Splendours of the GONZAGA

Catalogue

Edited by
DAVID CHAMBERS & JANE MARTINEAU

Exhibition 4 November 1981–31 January 1982
VICTORIA & ALBERT MUSEUM - LONDON

The Exhibition has been organized with
the assistance of the Italian Government and
the city of Mantua, and is sponsored
by *The Daily Telegraph* and the
CARIPLO - Cassa di Risparmio delle Provincie Lombarde

Cover

(Front) *Mantegna, Detail of "Meeting Scene" in* Camera Picta, Castello S. Giorgio, Mantua *(Cat. 29).*

(Back) *Dish with Gonzaga arms and music book,*
c. *1530 (Cat. 198).*

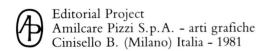

Editorial Project
Amilcare Pizzi S.p.A. – arti grafiche
Cinisello B. (Milano) Italia - 1981

PATRONS

H.R.H. The Prince of Wales

Senator Professor Amintore Fanfani
(President of Senate of the Italian Republic)

HONORARY COMMITTEE

Rt. Hon. Lord Carrington, P.C., K.C.M.G., M.C.

H.E. Sir Ronald Arculus K.C.M.G.

Rt. Hon. Lord Clark

Rt. Hon. Lord Hartwell

Rt. Hon. Norman St John Stevas M.P.

The Worshipful the Mayor of the Royal Borough of Kensington and Chelsea

Mr John Macrae

Mr Keith Geoffrey

Mr Anthony Letts

On. Emilio Colombo

On. Vincenzo Scotti

H.E. Andrea Cagiati G.C.V.O

Ambassador Sergio Romano

Dr Guglielmo B. Triches

On. Gianni Usvardi, Mayor of Mantua

H.E. Monsignor Carlo Ferrari, Bishop of Mantua

Professor Antonio Confalonieri

Dr Armenise Auletta

ACADEMIC COMMITTEE

Dr Roy Strong F.S.A.

Dr D.S. Chambers

Mr Anthony Radcliffe

Professor Sir Ernst Gombrich, F.B.A., F.S.A.

Sir Oliver Millar, K.C.V.O., F.B.A., F.S.A.

Professor J.R. Hale, F.B.A.

Dottoressa Ilaria Toesca–Bertelli

Dottoressa Rosa Maria Letts

Professor Mario Praz

Professor Cesare Brandi

Professor Mario Montuori

Dottoressa Adele Bellù

Professor Rodolfo Signorini

Acknowledgements

Lenders

Great Britain Her Majesty The Queen
Artemis Group, London; Visitors of the Ashmolean Museum, Oxford; City of Birmingham Museums and Art Gallery; Bodleian Library, Oxford; The British Library Board; The Trustees of the British Museum; The Trustees of the Chatsworth Settlement; Christ Church, Oxford; The Provost and Fellows of Eton College; Fitzwilliam Museum, Cambridge; The Wernher Collection, Luton Hoo; The Trustees of the National Gallery; National Portrait Gallery; The National Trust (Saltram House and Tatton Park); The Marquess of Northampton; The University of Oxford; Public Record Office, London; The Armouries, H.M. Tower of London; The Warburg Institute, University of London; Private Collectors.

Italy Museo del Palazzo Ducale, Mantua; Curia Vescovile, Mantua; Fondazione d'Arco, Mantua; Comune di Mantova (Biblioteca Comunale and Museo del Palazzo Te); Comune di Sabbioneta, Mantua; Dr Giampaolo Negri, Mantua; Museo Nazionale del Bargello, Florence; Pinacoteca di Brera, Milan; Galleria Giorgio Franchetti alla Ca' d'Oro, Venice; Biblioteca Casanatense, Rome; Museo Internazionale delle Ceramiche, Faenza; Biblioteca del Conservatorio "Giuseppe Verdi", Milan; Fondazione Museo Miniscalchi Erizzo, Verona; Biblioteca Estense and Galleria Estense, Modena; Museo Poldi Pezzoli, Milan; Biblioteca Giustiniani Recanati, Venice; Civiche Raccolte d'Arte e Pinacoteca, Castello Sforzesco, Milan; Galleria degli Uffizi, Florence; Private Collectors.

Austria Oesterreichische Nationalbibliothek, Vienna

Eire National Gallery of Ireland, Dublin

France Musée du Louvre, Paris; Château de Fontainebleau (dépôt du Musée du Louvre)

German Federal Republic Staatliche Museen, Berlin-Dahlem; Herzog Anton Ulrich-Museum, Brunswick; Kunstmuseum, Düsseldorf

Netherlands Museum Boymans-van Beuningen, Rotterdam

Philippines Metropolitan Museum, Manila (anonymous lender)

Spain Museo Arqueológico, Madrid

Sweden Nationalmuseum, Stockholm

Exhibitions Section and the organizers in addition to thanking the lenders listed above wish firstly to thank Dr Roy Strong and Dottoressa Toesca-Bertelli for their constant support. For organization concerning the loans from Italy thanks are owing to Cons. Massimo Baistrocchi (Ministry for Foreign Affairs, Department of Cultural Relations), Dottoressa Anna Forlani Tempesti and Dottoressa Rosetta Mosco (Ministry for Cultural Heritage), to the Italian Embassy in London, and in Mantua to the Staff of the Soprintendenza per i beni artistici e storici, to Don Giancarlo Manzoli of the Curia Vescovile, and to the Director of the Archivio di Stato, Dottoressa Adele Bellù. For their initiative concerning the model of Palazzo Te Dr Giancarlo Erbesato, Adolfo Poltronieri and the Director of the Istituto Statale d'Arte, Mantua, are to be warmly thanked, while the ready help at all times and in all ways of Professor Rodolfo Signorini has been of inestimable value. Generous advice and assistance concerning loans has been given by Keith Geoffrey (Arts Council), Michael Hirst (Courtauld Institute), Mme. Sylvie Béguin (Musée du Louvre), Dr Diether Graf (formerly of the Kunstmuseum, Düsseldorf) and Leslie Phillips (British Council, Madrid). Special thanks are also owing to Jonathan Alexander, David Alston, Professor Dennis Arnold, Timothy Bathurst, Alan Braham, Howard Burns, Joe Cowell, Caroline Elam, Iain Fenlon, Dr Alberto Falck, John Gere, Elizabeth McGrath, Professor Luigi Magnani, Jennifer Montagu, S. Nystad, Mario Ronchetti, Albi Rosenthal, Professor Edoard Safarik, Professor J.B. Trapp, Nicholas Turner and Julius Weitzner.

Page 161	Col. 2 line 5: *quadro che farà* Col. 2 line 21: *have*	*quadro grande che farà* *haver*
Page 169	Col. 2 line 1: woodwokers	woodworkers
Page 172	Plate **125** change to **126**	Plate **126** change to **125**
Page 174	Col. 2 line 26: appearence	appearance
Page 178	Col. 1 line 8: , Thetis is seen praying...	, Peleus is seen praying...
Page 180	No. 141 Col. 1 line 10: ΑΜΩΜΟΣ	ΟΛΥΜΠΟΣ
Page 185	No. 154 Title: (*c.* 1576)	(*c.* 1536)
Page 186	Col. 2 line 22: potrait	portrait
Page 187	Col. 1 line 12: ... façade), and which Col. 2 line 26: currency No. 157-9 Title: 8.4 cm/8.4 cm/8.42 cm	... façade), which curving 84 cm/84 cm/84.2 cm
Page 188	No. 160-3 Title: 5.35 cm/5.38 cm/5.34 cm/5.36 cm	53.5 cm/53.8 cm/53.4 cm/53.6 cm
Page 196	Col. 1 line 35: form	forms
Page 200	No. 197 Col. 1 line 4: ΑΜΩΜΟΣ	ΟΛΥΜΠΟΣ
Page 203	No. 203 Col. 1 line 18: covererd	covered
Page 212	No. 225 Col. 1 line 5: maried	married
Page 213	Col. 1 line 4: altarcloth.	altarpiece.
Page 229	Col. 1 line 2: sponse to Italy – its landscape in particular: a brilliant...	sponse to Italy, its landscape in particular a brilliant...
Page 234	No. 253 Col. 1 line 9: oulines	outlines
Page 244	No. 274 Col. 1 line 8: ocupation	occupation

Splendours of the Gonzaga

ERRATA   CORRIGE

Page IV (Acknowledgements):	Dr Giancarlo Erbesato	Dr Gianmaria Erbesato
	Professor Dennis Arnold	Professor Denis Arnold
Page XVIII-XIX (Genealogy):	Susanna (1447-61)	Susanna (1447-81)
	Dorotea (1449-62)	Dorotea (1449-67)
	Cecilia (1451-72)	Cecilia (1451-78)
Page XXI	Col. 2 line 6:	
	jowels	jowls
Page 38	Col. 1:	
	32. Lorenzo de' Medici,	33. Lorenzo de' Medici,
Page 78	Col. 2 line 39:	
	having letter	having a litter
Page 103	No. 2 Col. 1 line 4:	
	VERONENSIS	VERONENSI
Page 114	No. 23 Col. 1:	
	ADDITIONAL BIBLIOGRAPHY/ADDENDUM	ADDITIONAL BIBLIOGRAPHY: A. Luzio and R. Renier, "Il Platina e i Gonzaga", *Giorn. stor. della lett. ital.*, xiii, 1889, pp. 430-40. The *De principe* was...
Page 125	No. 35 Col. 2 line 1:	
	have	has
Page 130	No. 47 Col. 2 line 7:	
	(1445-96)	(1446-96)
Page 132	No. 49-50 Col. 1 title:	
	(1443-96)	(1446-96)
Page 135	Col. 1 line 5:	
	(Cat. 35)	(Cat. 55)
Page 141	Col. 2 line 13:	
	portrait	portraitist
Page 142	title line 4:	
	lenght	length
	No. 65 Col. 1 line 20:	
	iscription	inscription
Page 145	No. 71 Col. 1:	
	ADDENDUM/End of entry add initials	A.M.
Page 160.	No. 110 Col. 2 line 16:	
	negociate	negotiate

Contents

Foreword *by Dr. Roy Strong* — VII

Bibliography — IX

Introduction: The Gonzaga and Mantua *by D.S. Chambers* — XVII

Lancaster and Gonzaga: the Collar of SS at Mantua *by Ilaria Toesca* — 1

Gonzaga Tombs and Catafalques *by Rodolfo Signorini* — 3

Mantegna and Mantua *by Caroline Elam* — 15

The Gonzaga and Renaissance Architecture *by Howard Burns* — 27

The Gonzaga and Ceramics *by J.V.G. Mallet* — 39

Ceramic Tiles for the Gonzaga *by Mariarosa Palvarini Gobio Casali* — 44

Antico and the Mantuan Bronze *by Anthony Radcliffe* — 46

Isabella d'Este, Patron and Collector *by J.M. Fletcher* — 51

The Gonzaga Devices *by Mario Praz* — 65

Federico II Gonzaga as a Patron of Painting *by Charles Hope* — 73

"That rare Italian Master…" Giulio Romano, Court Architect,
Painter and Impresario *by E.H. Gombrich* — 77

The Gonzaga and Music *by Iain Fenlon* — 87

Charles I and the Gonzaga Collections *by David Howarth* — 95

Catalogue:

I. Foundations — 102

II. The Arts of Peace and War — 117

III. Isabella d'Este, the Insatiable Collector — 159

IV. Federico Gonzaga, the Terrestrial Jupiter — 180

V. The Beauty of Holiness — 203

VI. Pomp and Circumstance — 223

VII. Disintegration — 244

Contributors to the Catalogue

Entries written by the Editors are signed D.S.C. (D.S. Chambers) and J.T.M. (J.T. Martineau). Other entries are signed with initials of the following authors:

J.B.	Jacqueline Burckhardt	M.L.	Margaret Lyttelton
H.B.	Howard Burns	E.McG.	Elizabeth McGrath
L.C.	Lorne Campbell	J.V.G.M.	J.V.G. Mallet
D.E.	David Ekserdjian	A.M.	Andrew Martindale
C.E.	Caroline Elam	J.M.M.	Jean Michel Massing
L.F.	Lynda Fairbairn	G.M.	Germano Mulazzani
I.F.	Iain Fenlon	A.F.R.	Anthony Radcliffe
J.F.H.	J.F. Hayward	N.R.	Nicolai Rubinstein
M.H.	Michael Hirst	R.S.	Rodolfo Signorini
C.H.	Charles Hope	A.S.C.	Anna Somers Cocks
S.K.	Stephen Kolsky	I.T.	Ilaria Toesca
R.J.	Roger Jones	J.B.T.	J.B. Trapp
J.L.	Jim Law	G.W.	Guy Wilson

The Editors wish to thank all their collaborators listed above, and are grateful for help generously given within the Victoria and Albert Museum, particularly by Gillian Davies, who undertook the ordering of photographs as well as much other work, and by Lucy Cullen who prepared descriptive lists of medals; to Harold Barkley, Nicky Bird, Claude Blair, Anne Buddle, Ronald Lightbown, Anna Somers Cocks, Peter Thornton, Irene Whalley and others they are also grateful. Further thanks are owing for help given by Dott. Paride Berardi, Dott. Giancarlo Bojani, Monsignor Luigi Bosio, Luigi Bottura, Professor C.P. Brand, Edward Bresley, Professor Lanfranco Caretti, Tatyana Chambers, John Cherry, Sarah Dale, Albinia de la Mare, Ian Eaves, Dott. Giuseppe Frasso, Dott. Renzo Grandi, Rupert Hodge, Michael Holmes, M. Irwick Smith, Mark Jones, Ann Kettle, Jill Kraye, Giulio and Laura Lepschy, Maximilian Leutenmayr, Anna Maria Lorenzoni, Denis Mahon, Ann Marie Meyer, Alessandra Mottola-Molfino, Jennifer Montagu, Robert Nelson, Richard Palmer, Nicholas Penny, Graham Pollard, Dennis Rhodes, Ruth Rubinstein, Dott. Giancarlo Schizzerotto, Professor John Shearman, Archimede Sogliani, Anna Maria Tammassia, Antonia Tissoni-Benvenuti, Dott. Mario Vaini and Timothy Wilson.
Finally they would like to thank Dott. Sergio Lucioli, Angelo Salvioni and Guido Modena of Amilcare Pizzi S.p.A. who have made this Catalogue a tangible expression of Anglo-Italian collaboration.

Foreword

by Dr. Roy Strong, Director of the Victoria and Albert Museum

The idea of a Gonzaga exhibition was first suggested to me five years ago by Rosa Maria Letts. It seemed particularly appropriate that the Victoria and Albert Museum should provide the setting for an evocation of this great Renaissance dynasty. Like the Museum the emphasis of their collection was on the decorative arts of which they were massive patrons and collectors with aims very close to those of the V. & A.: to preserve the best of the art of the past and to stimulate that of the future.

This is the first time this Museum has set out to recreate the treasures of one Renaissance dynasty and, indeed, no attempt has ever been made to re-group these particular objects outside Italy. The task has been enormous and would certainly have been impossible without the unending support of the Italian Government. This exhibition is the climax of the thirtieth year of the 1951 Anglo/Italian Cultural Agreement. From the outset the idea of the exhibition was received with enthusiasm by Ilaria Toesca Bertelli, Dirigente Superiore, Soprintendenza per i Beni artistici e storici per le Province di Brescia, Cremona e Mantova. Her continued interest and practical assistance has been invaluable, while the generous support of the Mayor and Comune of Mantua has also been much appreciated.

The Italian Ambassador in London, His Excellency Andrea Cagiati, and his staff, particularly Professor Mario Montuori, Dr. Guido Lenzi, Dr. Leonardo Sampoli, Dr. Giorgio Mariotti and Signora Marcella Barzetti, have in every way assisted the complex negotiations that accompanied permission to borrow so many important works of art.

The sponsors of the exhibition, *The Daily Telegraph* and the CARIPLO-Cassa di Risparmio delle Provincie Lombarde, have made it possible for the Museum to present the Gonzaga family to a wide audience: *The Daily Telegraph* by providing a lavish publicity campaign and CARIPLO by publishing this catalogue containing much new scholarship.

Above all my thanks must go to David Chambers. The role he accepted, that of 'academic organiser', involved him in selecting all the objects. In addition, however, he personally negotiated many of the loans, advised on the design and willingly took on the endlessly varied tasks needed to get a show of this complexity off the ground. Credit for the catalogue also largely falls to him as he decided the format as well as writing many of the entries and acting as editor-in-chief. It is essentially his exhibition.

John Ronayne, the designer of the exhibition, deserves much praise for his immensely thorough research and for the success with which he has recreated the atmosphere of Mantua.

Rosa Maria Letts has worked tirelessly not just on the audio visual display and the concerts and lectures that accompany the exhibition, but also on every aspect of the show.

Within the Museum special thanks are due to Anthony Radcliffe who selected the sculptures and medals and spent many hours in consultation with the organizers. As usual I wish to express my gratitude to colleagues in other curatorial departments, particularly John Mallet, who have been unstinting in their help. But the greatest burden has inevitably fallen on the Exhibition, Design and Press and Information Sections. Of these I would like to single out Gill Davies who has been the vital link between almost too many complex chains. The result we hope is the greatest Renaissance exhibition to be seen in this country since the last war. Renaissance means rebirth and no message could be more apposite for this country at the present time.

Photographs

Photographic reproductions of documents from the Archivio di Stato, Mantua, have been generously provided for the exhibition by the Ministero per i Beni Culturali e Ambientali (Ufficio Centrale per i Beni Archivistici) and executed by Foto Giovetti, Mantua (reproduction of all archival material is permitted by Ministerial authorization no. 1751). The photographic half-scale facsimile of the *Camera Picta* (Cat. 29) was executed by Scala, Florence; CIBACHROME materials were donated by ILFORD Ltd. Most photographs of objects in the exhibition were supplied for the catalogue by the lenders; in addition a number of photographs were kindly provided by the Archivio Fotografico of CARIPLO. Photographs of objects from collections in Mantua were supplied by Foto Giovetti.

The following also provided photographs:
British Museum Photographic Services Pl. 18; Cat. 65
Foto Cavacchini, Mantua Pl. 15; Cat. 156
Conway Library, Courtauld Institute of Art Pl. 23, 33, 34; Cat. 38, 185, 189, 204
Museo di Capodimonte, Naples Pl. 20
Lynda Fairbairn Pl. 35, 36, 40; Cat. 203, 208, 209
Gabinetto Fotografico Nazionale Pl. 5, 6
Foto Giovetti, Mantua Pl. 1, 4, 7, 9, 10, 12-17, 19, 24, 25, 31, 32, 38, 39, 41; 56-61, 63, 64, 87, 88, 90-92; Cat. 35-37, 48, 202, 245
Kunsthistorisches Museum, Vienna Pl. 47-50
Foto Landesbildstelle Rheinland Cat. 157-165, 168-178
Pierangelo Monici, Mantua Pl. 8
National Gallery, London Pl. 98, 101
National Portrait Gallery Pl. 102
Stanley Parker-Ross Cat. 4
Museo del Prado Pl. 22, 81, 100
Documentation Photographique de la Réunion des Musées Nationaux Pl. 11, 27, 29, 30, 46, 51-55, 89, 99, 103
Galleria degli Uffizi, Florence Pl. 26, 52
Peter Macdonald and the Photo Studio of the Victoria & Albert Museum supplied, in addition to photographs of objects from the Museum's collections, Pl. 65-80 and Cat. 153, 206, 251, 254-256

Drawings and Diagrams

Plans of the Palazzo Ducale, Mantua (Pl. 3, 3a) and drawings to accompany the *Camera Picta* (Cat. 29) were prepared by Caroline Elam; reconstruction drawings to accompany Rubens's *Adoration* (Cat. 228) were prepared by Elizabeth McGrath, with acknowledgments to Ugo Bazzotti and photographic help from Stanley Parker-Ross.

Bibliography

Note: BIBLIOGRAPHY beneath essays and catalogue entries gives abbreviated references to works in the general bibliography which follows here; ADDITIONAL BIBLIOGRAPHY cites in full other works usually of importance only for the specific item, and these titles are not repeated.

ABBREVIATIONS USED

ASDM   Archivio Storico Diocesano, Mantua
ASM   Archivio di Stato, Mantua
ASMAG Archivio di Stato, Mantua, Archivio Gonzaga.
Atti Acc. Virgiliana   Atti e Memorie della Accademia Virgiliana di Mantova.
CNI   Corpus Nummorum italicorum, IV, Lombardia (Zecchi minori), Rome, 1913.
Corpus   see HILL, Corpus.
DBI   Dizionario biografico degli italiani.
S.T.C.   A Short-Title Catalogue of Books printed in England, etc. 1475-1640, London, 1926, 2nd edn, I-Z, London, 1976.
Thieme-Becker U. Thieme and F. Becker ed., Allgemeines Lexikon der bildenden Künstler, Leipzig, 1907-50.

Ademollo, 1888
A. ADEMOLLO, La bell'Adriana ed altre virtuose del suo tempo alla corte di Mantova, Città di Castello, 1888.

Affò, 1780
I. AFFÒ, Vita di Vespasiano Gonzaga, Parma, 1780; repr. Mantua, 1975.

Alberti, 1966
L.B. ALBERTI (ed. P. Portoghesi and G. Orlandi), De Re Aedificatoria, 2 vols, Milan, 1966.

Alexander and de la Mare, 1969
J.G. ALEXANDER AND A.C. DE LA MARE, Italian Manuscripts in the Library of Major J.R. Abbey, London, 1969.

Alexander, 1970
J.G. ALEXANDER, 'A manuscript of Petrarch's Rime and Trionfi', Victoria and Albert Museum Yearbook, II, 1970, pp. 24-40.

Alston and others, 1979
D. ALSTON, C. BURMAN, D. LANDAU, Catalogue: Prints by Mantegna and his School, Christ Church, Oxford, Oxford, 1979.

Amadei, 1955
F. AMADEI, Cronaca Universale della città di Mantova, I, II, Mantua, 1955.

Amadei, 1968
G. AMADEI, 'Il Pisanello a Mantova', Civiltà Mantovana, 17, 1968, pp. 287-321.

Amadei and Marani, 1978
G. AMADEI AND E. MARANI, I ritratti gonzagheschi della collezione di Ambras, Mantua, 1978.

Amadei and others, 1980
G. AMADEI, E. MARANI, M. ZANELLI, M.C. GRASSI, A. BELLÙ, Il Palazzo d'Arco in Mantova, Mantua, 1980.

Antwerp, 1977
Royal Museum, P.P. Rubens. Paintings-Oilsketches-Drawings, Antwerp, 1977.

Armand, 1883-87
A. ARMAND, Les médailleurs italiens de 15. et 16. siècles, 3 vols, Paris, 1883-87.

Askew, 1978
P. ASKEW, 'Ferdinando Gonzaga's Patronage of the Pictorial Arts: the Villa Favorita', Art Bulletin, LX, 1978 pp. 274-95.

Atlas, 1975
A. ATLAS, The Cappella Giulia Chansonnier. Rome, Biblioteca Apostolica Vaticana C.G. XIII. 27, I, Minden, 1975.

Ballardini, 1933, 1938
G. BALLARDINI, Corpus della Maiolica italiana, I, Le Maioliche datate fino al 1530, Rome, 1933; II, Le Maioliche datate dal 1531 al 1535, Rome, 1938.

Barblan, 1972
G. BARBLAN, Conservatorio di musica 'Giuseppe Verdi', Milano. Catalogo della biblioteca, fondi speciali I. Musiche della cappella di S. Barbara in Mantova, Florence, 1972.

Baroni, 1934
C. BARONI, Ceramiche italiane Minori del Castello Sforzesco, Milan, 1934.

Baschet, 1866[1]
A. BASCHET, 'Pierre Paul Rubens, peintre de Vincent Ier de Gonzague, Duc de Mantoue. (1600-1608)', Gazette des Beaux-Arts, XX, 1866, pp. 401-52.

Baschet, 1866[2]
A. BASCHET, 'Recherches de documents d'art et d'histoire dans les Archives de Mantoue', Gazette des Beaux-Arts, XX, 1866, pp. 318-39, 478-91.

Baschet, 1867[1]
A. BASCHET, Aldo Manuzio. Lettres et documents 1495-1515, Venice, 1867.

Baschet, 1867[2]
A. BASCHET, 'Pierre Paul Rubens. Rubens revient d'Espagne a Mantoue. (1604-1606)', Gazette des Beaux-Arts, XXII, 1867, pp. 305-20.

Battisti, 1965
E. BATTISTI, 'Il Mantegna e la Letteratura Classica', Atti del VI Congresso di Studi sul Rinascimento, Florence, 1965, pp. 23-56.

Baxandall, 1963
M. BAXANDALL, 'A Dialogue on Art from the Court of Leonello D'Este', Journal of the Warburg and Courtauld Institutes, XXVI, 1963, pp. 304-26.

Baxandall, 1965
M. BAXANDALL, 'Guarino, Pisanello and Chrysoloras', Journal of the Warburg and Courtauld Institutes, XXVIII, 1965, pp. 183-204.

Bazzotti-Belluzzi, 1980[1]
U. BAZZOTTI AND A. BELLUZZI, 'Le concezioni estetiche di Baldassare Castiglione e la cappella nel santuario di Santa Maria delle Grazie', Atti del Convegno di Studio su Baldassare Castiglione nel quinto centenario della nascita, Mantova 7-8 Ottobre 1978, ed. E. Bonora, Mantua, 1980.

Bazzotti-Belluzzi, 1980[2]
U. BAZZOTTI AND A. BELLUZZI, Architettura e Pittura all'Accademia di Mantova (1752-1802), Florence, 1980.

Béguin, 1975[1]
S. BÉGUIN ed., Le Studiolo d'Isabelle d'Este, Exhibition catalogue, Paris, Louvre, 1975.

Béguin, 1975[2]
S. BÉGUIN, 'Remarques sur les deux allégories de Corrège du Studiolo d'Isabelle d'Este', Revue du Louvre, IV, 1975, pp. 221-26.

Belluzzi and Capezzali, 1976
A. BELLUZZI AND W. CAPEZZALI, Il Palazzo dei lucidi inganni, Palazzo Te a Mantova, Mantua, 1976.

Beltrami, 1919
L. BELTRAMI, Documenti e memorie riguardanti la vita e le opere di Leonardo da Vinci, Milan, 1919

Bertazzolo, 1622
G. BERTAZZOLO, Breve relatione dello sposalitio fatto della Serenissima Principessa Eleonora Gonzaga con la Sacra Cesareo Maestà di Ferdinando II Imperatore, Mantua, 1622.

Bertolotti, 1885
A. BERTOLOTTI, Artisti in Relazione coi Gonzaga duchi di mantova nei secoli XVI e XVII, Modena, 1885.

Bertolotti, 1888
A. BERTOLOTTI, 'Le Arti Minori alla Corte di Mantova', Archivio Storico Lombardo, XV, 1888, pp. 259-318, 419-590, 980-1075.

Bertolotti, 1889
A. BERTOLOTTI, Le arti minori alla corte di Mantova nei secoli XV, XVI e XVII, Milan, 1889.

Bertolotti, 1889, 1977
A. BERTOLOTTI, 'La ceramica alla corte di Mantova nei secoli XV, XVI, XVII', Archivio Storico Lombardo, XVI, 1889, pp. 808-46. Reprinted Mantua, 1977.

Bertolotti, 1890[1]
A. BERTOLOTTI, Figuli, Fonditori e Scultori in relazione con la Corte di Mantova nei secoli XV, XVI, XVII, Milan, 1890.

Bertolotti, 1890[2]
A. BERTOLOTTI, Musici alla corte dei Gonzaga in Mantova dal secolo XV al XVIII. Notizie e documenti raccolti negli archivi mantovani, Milan, 1890.

Bettini, 1944
S. BETTINI, Giusto de' Menabuoi e l'arte del Trecento, Padua, 1944.

Blum, 1936
I. BLUM, *Andrea Mantegna und die Antike*, Strasbourg, 1936.

Bode, 1907[1]
W. BODE, *The Italian Bronze Statuettes of the Renaissance*, I, London, 1907.

Bode, 1907[2]
W. BODE, 'Pier Ilari Bonacolsi genannt Antico', *Kunst und Künstler*, V, 1907, pp. 297-303.

Bohatta, 1937
H. BOHATTA, *Bibliographie der Breviere 1501-1850*, Leipzig, 1937.

Braghirolli, 1876
W. BRAGHIROLLI, 'Luca Fancelli; scultore architetto e idraulico del secolo XV', *Archivio Storico Lombardo*, Anno 3, 1976, pp. 610-38.

Braghirolli, 1877
W. BRAGHIROLLI, 'Carteggio di Isabella d'Este Gonzaga intorno ad un quadro di Giambellino,' *Archivio Veneto*, XIII, 1877, pp. 370-83.

Braghirolli, 1878
W. BRAGHIROLLI, 'Lettere inedite di artisti del secolo XV cavate dall'archivio Gonzaga', *per nozze Cavriani-Sordi*, Mantua, 1878.

Braghirolli, 1881
W. BRAGHIROLLI, 'Tiziano alla corte dei Gonzaga', *Atti Acc. Virgiliana*, XIV, 1881, pp. 59-144.

Brand, 1965
C.P. BRAND, *Torquato Tasso*, Cambridge, 1965.

Brinton, 1927
S. BRINTON, *The Gonzaga. Lords of Mantua*, London, 1927.

Brown, 1966
C. BROWN, *Lorenzo Costa*, unpublished Ph. D. dissertation, Columbia University, 1966.

Brown, 1967-68
C. BROWN, 'The Chapel of St. Cecilia and the Bentivoglio Chapel in Bologna'. *Mitteilungen des Kunsthistorisches Institutes in Florenz*, 13, 1967-68, pp. 301f.

Brown, 1969[1]
C. BROWN, 'Little known and unpublished documents concerning Andrea Mantegna, Bernardino Parentino, Pietro Lombardo, Leonardo da Vinci & Filippo Benintendi', *L'Arte*, N.S. II no. 6, June 1969, pp. 140-64; no. 718, Dec. 1969, pp. 182-84.

Brown, 1969[2]
C. BROWN, 'Comus Dieu des Fêtes.. Allegories de Mantegna et de Costa pour le studiolo d'Isabella d'Este-Gonzague', *Revue du Louvre*, XIX, I, 1969, pp. 31-38.

Brown, 1969[3]
C. BROWN, 'Una testa di Platone antica con la punta del naso di cera'. Unpublished negotiations between Isabella d'Este and Niccolo & Giovanni Bellini', *Art Bulletin*, LI, 1969, pp. 372-77.

Brown, 1970
C. BROWN, 'Lorenzo Costa in Mantua. Five Autograph Letters', *L'Arte*, 11-12, 1970, pp. 106-17.

Brown, 1972
C. BROWN, 'New documents for Mantegna's Camera degli Sposi' *Burlington Magazine*, CXIV, 1972, pp. 861-63. Corrections in CXV, 1973, pp. 253-54.

Brown and Lorenzoni, 1972
C. BROWN AND A. LORENZONI, 'Isabella d'Este e Giorgio Brognolo nell'Anno 1496', *Atti Acc. Virgiliana*, N.S. XL, 1972, pp. 97-122.

Brown, 1973[1]
C. BROWN, 'An art auction in Venice in 1506', *L'Arte*, XVIII-XX, 1973, pp. 124-28.

Brown, 1973[2]
C. BROWN, 'Gleanings from the Gonzaga documents in Mantua - Gian Cristoforo Romano and Andrea Mantegna, I: Gian Cristoforo Romano and the impresa del crogiuolo', *Mitteilungen des Kunsthistorischen Institutes in Florenz*, XVII, 1973, pp. 153-59.

Brown, 1974
C. BROWN, 'Andrea Mantegna and the Cornaro of Venice', *Burlington Magazine*, CXVI, 1974, pp. 101-03.

Brown, 1976
C. BROWN, 'Lo Insaciabile Desiderio Nostro De Cose Antique': New Documents on Isabella d'Este's Collection of Antiquities', in *Cultural Aspects of the Italian Renaissance*, Essays in Honour of P.O. Kristeller ed. C. Clough, Manchester, 1976, pp. 324-53.

Brown and Lorenzoni, 1977-78
C. BROWN AND A. LORENZONI, 'The Grotta of Isabella d'Este', *Gazette des Beaux-Arts*, per. 6, LXXXIX, 1977, pp. 155-71, XCI, 1978, pp. 72-82.

Brown, 1980[1]
C.M. BROWN, 'Letter' *Burlington Magazine*, CXXII, 1980, pp. 69-70.

Brown, 1980[2]
C.M. BROWN, 'The "Triumphs of Caesar" of Andrea Mantegna and Francesco II Gonzaga's supposed trip to Germany in 1486', *Atti Acc. Virgiliana* N.S. XLVIII, 1980, pp. 111-16.

Bruns, 1950
G. BRUNS, 'Das Mantuanische Onyxgefäss', *Kunsthefte des Herzog Anton Ulrich-Museums*, Braunschweig, V, 1950.

Burchard and d'Hulst, 1963
L. BURCHARD AND R.-A. D'HULST, *Rubens Drawings*, Brussels, 1963.

Burckhardt, 1978
J. BURCKHARDT, 'Die Loggia dei Marmi von Giulio Romano im Palazzo Ducale in Mantova. Ein Beitrag zu einer Monografie'. Unpublished dissertation, Zurich, 1978.

Burns, 1979
H. BURNS, 'A drawing by L.B. Alberti', *Architectural Design*, 49, nos. 5-6, 1979, pp. 45-56.

Byam Shaw, 1976
J. BYAM SHAW, *Drawings by Old Masters at Christ Church, Oxford*, 2 vols., Oxford, 1976.

Cagnolati, 1928
T. CAGNOLATI, *Il crepuscolo di Ferrante Gonzaga*, Reggio Emilia, 1928.

Calzona, 1979
A. CALZONA, *Mantova città dell'Alberti. Il San Sebastiano: tomba, tempio, cosmo*, Parma, 1979.

Campori, 1879
G. CAMPORI, *Notizie Storiche e Artistiche, della Maiolica e della Porcellana di Ferrara nei Secoli XV & XVI*, 3rd ed., Pesaro, 1879.

Campori, 1885
G. CAMPORI, 'I pittori degli Estensi nel secolo XV', *Atti e memorie delle Deputazioni di Storia Patria per le provincie modenesi e parmensi*, ser. 3, III, 1885, pp. 525-603.

Canal, 1881
P. CANAL, *Della musica in Mantova*, Venice, 1881.

Canuti, 1931
F. CANUTI, *Il Perugino*, 2 vols., Siena, 1931.

Carpi, 1920
P. CARPI, 'Giulio Romano ai servigi di Federico II Gonzaga' *Atti Acc. Virgiliana*, N.S., 11-13, 1918-20, pp. 35-150.

Cartwright, 1903 etc.
J. CARTWRIGHT, *Isabella d'Este Marchioness of Mantua, 1474-1539*, 2 vols., London, 1903 etc.

Cartwright, 1908
J. CARTWRIGHT, *Baldassare Castiglione, The perfect Courtier. His life and Letters 1478-1529*, 2 vols., London, 1908.

Cavriani, 1909
C. CAVRIANI, *Le razze Gonzaghesche dei cavalli nel mantovano e la loro influenza sul puro sangue inglese*, Mantua, 1909, repr. 1974.

Cessi, 1913
R. CESSI, 'La cattura del Marchese Francesco Gonzaga di Mantova e le prime trattative per la sua liberazione', *Nuovo Archivio Veneto*, XXV, 1913, pp. 144-76.

Chacon, 1677
See CIACCONII

Chambers, 1977
D.S. CHAMBERS, 'Sant'Andrea at Mantua and Gonzaga patronage', *Journal of the Warburg and Courtauld Institutes*, XL, 1977, pp. 99-127.

Chambers, 1980
D.S. CHAMBERS, 'Francesco Cardinalino (*c.* 1477-1511) the son of Cardinal Francesco Gonzaga', *Atti Acc. Virgiliana*, N.S., XLVIII, 1980, pp. 5-55.

Chattard, 1762-67
G. CHATTARD, *Nuova Descrizione del vaticano*, 3 vols. Rome, 1762-67.

Cherry, 1969
J. CHERRY, 'The Dunstable Swan Jewel', *Journal of the British Archaeological Association*, 3rd ser., XXXII, 1969, pp. 38-53.

Chiappini, 1956
L. CHIAPPINI, *Eleonora d'Aragona, prima duchessa di Ferrara*, Rovigo, 1956.

Chiappini, 1967
L. CHIAPPINI, *Gli Estensi*, Milan, 1967.

Chompret, 1949
J. CHOMPRET, *Répertoire de la Majolique italienne*, Paris, 1949.

Ciacconii, 1677
A. CIACCONII, *Vitae et res gestae pontificum Romanorum et S.R.E Cardinalium...*, III, Rome, 1677

Cian, 1885
V. CIAN, *Un decennio della vita di M. Pietro Bembo*, Turin, 1885.

Cian, 1887
V. CIAN, 'Pietro Bembo e Isabella d'Este Gonzaga', *Giornale Storico della Letteratura Italiana*, IX, 1887, pp. 81-136.

Cipriani, 1963
R. CIPRIANI, *Tutta La Pittura di Andrea Mantegna*, Milan, 1963, English edn., London, 1963.

Clough, 1966
C.H. CLOUGH, 'The grave of Isabella d'Este', *Renaissance News*, XIX, 1966, pp. 96-97.

Clough, 1971
C.H. CLOUGH, *Pietro Bembo's Library as represented in the British Museum*, London, 1971.

Clough, 1972
C.H. CLOUGH, 'The Library of the Gonzaga at Mantua', *Librarium*, XV, 1972, pp. 50-63.

Coccia, 1960
E. COCCIA, *Le edizioni delle opere del Mantovano*, Rome, 1960.

Coletti and Camesasca, 1959
L. COLETTI AND E. CAMESASCA, *La Camera degli Sposi di Andrea Mantegna*, Milan, 1959.

Coniglio, 1958
G. CONIGLIO, *Mantova: La Storia*, I, Mantua, 1958.

Coniglio 1967
G. CONIGLIO, *I Gonzaga*, Milan, 1967.

Coryat, 1611
T. CORYAT, *Coryat's Crudities*, London, 1611; repr. 2 vols., 1905.

Cottafavi, 1934
C. COTTAFAVI, 'Palazzo Ducale di Mantova - I Gabinetti di Isabella d'Este - vicende, discussioni, restauri', *Bollettino d'arte*, XXVIII, 1934, pp. 228-40.

Cottafavi, 1935[1]
C. COTTAFAVI, 'Clarisse della famiglia Gonzaga in S. Paola di Mantova', *estratto* from *Le Venezie francescane*, IV, March 1935.

Cottafavi, 1935[2]
C. COTTAFAVI, *L'ordine cavalleresco del Redentore*, *Atti Acc. Virgiliana* XXIV, 1935, pp. 171-225.

Cottafavi, 1963
C. COTTAFAVI, 'Saggi inediti su edifici della Corte di Mantova: La Domus Nova (1936-7)', *Atti Acc. Virgiliana*, XXXIV, 1963, pp. 8-18.

Crowe and Cavalcaselle, 1912
J. CROWE AND G.B. CAVALCASELLE, *A History of Painting in North Italy*, 3 vols., London, 1912.

Conti, 1973
G. CONTI, *L'Arte della Maiolica in Italia*, Milan, 1973.

Dall'Acqua, 1974
M. DALL'ACQUA, 'Storia di un progetto albertiano, non realizzato: La ricostruzione della rotonda di San Lorenzo di Mantova', see *Mantua, Sant'Andrea*, 1974.

d'Arco, 1842
C. d'ARCO, *Istoria della vita e delle opere di Giulio Pippi Romano*, 2nd edn., Mantua, 1842.

d'Arco, 1845
C. d'ARCO, 'Notizie di Isabella Estense', *Archivio Storico Italiano*, 1845, App. II, pp. 205-326.

d'Arco, 1857
C. d'ARCO, *Delle arti e artifici di Mantova*, 2 vols., Mantua, 1857.

Davari, 1876
S. DAVARI, *Notizie storiche intorno allo studio pubblico... in Mantova*, Mantua, 1876.

Davari, 1884[1]
S. DAVARI, 'La musica a Mantova, Notizie biografiche di maestri di musica cantori e suonatori presso la corte di Mantova nei secoli XV, XVI, XVII tratte dai documenti dell'Archivio Storico Gonzaga', *Rivista storica mantovana*, I, 1884, p. 53 (reprinted with appendixes by G. Ghirardini, Mantua, 1975; but citations are of the orig. edn.).

Davari, 1884[2]
S. DAVARI, *Notizie biografiche del distinto maestro Claudio Monteverdi*, Mantua, 1884.

de Grummond, 1974
N.T. DE GRUMMOND, 'The real Gonzaga Cameo', *American Journal of Archaeology*, 78 no. 4, 1974, pp. 427-29.

de Terverant, 1958
G. DE TERVERANT, *Attributs et symboles dans l'art profane 1450-1600*, 2 vols., Geneva, 1958.

Dionisotti, 1958
C. DIONISOTTI, 'Battista Fiera', *Italia Medioevale e Umanistica*, I, 1958, pp. 401-18.

Dollmayr, 1901
H. DOLLMAYR, 'Giulio Romano und das classische Alterthum', *Jahrbuch der Kunsthistorischen Sammlungen des allerhöchsten Kaiserhauses*, XXII, 1901, pp. 178-220.

Dondi ed. Müller, 1857
N. DE DONDI, *Estratti del diario delle cose avvenute in Sabbioneta dal MDLXXX al MDC*, in G. Müller, *Raccolta di cronisti e documenti storici lombardi inediti*, II, Milan, 1857.

Donesmondi, I, 1613, II, 1616
I. DONESMONDI, *Dell'istoria ecclesiastica di Mantova*, vol.I, Mantua, 1613, vol. II, Mantua, 1616.

Donesmondi, 1625
I. DONESMONDI, *Vita dell'illustrissimo et reverendissimo monsignor F. Francesco Gonzaga vescovo di Mantova*, Venice, 1625.

Downes, 1980
K. DOWNES, *Rubens*, London, 1980.

Eikemeier, 1969
P. EIKEMEIER, 'Der Gonzaga-Zyklus des Tintoretto in der Alte Pinakothek', *Münchner Jahrbuch*, 3 Folge, XX, 1969 p. 75ff.

Einstein, 1971
A. EINSTEIN, *The Italian madrigal*, 3 vols., Princeton, 1949; reprinted, with additional index, 1971.

Elam, 1970
C. ELAM, *Studioli and Renaissance Court Patronage*, unpublished M.A. report, Courtauld Institute, London, 1970.

Equicola, 1607
M. EQUICOLA, *Dell'Istoria di Mantova*, Mantua, 1607.

Errante, 1915
V. ERRANTE, 'Forse che si, forse che no', *Archivio Storico Lombardo*, XLII, 1915, pp. 15-114.

Faccioli, 1959, 1962
E. FACCIOLI, *Mantova Le Lettere*, I, II, Mantua, 1959-1962.

Fehl, 1974
P. FEHL, 'The Worship of Bacchus and Venus in Bellini's and Titian's Bacchanals for Alfonso d'Este', *Studies in the History of Art*, Washington, National Gallery of Art, VI, 1974, pp. 37-95.

Fenlon, 1980
I. FENLON, *Music and patronage in sixteenth century Mantua*, I, Cambridge, 1980.

Ferrari, 1970
A. FERRARI, 'Fabbricate e giardini dei Gonzaga a Maderno', *Civiltà Mantovana*, XXII, 1970, pp. 276-77.

Ferro, 1623
G. FERRO, *Teatro d'imprese*, II, Venice, 1623.

Fink, 1950
A. FINK, 'Die Schicksale des Onyxgefässer', in *Kunsthefte des Herzog Anton Ulrich-Museums, Braunschweig*, V, 1950.

Fiocco, 1937
G. FIOCCO, *Mantegna*, Milan, 1937.

Fiocco, 1940
G. FIOCCO, 'Andrea Mantegna scultore', *Rivista d'arte*, XXII, 1940, pp. 224-28.

Florence, *Bronzetti*, 1962
Direzione Generale delle antichità e Belle Arti, *Bronzetti Italiani del Rinascimento*, Florence, 1962.

Florence, *Palazzo Vecchio*, 1980
Firenze e la Toscana dei Medici nell'Europa del Cinquecento. Palazzo Vecchio: committenza e collezionismo medicei, Florence, 1980.

Foerster, 1901
R. FOERSTER, 'Studien zu Mantegna und der Bildern im Studienzimmer der Isabella Gonzaga', *Jahrbuch der Preussischen Kunstsammlungen*, 22, 1901, pp. 78f and 154f.

Follino, 1587
F. FOLLINO, *Descrittione dell'infermità, morte et funerali del sereniss. sig. Guglielmo Gonzaga III Duca di Mantova e di Monferrato I*, Mantua, 1587.

Follino, 1608
F. FOLLINO, *Compendio delle sontuose feste fatte l'anno 1608... nella città di Mantova, per le... nozze... principe D.F. Gonzaga con... Margherita di Savoia*, Mantua, 1608.

Forrer, 1909
L. FORRER, *Biographical Dictionary of Medallists... BC 500-AD 1900*, London, 1909.

Forster, 1977
K.W. FORSTER, review art. in *Journal of the Soc. of Architectural Historians*, 36, 1977, pp. 123-25.

Foster and Tuttle, 1971
'The Palazzo del Te', *Journal of the Soc. of Architectural Historians*, XXX, 1971, pp. 267-93.

Forster and Tuttle, 1973
K.W. FORSTER AND R.J. TUTTLE, 'The Casa Pippi. Giulio Romano's house in Mantua', *Architectura*, 3, 1973, pp. 104-30.

Fortnum, 1873
C.D.E. FORTNUM, *A Descriptive Catalogue of the Maiolica, Hispano-Moresque, Persian, Damascus and Rhodian Wares in the South Kensington Museum*, London, 1873.

Fortnum, 1896
C.D.E. FORTNUM, *Maiolica*, Oxford, 1896.

Fossati, 1969
C. FOSSATI, 'Il Palazzo Gonzaga di Maderno', *Civiltà Mantovana*, XIX, 1969, pp. 30-47.

Fossi Todorow, 1966
M. FOSSI TODOROW, *I Disegni del Pisanello e della sua cerchia*, Florence, 1966.

Gallico, 1977
C. GALLICO, 'Guglielmo Gonzaga signore della musica', *Nuova rivista musicale italiana*, XI, 1977, p. 321.

Garin, 1958
E. GARIN, *Il pensiero pedagogico nell'Umanesimo*, Florence, 1958.

Gaye, 1839-40
G. GAYE, *Carteggio inedito d'artisti dei secoli XIV, XV, XVI*, 3 vols., Florence, 1839-40.

Gerola, 1908-09
G. GEROLA, 'Nuovi documenti mantovani sul mantegna', *Atti del r. Istituto veneto di scienze lettere ed Arti*, LXVIII, pt 2, 1908-09, pp. 905-15.

Gerola, 1918
G. GEROLA, 'Vecchie Insegne di Casa Gonzaga', *Archivio Storico Lombardo*, N.S. 5, XLV, 1918, pp. 98-110.

Gerola, 1929
G. GEROLA, 'Trasmigrazioni e Vicende dei Camerini di Isabella d'Este', *Atti Acc. Virgiliana*, Ser. II, XXI, 1929, pp. 253-90.

Gerola, 1930
G. GEROLA, 'Un'impresa ed un motto di casa Gonzaga', *Rivista d'arte*, XII, 1930, pp. 381-402.

Giacomotti, 1974
J. GIACOMOTTI, , *Les Majoliques des Musées Nationaux*, Paris, 1974.

Gilbert, 1980
C. GILBERT, *Italian Art 1400-1500: Sources and Documents*, Englewood Cliff, N.J., 1980.

Giovio, 1978
P. GIOVIO, *Dialogo dell'imprese militari e amorose*, ed. M.L. Doglio, Rome, 1978.

Golzio, 1936
V. GOLZIO, *Raffaello nei documenti*, Vatican City, 1936.

Gould, 1975
C. GOULD, *The Sixteenth Century Italian Schools*, National Gallery Catalogue, London, 1975.

Gould, 1976
C. GOULD, *The Paintings of Correggio*, London, 1976.

Gozzi, 1974
T. GOZZI, 'La basilica palatina di Santa Barbara in Mantova', *Atti Acc. Virgiliana*, XLII, 1974, pp. 3-91.

Grayson, 1955
C. GRAYSON, 'Un codice del "De Re Aedificatoria" posseduto da B. Bembo', in *Studi letterari. Miscellanea in onore di Emilio Santini*, 1955, pp. 181-88.

Grayson, 1960
C. GRAYSON, 'The Composition of L.B. Alberti's "Decem Libri de Re Aedificatoria"', *Münchner Jahrbuch der Bildenden Kunst*, XI, 1960, pp. 152-61.

Grove, 1980
GROVE, *The New Grove Dictionary of Music and Musicians*, ed. S. Sadie, 20 vols., London, 1980.

Hartt, 1958
F. HARTT, *Giulio Romano*, 2 vols., New Haven, Conn., 1958.

Hausmann, 1972
T. HAUSMANN, *Kataloge des Kunstgewerbemuseums Berlin, VI, Majolika, Spanische und Italienische Keramik vom 14. bis zum 18. Jahrhundert*, Berlin, 1972.

Heikamp, 1966
D. HEIKAMP, *L'Antico*, I maestri della Scultura No. 61, Milan, 1966.

Held, 1959
J.S. HELD, *Rubens. Selected Drawings*, London, 1959.

Held, 1966
J.S. HELD, Letter to the editor, *Art Bulletin*, XLVIII, 1966, pp. 468 f.

Hermann, 1910
H. HERMANN, 'Pier Jacopo Alari-Bonacolsi genannt Antico', *Jahrbuch der Kunsthistorischen Sammlungen der Allerhöchsten Kaiserhauses*, XXVIII, 1910, pp. 201-88.

Hill, *Corpus*
G.F. HILL, *A Corpus of Italian Medals of the Renaissance before Cellini*, London, 1930.

Hill, 1965
G.F. HILL, *Drawings by Pisanello*, (reprint) New York, 1965; first published 1929.

Hill and Pollard, 1967
G.F. HILL, rev. and enl. by G. POLLARD, *Renaissance Medals from the Samuel H. Kress Collection*, London, 1967.

Hill, rev. Pollard, 1978
SIR G. HILL, *Medals of the Renaissance* (1920), revised and enlarged by G. Pollard, London, 1978.

Hind, 1938-48
A. HIND *Early Italian Engraving*, 7 vols., London, 1938-48.

Hirschfeld, 1968
P. HIRSCHFELD, *Mäzene, die Rolle des Auftraggebers in der Kunst*, Munich, 1968.

Hope, 1980
C. HOPE, 'Mantegna's Classical World', *London Review of Books*, 19 June-2 July 1980, p. 16.

Huemer, 1966
F. HUEMER, 'Some observations on Rubens' Mantua Altarpiece', *Art Bulletin*, XLVIII, 1966, pp. 84-85.

Huemer, 1977[1]
F. HUEMER, *Portraits I* (Corpus Rubenianum Ludwig Burchard, XIX), London, 1977.

Huemer, 1977[2]
F. HUEMER, 'Rubens and the Mantuan Altar', *Studies in Iconography*, III, 1977, pp. 105-44.

Intra, 1884
G.B. INTRA, 'L'antica cattedrale di Mantova e le tombe dei primi Gonzaga', *Archivio Storico Lombardo*, XI, 1884, pp. 486-98 (reprinted Mantua, 1974).

Intra, 1888
G.B. INTRA, 'Il Castello di Goito', *Archivio Storico Lombardo*, XV, 1888, pp. 23-48.

Intra, 1895
G.B. INTRA, 'Il Monastero di Santa Orsola in Mantova', *Archivio Storico Lombardo*, XXII, 1895, pp. 67-85.

Jaffé, 1957
M. JAFFÉ, 'The Interest of Rubens in Annibale and Agostino Carracci: Further Notes', *Burlington Magazine*, XCIX, 1957, pp. 375-79.

Jaffé, 1961
M. JAFFÉ, 'The Deceased Young Duke of Mantua's Brother', *Burlington Magazine*, CIII, 1961, pp. 373-78.

Jaffé, 1977[1]
M. JAFFÉ, *Rubens and Italy*, Oxford, 1977.

Jaffé, 1977[2]
M. JAFFÉ, 'Rubens in Italy: A self-portrait', *Burlington Magazine*, CXIX, 1977, pp. 604-48; and ibid. (letter), pp. 848-49.

Jeppesen, 1950
K. JEPPESEN, 'The recently discovered Mantova masses of Palestrina', *Acta musicologica*, XXII, 1950, p. 36.

Jeppesen, 1953
K. JEPPESEN, 'Pierluigi da Palestrina, Herzog Guglielmo Gonzaga, und die neugefundenen Mantovaner-Messen Palestrinas', *Acta musicologica*, XXV, 1953, p. 147.

Johnson, 1975
E.J. JOHNSON, *Sant'Andrea: The Building History*, University Park, and London, 1975.

Jones, 1979
M. JONES, *The Art of the Medal*, London, 1979.

Jones, 1981
R. JONES, ' "What Venus did with Mars": Battista Fiera and Mantegna's "Parnassus" ', *Journal of the Warburg and Courtauld Institutes*, XLIV, 1981 (forthcoming).

Kenner, 1896
F. KENNER, 'Die Porträtsammlung des Erherzogs Ferdinand von Tirol', *Jahrbuch der Kunsthistorischen Sammlungen des Allerhöchsten Kaiserhauses*, XVII, 1896, pp. 101-274.

Krautheimer, 1969
R. KRAUTHEIMER, *Studies in Early Christian, Medieval and Renaissance Art*, New York etc., 1969.

Kristeller, 1901
P. KRISTELLER, *Andrea Mantegna*, London, 1901 (English edn.).

Kristeller, 1902
P. KRISTELLER, *Andrea Mantegna*, Berlin and Leipzig, 1902 (with documentary Appendix by A. Luzio).

Kube, 1976
A. KUBE, ed. O. Mikhailova and E. Lapkovskova, *Italian Majolica XV-XVIII Centuries, State Hermitage Collections*, Moscow, 1976.

Lamoureux, 1979
R.E. LAMOUREUX, *Alberti's church of San Sebastiano in Mantua*, New York etc., 1979.

Landau, 1979
D. LANDAU, 'Mantegna as engraver' in D. Alston, C. Bowman & D. Landau, *Prints by Mantegna and his school*, exhib. cat. Christ Church Picture Gallery, Oxford, 1979.

Lane, 1960
A. LANE, *Victoria and Albert Museum, A Guide to the Collection of Tiles*, 2nd edn., London, 1960.

Lange, 1898
K. LANGE, *Der Schlafende Amor des Michelangelo*, Leipzig, 1898.

Lauts, 1952, 1956
J. LAUTS, *Isabella d'Este*, Hamburg, 1952, Paris, 1956.

Lazzarini & Moschetti, 1908
V. LAZZARINI & A. MOSCHETTI, 'Documenti relativi alla pittura padovana del secolo XV', *Nuovo archivio Veneto*, ser. 2, XV, 1908, pp. 250-321.

Lehmann, 1973
P.W. LEHMANN, 'The sources and meaning of Mantegna's *Parnassus*', in P.W. Lehmann and K. Lehmann (eds.), *Samothracian reflections. Aspects of the revival of the antique*, Princeton, 1973.

Letts, 1980
R.M. LETTS, *Paola Malatesta and the Court of Mantua 1393-1453*, unpublished M. Phil. dissertation, Warburg Institute, London, 1980.

Levenson and others
J. LEVENSON, K. OBERHUBER, J. SHEEHAN, *Early Engravings from the National Gallery of Art*, Washington, 1973.

Levey, 1964
M. Levey, *The Later Italian Pictures in the Collection of Her Majesty the Queen*, London, 1964.

Levi, 1926
A. Levi, 'Rilievi di Sarcofagi del Palazzo Ducale di Mantova', *Dedalo*, VII, 1926, pp. 205-30.

Levi, 1931
A. Levi, *Sculture greche e romane del Palazzo ducale di Mantova*, Mantua, 1931.

Liebenwein, 1977
W. Liebenwein, *Studiolo*, Berlin, 1977.

Liverani, 1937
G. Liverani, 'Un nuovo piatto del servizio d'Isabella d'Este-Gonzaga', *Faenza*, XXV, 1937, pp. 89-93.

Liverani, 1938
G. Liverani, 'Ancora nuovi piatti del servizio d'Isabella d'Este-Gonzaga', *Faenza*, XXVI, 1938, pp. 90-92.

Liverani, 1938 and 1939
G. Liverani, 'Le Credenze Maiolicate di Isabella d'Este Gonzaga e di Federico II Duca di Mantova', *Rassegna dell'Istruzione Artistica*, IX, 1938, pp. 330-46. Reprinted in *Corriere dei Ceramisti*, XVII, 1939, pp. 1-17.

Liverani, 1958
G. Liverani, *La Maiolica Italiana sino alla comparsa della Porcellana Europea*, Milano, 1958 (English edn. under title *Five Centuries of Italian Majolica*, New York, Toronto, London, 1960).

London, Burlington Catalogue, 1913
Burlington Fine Arts Club, *Catalogue of a collection of Italian sculpture and other plastic arts of the Renaissance*, London, 1913.

London, 1953
Flemish Art 1300-1700, Royal Academy Winter Exhibition, 2 vols., London, 1953.

London, Arts Council, 1961
Arts Council of Great Britain, *Italian Bronze Statuettes*, London, 1961.

London, *Princely Magnificence*, 1980
Princely Magnificence: Court Jewels of the Renaissance, 1500-1630, Victoria and Albert Museum, London, 1980.

Longhi, 1934
R. Longhi, 'Risarcimento di un Mantegna', *Pan*, 1934, pp. 503ff.

Longhi, 1956
R. Longhi, *Officina Ferrarese*, Florence, 1956.

Luchini, 1904
L. Luchini, 'Il Panteon dei principi Gonzaga in San Martino dell'Argine', *Atti Acc. Virgiliana*, 1904, pp. 3-18.

Luzio and Renier, 1885
A. Luzio and R. Renier, 'Contributo alla storia del mal francese', *Giornale Storico della Letteratura Italiana*, V, 1885, pp. 408-32.

Luzio, 1886
A. Luzio, 'Lettere inedite di Fra Sabbà da Castiglione, *Archivio Storico Lombardo*, XIII, 1886, pp. 91-112.

Luzio, 1887
A. Luzio, *I precettori d'Isabella d'Este*, Ancona, 1887.

Luzio, 1888
A. Luzio, 'Cinque lettere di Vittorino da Feltre', *Archivio Veneto*, n.s. XVIII, 1888, pp. 329-41.

Luzio and Renier, 1890[1]
A. Luzio and R. Renier, 'Delle relazioni di Isabella d'Este Gonzaga con Ludovico e Beatrice Sforza', *Archivio Storico Lombardo*, XVII, 1890, pp. 74-119, 346-99, 619-74.

Luzio and Renier, 1890[2]
A. Luzio and R. Renier, 'I Filelfo e l'Umanesimo alla corte dei Gonzaga', *Giornale stor. della letteratura ital.*, XVI, 1890, pp. 119-217.

Luzio and Renier, 1893[1]
A. Luzio and R. Renier, *Mantova e Urbino, Isabella d'Este ed Elisabetta Gonzaga nelle Relazione Famigliare, e nelle Vicende Politiche*, Turin, 1893.

Luzio and Renier, 1893[2]
A. Luzio and R. Renier, 'Niccolò da Correggio', *Giornale Storico della Letteratura Italiana*, XXI, 1893, pp. 205-64.

Luzio and Renier, 1896
A. Luzio, 'Il lusso di Isabella d'Este, Marchesa di Mantova', *Nuova Antologia*, serie IV, 1896, LXIII, pp. 441-69; LXIV, pp. 294-324; LXV, pp. 261-86, 666-88.

Luzio and Renier, 1899, 1903
A. Luzio and R. Renier, 'La coltura e le relazioni letterarie d'Isabella d'Este Gonzaga', *Giornale Storico della letteratura italiana*, XXXIII, 1899, pp. 1-62; XXXIV, 1899, pp. 1-97; XLII, 1903, pp. 75-111.

Luzio, 1899
A. Luzio, 'La Madonna della Vittoria del Mantegna', *Emporium*, Nov. 1899, pp. 358f.

Luzio, 1908[1]
A. Luzio, 'Isabella d'Este e il sacco di Roma', *Archivio Storico Lombardo*, X, 1908, pp. 5-107, 361-425.

Luzio, 1908[2]
A. Luzio, *Isabella d'Este e Francesco Gonzaga Promessi Sposi*, Milan, 1908.

Luzio, 1909
A. Luzio, 'Isabella d'Este e Giulio II', *Rivista d'Italia*, XII, fasc. 12, Rome, 1909, pp. 837-76.

Luzio, 1911
A. Luzio, 'Le strane vicende di un quadro del Rubens', *Archivio Storico Italiano*, XLVII, 1911, pp. 406-13.

Luzio, 1913
A. Luzio, *La Galleria dei Gonzaga venduta all'Inghilterra nel 1627-8*, Milan, 1913 (repr. Rome, 1974).

Luzio, 1914-15
A. Luzio, 'Isabella d'Este e i Borgia', *Archivio Storico Lombardo*, XLI, 1914, pp. 469-553, 673-753; XLII, 1915, pp. 115-67, 412-64.

Luzio, 1917-18
A. Luzio, 'I carteggi dell'Archivio Gonzaga riflettenti Inghilterra', *Atti della R. Accademia delle scienze di Torino*, LIII, 1917-18, pp. 167-82, 209-22.

Luzio, 1922
A. Luzio, *L'Archivio Gonzaga*, vol. II, Verona, 1922.

MacClintock, 1966
C. MacClintock, *Giaches de Wert (1535-1596). Life and Works*, n.p., 1966.

Magnaguti I, 1913; II, 1915.
A. Magnaguti, *Studi intorno alla Zecca di Mantova*, I. *I Marchesi, 1433-1530*, Milan, 1913; II. *I Duchi 1530-1627*, Milan, 1915.

Magnaguti, 1923
A. Magnaguti, 'Numismatica Virgiliana', *Atti Acc. Virgiliana*, N.S. 45-46, 1921-23, pp. 276-93.

Magnaguti, 1957, 1965
A. Magnaguti, *Ex nummis historia*, vols. VII, IX, Rome, 1957, 1965.

Magnusson, 1977
B. Magnusson, 'Rubens som tecknare' in *Rubens i Sverige* (ed. G. Cavalli-Björkman), Stockholm, 1977, pp. 86-130, 154-65.

Maier, 1964
Ed. B. Maier, *Il libro del Cortegiano con una scelta delle Opere minori di Baldesar Castiglione*, 2nd. edn., Turin, 1964.

Mallet, 1981
J.V.G. Mallet, 'Mantua and Urbino', Gonzaga Patronage of Maiolica', *Apollo*, September 1981, pp. 162-69.

Mann, 1938, 1943
J. Mann, 'The Lost Armoury of the Gonzagas' *Archaeological Journal*, XCV, 1938, pp. 239-336; C, 1943, pp. 16-127.

Mann, 1975
N. Mann, 'Petrarch MSS in the British Isles', *Italia medioevale e Umanistica*, XVIII, 1975, pp. 139-527.

Mantua, *Mostra Iconog.*, 1937
Mostra Iconografica Gonzaghesca, ed. N. Giannantoni, Mantua, May-September 1937.

Mantua, *Mostra Mantegna*, 1961
Andrea Mantegna, exhibition Catalogue (Mantua, 1961), ed. G. Paccagnini, Venice, 1961.

Mantua, 1972
Pisanello alla corte dei Gonzaga, exhibition catalogue, ed. G. Paccagnini, Mantua, 1972.

Mantua, *Sant'Andrea*, 1974
Il Sant'Andrea di Mantova e Leon Battista Alberti, *Atti del Convegno* (1972), Mantua, 1974.

Mantua, *Tesori*, 1974
Tesori d'arte nella terra dei Gonzaga, Mantua, Palazzo Ducale, Sept.-Nov. 1974.

Mantua, *Convegno*, 1978
Mantova e i Gonzaga nella civiltà de Rinascimento: Atti del Convegno, Mantova 1974, Milan, 1978.

Mantua, *Rubens*, 1977
Rubens a Mantova, Catalogue ed. G. Mulazzani, U. Bazzotti, D. Mattioli, S. Muliari Moro, R. Navarrini, F. Negrini, Mantua, 1977.

Mantua, *Scienza*, 1979
La Scienza a Corte (published in association with the *Mostra*, 1979), ed. A. Franchini and others, Rome, 1979.

Marani, 1957
E. Marani, 'Una ricostruzione del duomo di Mantova nell'età romanica', *Bollettino storico mantovano*, 7, July-Sept. 1957, pp. 161-85.

Marani and Perina, II, 1961
E. Marani and C. Perina, *Mantova: Le Arti II*, Mantua, 1961.

Marani and Perina, III, 1965
E. Marani and C. Perina, *Mantova: Le Arti III*, Mantua, 1965.

Martelli, 1966
M. Martelli, 'I pensieri architettonici del Magnifico', *Commentari*, XVII, 1966, pp. 107-11.

Martindale, 1964
A. Martindale, 'The Patronage of Isabella

XIII

d'Este at Mantua', *Apollo*, LXXIX, 1964, pp. 183-91.

Martindale and Garavaglia, 1967
A. MARTINDALE AND N. GARAVAGLIA, *The Complete Paintings of Mantegna*, London and New York, 1967.

Martindale, 1979[1]
A. MARTINDALE, 'The Middle Age of Andrea Mantegna', *Journal of the Royal Society of Arts*, September 1979, pp. 627-40.

Martindale, 1979[2]
A. MARTINDALE, *The Triumphs of Caesar by Andrea Mantegna*, London, 1979.

Martinelli, 1626, 1628
G.A. MARTINELLI, *In funere serenissime Ferdinandi Mantuae ducis oratio*, Mantua, 1626; *Orationi nelle esequie del serenissimo Vincenzo II Gonzaga*, Verona, 1628.

Mayer, 1929
A. MAYER, 'Francesco Bonsignori als Bildnismaler', *Pantheon*, IV, 1929, pp. 345-55.

Mazzoldi, 1960, 1963
L. MAZZOLDI, *Mantova: La Storia*, II, Mantua, 1960; III, Mantua, 1963.

Meiss, 1957
M. MEISS, *Andrea Mantegna as Illuminator*, Glückstadt, 1957.

Meroni, 1966
U. MERONI, *Mostra dei Codici Gonzagheschi 1328-1540*, Mantua, 1966.

Milan, *Storia*, 1958, 1961
Milan, *Storia di Milano*, ed. G. Treccani degli Alfieri, IX, 1961; XI, 1958.

Milan, *Tiziano*, 1977
Omaggio a Tiziano, la cultura artistica milanese nell'età di Carlo V, Milan, 1977.

Millar, 1960
O. MILLAR, *Abraham van der Doort's catalogue of the collections of Charles I*, Walpole Society, XXXVII, 1960.

Millar, 1972
Ed. O. MILLAR, *The Age of Charles I*, Tate Gallery, London, 1972.

Montesinos, 1931
J. MONTESINOS, *Cartas inéditas de Juan de Valdes al cardenal Gonzaga*, Madrid, 1931.

Monteverdi, 1638
C. MONTEVERDI, *Madrigali guerrieri et amorosi... libro ottavo*, Venice, 1638.

Muentz, 1888
E. MUENTZ, *Les collections des Médicis an XVe siècle*, Paris, 1888.

Mulazzani, 1979
G. MULAZZANI, 'La fonte letteraria della "Camera degli sposi" di Mantegna', *Arte Lombarda*, n.s., 50, 1979, pp. 33-46.

Müller Hofstede, 1977
J. MÜLLER HOFSTEDE, 'Rubens in Italien', in Exh. *Peter Paul Rubens. Katalog I*, Cologne, 1977, pp. 13-354.

Mumford, 1979
I. MUMFORD, 'Some decorative aspects of the Imprese of Isabella d'Este', *Italian Studies*, XXXIV, 1979, pp. 60-70.

Mustard, 1911
W.P. MUSTARD, ed., *The Eclogues of Baptista Mantuanus*, Baltimore, 1911.

Neumann, 1968-69
J. NEUMANN, 'Aus den Jugendjahren Peter Paul Rubens', *Jahrbuch des Kunsthistorischen Institutes der Universität Graz*, III-IV, 1968-69, pp. 73-134.

Negri, 1954
L. NEGRI, 'Giovanni Battista Covo, l'architetto d'Isabella d'Este,' *Rivista d'Arte*, XXIX, 1954, pp. 54-96.

Neverov, 1977
O. NEVEROV, *Kameya Gonzaga*, Leningrad, 1977.

Noël Sainsbury, 1859
W. NOËL SAINSBURY, *Original Unpublished Papers illustrative of the life of Sir Peter Paul Rubens, as an artist and a diplomatist...*, London, 1859.

Nolhac and Solerti, 1890
P. NOLHAC AND A. SOLERTI, *Il viaggio in Italia di Enrico III re di Francia e le Feste a Venezia Ferrara, Mantova e Torino*, Rome, Turin, Naples, 1890.

Norman, 1976
A.V.B. NORMAN, *Wallace Collection, Catalogue of Ceramics*, I, London, 1976.

Norris, 1975
C. NORRIS, 'The Tempio della Santissima Trinità at Mantua', *Burlington Magazine*, CXVII, 1975, pp. 72-79.

Norton, 1957
P. NORTON, 'The lost Sleeping Cupid of Michelangelo', *Art Bulletin*, XXXIX, 1957, pp. 251-57.

Orioli, 1892
P. ORIOLI, *Arte ed iscrizioni della basilica di L.B. Alberti fiorentino o S. Andrea in Mantua*, Mantua, 1892.

Orioli, 1896
P. ORIOLI, *Il pensiero religioso civile, artistico. Reminiscenze, arte ed iscrizioni nel Duomo di Mantova*, Mantua, 1896.

Ozzòla, 1949
L. OZZÒLA, *La galleria di Mantova, Palazzo Ducale*, Cremona, 1949.

Ozzòla, 1951
L. OZZÒLA, *Il Museo d'arte medievale e moderna del Palazzo Ducale di Mantova*, Mantua, 1951.

Ozzòla, 1952
L. OZZÒLA, 'Restauro di un Rubens a Mantova', *Bollettino d'Arte*, XXXVII, 1952, pp. 77f.

Ozzòla, 1953
L. OZZÒLA, 'Mattonelle isabelliane', *Faenza*, XXXIX, 1953.

Paccagnini, 1956
G. PACCAGNINI, 'Dipinti di Domenico Feti a Mantua', *Critica d'arte*, n.s., III, 1956, pp. 578-84.

Paccagnini, 1960
G. PACCAGNINI, *Mantova, Le arti*, I, Mantua, 1960.

Paccagnini, 1961[1]
G. PACCAGNINI, 'Appunti sulla tecnica della "camera picta" di Andrea Mantegna', *Studi in onore di Mario Salmi*, 3 vols., Rome, 1961, vol. l, pp. 395-403.

Paccagnini, 1961[2]
G. PACCAGNINI, 'Il Mantegna e la plastica dell'Italia settentrionale', *Bollettino d'arte*, 4th ser., XLVI, 1961.

Paccagnini, 1969
G. PACCAGNINI, *Il palazzo Ducale di Mantova*, Turin, 1969.

Paccagnini, 1972
G. PACCAGNINI, *Pisanello e il ciclo cavalleresco di Mantova*, Venice, 1972; English edn., *Pisanello*, London, 1973.

Pächt and Alexander, 1970
O. PÄCHT AND J.J.C. ALEXANDER, *Illuminated Manuscripts in the Bodleian Library*, Oxford, vol. 2, *Italian School*, Oxford, 1970.

Panofsky, 1961
E. PANOFSKY, *The Iconography of Correggio's Camera di San Paolo*, London, 1961.

Paris-Brussels-Amsterdam, 1970-71
Dessins du Nationalmuseum de Stockholm: Collection du Comte Tessin (P. Bjurström), Paris-Brussels-Amsterdam, 1970-71.

Paris, 1977
Le siècle de Rubens dans les collections publiques francaises. Exh. Grand Palais, Paris, 1977-78 (J. Foucart, J. Lacambre etc.).

Pelati, 1973
P. PELATI, 'L'impresa del crogiuolo in tessuti gonzagheschi', *Civiltà Mantovana*, VII, 1973, pp. 312-22.

Perina, 1965
C. PERINA, *La basilica di S. Andrea in Mantova*, Mantua, 1965.

Pescasio, 1972
L. PESCASIO, *Pietro Adamo de Micheli Proto editore mantovano*, Mantua, 1972.

Piccinelli, 1653
F. PICCINELLI, *Mondo simbolico*, Milan, 1653.

Planiscig, 1930
L. PLANISCIG, *Piccoli bronzi italiani del rinascimento*, Milan, 1930.

Plon, 1887
E. PLON, *Les Maîtres italiens au service de la Maison d'Autriche. Leone Leoni et Pompeo Leoni*, Paris, 1887.

Polidori, 1953
G. POLIDORI, *Studi Artistici Urbinati*, II, Urbino (Accademia Raffaello), 1953.

Polidori, 1962
G. POLIDORI, 'Nicolò Pellipario, con particolare cenno ad una sua fase stilistica', *Pantheon*, XX, Jahrgang 1962, pp. 348-55.

Pope-Hennessy, 1961
J. POPE-HENNESSY, Rijksmuseum, *Meesters van het brons der Italiaanse Renaissance*, Amsterdam, 1961.

Popham and Pouncey, 1950
A.E. POPHAM AND P. POUNCEY, *Italian Drawings in the Department of Prints and Drawings in the British Museum, the 14th and 15th Centuries*, 2 vols., London, 1950.

Popham and Wilde, 1949
A.E. POPHAM AND J. WILDE, *The Italian Drawings of the XV and XVI Centuries in the Collection of His Majesty the King at Windsor Castle*, London, 1949.

Portioli, 1877-78
A. PORTIOLI, 'Monumenti a Virgilio in Mantova', *Atti Acc. Virgiliana*, 1877-78, pp. 3-30.

Portioli, 1879
A. PORTIOLI, *La zecca di Mantova*, Mantua, 1879.

Pouncey and Gere, 1962
P. Pouncey and J. Gere, *Italian Drawings in the British Museum, Raphael and his circle*, 2 vols., London, 1962

Praticò, 1949
G. Praticò, 'Lorenzo il magnifico e i Gonzaga', *Archivio storico Italiano*, CVII, 1949, pp. 155-71.

Prizer, 1978
W.F. Prizer, II, 'La cappella di Francesco II Gonzaga e la musica sacra a Mantova nel primo ventennio del cinquecento', *see above*, Mantua, Convegno, 1978.

Pungileone, 1818
P.L. Pungileone, *Lettere sopra Marcello Donati.. Medico del Duca Guglielmo Gonzaga etc.*, Parma, 1818.

Puppi, 1972
L. Puppi, *Il trittico di Andrea Mantegna per la Basilica di San Zeno Maggiore in Verona*, Verona, 1972; reviewed by V. Herzner, *Art Bulletin*, LVI, Sept. 1974, pp. 440-42.

Rackham, 1933
B. Rackham, *Victoria and Albert Museum, Guide to Italian Maiolica*, London, 1933.

Rackham, 1940
B. Rackham, *Victoria and Albert Museum, Catalogue of Italian Maiolica*, London, 1940.

Rackham, 1945
B. Rackham, 'Nicola Pellipario and Bramante', *Burlington Magazine*, LXXXVI, 1945, pp. 144-48.

Rasmussen, 1972
J. Rasmussen, 'Zum Werk des Majolikamalers Nicolò da Urbino', *Keramos*, 58, 1972, pp. 51-64.

Resti-Ferrari, 1926-27
M. Resti-Ferrari, 'Aggiunte al codice diplomatico mantegnesco del Kristeller', *Atti Acc. Virgiliana*, n.s., XIX-XX, 1926-27, pp. 263-80 (published separately, Modena, 1928).

Rhodes, 1954
D.E. Rhodes, 'A book from the Gonzaga Library at Mantua', *Journal of the Warburg and Courtauld Institutes*, XXII, 1954, pp. 377-80.

Rhodes, 1955, 1956, 1964
D.E. Rhodes, 'A Bibliography of Mantua', *La Bibliofilia*, LVII-LVIII, 1955-56; LXVI, 1964.

Richter, 1937
G. Richter, *Giorgio da Castelfranco*, Chicago, 1937.

Rigoni, 1927-28, 1970
E. Rigoni, 'Nuovi documenti sul Mantegna', *Atti del Reale Istituto Veneto di Scienze, Lettere ed Arti*, 87, pt. 2, 1927-28, pp. 1165-186. Reprinted in Idem, *L'Arte rinascimentale in Padova. Studi e documenti*, Padua, 1970.

Robert, 1969
C. Robert, *Die antiken Sarkophag-Reliefs* III, 3, Rome, 1969.

Rooses and Ruelens, 1887
M. Rooses and C. Ruelens, *Codex Diplomaticus Rubinianus*, I, Antwerp, 1887.

Rosenthal, 1962
E. Rosenthal, 'The House of Andrea Mantegna in Mantua', *Gazette des Beaux-Arts*, LX, 1962, pp. 327-48.

Rossi, 1888
U. Rossi, 'I medaglisti del Rinascimento alla Corte di Mantova. II, Pier Jacopo Alari-Bonacolsi detto l'Antico', *Rivista italiana di numismatica*, I, 1888, pp. 161-94, 433-38.

Rubsamen, 1943
W.H. Rubsamen, *Literary sources of secular music in Italy (ca. 1500)*, Berkeley and Los Angeles, 1943.

Ruysschaert, 1969
J. Ruysschaert, 'Miniaturistes "romains" à Naples', in T. de Marinis, *La Biblioteca Napolitana dei Re d'Aragona*, supplemento, To. I, Verona, 1969, pp. 263-74.

Salmatia (Salmazia), 1626
A. Salmatia, *Breve raguaglio del funerale fatto al sereniss. Ferdinando che fu Duca di Mantova e di Monferrato, dal sereniss. Signor duca Vincenzo [II] suo Fratello e successore*, Mantua [1626].

Salmazia, 1628
A. Salmazia, *Breve raguaglio del funerale Fatto al sereniss. Vincenzo [II] che fu Duca di Mantova e di Monferrato dal Serenissimo Signor duca Carlo suo zio e successore nella ducal chiesa di Santa Barbara di Mantova il dì 18 di febraro 1628*, Mantua [1628].

Schizzerotto, 1977
G. Schizzerotto, *Cultura e vita civile a Mantova fra '300 e '500*, Florence, 1977.

Schizzerotto, 1979
G. Schizzerotto, *Rubens a Mantova fra Gesuiti, principi e pittori con spigolature sul suo soggiorno italiano (1600-1608)*, Mantua, 1979.

Schloder, 1975
J. Schloder, 'Les Costa du Studiolo d'Isabella d'Este: sources iconographiques', *La Revue du Louvre et des Musées de France*, XXV, no. 3, 1975, pp. 230-33.

Schmitt, 1961
U. Schmitt, 'Francesco Bonsignori', *Münchner Jahrbuch der Bildenden Kunst*, 3. Folge, XII, 1961, pp. 73-152.

Schrade, 1964
L. Schrade, *Monteverdi. Creator of Modern music*, London, 1964.

Scott-Elliot, 1959
A. Scott-Elliot, 'The statues from Mantua in the collection of King Charles I', *Burlington Magazine*, CI, 1959, pp. 218-27.

Secco d'Aragona, 1956
F. Secco d'Aragona, 'Francesco Secco, i Gonzaga e Paola Erba', *Archivio Storico lombardo* 1956, pp. 210-61.

Shearman, forthcoming *Catalogue*
J. Shearman, *Catalogue of the Earlier Italian Paintings at Hampton Court*.

Sherr, 1978
R. Sherr, 'The publications of Guglielmo Gonzaga', *Journal of the American Musicological Society*, XXXI, 1978, p. 118.

Signorini, 1972
R. Signorini, 'Sugli affreschi della "Camera Picta"', 'I magi alla Camera degli Sposi', 'Il Mantegna firmò la sua camera', *Gazzetta di Mantova*, 21 & 23 May, 3 September, 5 October 1972.

Signorini, 1974
R. Signorini, 'Federico III e Cristiano I nella camera degli sposi di Mantegna', *Mitteilungen des Kunsthistorischen Institutes in Florenz*, XVIII, 1974, pp. 227-50.

Signorini, 1975
R. Signorini, 'Lettura storica degli affreschi della "Camera degli Sposi" di Andrea Mantegna', *Journal of the Warburg and Courtauld Institutes*, XXXVIII, 1975, pp. 109-35.

Signorini, 1976
R. Signorini, 'L'autoritratto del Mantegna nella Camera degli Sposi', *Mitteilungen des Kunsthistorischen Institutes in Florenz*, XX, 1976, pp. 205-12.

Signorini, 1977
R. Signorini, 'Il paesaggio dell'Incontro nell'affresco della "Camera degli Sposi" e le sue fonti', *Civiltà Mantovana*, XI, 1977, pp. 1-25.

Signorini, 1979
R. Signorini (ed.), *In traccia del Magister Pelicanus: Mostra documentaria su Vittorino da Feltre*, Mantua, 1979.

Strunk, 1947
O. Strunk, 'Guglielmo Gonzaga and Palestrina's Missa Domenicalis' in *Essays in music in the Western world*, New York, 1974, p. 94 (reprinted from *Musical Quarterly*, XXXIII, 1947, p. 228).

Tagmann, 1967
P.M. Tagmann: *Archivalische Studien zur Musikpflege am Dom von Mantua (1500-1627)*, Bern, 1967.

Tagmann, 1970
P.M. Tagmann, 'La cappella dei maestri cantori della basilica palatina di S. Barbara a Mantova (1565-1630): Nuovo materiale scoperto negli archivi mantovani', *Civiltà Mantovana*, IV, 1970, p. 376.

Tellini Perina, 1967
Tellini Perina, *Mantova: Duomo* (Tesori d'arte cristiana, 4), Bologna, 1967, pp. 449-76.

Taja, 1750
A. Taja, *Descrizione del Palazzo Apostolico*, Rome, 1750.

Tietze-Conrat, 1955
E. Tietze-Conrat, *Mantegna*, London, 1955.

Toesca, 1973
I. Toesca, 'Lancaster e Gonzaga: il fregio della sala del Pisanello nel Palazzo Ducale di Mantova', *Civiltà mantovana*, VII, 1973, pp. 361-77.

Toesca, 1974
I. Toesca, 'A Frieze by Pisanello', *Burlington Magazine*, CXVI, 1974, pp. 210-14.

Toesca, 1979
I. Toesca, 'More about the Pisanello Murals at Mantua', *Burlington Magazine*, CXVIII, 1976, pp. 622-29.

Toesca, 1977
I. Toesca, 'Altre osservazioni in margine alle pitture del Pisanello nel Palazzo Ducale di Mantova', *Civiltà mantovana*, XI, 1977, pp. 349-76.

Tonelli, 1797-1800
F. Tonelli, *Ricerche storiche di Mantova*, vols. I-II, Mantua, 1797-1800; vol. III, Mantua, 1798; vol. IV, Mantua, 1800.

Trapp, 1980
J.B. Trapp, 'The Poet and the Monumental Impulse', *Society for Renaissance Studies Occasional Papers*, 6, 1980.

Van de Velde, 1978-79
C. Van de Velde, 'L'intinéraire italien de Rubens', *Bulletin de l'Institute Historique Belge de Rome*, XLVIII-XLIX, 1978-79, pp. 238-59.

Varese, 1967
L. Varese, *Lorenzo Costa*, Milan, 1967.

Vasari ed. Milanesi
G. Vasari (ed. G. Milanesi), *Giorgio Vasari. Le opere. Le vite de' più eccellenti pittori scultori ed,*

architettori. Con nuove annotazione e commenti, 9 vols., Florence, 1878-85.

Vasić Vatovec, 1979
C. Vasić Vatovec, Luca Fancelli, architetto. Epistolario Gonzaghesco, Florence, 1979.

Venturi, 1888
A. Venturi, 'Gian Cristoforo Romano', Archivio Storico dell'Arte, I, 1888, pp. 49-59, 107-18, 148-58.

Venturi, 1889
A. Venturi, 'Ercole de' Roberti', Archivio Storico dell'Arte, II, 1889, pp. 339-60.

Venturi, 1896
A. Venturi, Vasari, Le Vite, vol. I: Gentile da Fabriano e Pisanello, Florence, 1896.

Venturi, VI, 1908; VII, 1914; X (1), 1935
A. Venturi, Storia dell'arte italiana, VI, Milan, 1908, VIII (3), 1914; X (1) 1935.

Verheyen, 1966
E. Verheyen, 'Correggio's Amori di Giove', Journal of the Warburg and Courtauld Institutes, XXIX, 1966, pp. 160-92.

Verheyen, 1967
E. Verheyen, 'Jacopo Strada's Mantuan drawings of 1567-1568', Art Bulletin, XLIX, 1967, pp. 62-70.

Verheyen, 1971
E. Verheyen, The Paintings in the Studiolo of Isabella d'Este at Mantua, New York, 1971.

Verheyen, 1977
E. Verheyen, The Palazzo del Te in Mantua.

Images of Love and Politics, Johns Hopkins University Press, Baltimore and London, 1977.

Vienna, 1977
Kunsthistorisches Museum, Peter Paul Rubens, 1577-1640 (G. Heinz, K. Schutz etc.), Vienna, 1977.

Vogel, 1887
E. Vogel, 'Claudio Monteverdi', Vierteljahrschrift für Musikwissenschaft, III, 1887.

von Falke, 1914, 1923
O. von Falke, Die Majolikasammlung Alfred Pringsheim in München, The Hague, vol. I, 1914; vol. II, 1923.

Wagner, 1959
Sir A.R. Wagner, 'The Swan Badge and the Swan Knight', Archaeologia, XCVII, 1959, pp. 129-39.

Wallen, 1968
B. Wallen, 'A Majolica Panel in the Widener Collection', National Gallery of Art, Report and Studies in the History of Art, Washington, 1968, pp. 94-105.

Wallis, 1905
H. Wallis, XVII Plates by Nicola Fontana da Urbino at the Correr Museum, Venice. A Study in Early XVIth Century Maiolica with Illustrations by Henry Wallis, London, 1905.

Ward-Jackson, 1979
P. Ward-Jackson, Victoria and Albert Museum: Catalogue of Italian Drawings, vol. I: 14th - 16th Century, London, 1979.

Wardrop, 1957
B. Fiera (ed. J. Wardrop), De Iusticia Pingenda, London, 1957.

Wardrop, 1963
J. Wardrop, The Script of Humanism, London, 1963.

Weiss, 1969
R. Weiss, The Renaissance Discovery of Classical Antiquity, Oxford, 1969.

Wethey, 1969, 1971, 1975
Wethey, The Paintings of Titian (3 vols.), London, 1969, 1971, 1975.

Weyerman, 1729
J.C. Weyerman, De Levens-beschryvingen der Nederlandsche Konst-schilders, I, The Hague, 1729.

Wind, 1948
E. Wind, Bellini's Feast of the Gods, Cambridge, Mass., 1948.

Wittkower, 1962
R. Wittkower, Architectural Principles in the Age of Humanism, London, 1962.

Woodward, 1897
W.H. Woodward, Vittorino da Feltre and other humanist Educators, Cambridge, 1897; repr. Columbia, 1963.

Yriarte, 1895
C. Yriarte, 'Isabella d'Este et les artistes de son temps', Gazette des Beaux-Arts, ser. 3, XIII-XIV, 1895, pp. 189f, 382f, 394f.

Zanoli, 1973
A. Zanoli, 'Sugli Affreschi del Pisanello', Paragone, 24, 1973, pp. 23-44.

View of Mantua, c. 1550 (see Cat. 72).

Introduction

Mantua and the Gonzaga
by D.S. Chambers

An Englishman, Thomas Coryat, who visited Mantua in 1608 when the Gonzaga were at the height of their grandeur, wrote "This is the citie which of all other places in the world I would wish to make my habitation in... London whiche both for frequencie of people and multitude of houses doth thrise exceed it, is not better furnished with gardens". London grew while Mantua, which even in its heyday had only 30-40,000 inhabitants, did not; and many of its original features (if not the abundance of gardens) are still recognizable. A later English visitor, Aldous Huxley, called it "the most romantic city in the world" and, in another context, a place "pregnant with the memory of splendour".

It is best approached from the east, where the rich agricultural land of the Lombard plain is suddenly interrupted by lakes; formed by the river Mincio as it flows on to join the Po, these lakes surround Mantua on three sides, making a strong defence. The long bridge which Còryat compared to London Bridge no longer exists, but from an asphalted causeway one discerns, often through mist or fog which prevails in this part of Italy, the outlines of the enormous precinct of the Gonzaga court: a complex of palaces built in different periods, the Castello di San Giorgio and the tower of the palatine church of Santa Barbara. Mantua was already distinguished as the birthplace of Virgil and the sanctuary (in the church of Sant'Andrea) of a relic of the Blood of Christ; these assets remained as a source of civic pride. But its central historical experience was to have been the seat of government of the Gonzaga dynasty from 1328 to 1708, and this is still monumentally evident.

The Gonzaga family rose as local landowners (originally their name was Corradi and they came from Gonzaga, south of the river Po); dominating Mantua and its territory they later became princes and patrons of European importance. The time span within this exhibition is mainly confined to two out of the four Gonzagan centuries; it begins effectively in 1433, when Gianfrancesco Gonzaga was created a Marquis by the Emperor Sigismund, thus transcending his merely urban – and in origin elective – office of Captain, and it ends with the disasters of 1627-30: financial crisis, male succession crisis, siege, plague and sack of the city by an imperial army sent to overthrow the adoptive heir:

events which provide a clear breaking-off point in the history of Gonzaga ascendancy. The Exhibition illustrates, therefore, the rise, heyday and decline of an ambitious family, its expressions of the princely virtue of magnificence, the propagation of its own historical legends, the influence upon it of humanist learning and ideas, its art collections and patronage. Greater cities and other famous dynasties and courts may be preferred to characterize Italian Renaissance civilization, but the longlasting Gonzaga of Mantua provide one of the most coherent and spectacular examples.

A sub-theme also runs throughout the exhibition, the relations of Gonzaga Mantua and England. The Gonzaga were somewhat exceptional among Italian princely dynasties in their many links with Northern Europe. Partly owing to Mantua's position (directly south of the Brenner Pass route into Italy) and its tradition of deference to the authority of the Emperor, the strongest of these links was German; there were many marriages with leading German dynasties, and a number with French. Although there were no English marriages, and only one Gonzaga is definitely known to have visited England, Duke Federico's brother Ferrante who met Henry VIII in 1544 and Queen Mary in 1555, diplomatic courtesies and gifts were for long exchanged until Reformation politics made it impossible in Queen Elizabeth's reign. Ambassadors had come and gone in both directions and there was certainly an awareness of Mantua in sixteenth century England, not least for its thoroughbred horses and Latin poetry. It may come as a surprise to find an Italian exhibition which begins and ends with portraits of Kings of England, but Henry VI has his place to represent goodwill towards the Gonzaga, which included the concession to use Lancastrian livery devices, and Charles I appears because he acquired a large part of the Gonzaga art collection in 1627-30.

What distinguishes the Gonzaga as a princely family? They emerged in the fourteenth century from a rather limited background; they had not the aristocracy of lineage of the Estensi of Ferrara or the Visconti of Milan, nor wealth on the scale of some of the patrician dynasties of Florence. They had to seek advantageous marriages and military leadership to gain reputation. By marriage the Gonzaga constantly widened the dis-

THE GONZAGA

N.B.: Dates of birth and death of Gonzaga rulers are shown. For dates of succession see the previous ruler's year of death.

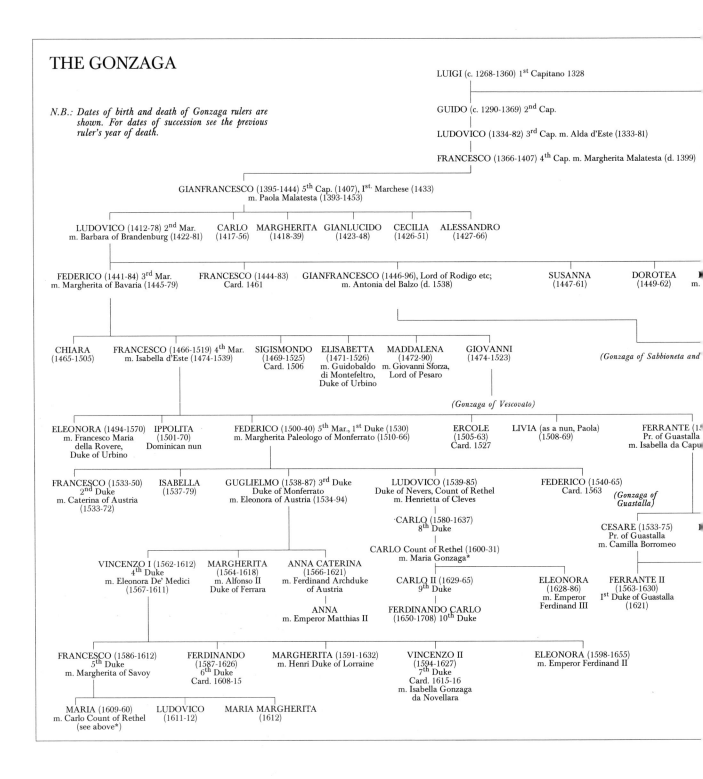

tance between themselves and other local families; not only did they go for prestigious Italian dynasties, the Malatesta of Rimini, Montefeltri of Urbino, the Estensi and (in the later sixteenth century) the ducal Medici of Florence, but – as already mentioned – for Hohenzollerns, Wittelsbachs and Habsburgs. Thanks to his good relations with the Emperor Charles V (for the Gonza-

ga, the advance of the Imperial and Spanish control in Italy was no tragedy) Marchese Federico was created Duke of Mantua in 1530 and through his marriage with Margherita Paleologo acquired for his heirs a second principality, Monferrato in Piedmont; his younger son Ludovico became by marriage Duke of Nevers in France. Only with the marriages of Duke Vincenzo I's off-

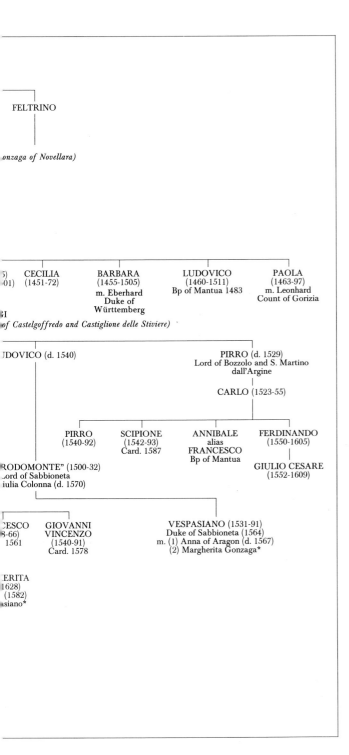

FELTRINO

(…onzaga of Novellara)

…5) …01)	CECILIA (1451-72)	BARBARA (1455-1505) m. Eberhard Duke of Württemberg	LUDOVICO (1460-1511) Bp of Mantua 1483	PAOLA (1463-97) m. Leonhard Count of Gorizia

…I …of Castelgoffredo and Castiglione delle Stiviere)

…JDOVICO (d. 1540)   PIRRO (d. 1529)
                                               Lord of Bozzolo and S. Martino
                                                      dall'Argine

                                               CARLO (1523-55)

PIRRO (1540-92)	SCIPIONE (1542-93) Card. 1587	ANNIBALE alias FRANCESCO Bp of Mantua	FERDINANDO (1550-1605)

…RODOMONTE" (1500-32)   GIULIO CESARE
…ord of Sabbioneta   (1552-1609)
…iulia Colonna (d. 1570)

…CESCO   GIOVANNI   VESPASIANO (1531-91)
8-66)   VINCENZO   Duke of Sabbioneta (1564)
1561   (1540-91)   m. (1) Anna of Aragon (d. 1567)
             Card. 1578   (2) Margherita Gonzaga*

…ERITA
1628)
(1582)
…siano*

who remained childless, and the third son, Vincenzo II, broke all traditions by marrying a Gonzaga relative, a widow too old for childbearing. The daughters did better; Margherita married the Duke of Lorraine and Eleonora in a sense reached the summit of Gonzaga ambitions, for she married the Emperor Ferdinand II in 1622. But this did not compensate enough for the consequence of her brothers' failure to leave a male heir; she could not stop her husband sending in the troops in 1629 to oppose the succession of the Gonzaga line of Nevers.

As military leaders the Gonzaga vaunted prestigious and lucrative captaincies on behalf of greater powers in the fifteenth and sixteenth centuries. The fame of their deeds came to be expressed in art and literature but in truth their war records were not wholly glorious. In the war of Visconti Milan against Venice Ludovico as Commander of the Venetian army was involved in its worst defeat (1448); Marchese Francesco failed to preserve discipline and to follow up the supposed victory he had won for the Italian League against the French at Fornovo (1495), and in 1509 he was taken prisoner in humiliating circumstances; Federico in general avoided the hot spots during the wars of the 1520's apart from his few weeks' defence of Pavia against the French in 1522. Minor episodes were inflated beyond their true significance in Gonzagan military mythography, although various members of the family not in the direct succession had highly professional military careers: for instance Gianfrancesco in the fifteenth or Ferrante of Guastalla and Vespasiano of Sabbioneta in the sixteenth century. But the rulers of Mantua were not distinguished as heroic warriors, and their posture as such reached a point of grandiose absurdity with Duke Vincenzo I's three expeditions against the Turks in Hungary in 1595, 1597 and 1601. Fortunately, after 1397 the Gonzaga were never tested by a full-scale military attack on Mantua itself, until 1629.

Their most recurrent strategic and defensive warfare was against the menace of the river Po in flood; their image as champion horsemen, ready to excel in battle, was best expressed by their passion for hunting, their fighting ranks not soldiers but dogs. Dogs and horsebreeding were among their strongest interests; the Gonzaga stables contained 650 horses in 1488, and many

spring did things go less well. The eldest son Francesco married Margherita of Savoy in 1608, which was supposed to secure good relations with the jealous Dukes of Savoy concerning Monferrato; because of his early death in 1612 it had the opposite effect. The second son, ex-Cardinal Ferdinando, renounced his mistress (denying a secret marriage) for Caterina de' Medici

1. *Celebration with fireworks outside the Palazzo Ducale and Cathedral, Mantua, of Eleonora Gonzaga's wedding to the Emperor, 1622 (Cat. 272).*

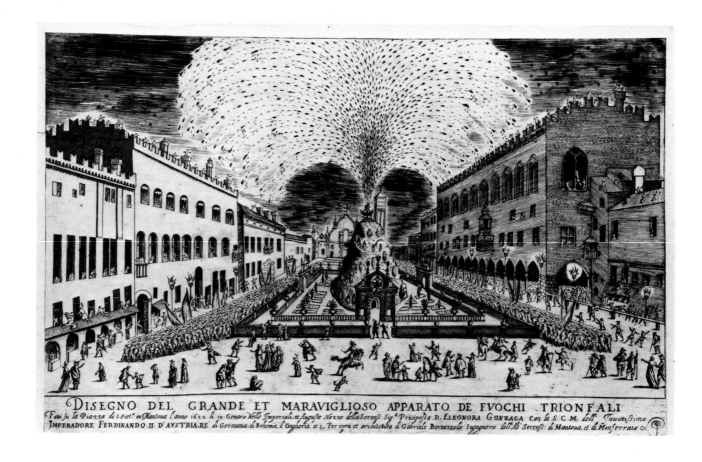

DISEGNO DEL GRANDE ET MARAVIGLIOSO APPARATO DE FVOCHI TRIONFALI
Fatti ſu la Piazza di S.Pietº in Mantoua l'anno 1622 li 19. Genaro Nelle Imperiali, et Auguste Nozze della Sereniſſ. Sigª Prin.peſſa D. ELEONORA GONZAGA con la S. C. M. dell' Inuittiſſimo IMPERADORE FERDINANDO. II. D'AVSTRIA.RE di Germania. di Bohemia, d'Onghería. et ç, Per opra et architettura di Gabriele Bertazzolo Ingegnero dell'Alt Sereniſſ. di Mantoua, et di Monferrato

of them excelled in races throughout Italy. Horses as gifts impressed other rulers; Henry VIII was supplied for years with selections from the Gonzaga breeds, and Duke Guglielmo wanted to give Henri III of France no less than two hundred horses when he came to Mantua in 1574.

Although the Gonzaga had seized power by violence in 1328, it was the oath Luigi the first Captain swore to rule by peace and justice which was emphasized as the earliest Gonzaga Triumph. The preservation of internal peace and relatively benign government was to characterize the regime. Palace conspiracies were rare and no Gonzaga was widely denigrated or assassinated as a tyrant. They provided security and employment, and gratified civic pride by their style as rulers, by the buildings they had erected and the distinguished visitors

they entertained: Pope Pius II in 1459-60, Emperor Charles V in 1530 and 1532, the King of Denmark in 1474, the King of France in 1574 to name but a few. They enjoyed a consensus of support from the leading urban and rural families they had outdistanced, from the petty nobility of the court which they fostered by knighthoods and favours, and from merchants and artisans whose business benefited from their presence in spite of the taxes which were raised. It may be that to dominate so small an urban society as Mantua was relatively uncomplicated and the greater number of the subject population in any case lived their menial lives in the country, many of them on Gonzaga estates; but stability and continuity were certainly among the dynasty's achievements. These even survived the potentially risky subdivisions of lands and authority among their

XX

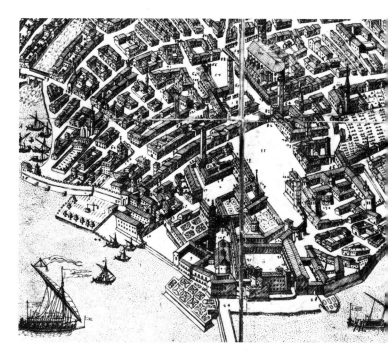

sons made by the first two marchesi Gianfrancesco and Ludovico. From the latter's third son Gianfrancesco (1446-96) were to descend the separate princely lineages of Bozzolo and Sabbioneta, and another principality in the sixteenth century, Guastalla, descended from Ferrante, the third son of Marchese Francesco II. In spite of such territorial compartments Gonzaga rule hung together, and the miniature magnificence of the lesser princely branches must also be recalled, though it cannot be equally represented in the exhibition. More serious for the Gonzaga regime in the century up to 1630 was the separation from its other territory, Monferrato, by a wide corridor of land under the control of the rulers of Milan. But this part of the story must be set aside.

If the Gonzaga family lived in many ways close to the soil, they also had conspicuously heavenward leanings which were expressed by their patronage of Mantuan churches and convents and their traditions of personal piety. The family not only acquired close contacts with and to some extent control of the local clergy but Gonzaga younger sons themselves entered the Church, while many daughters took the veil. By acquiring a cardinal's hat in 1461 for Francesco, the second son of Marchese Ludovico, the Gonzaga set a precedent for other Italian princely families. By 1615 there had been nine more Gonzaga cardinals, not to mention Gonzaga bishops, even a candidate for sainthood in Luigi Gonzaga, a disciple of St. Charles Borromeo. There was almost a Gonzaga pope in the person of Cardinal Ercole, who was a favourite candidate in several conclaves in the middle of the sixteenth century. The splendours of Gonzaga holiness reached a peak with Duke Guglielmo who founded the church of Santa Barbara within the Palace compound (which already contained an earlier church, Santa Croce, not to mention chapels or oratories) and his Habsburg wife Eleonora who assisted the Jesuits in their foundation of Santa Trinità. This religious strand of Gonzaga magnificence – which is not overlooked in the exhibition – reached its final extravagance with Duke Vincenzo I's illusion of himself as a crusading hero, his foundation of an Order of Christian knighthood and the construction within the Ducal Palace of a replica of the Scala Santa at Rome by his brother Cardinal Ferdinando.

In their earthly reality the Gonzaga can scarcely be characterized as splendid either in beauty or brains. Some exceptions come to mind; Duke Federico and his brothers Cardinal Ercole and Ferrante seem to have been better endowed than most of the line, which tended to heavy jowels, thick lips, deformities and chronic disease. Meanwhile only two of the Gonzaga rulers of Mantua, Marchese Ludovico and Duke Ferdinando, might be described as intellectuals. But nearly all of them were memorable as patrons and as such they come into clear focus as the subject for this exhibition, for the sake of works of art which they bought or caused to be made, built, written or performed. Over the two centuries 1430-1630 they persistently combined good judgment, luck and a readiness to spend money, which they did not always have to hand, on the best works and most interesting artists available, keeping in touch through advisers and agents with the centres of talent, Florence, Padua, Venice, Rome and elsewhere. What narrows the focus is that nearly every major artist was imported; we are concerned with Gonzaga court art rather than Mantuan art, and what did grow up from local roots owed most to Gonzaga impetus. In presenting the Gonzaga as a dynasty of collectors attention must be concentrated on a few rather than all; inevitably a personality obtrudes who was only a Gonzaga by marriage, Isabella d'Este, for she was hovering over the Mantuan court for nearly fifty years (1490-1539). Isabella's contribution forms only a part, however, within a long tradition which reached its climax in the accumulations of Dukes Vincenzo I and Ferdinando. Of paintings alone over two thousand were listed in the inventory drawn up in 1627, and these do not include

3. *Palazzo Ducale, Mantua: Plan showing upper floor level with principal apartments mentioned in essays and Catalogue.*

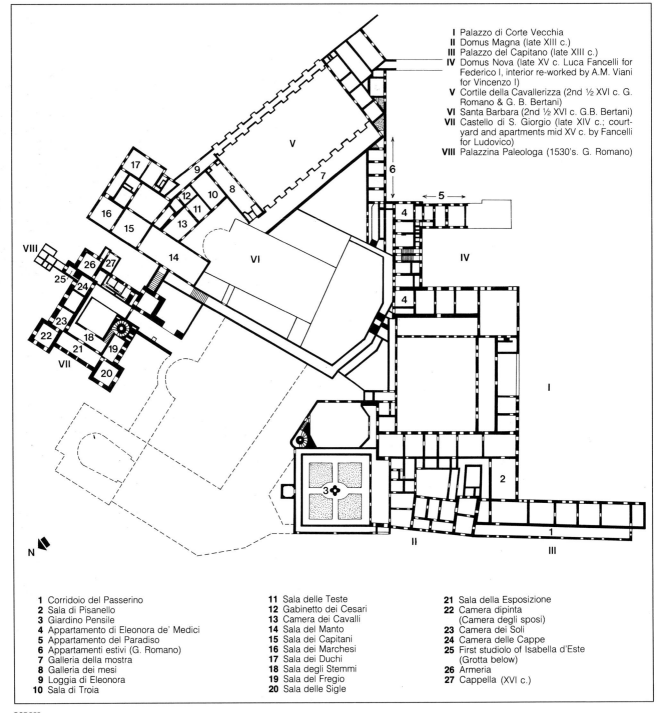

I Palazzo di Corte Vecchia
II Domus Magna (late XIII c.)
III Palazzo del Capitano (late XIII c.)
IV Domus Nova (late XV c. Luca Fancelli for Federico I, interior re-worked by A.M. Viani for Vincenzo I)
V Cortile della Cavallerizza (2nd ½ XVI c. G. Romano & G. B. Bertani)
VI Santa Barbara (2nd ½ XVI c. G.B. Bertani)
VII Castello di S. Giorgio (late XIV c.; courtyard and apartments mid XV c. by Fancelli for Ludovico)
VIII Palazzina Paleologa (1530's. G. Romano)

1 Corridoio del Passerino
2 Sala di Pisanello
3 Giardino Pensile
4 Appartamento di Eleonora de' Medici
5 Appartamento del Paradiso
6 Appartamenti estivi (G. Romano)
7 Galleria della mostra
8 Galleria dei mesi
9 Loggia di Eleonora
10 Sala di Troia

11 Sala delle Teste
12 Gabinetto dei Cesari
13 Camera dei Cavalli
14 Sala del Manto
15 Sala dei Capitani
16 Sala dei Marchesi
17 Sala dei Duchi
18 Sala degli Stemmi
19 Sala del Fregio
20 Sala delle Sigle

21 Sala della Esposizione
22 Camera dipinta (Camera degli sposi)
23 Camera dei Soli
24 Camera delle Cappe
25 First studiolo of Isabella d'Este (Grotta below)
26 Armeria
27 Cappella (XVI c.)

3a. *Palazzo Ducale, Mantua: Plan showing ground floor level of* Corte Vecchia.

4. *Palazzo Ducale and (left, foreground) the Cathedral, Mantua: view from north.*

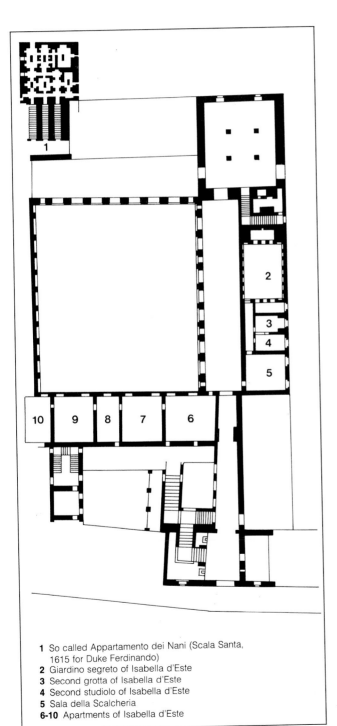

of course unmoveable mural and ceiling decorations or much of the contents of other Gonzaga residences (apart from more distant villas and castles, there were at least six in the city's immediate vicinity, the most recent being Duke Ferdinando's *La Favorita* built on an enormous scale). Given such abundance, Vincenzo II's decision in 1627 to unload some of his assets for money seems not intrinsically unwise. An exhibition cannot convey the quantity (in any case an overwhelming proportion of everything has been lost or destroyed) but something of the quality and variety of the Gonzaga collections can still be retrieved. For all his raptures about Mantua in 1608, the Englishman Coryat mentioned at the beginning seems to have had no conception at all of the Gonzaga treasures, apparently he did not enter any of the palaces, nor does he even record setting eyes upon a Gonzaga. Visitors to this exhibition may have in some respects a fuller experience than he did.

1 So called Appartamento dei Nani (Scala Santa, 1615 for Duke Ferdinando)
2 Giardino segreto of Isabella d'Este
3 Second grotta of Isabella d'Este
4 Second studiolo of Isabella d'Este
5 Sala della Scalcheria
6-10 Apartments of Isabella d'Este

5.   *Pisanello, Tournament,* mural painting *(Palazzo Ducale, Mantua).*

6.   *Detail of above, showing frieze with SS collars, swan pendants and marigold flowers.*

Lancaster and Gonzaga: the Collar of SS at Mantua
by Ilaria Toesca

It was in July 1389 that Francesco Gonzaga, first of this name as ruler of Mantua and the fourth of his family to hold the title of Imperial Vicar, travelled to Paris as an escort to Valentina Visconti. She was the daughter of Gian Galeazzo, Lord of Milan, and was to be married to Louis d'Orléans, brother of King Charles VI of France.

Francesco was chosen for this honour by the bride's father, a refined gentleman who styled himself *comte de Vertus* (Italian: *conte di Virtù*), a French title of nobility he had acquired through his first wife, Isabelle de Valois, daughter of King Jean II (le Bon). Francesco Gonzaga must have been rather flattered in being entrusted with this task by the powerful Lord of Milan, who was also a close relative. In 1389 Agnese Visconti was still Francesco's wife; she was daughter of the cruel Bernabò Visconti, Giangaleazzo's uncle; hence the Mantuan lord and his Milanese wife were second cousins to the new Duchess of Orléans.

Kinships of this kind may mean something to the historian; even more to the art historian. They can indicate some of the channels through which cultural influence could travel. Valentina Visconti's marriage to the Duke of Orléans is a good example of this.

The marriage provided an opportunity for the Mantuan party to travel farther on, after the ceremonies at Paris had finished. In a letter written in Paris to his mother and his wife, dated 16 September 1389[1], Francesco announces his intention to visit Bruges, Ghent and England *ad videndum partes illas* ("in order to see those lands"). Unfortunately no letters survive from Bruges, Ghent or England, to let us know where the travellers halted, what they saw, whom they met, or what they brought home. If – as we think it probable – they stayed in London, they may have been received there by high ranking relatives, since Violante Visconti, Gian Galeazzo's sister, had once been married to Lionel, Duke of Clarence.

If the Lombard party was received at court, the occasion would not have passed without the customary celebrations, even if there were also diplomatic talks. Francesco Gonzaga's letter home is so far the earliest proof of direct connections between his family and England.

Though Agnese Visconti was beheaded at Mantua for adultery in 1391, Francesco's relations with the Visconti remained good. By the time of his death in 1407 another of the Visconti women, Lucia, daughter of "Melan grete Barnabo Viscounte,/God of delit, and scourge of Lumbardye"[2] had established herself in England, having married Edmund Holland, Duke of Kent. She was poor Agnese's sister, hence, for a period, Francesco Gonzaga's sister-in-law. She lived until 1427 although her young husband, Richard II's half-brother, died in 1408. Many years before, there had been serious talks of a marriage between Lucia Visconti and Henry Bolingbroke (later Henry IV).

Such complicated family ties may prove rather amusing if we translate them from the formality of written documents into terms of real life, and they may help in recapturing a glimpse of the multifaced implications of such intricate events. The links between Mantua and England exemplified by Henry VI granting Gianfrancesco Gonzaga permission to distribute fifty of his SS collars to fifty of his best men (Cat. 6) go back further than we first thought. For once, the written document (Henry VI's grant) has a visual counterpart. The exquisite frieze that forms the top border of what is left of Pisanello's murals in the Mantuan Palazzo Ducale – a frieze that William Morris would have loved – puts a strong emphasis on the English royal livery, which is entwined with elegant marigold flowers, an emblem of the Gonzaga family. But the story did not start there. In 1416 an SS collar was already at Mantua in the possession of Gianfrancesco; but when did the Gonzaga obtain it? Maybe the young Earl of Derby, stopping at Mantua on his way back from Venice in 1393 (this was the time when he became betrothed to Lucia Visconti), could have given such a collar to Francesco, whom, anyway, he might also have met previously in Venice, where the Gonzaga frequently lived, being Venetian patricians. But this is romantic speculation. Another possibility may have occurred later on, when Lucia Visconti was escorted to England to marry Edmund Holland in 1407: but it is doubtful that she could have tolerated the company of the man who had sentenced her sister to death.

The fact that the collar is not listed among the jewels belonging to Francesco (a very accurate inventory was compiled in 1395), nor in the 1408 list of those belonging to Gianfrancesco makes us feel inclined to believe that it was between 1408 and 1411 that the Lancastrian badge was given to the Lord of Mantua, either by Henry IV or Henry V.

At that time the Gonzaga did not hold the title of Marquis of the Holy Roman Empire, although they had had an invalid promise of it from the deposed Emperor Wenceslaus of Bohemia in 1403. The investiture, from the Emperor Sigismund, took place in 1433. So one may incline to think that there was some specific reason for putting such a strong emphasis on royal English connections, perhaps an event of importance which we have yet to discover.

In any case, Henry VI's decision to grant Gianfrancesco Gonzaga the right to distribute fifty Lancastrian collars resulted in producing the best of unwritten documents: a large painted hall, which the Lord of Mantua wished to be decorated with chivalric scenes (Cat. 9, 12). Unfortunately only a portion of Pisanello's murals has survived (moreover they were left in an unfinished state) and their precise subject still awaits full explanation.

Since the Lancaster collar appears not only in the frieze, but also within the great "Tournament" scene, there should be some theme to connect the whole programme. The Royal livery is shown on the caparisons of some of the horses, so that those knights who are riding them are distinguished from the others. But because those same knights also wear the Gonzaga heraldic colours, the combination of the two features cannot be a casual one.

Specifically what did the Mantuan ruler order his painter to represent? Perhaps something connected with a real event, even if under the cover of some chivalric romance story? We cannot tell: and this is a great pity. Of course, the well-furnished palace library could provide more than one example for the patron to show the painter what he intended to have portrayed on the walls of his new hall. For example the *Entrée de Spagne*, a manuscript of the fourteenth century (Biblioteca Marciana, Venice, Fr. Z.21=257) was there, with a number of boldly illuminated pages (not the usual *bas de page* scenes illustrating the text), with fights portrayed on a large scale, and with no break in continuity over contiguous pages. Later Pisanello was to handle the corner between two walls of the hall in the same manner[3]. But

this is just a random example that we can still check, while so many princely halls decorated according to the same principles are now lost.

Again factual, not written, evidence of the role the SS collar had in the Gonzaga court is provided by a small object, of the utmost rarity, found a short time ago[4] in a storeroom of the Palazzo Ducale. Small as it is, and worn by use, it tells us more than many lengthy texts: but its significance could not have been completely understood had not the story of the SS collar at Mantua been reconstructed. It is a hawk's hunting hood, made of leather, once gilt; it is adorned with a punched decoration showing two swans, marigolds, and two scrolls, each inscribed with a minute letter "S". It should be dated not later than the middle of the fifteenth century because of certain gothic features. It enables us to recapture something from the world to which both the SS collar and the Pisanello murals belonged: a world of courtly refined society.

In later times, relations between the court of Mantua and that of England do not appear to have continued, perhaps owing to the fact that Mantuan politics became increasingly involved with German and Imperial relationships. The last we hear about the SS collar comes from a letter[5] of Barbara of Brandenburg, Ludovico's German wife, who in 1451 ordered it to be pawned in Venice.

Notes

BIBLIOGRAPHY: See General Bibliography under Cherry; Toesca.

1. ASMAG, 2093, no. 63. Still unpublished as far as I know.
   Magnificis matri et Consorti nostris carissimis domine margarite de Gonzaga ac Agneti de Vicecomitibus etc.
   Magnifice mater et Consors nostre carissime. Ad vestram consolationem Significamus vobis per presentes quod omnipotentis gratia cum tota comitiva nostra sani Sumus illud idem de vobis ac natis nostris reaudire Cupientes. Die Sabati proxima futura hinc discedemus et Bruzes ac Guantum indeque usque in Angliam nos transferemus ad videndum partes illas. Ex quo stetis de bono velle usque ad nostri redditum mantuam quam cito revertemur. Valete cum dei gratia.
   Franciscus de Gonzaga Mantue etc.   Datum parisius XVI Septembris
   Imperialis Vicarius Generalis   mccclxxxviiij
2. See Chaucer, *The Monk's Tale*, lines 2399-2401.
3. Venice, Marciana Library, Fr. Z.21=257, f. 160ᵛ-161ʳ. See also P. Toesca, *La pittura e la miniatura nella Lombardia*, 1912, 2nd ed., Turin, 1966, p. 165.
4. Shortly to be published by the author of the present note.
5. Kindly pointed out to me by Prof. Rodolfo Signorini, to whom I wish to express my thanks here. The letter is to be found in ASMAG, b. 2095, and is dated 21 February 1451.

Gonzaga Tombs and Catafalques
by Rodolfo Signorini

Sic transit gloria mundi: the famous saying applies even to the tombs intended to immortalize the fifteen Gonzagas who ruled Mantua from 1328 to 1627, for no trace of them remains. Some were shifted from their original sites and broken up in the process, but most of them disappeared through vandalism, particularly in the wave of destruction which followed the arrival of Napoleon's troops early in 1797[1]. However some scattered evidence can be assembled about these former monuments and those of Gonzaga consorts, and about a number of more grandiose projects which were never realized at all.

The places favoured for Gonzaga burials varied; several different churches in Mantua shared the honours and the Gonzaga tombs were never assembled together. Although there were various plans for such a thing, there never was a proper Gonzaga mausoleum.

The cathedral of San Pietro contained the tombs of the first Gonzaga Captain, Luigi (d. 1360) and of his wives and two of his sons[2]. The inscription commemorating one of the latter, Azzone[3] (d. 1412) is all that survives of these early Gonzaga monuments (Pl. 8). Although it is recorded that they were specially cleaned in December 1543[4], two years later they were dismantled when work began on reconstructing the cathedral's interior according to Giulio Romano's design[5]. Guido Gonzaga, the second Captain (d. 1369) chose to be buried in the church of San Francesco and planned to have a marble tomb in the chapel dedicated to St Louis of Toulouse (Pl. 9). His son Ludovico the third Captain (d. 1382) and his widow Alda d'Este (d. 1381) were also buried there[6]. The effigy of Alda lay upon a sarcophagus decorated with statuary (some fragments of which remain); this rested upon four columns with lions at their base. Francesco I (d. 1407) also chose to be buried in this chapel[7]. Nothing of his tomb remains (it too was a structure resting upon columns) but the effigy survives from the tomb of his second wife, Margherita Malatesta (Pl. 10), and documents describe this elaborate work commissioned from Piero Paolo delle Masegne[8]. Therefore by the time of Gianfrancesco Gonzaga, the first Marquis, a tradition had been established of burials and monumental tombs in the chapel of St Louis of Toulouse (which also came to be known as the Chapel of the Princes and was later dedicated to St Bernardino

of Siena)[9]. Gianfrancesco stipulated in his will of 23 September 1444 that he should be buried in his father's tomb there[10]. But the tradition of setting up an adjacent tomb for the ruler's wife was discontinued, for his devout widow Paola Malatesta (d. 1453) wanted for herself a humble grave outside Corpus Domini, the church of her own conventual foundation of the Clarisses of St Paola[11]. Similarly, although Marquis Ludovico (d. 1478) was buried in the same chapel as his ancestors in San Francesco[12] (nothing is known of any monumental tomb design, in spite of his interest in sculpture and architecture) Barbara of Brandenburg (d. 1481) preferred to be buried in the chapel of Sant'Anselmo in the cathedral, which was probably the first chapel on the right as one entered[13]. A tomb was designed for her by Andrea Mantegna but never erected[14] and the poet Fausto Andrelino of Forlì was invited to compose an epitaph in the ancient manner (*prisco more*)[15]. It appears that when the wives survived their husbands they preferred, either from modesty or other considerations, to be buried elsewhere. But Margherita of Bavaria (d. 1479) predeceased Federico, the third Marquis, and according to a letter of Francesco Secco of 14 October 1479 requested in her will to be buried humbly in the floor of the chapel at San Francesco wearing the habit of a Franciscan tertiary (*a San Francesco in la capella delli Signori ma in terra*)[16]. Federico himself (d. 1484), according to his will of 21 April 1479, requested like his ancestors an unceremonious burial in the family tomb (*in ecclesia Sancti Francisci, in monumento illustrium dominorum progenitorum meorum, sine aliqua pompa aut cerimonia*)[17].

Slightly more is known about the burial of Marquis Francesco (d. 1519). In his will of 29 March 1519[18] he had expressed the wish for his body, clad in the Franciscan habit, to be placed "in the chapel of the illustrious Gonzaga lords"; on the evening of 30 March 1519 these wishes were carried out and he was laid there in a coffin covered with black velvet surmounted by the Gonzaga arms[19]. A drawing survives (Pl. 7) of the grandiose catafalque in the form of a pyramid which was erected in San Francesco for the solemn ceremonies performed in his memory on 11 and 12 April 1519[20]. It was lit by candles and decorated with the heraldic arms and military standards of the major powers he had served as a

7. *Catafalque of Marchese Francesco Gonzaga (d. 1519)*
    (ASMAG b. 85 reg. 10 c. 125r).

8. *Inscription to Azzone Gonzaga (room in tower of the*
    Cathedral, Mantua).

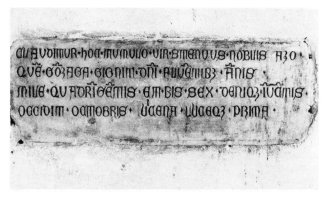

ing place and that of Isabella d'Este. She survived him for nearly twenty years, and following the precedent of Paola Malatesta wished (according to her will of 22 December 1535)[23] to have herself buried at Corpus Domini (Santa Paola) not outside the church, however, like Paola, but in the choir. Giulio Romano designed for Isabella (d. 1539) an elaborate catafalque[24], with the figure of Rachel weeping for her children, but nothing is known of any plan for a monumental tomb. Two later sources are at variance about the interment of the bodies of husband and wife together. One states[25] that Francesco was buried in the chapel of San Bernardino (i.e. in the family chapel in San Francesco); the other[26] that Isabella was buried, as she had wished, in the convent of the Order of S. Paola (Corpus Domini) and it was traditionally believed that the body of the Marquis was moved there[27]. This was scarcely sufficient as evidence for the identification made of two skeletons unearthed in 1965 beneath the choir as the remains of Francesco and Isabella[28] (Pl. 12). Even less convincing was the attempt to identify the male skull as Francesco's from a comparison with his head in Mantegna's painting of the *Madonna della Vittoria* (Pl. 29).

Documentation about burial arrangements at S. Paola complicates the problem. In her will Isabella had made no mention of her husband's body. Her son Duke Federico, who soon after she died drew up a will (26 June 1540)[29] a few days before his own death, stated that he wished to be buried with her in S. Paola (*nella sepultura che si ha da fare per el corpo della madama marchesa sua madre, quale sepoltura si faccia capace anco del corpo di sua excellentia*): there is no mention of his father. Although

commander, Pope Julius II, the Emperor Maximilian, Louis XII King of France, the Republic of Venice and the Duchy of Milan. On the summit was the sarcophagus with an effigy in armour upon its lid. A drawing attributed to Alfonso Cittadella (Pl. 11) suggests that later a monumental tomb was projected for him, either by his widow Isabella d'Este or his sons[21]. It shows a soldier in antique armour lying upon a sarcophagus with an inscription (partly concealed by his dangling sword) mis-spelling his name and labelling him as the third instead of the fourth Marquis; but the *impresa* of the crucible (*crogiuolo*) clearly associates the drawing with him[22].

Some confusion has arisen about Francesco's final rest-

4

Federico and his son Francesco, the second Duke (d. 1550) were buried in S. Paola, later (as will be mentioned below) they were moved elsewhere, so the male skeleton found in 1965 – in a grave which, incidentally, was intended for only one body – cannot have belonged to either of them. To complicate matters further, Federico's widow Margherita Paleologo stated in her will dated 21 May 1563[30] that she wished to be buried in Corpus Domini where her son lay in the same tomb as her husband (no mention is made of her mother-in-law). Traces of the tomb of Margherita (d. 1566) in the choir revealed that it was made to contain three bodies, presumably those of Isabella, Federico and Margherita. In 1782 inscriptions were recorded in S. Paola relating to them, also to Federico's sister Livia (d. 1569), who had taken the name of Paola when she became a nun, and his son Francesco[31].

Duke Federico's burial arrangements had broken the long tradition of entombment in San Francesco for Gonzaga rulers. It may be that the chapel of St Louis of Toulouse had become too crowded (it also contained a monument representing the Holy Sepulchre); no more tombs were added, and in September 1601 one of the Gonzaga monuments there was damaged by a thunderbolt[32].

Meanwhile Duke Guglielmo planned to have a Gonzaga mausoleum beneath the presbytery of the ambitious palatine church of St Barbara, designed for him by G.B. Bertani[33]. According to his will drawn up on 13 May 1569 he planned that his own body and the bodies of his successors, but of no one else should be buried there ("*... sepelliri voluit in ecclesia sub titulo sanctae Barbarae, errecta prope castrum civitatis Mantuae, et in monumento sive sepulcro in eadem ecclesia construendo apud murum sanctuarii [...] et in ipso sepulcro [...] voluit et ordinavit [...] collocari cadavera illustrissimorum dominorum Mantuae ducum tantum illorumque filiorum qui [...] in dignitate ducatus successissent, nollens aliquo futuro tempore ulla alia cadavera preter suprascripta in dicto sepulcro collocari*")[34].

Elaborate funeral ceremonies on 18-19 September 1587 followed Duke Guglielmo's death. According to one account[35] there were two pyramidical catafalques; one, lit with burning tapers, was in the courtyard of Santa Croce in the Corte Vecchia area of the Palace, where first the coffin and effigy of the Duke were placed, and

a second grander catafalque was in Santa Barbara[36]. The plaster effigy of Guglielmo, upon the brocade-draped coffin, portrayed him wearing his ducal robes of white damask and a crown; on the right hand lay the rod of office, on the left the belt, sword and dagger, and the spurs were at the feet; everything was painted

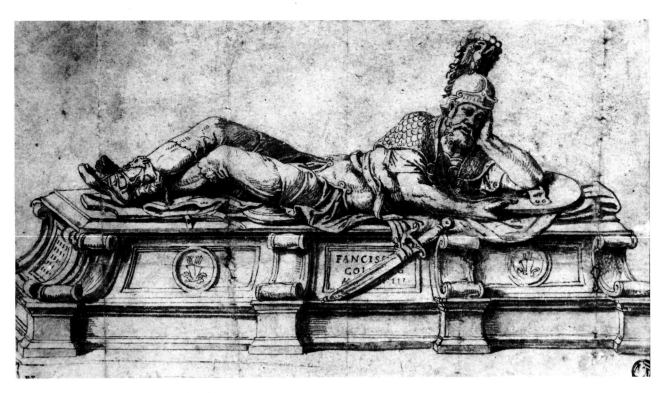

in white and gold. The Santa Barbara catafalque, designed by the Florentine Francesco Trabalesi, Prefect of the Building Works, was made in imitation of a building in stone "of melancholy colour" in the Ionic style (... *tutto lavorato d'opera Ionica, finto di pietra macigno, che apunto si scorge color melanconico*); it had eight façades, four of them open in the form of doorways; inside a flight of five steps led to the temporary tomb. But another description is given of this catafalque, as a rotunda surmounted by a pyramid with statues of Fortitude, Justice, Prudence and Faith, with smaller pyramids and other sculptural figures around it[37].

The site of the burial crypt to which the coffin was afterwards borne lay behind the flight of semi-circular steps of diminishing width which ascend to the sanctuary, and which were noted[38] to be like the Gonzaga *impresa* of Mount Olympus, with the high altar completing the effect by corresponding to the altar labelled *Fides* which appears at the summit of the mountain, (Pl. 94). The crypt was divided into three sections, a lesser chamber designed for the bodies of princesses and two

chapels dedicated respectively to the Virgin and the Holy Cross. The coffins were to be placed on stone shelves around the walls. Of all this little trace remains as the site was badly damaged by flooding, but Guglielmo had already stipulated in his will of 1569 that the remains of his father and elder brother, Dukes Federico and Francesco, were to be placed in Santa Barbara (".. *in ipso sepulcro transferri voluit et ordinavit cadavera... Federici genitoris sui et.. Francisci olim eius fratris, Mantuae ducum*"). Perhaps the decision to move them from Santa Paola was made partly on the grounds that a female convent was considered not to be a suitable resting-place for Dukes of Mantua (Isabella and Margherita could happily be left where they were) but it was also a way of magnifying the importance of Santa Barbara. The translation may have taken place soon after 1569[39], or more probably at the time of Guglielmo's own funeral, when the remains were put on display[40], placed in new coffins because damp had damaged those in which they had lain previously and dispersed the bones. Guglielmo's wife Eleonora of Austria (d. 1594) did not

join him in the crypt of Santa Barbara but was buried in the Jesuit Church of Santa Trinità (her bones were removed in 1856 to the cathedral)[41]. Meanwhile Vincenzo I had a marvellous catafalque erected in her honour in Sant'Andrea; it was displayed to public view on 1 October 1594[42]. The catafalque was square in form and reached the vault of the church; on each side there was a door and at each corner four columns supported the images of fifty Austrian notables. The top of the catafalque was covered by a large cupola surmounted by a cross borne by two angels. Beneath it lay an effigy of the Duchess in mourning robes. All around there were Gonzaga and Habsburg emblems and mottoes. Four narrow staircases gave access to a balcony from which these details and the sarcophagus could be viewed, and the whole catafalque was lit by a great number of candles. The portico and interior of the church were decorated with funerary ornamentation and there were also paintings representing episodes in the Life of Christ. At the main entrance were four gigantic statues symbolizing the cities of Mantua and Casale Monferrato and the rivers Po and Mincio.

Duke Vincenzo had no intention of continuing his father's project for a Gonzaga mausoleum in Santa Barbara. In his first will dated 28 November 1587, only a few months after Guglielmo's death (14 August) Vincenzo stipulated that he should be buried in San Francesco reviving the ancient family tradition (*sepeliri voluit in ecclesia sancti Francisci Mantuae, specialiter in capella inclitae domus Gonzagae.. in uno sepulcro ibi construendo*)[43] but this was revoked in his second will (29 July 1595)[44] in which he declared that his body should be buried in the crypt of Sant'Andrea according to an entirely new scheme, the drawing for which has also now been found (see Cat. 222, Pl. 13). Probably inspired by the new Prefect of the Ducal Buildings, Antonio Maria Viani, this scheme consisted of a chapel in the form of a Greek cross with thirty bays around the walls. Within alternating niches were to be placed the tombs of the twelve Gonzaga rulers of Mantua up to and including Vincenzo himself, and of their respective wives. The majority of these tombs were simply memorials; in fact the will laid down that the bodies of Guglielmo and Eleonora should not be removed there, nor ought those of earlier princes who had specified their place of burial. Perhaps

only the remains of Luigi, the first Captain (moved in 1545), were to be installed in the new site. From both the drawing and the will it is clear that within the niches there were to be marble busts of the wives and life-size statues of the Gonzaga rulers, kneeling in adoration before the relic of the Precious Blood of Christ kept in the sanctuary in the centre of the crypt. The whole chapel was to be faced with marble and the vault to be supported by many columns. All these provisions were confirmed in the next will of Vincenzo, dated 17 July 1601[45], but in another dated 18 July 1608[46], he specified that he did not wish to be buried in a recumbent position but on a marble throne (*non quidem, ut moris est, iacendo, sed sedendo super cathedra marmorea ad hoc parata, non autem in arca lignea includatur*).

In his final will of 3 February 1612[47] Vincenzo clarified that he wanted his body to be displayed sitting on a throne with his sword (... *sedendo cum suo ense apposito super cathedra marmorea*), and after forty hours to be buried in this position in the same small chamber (*camerino*) of the crypt where his wife Eleonora had been placed the previous year. This *camerino* is not mentioned in the earlier wills, nor can it be identified from the drawing; it implies a provisional arrangement since the project was far less complete than references in the wills suggest, apart from the statue of Duke Guglielmo (Pl. 16) presumed to be for it (see Cat. 223) and the empty

13.   *Plan for projected Gonzaga Mausoleum in the crypt of Sant'Andrea, Mantua (Cat. 222).*

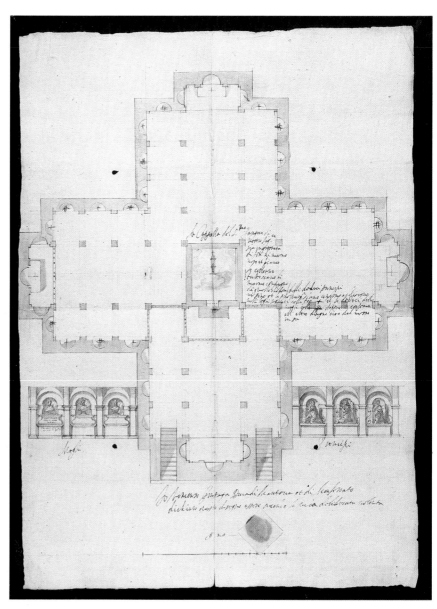

14.   *Sant'Andrea, Mantua: crypt.*

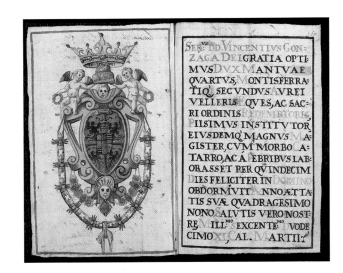

niches. In fact, when Vincenzo died (Pl. 15) his maca-bre instructions were disregarded and his body was placed in a coffin, though there was a marble throne nearby with an epitaph above it in gold letters upon black marble[48]. Although neither his tomb nor Eleono-ra's nor the *camerino* have ever been found (the niches were filled in and the whole crypt was much altered in the nineteenth century) (Pl. 14), inscriptions relating to them were removed to the upper church in 1836[49].

The grandiose catafalque for Duke Vincenzo's funeral which was erected in Sant'Andrea evidently reflected the scheme for the crypt mausoleum. Upon it were eleven pictures illustrating the achievements of his eleven predecessors, funerary monuments and portraits of them and also eleven pictures showing Vincenzo's own deeds, to prove that in him the virtues of all had been combined[50].

Neither the predecessors nor the successors of Duke Vincenzo I ended up with him in Sant'Andrea, apart from his two grandchildren who died in infancy and were buried there in 1612[51]. Their father, Vincenzo's eldest son Duke Francesco, himself died in December 1612 after a reign of only ten months, and was buried in Santa Barbara[52]. Duke Ferdinando in his will dated 1 October 1626[53] had expressed the wish to be buried where his parents lay (*in camerino subterraneo ubi adservan-tur cadavera eius genitorum... in ecclesia Sancti Andreae*). But the twenty-six, not twenty-four nor thirty, niches in the crypt (clearly visible also in a drawing of 1788)[54] were blocked up in 1873[55], and clearly Ferdinando's in-structions had been disregarded, for the will of his wid-ow Caterina de' Medici, dated 19 June 1627[56], stipulated that her body should be buried without pomp in Santa Barbara next to her husband (*voglio che il cadave-re... sia sepolto nella chiesa di Santa Barbara di Mantova appresso la sepoltura del... mio amatissimo consorte*).

His successor, Vincenzo II (d. 1627) broke all past con-ventions by arranging that he should be buried before the high altar of the church of San Maurizio[57]: of this tomb no trace remains.

For both Ferdinando and Vincenzo II elaborate cata-falques in Santa Barbara were designed by an unknown Jesuit and constructed by the court architect Viani. Full descriptions of them have survived[58] as well as the text of the funeral orations[59]. Ferdinando's was in the form of a pyramid with three doors; inside a fictive tomb showing the Duke guarded by the imperial eagles could be seen, together with similar tombs commemorating all five preceding dukes. On the outside were statues symbolizing the cities of Mantua, Viadana, Casale Monferrato and Alba; personifications of theology, phi-losophy, poetry and erudition in all of which Ferdinan-do excelled, and around the pyramid the virtues of Pru-dence, Justice, Fortitude and Temperance. Zodiacal signs decorated the church and symbolized other aspects of the Duke's character; most interesting perhaps was the Scorpion shown in the act of stinging itself for having killed the sun. For Duke Ferdinando, whose favoured emblem was the sun[60], had died at the end of October 1626 under the sign of Scorpio. In contrast the theme for the catafalque of Vincenzo II was the moon; one of his emblems had been a full moon facing the sun and less than a month after his death there was an eclipse of the moon (20 January 1628). A large pyramid containing the temporary tomb of the Duke in faked lapis lazuli was surrounded by six smaller pyramids commemor-ating the previous Dukes and their planets; there were twelve steps lit by candles and above the large pyramid was another lit to represent the moon; the whole was surmounted by an urn in imitation bronze with a cross at the top.

The only Gonzaga tombs which have survived intact as monumental objects are those of some of the younger

16. *Statue of Duke Guglielmo Gonzaga at prayer (Cat. 223).*

sons of rulers of Mantua, or of their nephews and cousins belonging to cadet branches of the family. The Gonzaga who entered the Church have fared slightly better than their secular relatives, though no trace remains of the tomb of the first Cardinal of the family, Francesco (d. 1483) who was buried, as his will required, in San Francesco alongside his father[61] (*in capella ubi illustres quondam progenitores mei sepulti sunt... iuxta archam sive sepulturam illustris quondam genitoris mei*). His brother Ludovico (d. 1511) who became Bishop of Mantua, and their nephew Cardinal Sigismondo (d. 1525), had some curious posthumous adventures and ended up sharing a monument in the cathedral. Ludovico was first buried there in the chapel of Sant'Anselmo, where his mother Barbara lay, and for the solemn obsequies an illuminated catafalque was set up[62]. Later his remains were transferred to the chapel of Santa Maria dei Voti[63] in the cathedral and then to the sacristy. Cardinal Sigismondo's corpse started off in the last named chapel, but in 1537 it was transferred to the nearby church of San Paolo[64] and was later moved to the cathedral sacristy. In February 1566 the two prelates were disturbed again, and their coffins were put in the chapel of Santa Maria dei Voti[65], but in September the same year the Chapter account books record with asperity "that brute of a vicar" had ordered that the two restless coffins should be moved again to a site beneath the tower[66], and inscriptions were painted on both of them[67]. They ended up in the presbytery with the monument that still survives (Pl. 17) sometime during the episcopate of Francesco Gonzaga (1593-1620)[68]. Cardinal Ercole Gonzaga (d. 1563) was buried in a simple wooden coffin, covered in velvet, now on the wall of the cathedral sacristy[69], and Cardinal Federico (d. 1565), brother of Duke Guglielmo, had a simple inscribed tablet behind the High Altar[70], as did bishop Francesco (d. 1620) in the presbytery[71]. For the second Cardinal Francesco Gonzaga (d. 1566), son of Ferrante, there is a modest stone inscription in the church of San Lorenzo in Lucina in Rome[72], though two drawings in the British Museum may relate to projects for a grander tomb; one of them gives his date of death (see Cat. 221) the other is much more elaborate; both are decorated with Gonzaga arms and eagles (Plate 18). Also in Rome, in the church of Sant'Alessio, is an elegant

17. *Cathedral, Mantua: Inscription to Bishop Ludovico and Cardinal Sigismondo Gonzaga.*

18. *Study for a tomb possibly of Cardinal Federico Gonzaga (d. 1565) or of Cardinal Francesco Gonzaga (d. 1566) (British Museum, Department of Prints and Drawings) (see Cat. 221).*

19. *Church of the Incoronata, Sabbioneta: Tomb of Vespasiano Gonzaga, Duke of Sabbioneta.*

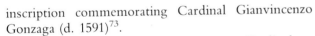

inscription commemorating Cardinal Gianvincenzo Gonzaga (d. 1591)[73].

The most imposing tomb of a Gonzaga Cardinal on Mantuan territory is, paradoxically, that of Cardinal Scipione (d. 1593), a very distant relation of the ruling line; his portrait bust dressed in a *mozzetta* (bishop's cape) is in the Gonzaga mausoleum of the parish church of San Martino dall'Argine, where his branch of the family lived[74].

There is a striking contrast between the tombs of two of the most famous lay members of the family during the sixteenth century who were not in direct succession to the Mantuan dukedom. Ferrante (d. 1557) Lord of Guastalla, former Viceroy of Sicily and Governor of Milan, ended, like his brother Cardinal Ercole, in a simple wooden coffin on the wall of the sacristy in Mantua cathedral[75]. But Vespasiano Gonzaga, Duke of Sabbioneta and three generations removed from the ruling line of Mantua, had the one distinctly grand monumental tomb to survive (Pl. 19). Designed by Giovanni Battista della Porta, it stands in the church of the Incoronata, Sabbioneta; above it, in accordance with Vespasiano's will was placed the bronze statue

of the Duke (1588) by Leone Leoni, formerly on a marble pedestal in front of his palace, presenting him in the aspect of a triumphant emperor[76].

APPENDIX: EXTRACT FROM THE SECOND WILL OF DUKE VINCENZO GONZAGA, 29 JULY 1595

(ASMAG, Magistrato Camerale Antico, b. B b I, fasc. 4, 3, cc. (1r-2v)

[...] corpus [...] suum sive cadaver, cum ab eo anima fuerit separata sepelliri voluit et mandavit in capella inferiori et subterranea sacrosancti sanguinis Christi, in ecclesia sancti Andreae de Mantua [...] Quam quidem capellam ampliari voluit et mandavit tantum quantum capit circumferentia interior capellae maioris et superioris quae esset finienda dictae ecclesiae, construique et ornari mandavit cum columnis presertim et incrostaturis marmoreis et cum viginti quattuor sepulcris marmoreis principum familiae Gonzagiacae, incipiendo ab Aluisio inclusive et sequendo usque ad dictum dominum testatorem, necnon et dominarum uxorum singulorum ipsorum principum, illarum scilicet a quibus linea principum processit, respectu quidem eorum principum qui plures uxores habuerunt, in quibus sepulcris ponantur sigillatim cadavera et cineres respective prefati domini testatoris et aliorum praefatorum dominorum principum, et praedicta omnia et infrascripta fieri debeant omnibus expensis infrascripti domini heredis et iuxta exemplar et, ut vulgo dicitur, dissegno

11

mihi infrascripto notario per eius celsitudinem traditum et manu ipsius serenissimi domini subscriptum et suo familiari sigillo signatum in praesentia superiorum dominorum testium et mei notarii praefati, et penes presens testamentum asservatum, declarans quod, etsi sepulcra omnia praefatorum construi debeant, non tamen amoveantur cineres et reliquiae serenissimorum suorum patris et matris et aliorum locis et sepulcris in quibus reperiuntur et ipsi specialiter recondi debere ordinaverunt [...]

Notes

The author wishes to thank Dr Roberto Navarrini, Director of the Archivio di Stato of Brescia, for his valued help.

1. See contemporary comments by Paolo Predella, collector of Mantuan inscriptions; ms. in Accademia Virgiliana, Mantua.

2. Intra, 1884; Marani, 1957; Paccagnini, 1960, pp. 115, 120 n. 19.

3. Orioli, 1896, p. 258.

4. ASDM, Fondo Capitolo della Cattedrale, Serie libri di massaria (1543), c. 101v.

5. Ibid. Liber "S. Andrea" (1545) c. 80r-81r; cf. I. Daino, "De origine... de Gonzaga", ms. in ASMAG, b. 416. cc. 145r-147v; Marani, 1962, pp. 212-214; Tellini Perina, 1967.

6. Tonelli, II, 1797-1800, p. 217; Amadei-Marani, 1978, pp. 21-22; Schizzerotto, 1977, pp. 95-96 n. 11.

7. Schizzerotto, 1977, pp. 85-95, Amadei-Marani, 1978, pp. 25-32.

8. Paccagnini, 1960, pp. 241, 250-251, n. 64.

9. Schizzerotto, 1977, pp. 92-93.

10. ASMAG, b. 330 c. (1v).

11. Signorini, 1979, pp. 43-44, cf. Donesmondi, I, 1613, p. 383; Cottafavi, 1935, I, pp. 2-5.

12. See below n. 61.

13. Amadei, I, 1955, pp. 673-674; the chapel had a round window (ochio) facing the piazza which was mended in December 1532, ASDM, Fondo Capitolo della Cattedrale, Serie libri di massaria (1532) c. 86v.

14. Resti-Ferrari, 1928, pp. 15-18.

15. I. Affò, Memorie di Ludovico Gonzaga vescovo di Mantova, Biblioteca Comunale, Mantua, MS. 1265 (I.IV.78) p. 46.

16. ASMAG, b. 2422; cf. Amadei, II, 1955, pp. 239-241; Tonelli, II, 1797, p. 407; Amadei-Marani, 1978, pp. 43-44.

17. ASMAG, b. 330.

18. Ibid. His brother Giovanni also wished to be buried there; will dated 10 February 1514 in ASMAG b. 333 cc. 167v-168r.

19. ASMAG, b. 85 Lib. 10 (1341-1520) c. 135v.

20. Ibid. 137v-138v. Cf. Bazzotti-Belluzzi, 1978, pp. 126, 134-35, n. 37, fig. 7.

21. Hartt II, 1958, pp. 302, 326 (docs. 198, 200); fig. 514. For other projects and a drawing by Raphael see Marani and Perina, 1961, II, p. 197.

22. On the crogiuolo, Brown, 1973, pp. 153-159.

23. ASMAG, b. 330; cf. Amadei, 1955, II, p. 582.

24. Hartt II, 1958, pp. 211, 327. The document (ASMAG, Autografi, cass. 7) was incorrectly transcribed; "rachilli" should read "Rachelle"; "cotapalcho" should read "catafalcho"; "in Feb. 1 di 6 da in mrxo a di" should read "schudi 6 d'or inn oro".

25. Amadei, 1955, II, pp. 457-458.

26. Tonelli, 1798, III, p. 77, Amadei, 1955, II p. 582.

27. Marani, 1966, pp. 22-30; Clough, 1966, pp. 96-97, Amadei-Marani, 1978, pp. 45-48, 255-56.

28. *Gazzetta di Mantova*, 12.ix.1965, 10.ix.1978, 13.vii.1980, 24-25.ii.1981.

29. ASMAG, b. 330.

30. ASMAG, b. 332 c. 3r.

31. Marani, 1966, pp. 24, 28-30.

32. Luzio, 1922, p. 39 no. 1; letter to Annibale Chieppio, 12 Sept. 1601 in ASMAG, b. 2684 fasc. vii.

33. Gozzi, 1974; Fenlon, 1980, pp. 95-117.

34. ASMAG, b. 333.

35. G.B. Vigilio, *L'insalata*, ms. in ASM, Fondo d'Arco, 168 cap. 79.

36. Follino, 1587, gives the fullest description.

37. Donesmondi II, 1616, pp. 272-73; G. Mambrino, *Dell'historia di Mantova* ms. in ASM, Fondo d'Arco, 80 pp. 754-57.

38. Follino, 1587, p. 10: *...si levò il corpo dal catafalco et fu portato alla sepoltura altre volte d'ordine suo fabricata sotto la salita de' gradi della scala, che camina nella Capella maggiore dov'è l'Altar grande, li quali sono de marmo et fatti in forma dell'impresa del monte Olimpo, quale già portava et egli et tutti gli suoi antecessori Gonzaghi.*

39. Donesmondi II, 1616, p. 208; Followed by Mambrino, ms. cit. pp. 754-55 incorrectly give the date of the translation as 1564, which would have greatly upset Margherita Paleologo's burial arrangements (above n. 30). Marani, 1966, p. 24 gives it as 1566 but the document cited does not mention the subject (and is in ASMAG b. 2575 not 2576).

40. ASDM, Fondo S. Barbara, Diario di S. Barbara 1572-1602 p. 489.

41. Schizzerotto, 1979, pp. 41, 57 n. 77; Amadei-Marani, 1978, pp. 59-60.

42. Amadei, 1955, III, pp. 120-21; Donesmondi II, 1616, pp. 316-317.

43. ASMAG, Magistrato Camerale Antico b. B b I, fasc. 4, 1, cc. (1r-2r).

44. *Ibid.*, fasc. 4, 3 cc. (1r-2v). See Appendix below essay.

45. *Ibid.*, fasc. 4, 6. cc. (2r-2v) and ASMAG b. 330.

46. *Ibid.*, fasc.4, 9 cc. 1r-1v.

47. *Ibid.*, fasc. 4, 10, cc. 1r-2v.

48. Tonelli, IV, 1800, pp. 37-42.

49. ASM, Arch. Portioli, ms. *Lapidi nella basilica di Sant'Andrea etc.... 1835[-36]* p. 27 nos. 48, 49. Orioli, 1892, pp. 66-67 mentioned the unsuccessful search already made in 1811; later excavations are reported in January 1873 in ASDM, Fondo Basilica di Sant'Andrea, b. 354 (8) para. 6.

50. Donesmondi, II, 1616, pp. 476-477; Mambrino, ms. cit., pp. 916-917.

51. ASMAG, b. 393 for details with inscription of burial of the *puttina* Maria Margherita, d. 12 September 1612, and ASM, Carlo d'Arco, *Iscrizioni... in Mantova e nel mantovano*, ms. vol. 228 (loose pages) concerning burial of the infant Ludovico, d. 3 November 1612; Donesmondi II, 1616, pp. 482-484; Amadei III, 1955, pp. 288-289.

52. Mambrino, ms. cit., p. 927; Amadei, III, 1955, p. 290.

53. ASMAG, b. 330 (f.2v).

54. Bazzotti-Belluzzi, 1980, p. 47.

55. ASDM, Fondo Basilica di Sant'Andrea, b. 354 (8) para. 6.

56. ASMAG, b. 332, cf. Amadei III, 1955, p. 380; Mambrino, ms. cit., p. 976.

57. Amadei, III, 1955, pp. 402-03.

58. Salmatia, 1626; Salmatia, 1628.

59. Martinelli, 1626; 1628.

60. On the respective emblems see Magnaguti, 1965, p. 106; Ferro, II, 1623, p. 463; Picinelli, 1653, pp. 5, 22; Tonelli, IV, 1800, p. 110.

61. ASMAG, b. 333, c. 83r., cf. Chambers, 1980, pp. 8, 28.

62. Described in letters of Amico Maria della Torre to Federico Gonzaga, 2, 13 February 1511 (ASMAG, b. 2482 c. 168r., 170r.).

63. Perhaps in 1545 at the time of the rebuilding of the cathedral.

64. ASDM, Fondo Capitolo Cattedrale, Serie Libri di massaria (1537) c. 81v (13 August 1537).

65. ASDM, Fondo Capitolo Cattedrale, serie Filze di fatture etc. (1539-97) filza 690; Serie Libri di massaria (1566) c. 217r.

66. *Ibid.* Serie Libri di massaria (1566) c. 223r: *speso per far levare ad instanza di quell'animale del vicario le due irrequiete casse del cardinale Sigismondo e del vescovo Ludovico...*

67. *Ibid.* Serie Miscellanea b. 2a, fasc. Memorie riguardanti la chiesa Cattedrale dal 1395 in poi (10 Sept. 1566). Among other payments are sums of 1 lira 5 *soldi* to *domino Aluigi che scrisse in carta di lettere antiche imbroccate sopra la cassa del vescovo Ludovico,* "Ludovico Gonzagae Episcopo Mantuano Magni animi magnique consilii viro" and of 1 lira 1 soldo to *maestro Giuliano pittore che dipinse sotto la cassa del cardinal Sigismondo, sul muro in lettere antiche:* "Sigismondo Gonzagae qui cum generis splendore naturae bonitatem adaequavit".

68. Amadei, II, 1955, p. 413; Amadei-Marani, 1978, pp. 93-94.

69. Amadei, II, 1955, pp. 733-34; Tonelli 2, III, 1798, p. 134; Ciacconius, 1677, III cols 481-485; Schrader, 1592, p. 339.

70. Amadei, II, 1955, p. 739; Tonelli, III, 1798, p. 141; Ciacconius, 1677, III col. 943.

71. Donesmondi, 1625, p. 179; Amadei, III, 1955, p. 60.

72. Ciacconius, 1677, III col. 934; Amadei, II, 1955, pp. 761-63; Amadei-Marani, 1978, pp. 151-52; Tonelli, III, 1798, p. 143.

73. Ciacconius, 1677, IV col. 67; Amadei, III, 1955, pp. 63-64; Amadei-Marani, 1978, pp. 237-38.

74. Luchini, 1904, pp. 9-18.

75. Amadei, II, 1797, 697-98; Amadei-Marani, 1978, pp. 79-80; Schrader, 1592, p. 339.

76. Dondi, ed. Müller, 1857, p. 338; Affò, 1975, p. 58; Forster, 1969, pp. 19-24.

20.   *Mantegna*, Portrait of Francesco Gonzaga (Protonotary and later Cardinal) as a boy, c. *1460 (Museo di Capodimonte, Naples)*.

Mantegna at Mantua
by Caroline Elam

In 1460 Andrea Mantegna travelled up the river from Padua to Mantua, where he was to remain for the rest of his life. For three years Marchese Ludovico Gonzaga had been trying to persuade him to enter his service as court artist. In 1459, Ludovico had almost despaired and began to negotiate with an obscure and bizarre painter of Hungarian origin, Michele Pannonio, who worked at Ferrara[1]. Had Pannonio been appointed instead, our vision of Ludovico Gonzaga and his family, which depends so much upon Mantegna's group portrait in the Castello S. Giorgio, would have been very different. For this portrait is not simply a record of how Ludovico saw himself and his family, but is equally an image imposed by Mantegna's highly individual art. Ludovico and his successors were aware that their image was in Mantegna's hands, and that their reputation for good judgement would rest partly on their patronage of this great artist. In 1489 Ludovico's grandson Francesco wrote to Mantegna of the *Triumphs of Caesar*, "While they are the work of your hand and your genius (*ingegno*) we nonetheless take glory in having them in the house"; and in a decree of 1492 he observed that a ruler's immortality is gained by the honouring of men of *virtù*, citing hoary examples from antiquity such as Alexander's patronage of Lysippus and Apelles. Mantegna's predecessor at Mantua, Pisanello, was extolled in much the same terms by Alfonso of Naples[2]. Mantegna's forty-six years in Mantua are more abundantly documented than the life of any other fifteenth century artist and afford us a unique glimpse of the actuality of life as a court artist; this documentation also suggests some answers to questions about the nature and effects of artistic patronage in the fifteenth century.

Although Mantegna had agreed in principle to go to Mantua in January 1457, it was three years before he arrived there. Apart from commitments in Padua and Verona, he may have been delayed by doubts about the move. He had had only one brief experience of a court before, when as an eighteen year-old he painted a double portrait for Marquis Leonello d'Este of Ferrara[3]. Leonello was Ludovico's brother-in-law, and may once have recommended Mantegna to him, although the artist's precocity had already earned him an enormous reputation. He had painted much of an important fresco cycle in the Eremitani in Padua (now largely destroyed) and was completing a novel type of altarpiece for San Zeno, Verona. His combination of the perspective experiments of Donatello (in Padua 1443-54) with an ultra refined painting technique and an unrivalled understanding of antiquity had endeared him to a circle of learned patrons and humanist scholars in Padua and Verona. The appeal of Mantua, on the other hand, was less obvious; it was a small, unhealthy town and the Gonzaga were inferior in wealth and status to the rulers of neighbouring Ferrara or Milan. They had, however, established a reputation for enlightened patronage of writers and artists disproportionate to their resources. Alberti's appearance in Mantua in 1459 would have been an added attraction for Mantegna.

The terms of employment were set out in a letter of 1458. Ludovico offered Mantegna a salary of 180 ducats a year, in monthly payments, a house to live in, enough grain to feed six people, firewood and free removal to Mantua by boat. He added that if Mantegna came he would find this allowance "the least of the rewards" he would receive. The salary was quite generous for an artist still in his twenties, though in 1470 it was still the same and Ludovico wrote to Milan: "He gets from us 15 ducats a month, his house and other privileges, which is a great expense[4]." Only in 1505 is an increase recorded, but by this time Mantegna was sometimes paid for individual works[5]. The chronically insolvent Gonzaga often failed to pay the salary, reducing Mantegna to write begging letters. It was easier for his patrons to dole out "other rewards" in the form of property grants. Mantegna was able to add to the two estates he received in this way at Boscoldo (1472) and Borgoforte (1492) by buying other country holdings for himself, and by 1476 had laid the corner-stone for a town house, built over the next twenty years[6]. Mantegna's house, with its round courtyard (Pl. 31) reminiscent of Francesco di Giorgio's reconstructions of Roman houses is of great architectural interest[7]. In 1502 Mantegna exchanged the house, perhaps never his main dwelling, with Marquis Francesco Gonzaga for a market building in the town centre yielding an income[8]. He was still paying for yet another house "in order not to go here and there a vagabond" two months before his death. Mantegna's yearning for status was indulged by his

21.	*Mantegna,* Triptych *(Galleria degli Uffizi, Florence).*

22.	*Mantegna, Detail from* The Death of the Virgin, *showing the lake and Ponte S. Giorgio, Mantua (Museo del Prado, Madrid).*

patrons and promoted by his own efforts. While Ludovico was bargaining to get him, he had already acquired rights to a Gonzaga motto and the coat of arms which appears on his early seal[9]. In 1469 he went to Ferrara to obtain the title of Palatine Count from the Emperor. "He hopes to get the title free" reported Ludovico's secretary, but this was optimistic since Frederick III financed his Italian trip by the sale of such honours[10]. By 1484 he had been made a knight "of the gilded militia", and emblazoned this dubious title on the wall of Pope Innocent VIII's chapel in the Belvedere[11]. Although few artists could boast such nominal honours in the fifteenth century, few would have striven so hard to obtain them.

Mantegna's surviving letters are taken up with a stream of complaints about money and feuds with his neighbours. Francesco Aliprandi, denying the charge of stealing five hundred apples from Mantegna, wrote to the Marchese in 1475 "He is so hostile and unpleasant

that... he's never had a neighbour with whom he hasn't gone to law". Mantegna had acquired his litigiousness in Padua, a University city famous for its law faculty, where he had become a veteran of the courts before the age of twenty-five. A note of regret can almost be detected in his letter of 1480, complaining that Gonzaga cows had got into his vineyard but that respect for his patron made him reluctant to sue. In 1475 he took the law into his own hands when he set a gang to beat up two engravers who had pirated his designs, and later had one of them accused of sodomy. Bembo's reference to Mantegna's well-known "*cortesia e gentilezza*" in 1506 must surely be sarcastic.

Mantegna's activities were closely circumscribed by his patrons. He could not undertake outside work without Gonzaga permission, as we hear from letters written in 1470 and, long after, in 1505[12]. In the latter year a hopeful patron wrote to Marchese Francesco "I know that in things of this sort he is dependent on your most illustrious Lordship's will, since he is your subject and given up to your service". Mantegna had to take on the routine work expected of a court artist: designs for heraldic devices, vases, purses, tombs and tapestries[13]. In fact a tapestry to Mantegna's design was sufficiently well known to be classed by Marcantonio Michiel in 1519 as among the most celebrated works of the day in that medium. He also supervised and supplied designs for the lost decoration of several Gonzaga country villas and castles. The most common task for a court artist was portraiture, but in this Mantegna was not always to please.

Mantegna's first major undertaking for Marchese Ludovico was the decoration of his new apartments in the Castello S. Giorgio. Even before Mantegna arrived he had advised on the chapel here, which Ludovico described to him in 1459 as "made in your way". If the Marchese wanted it to be ready for the papal Congress in that year he was to be disappointed, for the work was only finished in 1464. The chapel was dismantled in the sixteenth century but Vasari's brief description of a *tavoletta* "with figures not very large but very beautiful"[14] and the reference to gilding frames in 1464 might suggest that small pictures were set into gilded wooden panelling. Three ill-assorted panels now framed together and known as the Uffizi triptych (Pl. 21)

are generally thought to have come from the chapel[15]. The unusual concave shape of the main panel, *The Adoration of the Magi*, suggests that it was intended to be set into a niche. The *Circumcision*, with its sumptuous architectural setting of coloured marbles and gilded reliefs, is a fitting tribute to the patron of Alberti. A fourth painting, the *Death of the Virgin* (Pl. 22) appeared in Ferrara in the late sixteenth century and probably belongs in the same series[16]. The beautiful view across the Lake is the only topographical representation of Mantua or its surroundings in Mantegna's work. In 1468 he painted a similar type of panel for Ludovico, a *Christ in Limbo (istoria del Li(m)bo)*. A panel of this subject in a private collection may be Mantegna's original composition, also known in other painted and engraved versions[17]. The elongated figures and delicate colours would date it to these years. (Pl. 23).

Mantegna's most famous work (see Cat. 29), the *Camera Picta* (the so-called *Camera degli Sposi*) is inconceivable

except in the context of a fifteenth century court. Originally this square tower room in the Castello was an audience chamber, not the bedroom implied by its modern title, although rooms seldom had single functions in the fifteenth century. Rodolfo Signorini has shown the painting was begun in 1465 and finished in 1474[18]; the date 1465 is incised – probably in Mantegna's hand – in the plaster of a window jamb, and the artist's dedicatory inscription is also dated: "For the illustrious Ludovico, second Marchese of Mantua, best of princes and most unvanquished in faith, and for his illustrious wife Barbara incomparable glory of womankind, his Andrea Mantegna of Padua completed this slight work in the year 1474". This elaborate inscription in which the artist dedicates the work to his patrons marks a significant change in the attitude to the artist in the fifteenth century. Even the apparently self-deprecating description of the work as *opus tenue* may conceal a self-satisfied pun, since *tenue* could also mean "fine" or "subtle", and was so used later to describe Mantegna's frescoes in Rome[19]. In 1470 Ludovico complained that Mantegna had completed less than half of his *camera*[20]. Two visits to Tuscany, in 1466 and 1467, had intervened, but Mantegna's slow pace of work was already notorious. The room took nine years to paint, the last section being the "Meeting" scene left of the entrance door.

For sixteenth century observers the *trompe l'œil* vaulted ceiling was the most remarkable part of the room. Here illusion and reality are intriguingly blurred even in the Identities of those who surround the fictive open oculus: fashionably coiffed court ladies hobnob with winged putti, one of whom threatens to drop an apple on our heads. This kind of visual pun is entirely characteristic of Mantegna. In the painted lozenge-shaped compartments into which the ceiling is divided we seem to see stucco roundels of the first eight Caesars. Their presence here, and the fact that Augustus wears a crown, may be intended to remind us that Mantua owed its allegiance to "his Caesarian majesty" the Holy Roman Emperor, whose portrait appears below. The putti holding the surrounding wreaths contain some of Mantegna's most beautiful passages of painting (Pl. 24), while the scenes from the myths of Orpheus, Arion and Hercules in the triangular sections below are boldly conceived and dramatically animated.

The *Camera degli Sposi* vault represents the first attempt at the kind of illusionistic ceiling painting which was to obsess Italian artists for the next two centuries. By contrast the group portraits below were a more familiar genre in mid-fifteenth century court art. It is Mantegna's illusionistic skill that makes these frescoes so compelling, and convinces us, quite wrongly, that we are looking at an actual historical event.

In the badly damaged "Court Scene" Mantegna succeeds remarkably in animating a multiple portrait group. The overall impression of the "Meeting" wall, however, is more awkward, despite the ravishing and minutely painted landscape. In the "Meeting" itself profile and three-quarter views of faces seem somewhat mechanically combined, with little sense of interaction; the figures are more formal and less relaxed than in the "Court" scene. The reason may partly be that not all the portraits were part of the original scheme. We now know that Barbara of Brandenburg's brother-in-law, the King of Denmark, was inserted here because he visited Mantua in 1474, the year Mantegna completed the frescoes[21]. The fact that he and the Emperor Frederick III appear as relatively insignificant members of the group, is admittedly a shock to our groping attempts at understanding Renaissance social decorum. Apparently it was accepted at the time, since we learn of the Duke of Milan's fury in 1475 that Ludovico had included the portraits of "the two most wretched men in the world" while leaving out the Duke himself. Ludovico tactfully replied that he would have included the Duke had the latter not objected so strongly to portrait drawings by Mantegna in the past, for "it is true that Andrea is a good master in other things, but in portrait painting he could have more grace, and doesn't do so well"[22].

The presence of these two monarchs proves that the "Meeting" cannot represent a single historical event, since their visits to Italy were five years apart in time, and the Emperor came to Ferrara, not Mantua. They confirm, however, the emphatic dynastic character of the scenes: the temporal Gonzaga succession is traced from Ludovico through his son Federico to his grandson Francesco, while the family's ecclesiastical ambitions are seen to be invested in Cardinal Francesco, Ludovico the future bishop, and Sigismondo later a cardinal, who all link hands.

How seriously should we take Ludovico's deprecatory remark that Mantegna's portraits could "have more grace"? Certainly he was no flatterer, but Ludovico and Barbara continued to tolerate his frank depictions, since in 1477 the artist complained of having to paint them while they were out of town. A vainer sitter, Isabella d'Este, turned down a portrait by Mantegna in 1493 on the ostensible grounds that "it looks nothing like us", but no doubt because her double chin was not spared. After Ludovico's death in 1478 and the division of the Mantuan territory, the new Marchese Federico was left with less revenue to fulfil his commitments, including Mantegna's salary. Federico, however, appreciated Mantegna's genius and kept the artist at work during his brief marquisate, even if the only documented references are to designs for vases in the Marchese's *studioli*, and to an unidentified room which Mantegna was painting for him in 1484. The only major painting obvious-

27.   *Mantegna, Study for the Standard-Bearers in the* Triumphs of Caesar *(Musée du Louvre, Cabinet des Dessins).*

28.   *Mantegna, Detail of Vase-Bearer in the* Triumphs of Caesar *(H.M. The Queen, Hampton Court).*

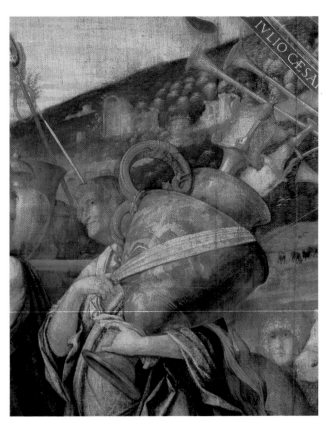

ly dating from these years is the *St. Sebastian* in the Louvre, associable with the marriage of Federico's daughter Chiara to Gilbert de Montpensier in 1481. Allowing for the difference in medium, this canvas is stylistically close to the *Camera degli Sposi*. Canvas was used rather than panel partly because the painting travelled to Aigueperse; in 1477 Mantegna suggested that portraits should be painted on canvas if they were to be sent some distance, in which case they could be rolled on a rod. He had already painted on canvas when in Padua, but he used it increasingly often; his workshop considered it to be especially suitable for large-scale decorative pictures[23]. But he continued to paint in tempera, using oil only for the final glaze and varnish.

In 1479 Mantegna coupled a plea for funds with a request for Federico's advice about an outside commission. Was this a threat to leave Gonzaga service if more money were not forthcoming? He was in the next years to make a direct approach to Lorenzo de' Medici, who in 1483 had made a detour to Mantua "just to see the city", looking at paintings and antiquities in Mantegna's collection. Just after Federico's death in 1484 the artist wrote to Lorenzo asking for financial help to complete his house. But it has not been noticed that in

1481 the artist had sent Lorenzo a picture to Florence, acknowledged on the 2 March[24]. Since in 1484 Mantegna refers to "the additional support of some work of mine", he may have sent a second picture then. The Medici inventory of 1492 records a lost *Judith and Holofernes* encased in a box, just the kind of small cabinet picture that Mantegna sent to friends and patrons[25]. But if a second picture was sent it might well be the *Madonna of the Stonecutters* in the Uffizi, described by Vasari in 1568 as among Francesco de' Medici's dearest possessions[26] (Pl. 26).

Federico would not have discouraged this apparently spontaneous gesture of 1481 towards Lorenzo. In these years Federico was fighting alongside the Florentines and also attempting to pay off his father's debts to the Medici bank[27]. Perhaps this episode is a subtle example of the diplomatic use of Mantegna's paintings. In 1499 Isabella d'Este attempted to win over the French by giving Cardinal d'Amboise a small *St John the Baptist* by Mantegna incorporating the Cardinal's portrait and coat of arms[28].

Mantegna was prepared to carry out such commissions quickly if they were relatively straightforward: refusing on his behalf a specific commission from the Du-

29. *Mantegna, Madonna della Vittoria (Musée du Louvre, Paris).*

chess of Milan, Federico reported in 1480: "He says this would be more like the work of a miniature painter than his own because he is not accustomed to doing small figures. He would be better at doing a Madonna or something else about one and a half *braccia* long". Many of Mantegna's surviving small Madonnas must have been produced as presents, like the Madonna Francesco Gonzaga gave his future mother-in-law as a Christmas gift in 1485. The small grisaille paintings of Old Testament or classical subjects which his studio produced in increasing numbers probably served a similar function.

Federico Gonzaga is the least well known of Mantegna's patrons; as a boy he received poor school reports from the bad-tempered humanist Filelfo[29]. When Marchese, however, he made touchingly strenuous efforts to understand the arts: while building his vast extension to the Ducal Palace, the Nova Domus, he asked for the designs of the most up-to-date palace in Italy, the Palazzo Ducale of Urbino, and consulted its architect, Francesco di Giorgio, about his design for chimneys that did not smoke[30]. He also had two *studioli* where he collected antiquities, and tried conscientiously to understand the epic poems sent him by Filelfo's son, Mario[31].

Federico's aspirations may be relevant to the unsolved problem of who commissioned Mantegna's masterpiece, the *Triumphs of Caesar*. Even if Mantegna suggested the initial idea himself, whoever allowed him to embark on this extraordinary series of canvases not only gave him the opportunity to create a unique work of art completely suited to his nature, but must also have been aware that the project would take many years to complete, given the artist's notorious slowness and the unprecedented scale of the work.

References to Mantegna working on the *Triumphs* all come from Francesco's reign (1484-1519), and it is usually assumed that he commissioned them. Recently, however, Professor Martindale has argued in his catalogue of the paintings that they were started for Ludovico (d. 1478)[32]. His argument rests on two assumptions: firstly that because of Mantegna's very slow rate of work and his other commitments the canvases would have taken at least twelve years to complete; and secondly that eight of the nine paintings must have

been painted before Mantegna's trip to Rome in 1488-90 since only one, the *Captives*, shows the familiarity with Roman street architecture that Mantegna could have acquired there. This canvas, however, no more resembles Rome than any of the others; indeed it is remarkable how little Mantegna's general vision of antiquity, formed by the monuments of Verona, was affected by his visit to Rome, even though references to specific Roman building and sculpture appear in his work both before and after. Moreover the evidence of Mantegna's preliminary work on the cycle suggests a different chronology.

Versions of several drawings by Mantegna for the *Triumphs* suggest that he worked out the whole cycle beforehand in a preliminary form. One such drawing, for the *Captives*, known from a copy, already shows the same conception of a street scene as found in the final canvas. An interesting feature of this and other preliminary drawings for the *Triumphs* is that the perspective viewpoint is much higher than the *di sotto in su* construction favoured in the canvases, suggesting an earlier stage of design. (In fact, Mantegna almost always changed the perspective construction between drawing and painting, as though he needed to work out the composition and poses before he applied his techniques of recession and foreshortening). The studies for the *Captives* and the *Senators*, with the heads of the figures almost on one level, are often said to recall Roman processional reliefs like the *Ara Pacis* (not discovered, however, till the next century). But the way Mantegna shows the figures walking three or four abreast with overlapping profiles has a closer precedent, the famous lost fresco by Masaccio, showing the consecration of S. Maria del Carmine in Florence.

Since there is no hard evidence that either Ludovico or Francesco was the patron of the *Triumphs*, there is perhaps room for a third suggestion, that they were started for Federico. The first reference we have to them in 1486 suggests they were well under way: in that year Ercole d'Este Duke of Ferrara, visited "the Triumphs of Caesar, which Mantegna is painting, which he liked very much". Even two canvases in the two years since Federico's death would have represented unusually fast progress for Mantegna, allowing little time for the laborious preliminary planning. Conversely neither the style of the paintings nor the silence in the documents suggests that they were begun over eight years before Ercole's visit. Even the vexed question of the intended location would be solved if it could be shown that they were commissioned by Federico and intended for the *Nova Domus*.

The patron of the *Triumphs*, whoever he was, must have wanted to identify himself with the most famous general of antiquity. The cult of Julius Caesar was widespread in the fifteenth century: the scholarly Leonello d'Este wrote Caesar-like commentaries on his own life. All three of Mantegna's Gonzaga patrons were condottieri, but Ludovico did not stress his military role in his last years, whereas Federico spent most of his short reign on the battlefield. Undoubtedly Francesco became closely associated with the *Triumphs* later on, and was often referred to as Caesar: his medals nearly always present a military image. The rival claims of the Gonzaga rulers to be the patron of Mantegna's great work will only be settled by much closer study of their lives and personal imagery.

But the *Triumphs* are, in Francesco's words, the product of Mantegna's *ingegno*. Into them the artist poured all his passionate commitment to antiquity, seen not as a dead subject for archaeological study, but as an inexhaustible source of visual riches. It is entirely appropriate that he should have used as his literary starting point Flavio Biondo's *Roma Triumphans*, which shares his own enthusiasm for the ancient world, continually reinforcing the use of written sources with acute visual observation and modern parallels. Mantegna's freely moving figures are in the liberated style of his later works: fluttering draperies and pennants have an independent life and vivacity; even the horses have ringlets, and share in the exuberant sense of fun which is an underestimated aspect of Mantegna's work.

Mantegna's last Gonzaga patron, Francesco, became Marchese at the early age of eighteen. "The disposition of this new lord renews my hopes, seeing him all inclined towards *virtù*", wrote Mantegna to Lorenzo de' Medici a month later. Francesco, who praised him to the Pope as "an outstanding painter whose like our age has not seen", allowed Mantegna his most prolonged absence from Mantua, the two years (1488-90) it took him to paint Pope Innocent VIII's chapel in the Villa Belvedere at the Vatican palace. No doubt the Marchese hoped to smooth the path for his brother Sigismondo's cardinalate, eventually achieved under Julius II. The chapel in Rome, praised by Vasari for its narrative realism, was destroyed in the eighteenth century[32].

Although he must have been excited at the opportunity to study Roman antiquities, Mantegna was less pleased by the Pope's ungenerous patronage. "I have nothing from our lord except expenses and housekeeping, so

that I should be better off at home", he complained. These affectionately gossipy letters to Francesco from Rome show that Mantegna was anxious to return to his incompleted *Triumphs*. Despite Francesco's unintellectual temperament, his preference for horses and chivalric romances to collecting and the classics, he was a sympathetic patron. His most memorable portrait is in Mantegna's *Madonna della Vittoria* (Plate 29), a beautiful painting with a rather sordid *raison d'être*. It was commissioned in 1495 to commemorate Francesco's inconclusive victory over the French in the Battle of Fornovo. Anti-semitism, whipped up by the Marchese's brother the protonotary Sigismondo and a fanatical friar, was exploited to stimulate patriotic religious feeling. An unfortunate Jew, who had quite legally destroyed a Madonna frescoed on his house, was obliged to pay not only for Mantegna's picture but also for a new church to house it, built on the site of the destroyed fresco. Here a popular cult developed, fostered by a carefully stage-managed procession on the first anniversary of the battle in which Mantegna's painting was carried in a *tableau vivant* from the artist's house to the new church. The altarpiece is marvellously calculated to suit this factitious devotion: the garlanded canopy over the Madonna's throne echoes the processional decorations and the proto-Wagnerian warrior saints are deliberately enlarged to protect the kneeling Francesco. "It was an incredible thing to see", a courtier reported to Francesco. "The crowds could never tire of looking at such a worthy work, especially – apart from the Virgin – at the image of Your Illustrious Lordship, which moved everyone to tenderness".

Observing the procession from a nearby house was Francesco's wife, Isabella d'Este. Isabella's patronage of Mantegna is marked by respect for his gifts tempered with irritation at his slowness of work. It was in my view her realisation that Mantegna would never complete enough paintings to fill her *studiolo* that turned Isabella to the idea of collecting works from "the most excellent artists in Italy"[34]. But Mantegna's canvases remained the paragons with which the arriving works from Perugino and Costa[35] were unfavourably contrasted, and which served to frighten off his brother-in-law, Giovanni Bellini, altogether. Mantegna's first painting for the *studiolo*, the *Parnassus* (completed 1497), is one of his masterpieces (Pl. 89). Mars and Venus preside over the dance of the Muses accompanied by Apollo's lyre, with Mercury and Pegasus in attendance. Pictorial harmonies suggest the harmonious intervals of music, and the technique – a combination

of gouache and oil varnish on canvas – produces a softer, less "stony" effect than ever before. The subject, whose precise allegorical meaning (the *bello significato* insisted on by Isabella) continues to elude iconographers, brought out the best in Mantegna's art and wit. Contemporaries were perhaps equally in the dark, since the doctor-poet Battista Fiera (see Cat. 96-100) had to apologise for making the not unnatural equation of Venus with Isabella herself. He had failed to remember the adulterous connotations of Venus's harmonious union with Mars:

"But, all unwary, he had not seen the Blacksmith's wrath,
Stretching out avenging hands to Mars…"

The irate presence of the cuckolded Vulcan suggests that we should not take the subject of the *Parnassus* as seriously as some have supposed.

Perhaps this kind of misunderstanding accounts for the plethora of identifying labels which appear in Mantegna's second picture for the *studiolo*, the *Expulsion of the Vices* (1502) (Pl. 30). We may feel that this heavily moralising subject was particularly congenial to Isabella, but equally laborious for Mantegna to realise in visual terms. In fact it corresponds very closely with the artist's own increasing obsession with the idea of the opposition of ignorance to virtue, and conversely of vice to truth[36]. This was the theme of the famous *Calumny* of Apelles, which Mantegna drew[37], and allegories of this sort are numerous in his late work (Cat. 125-126).

In 1506 Mantegna was working very slowly on a third *studiolo* composition, a *Story of Comus*. Still short of funds, still trying to acquire a house, he was forced to sell Isabella his beloved antique bust of Faustina (Cat. 121-22). Isabella was not diverted by compassion for the dying artist into acceding too readily to the asking price of 100 ducats. But Mantegna, however sick, was a match for Isabella in toughness and obstinacy and she eventually paid the full price. A month later Mantegna was dead. "I believe our Lord God will use him to make some beautiful work", wrote Lorenzo da Pavia. There now ensued an unseemly struggle over the artistic estate. Apart from the embryonic *Comus*, which Isabella must have silently appropriated, at least five paintings remained in the artist's studio. Not all were necessarily works of the last years: for although the *St. Sebastian* (Ca' d'Oro, Venice) is obviously a late work (its haunting inscription reads *Nil nisi divinum stabile est; cetera fumus* ("nothing but the divine is stable; the rest is smoke"), the *Dead Christ* (Cat. 33) seems to date from an earlier period. The *Reception of Cybele* (National Gallery) was initially appropriated along with the *Dead Christ* by Cardinal Sigismondo, but returned after a rather embarassed exchange of courtesies to its rightful owner, Francesco Cornaro.

The remaining two works were destined for Mant-

24

egna's own funerary chapel in Sant'Andrea, the rights to which he had acquired in 1504. There can be no doubt that Mantegna himself planned the chapel's beautiful decoration (Pl. 32), for which he left five hundred ducats in his will. It repeats the dedication (to St. John the Baptist) and several of the illusionistic decorative ideas of the Chapel of Innocent VIII. The mural painting must have been largely carried out by Mantegna's painter sons, who were capable of imitating their father's style, although there is a tradition that the young Correggio intervened in the panels. A bronze bust of the artist (Cat. 30), his face etched by powerful lines of discontent and melancholy, completes the ensemble. It is hard to think of another Renaissance artist who arranged for himself to be so richly commemorated.

Although Mantegna might have made more money at a richer court or in the free markets of Padua, Venice or Florence, he could hardly have found greater protection, or more opportunity to work in his own manner than was offered him by the Gonzaga. It might be claimed that the lack of competition in Mantua gave the artist little incentive to develop or even to change his style. Indeed Vasari saw him as one of the many late fifteenth century artists who fell short of the challenge of the third *maniera*, what we should call the High Renaissance. But we should be grateful that Mantegna did not follow in the footsteps of Leonardo da Vinci or Giovanni Bellini, but rather remained in Mantua to paint the *Parnassus*, and the *Triumphs of Caesar*, which, as Vasari conceded, "could not be more beautiful"[38].

Notes

For Mantegna in Mantua see especially Kristeller, 1901; Tietze-Conrat, 1957; Marani and Perina, 1962; Martindale, 1979. For works discussed, see also Mantua, *Mantegna* cat., 1961; Martindale and Garavaglia, 1967. Documents and letters are in Kristeller, 1902, Gerola, 1908-09; Resti-Ferrari, 1928; Brown, 1969, 1972, 1973, 1974, 1977 and 1978; Signorini, 1972, 1974, 1975; Martindale, 1979[2]. All letters and documents are from Luzio's documentary appendix to Kristeller, 1902, unless otherwise indicated.

1. Tietze-Conrat, 1955, p. 11.

2. Venturi, 1896, pp. 59-60.

3. Campori, 1885, p. 357.

4. Brown, 1972, p. 862.

5. ASM, Autografi 7, fol. 128 gives references to salary payments to Mantegna from the *Libro di Entrata e spese del Massario generale*, including an increase to 930 lire in 1505. Mantegna was paid 110 ducats for the *Madonna della Vittoria*. In 1506 Isabella d'Este refused him a 27 ducat advance on the *Comus*.

6. Gerola, 1908-9, and Resti-Ferrari, 1928, supplement Kristeller.

7. Rosenthal, 1962. The courtyard may also be a reference to Pliny the Younger's Laurentine villa as interpreted in Flavio Biondo, *Roma Triumphans*, 1472, bk. ix.

8. Gerola, 1908-9, p. 914.

9. Coat of arms seal used by Mantegna 1463-68; Caesar's head seal 1472-94; initial "M" seal 1505-06.

10. Signorini, 1974, p. 228.

11. He is described as *spectabilis eques* on 13 March 1484 during Federico's marquisate (Gerola, 1908-09, p. 911, checked in ASM, Notarile, Estensioni 1484, fols. 843r., v.) It is usually assumed (e.g. Kristeller, 1901, p. 203) that Marquis Francesco made Mantegna a knight in 1488.

12. Brown, 1972, p. 862, and Brown 1974.

13. Resti-Ferrari, 1928, on design for Barbara of Brandenburg's tomb (1482); Brown, 1974, p. 102 on purse for Giulia della Mirandola (1469).

14. Vasari, ed. Milanesi, III, p. 396.

15. First recorded in Medici collection at Casino di San Marco in 1588; Florence, *Palazzo Vecchio*, 1980, pp. 253-54; they could have passed to the Medici during the negotiations over the marriage of Vincenzo Gonzaga and Eleonora de' Medici (1584).

16. Longhi, 1934.

17. Sold at Sotheby's 11 July, 1973.

18. Signorini, 1974.

19. R. Maffei, *Commentariorum urbanorum*, 1506, bk. xxi, p. 300.

20. Brown, 1972, p. 862.

21-22. Signorini, 1974.

23. Kristeller, 1902, doc. 111, letter of 16 July 1491.

24. M. Del Piazzo, *Protocolli del Carteggio di Lorenzo il Magnifico*, Florence 1956, p. 136: *A Andrea Mantinia, dipintore a Mantova; lettera grata per la dipintura et opera sua mandata, ringraziandola, etc.* My thanks to Nicolai Rubinstein for this reference.

25. Muentz, 1888, p. 78.

26. Vasari ed. Milanesi, III, p. 402. The painting is not recognisably listed in the 1492 Medici inventory.

27. Praticò, 1949.

28. Luzio, 1901, p. 155.

29. Martindale, 1979[2], p. 45.

30. Cottafavi, 1963.

31. Braghirolli, 1876, p. 619; Marani and Perina, 1962, p. 119, n. 12.

32. Martindale, 1979[2].

33. Full descriptions in Chattard, 1762-67, iii, pp. 139-44; Taja, 1750, pp. 401 f.

34. Canuti, 1931, ii, p. 208.

35. Luzio, 1913, pp. 206-7; 1909, pp. 864-65.

36. Twice, in letters of 1489 and 1491 he cites the Latin tag *Virtuti semper adversatur Ignorantia* ("Virtue is always opposed by Ignorance").

37. Popham and Pouncey, 1950, no. 158.

38. Vasari ed. Milanesi, IV, p. 11, III, p. 400.

33.   *View of Mantua across the former Ponte di San Giorgio.*   34.   *View over the centre of Mantua looking east.*

The Gonzaga and Renaissance architecture
by Howard Burns

Despite the titles of its rulers, and the recognition and respect accorded to them, the Gonzaga state was in many ways a vast estate, dotted with Gonzaga residences, rather than a state in the modern sense. The ruler personally controlled everything from building a new church or digging a new canal to organising hospitality for the great personages on whose support and protection the ruling house depended. Mantua's key position in the north Italian system of communications (the Po, that great watery autostrada of the time flowed through the state) brought a stream of important visitors to be entertained and impressed. The Gonzaga had only one city, Mantua itself, and perhaps because of this created numerous splendid country villas. Ostentatious hospitality was a habit not only of the Gonzaga, but became instinctive for their immediate dependents as well. The architect Fancelli wrote to Ludovico in 1472 thanking him for having sent an architectural drawing by Mantegna: "the drawing which I have received from you pleases me first of all because I can understand the work from it, and secondly because frequently ambassadors and lords come, and to honour them one seeks to show them stupendous works, and I will now have this marvellous drawing to show…"[1]

It was above all because Mantua was not a state of the first importance that the Gonzaga made it a leading architectural centre. Its position was potentially ambiguous, hovering between the leading dukedoms and truly petty states like Carpi and Camerino[2]. Within broad limits prestige was a question of presentation and the Gonzaga in their hospitality, their horses, their artistic collections and their buildings, all matters to which they gave constant and expert attention, sought to present themselves and their city in the best possible light. Their expenditure paid off: Ludovico obtained a cardinal's hat for his son and was a respected figure among Italian rulers and military commanders; his children and grandchildren made advantageous marriages with other princely dynasties.
Federico, Captain General of the Church, had the acumen to default on his obligations towards Clement VII and instead to court and entertain Charles V, the dominant figure in Italian politics in these years, thereby securing his own position, as well as helping the career of his brother Ferrante (another important architectural patron), who rose to be Viceroy of Sicily, and Governor of Milan (Cat. 146). In 1530, in the course of his visit Charles V made Federico Duke of Mantua. By his marriage in October 1531 to Margherita Paleologo Federico became heir to the Marquisate of Monferrato[3], of which he assumed control in 1536. Thus the three Gonzaga brothers, Federico, Ferrante, and Cardinal Ercole, who ruled the state after Federico's death in 1540, came to assume an influence much greater than one would expect from the ruling family of a prosperous territory not much bigger than an English county.

No building stone was available locally. It had to be imported either from Verona (like the red marble used at Revere), from Vicentine quarries (like the hard white stone used at San Sebastiano), or from Venice (like the already cut Istrian stone "prefabricated" by Pietro Lombardo for a votive chapel)[4]. The whole character of architecture in Mantua was influenced by the need to produce impressive effects with brick, stucco and terracotta. Architects and patrons thought and calculated easily in terms of bricks, not only for wall thicknesses but for the totals required. Fancelli states that the vault (of the portico?) of San Sebastiano (Cat. 35) is four bricks thick (about 60 cms.) and contains 15,000 bricks, and Ludovico himself estimated that Sant'Andrea would require 2,000,000 bricks[5]. When Alberti wrote to Ludovico about his design for Sant'Andrea, saying that it "would cost much less" than Manetti's, one can guess that Manetti, who in Florence was architect at San Lorenzo, had produced a Brunelleschian church design with stone columns – a solution well suited to Florence, with stone quarries near the city, but prohibitively expensive in Mantua[6]. Similarly the Palazzo Te, is almost entirely a brick and stucco building, in which Giulio developed Bramante's idea (realized in his House of Raphael) of imitating masonry in cheaper materials. The lack of local stone was in fact an advantage for the Gonzagas and their architects: it encouraged the bold structural solution of Sant'Andrea and made possible the ornate and sometimes bizarre effects for which Giulio strove. It enabled more to be built than would have been possible if stone construction had been the norm for important buildings. The Gonzaga's building enterprises were many, and their income limited[7]. They were also patrons in a hurry, and brick construction saved not only the cost of stone but stonemasons' wages and the considerable time needed to handcut architectural details.

From Ludovico onwards the Gonzaga resolved to follow the modes of the leading artistic centres and to seek the collaboration of the best designers. Ludovico in the course of the 1450's opted for the new style which had been first created in Florence by Brunelleschi, and in this choice was certainly influenced by his own contacts with Florence and the Medici, and possibly by an admiration for antiquity derived from his studies under Vittorino da Feltre. The *all'antica* style was moreover appropriate to Virgil's city. The Florentine architect Antonio Manetti visited Mantua in the 1450's, and probably made executed designs for Revere (Cat. 34) and unexecuted ones for Sant'Andrea. The Marchese also took into his service a gifted young Florentine stonemason, Luca Fancelli, who within a decade of his arrival in 1450 became superintendent of all the more demanding projects. Most important of all were the close relations Ludovico established with Alberti, who became a regular visitor and correspondent. Filarete, writing in the early 1460s with the aim of converting his readers and his patron, Francesco Sforza, to the new architectural style, could already back up his argument by saying that "the lord of Mantua, who has a very great understanding" of architecture, would not use "the ancient way" of building were it not "more beautiful and more functional"than the medieval style which it had replaced[8].

Sixty years later Marchese Federico was also enthusiastically committed to the newest architectural style, that of Bramante, Peruzzi (Cat. 187) and Raphael. On his accession in 1519 he sought designs for a monument to his father from the leading artists in Rome, and in 1521 sent his court painter Lionbruno to Rome for a refresher course[9]. Federico wrote to Castiglione his ambassador: "Knowing what excellent talents master Lorenzo Liombruno our painter has... as it will be also to our honour and that of our country we reckon that coming to Rome would be of much benefit to him... we wish that he be directed ... to seeing those beautiful ancient and modern things in Rome and especially the works of Michelangelo and those of the late Raphael of Urbino and these others which in your judgement are excellent, so that he should return well instructed and full of things to imitate"[10].

In 1532 the architect Battista Covo undertook a similar study trip, and wrote to the Duke signing himself "Bap.ta da Covo who is learning architecture", and saying that he had received a letter "in which Messer Giulio Romano advises me of certain special places which I have to see" – perhaps not only for Covo's benefit, but because Giulio wanted drawings of them[11].

The first fifteen years of Ludovico's rule (he became Marchese in 1444) seem to have been taken up with improving the security and communications of the territory[12]. His first major architectural enterprise was the palace of Revere (Cat. 34) which documents his abandonment of a late Gothic in favour of an *all'antica* style. His intensive concern with urban development and building in Mantua itself begins in the years 1459-60, the period in which Alberti first became a regular visitor, and Mantegna was engaged as court artist. Ludovico's concern with the appearance of his city was connected with his successful efforts to have Mantua chosen by Pius II as the setting for the Congress to discuss a crusade against the Turks: Pius II was resident in the city from 27 May 1459 until 19 January 1460[13]. During this time he probably discussed his plans for the miniature city of Pienza, which he was constructing, with Ludovico and Alberti. A revealing letter from Ludovico to Alberti, dated 13 December 1459 asks Alberti if he could send a copy of Vitruvius by return of courier as Pius had asked to borrow it. The Pope, however, was not impressed by Mantua: "the place was marshy and unhealthy; the heat was intense ... very many were catching the fever; nothing was to be heard except the frogs"[14]. After the conclusion of the Congress an agent of Ludovico's reported a conversation he had had in Venice with a papal ambassador: "he greatly praised Your Lordship and Mantua ... saying that apart from the mud there was no city in the world more adapted or convenient for the Papal court... I replied to him that Your Excellency had begun paving the *piazze* and wanted go on to do the rest of the city"[15].

35. *Revere:* Portone *of Ludovico Gonzaga's Palace.*

36. *Revere:* Loggia *in courtyard of Ludovico Gonzaga's Palace.*

Criticisms of this sort led Ludovico to set under way an ambitious programme of renovation and embellishment, which may have already included the idea of rebuilding Sant'Andrea as well as the construction of San Sebastiano and the paving and cleaning up of the whole city, above all the central *piazze*, and the modernization of the Palazzo del Podestà. The ambitious idea of demolishing and rebuilding the round Romanesque church of San Lorenzo, so as to create a handsome central piazza came to nothing, and changes at Sant' Andrea were blocked until March 1470 by the determined opposition of Abbott Nuvoloni[16]. The paving went ahead, however, so did painting of shop fronts, the work on the Palazzo del Podestà, and on San Sebastiano. Alberti's close involvement with Ludovico's plans can be seen from the letter he wrote to the Marchese on 27 February 1460: "The working drawings for San Sebastiano, San Lorenzo, the loggia, Virgil, are done, – I think they will not displease you"[17].

By 1460 Leon Battista Alberti (1404-1472) was already the most respected authority on architecture for all those who were anxious to revive "the ancient way of building". His literary activity, his comprehensive and lucid architectural treatise (Cat. 38), his membership of a distinguished Florentine family and his close connections with the Florentine élite and with the leading courts of central and northern Italy gave him a unique prestige and standing[18].

He had great artistic flair, and expressed his highly original suggestions with clarity, brevity and self confidence (Cat. 36). He had already advised Pope Nicholas V and Pius II on architectural matters and had designed the Tempio Malatestiano in Rimini and the Palazzo Rucellai in Florence. Alberti was a man of letters, and lived off his official salary and ecclesiastical livings, not from being paid for making designs, and supervising their execution, as Fancelli did. On the other hand he was not an intellectual who never left his study. He was compulsively drawn to making architectural designs and solving architectural problems, even when he had not been called upon to do so, and he tells us that this was one of the ways he used to free himself of the feelings of stress to which he was probably excessively prone[19]. He was deeply interested in construction techniques, and enjoyed talking to craftsmen about their

29

methods. His many interests and commitments often kept him away from the building site, but when present he followed progress closely, and when he was away patrons like Sigismondo Malatesta and Ludovico Gonzaga saw to it that he should be kept informed, and his wishes followed, sometimes sending local architects on long journeys to consult with him[20]. Ludovico was fortunate to have obtained the friendship of this extraordinary man, who complemented in the architectural field what Ludovico had available in painting from Mantegna. There was probably some exchange of ideas between the two, and Mantegna possibly had access to Alberti's now lost drawings, which could well have influenced the architecture represented in the *Camera degli Sposi*[21]. The tone of Ludovico's letters to Alberti is extremely courteous and attentive, in contrast to his often boisterous and facetious exchanges with Fancelli: "We see in your letter what you write about having hurt a testicle" – by falling in Sant'Andrea – "to which we reply that the Lord God lets men punish themselves in the place where they sin"[22].

Ludovico entertained Alberti in Mantua, made a villa available to him when he wanted to rest in the country, advised him about the purchase of land near Mantua, and actively lobbied in Rome on his behalf[23]. He strongly backed all Alberti's ideas ("since it seems so to him, so it seems also to us") and when Fancelli made an alternative model, probably for San Sebastiano, this provoked such a strong reaction from the Marchese that Fancelli wrote to him that "as soon as I got back home I burned it"[24]. Ludovico was ready to stand up for Alberti's novel ideas even in the face of his son's sarcastic comments (Cat. 35) and of opposition in Florence to Alberti's design for the choir of the Annunziata, for which he was paying[25].

Ludovico's only fault as an architectural patron was that in his enthusiasm for building he started more projects than he could possibly complete. He built or improved numbers of country residences. The work at Alberti's San Sebastiano (Cat. 35) and Sant'Andrea (Cat. 36-37) went ahead very rapidly at first, but then Sant'Andrea came to eclipse the earlier church project, and even Sant'Andrea lost its impetus because of work on public buildings. Money that might have gone towards building in Mantua was spent on the Annunziata in Florence[26]. Ludovico was however an energetic and attentive general manager for all his building projects, he followed their progress closely, came up with sensible ideas of his own, and enjoyed referring to himself as the pupil and Fancelli as the "master"[27].

Despite some disagreements, and Fancelli's laments about not getting paid, Ludovico's relations with the man who became his leading architect became progressively closer, so that the two became collaborators rather than simply patron and architect. Luca Fancelli (c. 1430-1495) came, like many Florentine stonemasons, from Settignano[28]. He first arrived in Mantua about 1450, and his initial activity would have been as a highly skilled stonemason, capable of designing the details he executed in an up-to-date Florentine style. The portal at Revere is his most notable early work (Pl. 35). Fancelli however rapidly extended his expertise to cover woodwork, construction in brick, general direction of major enterprises and (witness his ill fated model) building design. He maintained close contact with Florence, where his family lived, and went there frequently. Later in his career he was in contact with Lorenzo de' Medici, who appreciated his merits, and had him appointed as architect of the Florentine cathedral in 1491[29]. He never became a provincial figure, and his many surviving letters show him as lively and intelligent: in a letter to Lorenzo de' Medici he criticises the Cathedral in Milan for being "without bones and without proportion" and he furnished Francesco Gonzaga with an account of Columbus' discoveries[30].

Without him Sant'Andrea, begun in the year of Alberti's death, could not have been built. For as Ludovico wrote to his wife about the building in 1477, revealing at the same time his own feeling for Alberti's architecture: "This work cannot be built without Luca, for no one but he understands it ... Johanino is a sensible person,... but he doesn't understand these subtle works because he is used to making his houses and barns in the country, and goes after cut-price solutions, while these beautiful things cannot be made without great expense"[31].

Fancelli was not however only an able executor of Alberti's ideas. His Nova Domus, built for the Marchese Federico I between 1480 and 1484, though it owes its

twin towers to Revere, and its pilasters to Alberti's Palazzo Rucellai, is a very original work, which anticipates sixteenth century architectural developments[32].

Federico Gonzaga seems to have been as interested in building as his father, despite the heavy debts to Lorenzo de' Medici and others which Ludovico had left him[33]. Work continued at San Sebastiano and Sant'Andrea after his accession, and Federico pressed ahead with the Nova Domus, intended as a fine new residence for himself within the old palace complex. Like his father before him and his grandson after, he was anxious to follow the best models, and to take the best advice. Thus he obtained plans of the palace at Urbino, and though he found them hard to understand, he hoped to "derive excellent models" from them[34]. He also wrote to Francesco di Giorgio the director of all architecture and artistic work at Urbino, whose role, given the close contact between the two courts, possibly furnished the model for the position of general superintendent of works in Mantua. The problem was smoking fireplaces: "as we at present are building in our palace we would desire to understand the system of the fireplaces made in that palace [Urbino] which ... never

smoke"[35]. Francesco di Giorgio politely declined the invitation to come to Mantua, but sent a drawing of the fireplaces "advising your most Illustrious Lordship that in past years they too used to smoke, but I fixed them in such a way that they function very usefully without the least appearance of smoke"[36].

When Federico died in 1484 all work on the Nova Domus stopped. The new Marchese, Francesco, seems to have been the least interested in architecture of all the rulers of Mantua, and as a result of his military involvements had little money available to spend on building. Moreover, thanks to the efforts of his father and grandfather he had less need to build, as the town and territory were now furnished with many modern buildings. Work was continued at Sant'Andrea as a result of the efforts of the building committee, and not of Francesco, who on the contrary only the year after his accession borrowed 110 ducats from the building fund of the church, not repaid by 1490[37]. Francesco had some work done on his villas, but his main project was the palace of San Sebastiano, opposite the church, which characteristically he constructed in part with materials intended for San Sebastiano itself[38]. After his "victory" at Fornovo Francesco resolved to build a votive chapel, for which the design was commissioned from the Venetian architect and sculptor/stonemason Pietro Lombardo (in itself a sign that there was by now no architect of real distinction in Mantua) who also supplied all the stone details. In this case too Francesco was in no hurry to pay, and Pietro's letters to him become progressively more pressing and sarcastic[39]. The chapel seems never to have been erected, despite being a religious vow, though the stone work which was intended for it seems to have been used in the construction of the later chapel of the Sacrament (Cat. 154) at the head of the left transept of the cathedral. The character of the capitals, and of the ornate *all'antica* cylindrical pedestals below the columns recalls works like the Cornaro Chapel in SS. Apostoli in Venice, and the pedestals of the first floor windows overlooking the Cortile dei Senatori in the Palazzo Ducale in Venice[40]. There is no surviving indication of how these elements were intended to be used in the original design.

Under Francesco the embellishment of the city continued, but largely as a result of a palace and house building by nobles and courtiers, an aspect of urban improvement which goes back to the time of Ludovico. One of the new houses built in Francesco's time was that of Mantegna, opposite San Sebastiano, with its handsome and totally unprecedented round cortile (Pl. 31). This may have been designed by Mantegna himself, possibly under the influence of Francesco di Giorgio's theoretical drawings[41].

With the accession of Federico in 1519 a new period of modernization and innovation began[42]. Even before the arrival of Giulio Romano in Mantua in November 1524 taste was changing. Falconetto's frescoes in the Palazzo d'Arco were executed around 1520, and work was under way in the new apartment of Isabella d'Este in the palace in 1522-23[43]. Her elegant little cortile, the *giardino segreto*, surrounded by an Ionic order raised on pedestals, with pedantically Vitruvian bases, itself raises an interesting question of attribution: it may be that Isabella's stonemason Battista Covo was capable of designing a work of this sort, but it seems more likely that the design came from Mantua[44] (Pl. 56).

Giulio Romano was as great a catch as Alberti and Mantegna had been. Despite his relative youth (he was almost the same age as Federico) by the time he came to Mantua he had a very considerable experience of painting, and of the design of buildings and their internal decoration (see essay by Gombrich below). The status, high salary and important offices which Federico accorded him were no more than he deserved for his contribution to Federico's prestige and advancement, above all in 1530 when Charles V visited Mantua. On that occasion one of the Venetian ambassadors wrote to his government that "certainly so much gold, tapestries, paintings and fineries were there, that it was said that those palaces resemble the immensely rich ones of the Sultan"[45].

In Mantua Giulio's skills and energy were not only devoted to the villa at Marmirolo (now destroyed), the Palazzo Te (Cat. 156-167) and the Ducal Palace itself, but to designs for private citizens, including his own beautiful house (1538-1546) and his general supervision of town planning and improvements to the streets[46]. Vasari writes that Giulio "made for the whole of that city of Mantua ... so many designs for chapels, houses, gardens and façades and took such delight in embellishing and adorning it, that he transformed it in such a way that where it was formerly in the grip of mud and full of foul water at certain times and almost uninhabitable, it is today, through his industry, dry, healthy and altogether beautiful and pleasing"[47]. Vasari describes how he raised the street level in areas subject to flooding, demolishing "small and flimsy little houses" and rebuilding "larger and more beautiful ones for the advantage and convenience of the city". He writes that despite widespread opposition the Duke ordered that "no one in that city could build without Giulio's license" and that "one could not build, above all in the city, palaces or other things of importance, save after his designs". The real character of Giulio's role is clear: he controlled the total appearance of the city in the interests of the Duke. Cardinal Ercole jokingly could say to Vasari that Giulio was more the proprietor of the state, than he was himself[48]. Of the success of his work there was no doubt: the Venetian ambassador in 1588 has not a word to say about the mud which assailed Pius II's

court, but simply that Mantua "is most pleasing for the great quantity of great and beautiful palaces, and above all for the spacious streets, which are marvellously long and straight"[49].

Giulio's fame in his own time and thereafter has rested above all on the Palazzo Te whose history and design has been carefully investigated in recent years (Cat. 156).

It was as Serlio wrote "truly an example of Architecture and painting for our times", the embodiment of all the artistic qualities most admired in the middle decades of the Cinquecento: inventive, surprising, elegant, complex but basically unified, allusive, learned, novel but not actually subversive of accepted architectural norms[50]. The difficulties of fitting a coherent exterior articulation to already existing rooms, and of closing, in a second phase, what had probably been a U shaped complex open towards the east provoked Giulio into creating an exterior architecture which seeks to distract attention from irregularities, and which boldly (and for the first time) abandons on the garden façade any idea of a regular rhythm, but instead merely makes the elevation symmetrical on either side of its central axis[51].

Giulio need not have resolved the matter in this way, but obviously enjoyed the outcome, as did his patron.

On the garden façade, the presence of fireplaces in the walls of the two outer rooms broke the regular sequence of piers, columns and arches. Looking at the building now the resulting change in the rhythm hardly strikes one as significant. Giulio, however, wilfully accented the oddities of the lower level by creating the now destroyed upper *logge* of slender columns as a commentary on it. They are, moreover, out of scale with the heavy attic they support.

The palace is not meant to be taken too seriously. It is as Vasari says made "in the *guise* (my italics) of a great palace", to provide an apartment for Federico's mistress Isabella Boschetti, with some fine rooms in which Federico could stay on occasion and use when he came to visit the stables or play in the tennis court[52]. Above all it was a place to hold splendid entertainments. It was the sort of building in which licenses and surprises were not only permitted, but almost expected. The famous slipped triglyphs, and the slightly raised keystone of the blank windows which go with them, so far from being an intimation of the dissolution of things may be a reference to the haste with which the building had to be completed, and in any case are a witty touch[53]. They also serve to enliven the *cortile* bays by establishing a central emphasis.

33

39.   *Palazzo Ducale, Mantua: Cortile della Cavallerizza.*

40.   *Palatine Basilica of Santa Barbara, Mantua: façade.*

Giulio's range of allusion is wide, but the different components are fused into a fluent personal style. The square plan and the atrium with four columns relate to reconstructions of the ancient Roman house, the motif of the upper court of Bramante's Cortile del Belvedere is quoted on the west exterior façade, and the alternating arches and trabeations of the Villa Lante reappear on the garden façade. But, as has been pointed out, the references are not all to Roman and antique buildings; other villas of the Gonzaga, with their *logge* and their fishponds, probably also influenced the design[54]. The *Loggia di Davide* is a grander version of the *loggia* at Revere, and where Revere has paired columns, the columns at the Te for structural reasons as well as impressiveness, are in groups of four, as in the *cortile* of the Ducal Palace in Venice.

In the twenty years in which Giulio worked in Mantua his style cannot really be said to change: the effects he created merely differ from building to building, according to the character of the commission and the problems it presented. He continues quoting inventively from a fixed stock of motifs taken from Bramante, Raphael and the antique; he does not, like Palladio, periodically reconsider the models he should follow. The richly ornamented but basically sober painted architecture of the *Sala dei Cavalli*, early in his Mantuan career is similar in spirit to parts of later works like the Duomo (Cat. 203) and San Benedetto Po (Cat. 208). He is consistently imaginative in designing rusticated treatments, whether in high relief as in his marvellous unexecuted designs for the Porta della Cittadella or in low relief, for the façade of his own house.[55]

From the Palazzo Te onwards Giulio displayed his flair for transforming pre-existing buildings. His skill did not depend on the budget: as well as inserting a beautiful ideal reconstruction of an early Christian basilica into the nave of the cathedral in Mantua[56] (Cat. 203), he explained to the city council of Vicenza how to rebuild the *logge* of the Basilica at minimum cost. In all his architectural works, as befitted a reader of Alberti, he gave close attention to beauty, function and structure, and remained pertinently and elegantly "antiquely modern and modernly antique"[57]. Cardinal Ercole Gonzaga was right to feel he had lost his right hand when Giulio died in November 1546: the Gonzaga were nev-

er again to have such a fine architect in their service[58]. The architecture of Mantua from Alberti's arrival in the city in 1459 till Giulio's death in 1546 had considerable influence on architectural developments elsewhere in Italy. Ludovico Gonzaga was already for Filarete a model patron. Lorenzo de' Medici (who had visited Mantua in 1483) asked Fancelli for a model of San Sebastiano in 1485. The church of the Carceri in Prato, which has a Greek cross plan designed by Giuliano da Sangallo in 1485, was possibly influenced by the Mantuan church[59].

Sant'Andrea was one of the most influential of all Quattrocento buildings. Its coffered barrel vault was echoed within a decade of Alberti's death in Bramante's S. Maria presso San Satiro in Milan, and its paired pilasters raised on pedestals, alternating with arches, provided the point of departure for the nave elevation of Bramante's St. Peter's and for his upper Cortile del Belvedere. The structural arrangement at Sant'Andrea, with no side aisles and the walls between the chapels buttressing the barrel vault reappears in many later churches, including Genga's San Giovanni Battista in Pesaro, Vignola's Gesù, and Palladio's Redentore.

The influence of Giulio Romano's Mantuan works was also very great. His lively and varied rusticated details were echoed in Serlio's books of architecture, and thus reached a very wide public. They also influenced Sanmicheli: both the smooth rustication of the lower part of the façade of Palazzo Canossa, and the rough blocks of the Porta Nuova derive from Giulio. So too does the rustication of the Palazzo Thiene in Vicenza, a building which if it was not designed in outline by Giulio (as seems likely) at least shows Palladio very much under his influence[60]. The cortile windows of the Palazzo Te also appear in an early palace projects by Palladio[61].

Giulio's skill as a moderniser of older structures (and the usefulness in these transformations of the serliana) was doubtless noted by Palladio, as would appear from his design for the *logge* of the Basilica in Vicenza. The stucco and painted decorations of Veronese and Vicentine interiors often derive directly from Giulio: Palladio's Palazzo da Porto Festa even has a room painted by Domenico Brusasorzi with the *Fall of the Giants*[62].

Giulio himself was a model for the noble painter and architect (the Vicentine council minutes refer to him as

"no common architect, celebrated to the highest degree") and through his success and life style, he helped to increase the standing of his profession[63]. Giulio's complex, learned, inventive and fluently eclectic style doubtless had considerable influence on Pirro Ligorio, as well as providing the best demonstration of an approach which was congenial to Vasari (above all in the Uffizi), Sansovino, Vignola and Alessi, even when they were not quoting specific motifs from him. There is a marked tendency in the latter half of the sixteenth century for patrons and artists to create buildings with a strongly local flavour, through the imitation of local antiquities (as in Verona) or of the works of a great local artist (Michelangelo in Florence, Palladio in Vicenza). Mantua is no exception, and a Giuliesque manner became the norm for most important Gonzaga buildings. This can already be seen in Bertani's works: the Cortile della Cavallerizza (Pl. 39) and the façade of

Santa Barbara (the interior is much less happy) are distinguished compositions in the Giuliesque manner (Pl. 40)[64].

This style was decently maintained into the early seventeenth century by the Ducal prefect of buildings, Antonio Maria Viani[65]. The last, and one of the most original works produced in this tradition for the Gonzaga was the Villa La Favorita (Pl. 41) built for Duke Ferdinando by his personal architect Nicolò Sebregondi, between 1613 and 1624[66]. The Villa, while making obvious references to the Palazzo Te has a completely individual character, and is impressive even in its present ruined state.

Mantua was by no means a paradise for Renaissance patrons, architects and workmen. Cash was often short, Luca Fancelli complained that he had received no salary for sixteen years[67]. Plague could stop work, fever among the workmen slow it down, and keep the architect in bed, as it did to Fancelli in the early stages of the construction of the Nova Domus[68]. Rain and frost could badly damage walls and vaults which had not been properly covered, and might necessitate extensive repairs, or even reconstruction[69]. But for all this, in the century between 1450 and 1550 Mantua was one of the most consistently vigorous architectural centres after Rome, Venice, Florence and Milan. And at a distance, or to the occasional visitor it did seem to offer ideal conditions for the architect, with Giulio Romano

living, as Cellini put it, "like a lord", and commanding a full time and highly skilled workforce: "it is not enough to have fine ideas and no one to realize them" wrote Genga in 1538, in a moment of extreme exasperation with the conditions under which he worked for the Duke of Urbino, "and we are here in Pesaro and not somewhere else, where the workmen are as they are, ... and this damned well isn't Mantua, where if there aren't the workmen, the Lord Duke makes them come and retains them with salaries so as to have them when he wants them..."[70].

Notes

1. Vasić Vatovec, 1979, pp. 183-84.

2. A contemporary gave the incomes in 1492 of e.g. Venice as 1,000,000 florins; Milan, 600,000; Ferrara, 120,000; Mantua, 60,000; Pesaro, 15,000. (*Le Carte Strozziane del R. Archivio di Stato di Firenze, Inventario,* Ser. I, vol. II; p. 833).

3. Verheyen, 1977, pp. 18-19; B. Navagero (1540) in E. Alberi, *Relazioni degli Ambasciatori Veneti al Senato,* Ser. II, vol. II, Florence, 1841, pp. 17-21.

4. See p. 32 below.

5. Cat. 36 and Chambers, 1977, p. 126: "serà posto in opera dui milioni de prede al credere nostro" (letter of 2 January to Cardinal Francesco Gonzaga).

6. See Cat. 36.

7. Building was as much a way of concealing poverty as of advertising wealth. Navagero (1540) estimated the Duke's income as *c.* 90-100,000 *scudi*, Cardinal Ercole's as 20,000 *scudi*. He wrote that Federico's "expenses were very heavy... because his Excellency spent a great deal on stables and buildings, and much in maintaining a great court, which amounted to 800 or more mouths to feed" (p. 10). He adds that Ercole made large cuts, spending less on the stables and reducing the court to 350.

8. Filarete, 1969, p. 228. Ludovico Gonzaga may well be the lord who explains how "these moderns used to please me too, but then once I had begun to appreciate these ancients, I came to hate the moderns", largely as a result of his contact with Florentine architecture (*ibid*, p. 380).

9. Federico's taste was formed when he was a hostage in Rome, 1510-13 (Luzio, 1886); on the tomb designs see Marani, 1961, p. 197.

10. D'Arco, 1857, II, p. 87.

11. Bertolotti, 1885, pp. 4-5.

12. Calzona, 1979, pp. 131-132.

13. Lamoureux, p. 135.

14. Lamoureux, doc. L, and p. 131.

15. Dall'Acqua, 1974, pp. 233-34.

16. Dall'Acqua, 1974; Chambers, 1977.

17. Braghirolli (1869) and others omitted the word 'Virgilio'; cf. correct reading by C. Grayson, in L.B. Alberti, *Opere Volgari,* III, Bari, 1973, p. 293. Though 'Virgil' might refer to a monument to Virgil (Cat. 92) Alberti probably meant the Palazzo del Podestà, often called the Palazzo di Virgilio from the statue which adorns it (Vasić Vatovec, pp. 148-58).

18. G. Mancini, *Vita di Leon Battista Alberti,* 2nd ed., Florence 1911 (repr. Rome, 1967).

19. Burns, 1979, p. 55, n. 38.

20. e.g. Lamoureux, docs. XIX and XXI; Calzona, doc. 52; and Ludovico to Alberti, 13 October 1464: "We have decided to send Lucha over there to you... to tell you how much has been done so far at San Sebastiano and to inform himself about what more you think should be done". (Vasić Vatovec, pp. 95-96).

21. e.g. The circular mausoleum on a square base and the loggia at the foot of the hill, though whatever Mantegna's debt to Alberti, he was himself an imaginative inventor of *all'antica* architecture, as the Eremitani frescoes show.

22. Letter of 2 August 1475 (Vasić Vatovec, p. 135).

23. Lamoureux, docs. II, XXXI, XXXXII, XLII; Calzona, doc. 56; Ludovico, however, in 1461 was not able to employ Alberti's brother Carlo (Lamoureux, doc. XIV).

24. Fancelli to Ludovico, 1462 (?): Vasić Vatovec, p. 88.

25. Lorenzo de' Medici, *Lettere,* I, 1460-1474, ed. R. Fubini, Florence, 1977, pp. 275-78.

26. Ludovico wrote in irritation to P. del Tovaglia that it would be better to spend the money "here in Mantua, which has greater need of a beautiful tempietto or two than has Florence" (*ibid.,* p. 276).

27. Vasić Vatovec, pp. 17, 350-51.

28. *Ibid.,* pp. 3-33.

29. *Ibid*, p. 22; the post was *"il più stimato uficio d'Italia per architectura"* according to Fancelli (*ibid*, p. 66). Cf., for other indications of Fancelli's reputation, *ibid*., pp. 412-425.

30. *"Questo edificio sanza osa e sanza misura"*, *ibid*. p. 60; pp. 71-72.

31. *Ibid*, p. 139.

32. Cottafavi, 1963, pp. 8-17; Vasić Vatovec, pp. 224-232.

32. Lorenzo de' Medici, *Lettere*, III, 1478-1479, ed. N. Rubinstein, Florence, 1977, p. 124.

34. Federico to the Duke of Urbino, 10 July 1481: *"essendo certi che ne poteremo ricavare de boni exempii"* (Vasić Vatovec, p. 238); Federico to the Duke, 20 August 1481: *"Per adesso non posso ben intendere ditto designo che lo e pur dificile"* (*ibid*., p. 240).

35. Letter of 18 February 1484, publ. Cottafavi, 1963, pp. 14-15.

36. Francesco di Giorgio to Federico, Urbino, 12 March 1484, ASMAG, b. 847, n. 215.

37. Vasić Vatovec, p, 147.

38. Lamoureux, doc. LXII.

39. Luzio and Renier 1888; Brown, 1969.

40. Cf. P. Paoletti, 1893, fig. 119 and Pls. 75 and 97.

41. Marani, 1961, pp. 147-50; Rosenthal, 1962; Campagnari, 1975.

42. See nn. 9-11.

43. G. Schweikhart, in Marini, 1980, pp. 92-94.

44. Negri, 1954, pp. 79-81: Tullio Lombardo, who was involved in the decoration of the apartment might well have designed the *giardino segreto*.

45. Sanudo, *Diarii*, LIII, col. 106.

46. K.W. Forster and R.J. Tuttle, "The Casa Pippi: Giulio Romano's House in Mantua", *Architectura*, 2, 1973, pp. 104-130; S. Davari, *I palazzi dei Gonzaga in Marmirolo*, Mantua 1890 (repr. 1974); Belluzzi and Capezzali, 1976, pp. 44-47. The beautiful villa (apparently already built in 1542), part of the Gonzaga farm complex called La Spinosa, was probably also designed by Giulio; Campagnari and Ferrari, in *Corti e Dimore del Contado Mantovano*, Florence, 1969, pp. 35-479.

47. Vasari, ed. Milanesi, V, 1906, pp. 547-48.

48. *Ibid*, pp. 548 and 553.

49. Francesco Contarini (1588) in Alberi, *Relazioni degli Ambasciatori Veneti al Senato*, ser. II, vol. V, Florence, 1841, p. 367. S. Razzi, *Diario di Viaggio di un ricercatore* (1572), ed. G. di Agresti, O.P., in *Memorie Domenicane*, N.S. 1971, n. 2, p. 150: *"sono in Mantova assai palazzi, belle contrade et ornatissime chiese"*.

50. Serlio, IV, 1537, fol. 133 v., quoted Verheyen, 1977, p. 56, n. 3: *"essempio veramente di Architettura et di pittura a nostri tempi"*. Cf. Shearman, in Boll. C.I.S.A., 1967, pp. 354-68, 434-38; Belluzzi and Capezzali, 1976, pp. 39-55.

51. Compare Peruzzi's Palazzo Massimi alle Colonne in Rome, where all four sides of the cortile are different.

52. Belluzzi and Capezzali, 1976, pp. 17-23.

53. Verheyen, 1977, p. 48.

54. Belluzzi and Capezzali, 1976, pp. 39-55.

55. The Porta della Cittadella designs are published by Gombrich, 1935, and Hartt, 1958. The bizarre Rustica in the Cortile della Cavallerizza (Pl. 39), which has been attributed to Giulio (Hartt, 1958, I, pp. 186-192) does not have the force and inventiveness of Giulio's rusticated designs, and the striking idea of using Salamonic colums on a "palace" façade is frittered away in an elevation which lacks strong visual tensions. The works is not mentioned by Vasari, and the documents indicate only that it existed by 1556, and that the apartment in the interior was only completed in 1561 (Cottafavi, 1939, pp. 5-12).

56. On Giulio's recommendations for the Basilica see Burns, 1975, pp. 29-30.

57. P. Aretino, *Lettere sull'Arte*, ed F. Pertile and E. Camesasca, I, Milan, 1957, p. 215; cf E Gombrich, "The Style all'Antica: Imitation and Assimilation", in *Norm and Form*, London 1966, pp. 112-128.

58. Gaye, II, Florence, 1839, p. 501; Verheyen, 1977, pp. 5-7, and p. 83 here. Cardinal Ercole's awareness of the lack of anyone of comparable quality in Mantua to take Giulio's place is manifest from his invitation to Genga to make designs for the Vescovado and the façade of the Duomo (Vasari, ed. Milanesi, VI, p. 321) which in itself implies an unfavourable assessment of Bertani as an architect.

59. A. Reumont, *Archivio Storico Italiano*, ser. III, XIX, 1874, p. 418; Vasić Vatovec, pp. 424-425.

60. Burns, 1975, pp. 36-37 (with bibliography).

61. R.I.B.A. XVII/6: see Burns in Marini, 1980, p. 119; D. Lewis, *The Drawings of Andrea Palladio*, Washington, 1981, pp. 88-89.

62. A.C. Calcagni in Marini, 1980, pp. 172-85; E. Forssman, *The Palazzo da Porto Festa in Vicenza*, 1973, pp. 63-65.

63. G. Zorzi, *Le opere pubbliche e i palazzi privati di Andrea Palladio*, Venice, 1965, p. 44: *"architeti non vulgaris immo celebris et nominati"*.

64. The interior of Santa Barbara, with its combination of vaults and square "domes" seems to be generally inspired by the structural scheme of the church of San Salvatore in Venice. For the building history see T. Gozzi, *La Basilica Palatina di Santa Barbara in, Accad. Virgiliana di Mantova. Atti e Memorie*, N.S. XLII, 1974, pp. 3-91. The plan of the closed nave bays reflects the plan of the portico of San Sebastiano (as does also the portico of the Spinosa); there crypt is more successful than the church itself. On the Cavallerizza see Cottafavi, 1939.

65. Marani, 1965, pp. 161-206.

66. Marani, 1965, pp. 175-78; D. Niccolini, "Una piccola Versailles gonzaghesca: La Favorita", in *Corti e Dimore del Contado Mantovano*, Florence, 1969, pp. 65-80.

67. Vasić Vatovec, p. 56. He was, however, recompensed in other ways: *ibid*, pp. 125-26; 142-43.

68. Fancelli to Ludovico, 24 September 1477: *"qui non n'è che possino lavorare: sono tutti amallati"* (Vasić Vatovec, p. 141); Verheyen, 1977, p. 141, doc. 42; Vasić Vatovec, p. 233.

69. Lamoureux, docs. XIX and XXII.

70. G. Gronau, *Documenti artistici urbinati*, Florence, 1936, p. 137.

The Gonzaga and Ceramics
by J.V.G. Mallet

Perhaps because the region in which Mantua lies did not yield suitable clays, the town was not famous during the Renaissance for the tin-glazed pottery known as maiolica. The characteristic ceramic products of the district, to judge from excavated fragments, were common lead-glazed wares or quite modest slipwares with scratched (*sgraffito*) decoration[1]. Nor does the *sgraffito* technique seem to have been put to such ambitious use at Mantua as it was under the d'Este dynasty in Quattrocento Ferrara. We may hope to learn more from the exhibition of ceramics which is to open in the Palazzo Ducale at Mantua while the present Catalogue is in the press[2].

Potters there certainly were at Mantua, and they received privileges during the reign of Marchese Ludovico (1444-78)[3]. But there is little documentary evidence to suggest that many of them made tin-glazed wares: Antonio di Gatti may have done, around 1541[4]; Tommaso Scaldamuzza of Faenza clearly did in 1552[5]. In 1592-93 Duke Vincenzo I encouraged potters from Albisola near Genoa to settle in Mantua and produce maiolica and porcelain, and it has been suggested that this initiative may be connected with the protection extended by Luigi Gonzaga, Duke of Nevers, to the Conradi family of potters from Albisola at about the same time[6]. However it was reported in 1601 that no maiolica was being produced in Mantua[7], and attempts were made to encourage Scipione Tamburino in 1615-18[8] and Lazzaro Levi in 1626[9].

Since there was little locally produced fine ware the Gonzaga had to rely on imports for the more showy of their ceramic needs. It is these ceramics acquired by the Gonzaga from outside their domains, either by gift or purchase, that will be discussed here, including the highly distinguished group of surviving maiolica which can be associated with the family on heraldic grounds. Tiles are described in a separate essay.

A central figure in the Gonzaga's patronage of ceramics, as of other arts, was Isabella d'Este. In 1494, four years after her marriage, she sent back for repair in her native Ferrara a plate that had been broken in three. Since the Ferrarese Ducal pottery workshop was concerned, it seems likely that the repair was effected by fusing the bits together with glaze mixture. In returning this valued piece, her mother, the Duchess of Ferrara, threw in another as a gift, while the writer of the letter from which we learn of the incident ordered for Isabella half a dozen pieces that may either have been refined slipware or, since the workmen involved were apparently from the Marches, where *sgraffito* was little practised, an early form of maiolica decorated with white on white[10].

Much later, in 1523, Isabella received from that passionate experimenter in pottery and other hand-crafts, her brother, Alfonso d'Este Duke of Ferrara, a gift of pottery and imitation stones that was delivered to her by their maker, Maestro Antonio da Faenza. In thanking Alfonso, Isabella remarked that these gifts would be most useful for her *Cucina Segreta*, and ordered further items[11]. Isabella was also ordering *vasi de la porcellana* from Urbino in 1510[12], at that date presumably not true porcelain but maiolica, though perhaps decorated in blue and white out of respect for the Chinese product. Again, in 1518 she ordered some plates of fine maiolica from Venice and Faenza[13]. In 1527 Isabella reluctantly accepted from a Roman dealer two maiolica vessels in part payment of an obligation incurred before the Sack of that year[14]. But of the circumstances surrounding the commissioning of the magnificent Este-Gonzaga Service of maiolica represented in this exhibition by Cat. 131-138, no documentary trace has been found.

The Este-Gonzaga Service has for many years, and rightly, been attributed to perhaps the greatest of all painters of *istoriato* maiolica, the man who inscribed a mere handful of pieces with a monogram that has been read as Nicolò, in one instance followed by the words "da Urbino". We have only two fixed points around which to reconstruct the sequence of Nicolò da Urbino's career: a dish dated 1521 in the Hermitage, Leningrad, and a dish in the Bargello, Florence, inscribed as having been painted in the Urbino workshop of Guido Durantino in 1528. Almost all else, including the belief that Nicolò is the same individual as a Nicola Pellipario, father of Guido Durantino, and that he began his career at Castel Durante, appears to be art-historical myth[15]. It has usually been claimed that the Este-Gonzaga service was painted in or soon after 1519, the year when Isabella was widowed, and unconvincing or inconclusive attempts have been made to read the subjects and *imprese* that appear on the pieces as evidence of mourning[16]. The unsupported word of Frati, as recorded years later by Fortnum, that there once existed a vase, dated 1519 and supposedly forming part of the Service, has been used in confirmation of this dating[17], the only hollow vessel with the Este-Gonzaga arms that has ever been illustrated, however, is an undated ewer that may not even belong to the Service[18]. On inconclusive historical grounds Burr Wallen suggested a date soon after 1521, when the Ducal family of Urbino returned from an exile much of which had been passed near Mantua[19]. Yet if we compare the Este-Gonzaga pieces with the two dated pieces mentioned above, I believe it will be found that the Service is far less like the Hermitage dish of 1521[20] than the Bargello dish of 1528. We know from datable pieces by other artists of the Duchy of Urbino that the *istoriato* style of maiolica decoration was evolving very rapidly between 1520 and 1530, from a pale, blue-toned style towards a stronger and eventually warmer palette. I do not believe Nicolò was so far ahead of his contemporaries in this development as has been assumed, and, on stylistic grounds, the Este-Gonzaga Service looks as if it should be dated around 1525. In confirmation of this dating it may be pointed out how similar in balance of colour is a plate of Nicolò's school with a lustred date 1524 on its back[21] to the Este-Gonzaga dish with Peleus and Thetis (Cat. 136) which was recently on view beside it in the Fitzwilliam Museum at Cambridge. Isabella could have ordered or been given the Este-Gonzaga Service when she passed through Pesaro, close to Urbino, on her way to Rome in February 1525, when she was fêted by her daughter Eleonora and son-in law Francesco Maria della Rovere, the Duke and Duchess of Urbino[22].

It is tempting to seek, in the oddly assorted choice of subjects − mythological, historical and biblical − that adorn the Este-Gonzaga Service, evidence of some recondite "programme" such as Isabella liked to impose on the easel painters from whom she commissioned work; it is tempting also when comparing the enigmatically poetic Este-Gonzaga Service with the relatively prosaic narrative pieces that bear the arms of Duke Federico, to explain this contrast in terms of the divergent tastes of mother and son. I suspect, however, that the reason for the difference lies in the development of Nicolò's style. A famous service in the Museo Correr, which is generally agreed to have been painted by Nicolò somewhat earlier than the Este-Gonzaga Service, is as odd as the latter Service in its range of subject matter and is even more hauntingly poetic in expression. Equally, all the work that may be attributed to Nicolò after 1530 is, like the work he did for Federico at that time, relatively inexpressive and coarse in handling, though still superior to most of the work of Nicolò's Urbino contemporaries.

Nicolò's work for Federico comprises pieces that bear his Mount Olympus device (Cat. 197) and others similar in style that bear his arms quartered with those of Margherita Paleologo, whom he married in 1531 (Cat. 194-195).

An interesting letter of August 1530 in answer to enquiries from the Mantuan court about the cost of an Urbino *istoriato* service, may mark the opening moves in Federico's patronage of Nicolò[23]. On the other hand another plate (Cat. 196), which bears the Gonzaga-Paleologo arms but is signed by Francesco Xanto Avelli, Nicolò's Urbino rival, may have been considered as part of the same service as the other Gonzaga-Paleologo pieces, in which case its date, 1533, is probably theirs also. An intriguing dish in the Lehman Collection at the Metropolitan Museum, New York, might perhaps also be associated with Federico II, despite its lack of any distinguishing coat of arms or insignia[24]. This dish is painted with a most unusual subject of a man in armour kneeling to receive a baton from a pope, a scene witnessed by a throng of clerics and two further men in armour holding flags. It is tempting to read this scene as Federico being appointed Captain General by Leo X in 1521, though if so, it is likely that the scene was painted ten or more years after the historical event, for the painter of the dish is assuredly Nicolò da Urbino in much the stage of his development represented by the Olympus and Gonzaga-Paleologo pieces. Other possibilities deserve investigation.

There have been recurrent attempts to associate Giulio Romano with the design or even the execution of maiolica for Federico. A circular drawing[25], an inventory of 1665[26] and the writing on the old frame in

which Cat. 194 used to be set[27] have all been called as evidence for this. While it is not impossible that a major artist like Giulio should have been asked to design maiolica for the table, as Battista Franco and Taddeo Zuccaro both did later, the evidence so far produced is not impressive: circular drawings could also serve for silver or for circular panel paintings; the inventory of 1665 belongs to the period when almost any fine Urbino piece was being attributed by collectors to Raphael and his pupils, and the inventory renders itself implausible by attributing ware to Raphael as well as to his pupil, Giulio; as for the frame inscribed *quam Julius Pi(pi) dictus – Romanus delineavi(t)* and dated 1536, the piece it surrounded (Cat. 194) has nothing in its decoration to suggest Giulio's style, and lies wholly within the usual range of Nicolò's unaided competence. The evidence now published by Signora Gobio Casali (essay below) concerning an attempt to involve Giulio in the design of floor-tiles, an architectural use of maiolica, is another matter.

Several pieces of maiolica bear the arms granted to the Gonzaga by the Emperor Sigismund in 1433. If cadet members of the family refrained from using these arms without any heraldic difference, then we have only to determine the date of these wares in order to discover which ruler of Mantua first owned each of them. On this assumption, a Castel Durante or Urbino dish in the Hermitage probably belonged to Federico in the earliest years of his rule[28]. Three other pieces (Cat. 198, 199, 200) have plausibly been dated around 1525 and would therefore seem to have been Federico's. A fine plate at Chicago[29] painted with the same arms surmounted by a ducal coronet appears to emanate from the workshop of the Fontana family at Urbino around 1550-70, and hence presumably belonged to Duke Guglielmo. A rather different problem is posed by Cat. 201 since the arms on it are encircled by the collar of the Golden Fleece and surmounted by a coronet somewhat different in shape from those on the other pieces. Cat. 201 looks as though it might have been

41

43. *Dish with a legend of Trajan, from Este-Gonzaga Service (Cat. 137), painted by Nicolò da Urbino, c. 1525.*

made at Cafaggiolo around 1515-35, and the only Gonzaga who held the Order of the Golden Fleece within these years was Ferrante (1507-1557) Duke of Ariano, who received it in 1531. A plate formerly in the Marryat Collection[30], painted by Francesco Xanto Avelli in 1541 with the storming of La Goleta, also bears the arms of Ferrante, impaling those of his wife Isabella di Capua, quartering those of her mother's family, the del Balzo of Naples. Once again Ferrante's arms are encircled with the collar of the Golden Fleece; Ferrante had accompanied Charles V on the expedition to La Goleta in 1535.

Various other matrimonial alliances of the Gonzaga are called to mind by the armorial bearings on maiolica. An unusual white hexagonal tray, in the collection of Dr. Gianpaolo Negri, with what look like two eggcups and a salt cellar (perhaps an early example of the *cadenas* later found in silver?)[31] is probably from Faenza in the early seventeenth century and bears the arms of Duke Vincenzo I who received the Golden Fleece, with which his arms are shown, in 1589. The marriage of Anna Caterina Gonzaga, daughter of Duke Guglielmo, to Ferdinand Archduke of Austria in 1582, is reflected in a set of plates, two of which survive at Berlin[32] and two at Innsbruck[33]. These are in the style of the Faenza *bianchi*, though it has quite plausibly been suggested that they may have been made by emigré potters working in the Tyrol, of which Ferdinand was ruler after 1564. A white jug at Prague, more probably made at Faenza itself, also bears the arms of Ferdinand and Anna Caterina[34].

Of later Gonzaga ceramics little remains to be said. We know that in 1593 a priest, Zucconi da Faenza, presented the Duke of Mantua with three *fontane* and two inkstands of Faventine workmanship[35], probably as part of a campaign by the potters of Faenza to obtain free entry for their products to Mantuan territory. A more exotic gift was sent to the Duke in 1598 from Pera (Beyoghlu, a suburb of Istanbul) by Edoardo da Gagliano, who described the ceramics included in his present as "thirty pieces of the gilded maiolica of this city"[36]. This was presumably Isnik pottery, which was well enough known in Italy to be copied in the late 16th and early 17th centuries, especially at Padua.

Despite the sack of Mantua in 1630, the inventory of

1665 shows that Duke Carlo II still possessed considerable quantities of *istoriato* plates, an *istoriato* wine cooler and nine *baccine*[37]. These are described as being in cabinets or cupboards (*armario* is the word used) probably designed for display since the pieces were prized as supposed works by Raphael and Giulio Romano. It is uncertain whether the finest *istoriato* wares were ever used at table; pieces like those comprising the Este-Gonzaga service normally show little sign of wear. A rather roughly painted Urbino service decorated with grotesques and bearing the *impresa* of Alfonso II d'Este of Ferrara, who married Margherita Gonzaga in 1579, was almost certainly intended for use; it is hard to see, otherwise, why the little ewers should have been inscribed with the words *olio* and *aceto* (oil and vinegar)[38]. Federico II, it was reported, liked eating off porcelain[39], and it may be that delicacies that could be eaten in the fingers without too much use of the knife were on special occasions consumed off even the most finely painted maiolica plates. Scattered though they now are throughout the collections of the world, the survivors of these fragile tin-glazed wares, with their brilliant polychromy and vivid draughtsmanship, can give us some idea of the visual splendour of life at the Renaissance court of Mantua.

Notes

1. Baroni, 1934, pp. 137-175.

2. *Ceramiche nel Palazzo Ducale di Mantova*, June-August, 1981, Catalogue by G. B. Siviero and others.

3. Bertolotti, 1890, p. 9.

4. Bertolotti, 1890, p. 18.

5. Bertolotti, 1890, pp. 23-24.

6. Campori, 1879, pp. 80-81; Bertolotti, 1890, pp. 27-28; Nicola Balbis, "Note sulle famiglie dei ceramisti Conradi a Nevers", *Atti del centro Ligure per la storia della Ceramica*, X, 1977 (1980), pp. 237-240.

7. Bertolotti, 1890, p. 36.

8. Campori, 1879, pp. 81-83; Bertolotti, 1890, pp. 37-40.

9. Campori, 1879, p. 84.

10. Campori, 1879, pp. 12-13; Bertolotti, 1890, p. 16.

11. Campori, 1879, p. 21; Bertolotti, 1890, pp. 32-33.

12. Campori, 1879, pp. 29-30; Bertolotti, 1890, p. 30.

13. Campori, 1879, p. 20.

14. Cartwright, 1903, II, pp. 274-75.

15. Wallen, 1968.

16. Falke, 1923, introductory essay to vol II; Rasmussen, 1972, pp. 57-62; against this view see Wallen, 1968, p. 103, note 9.

17. Fortnum, 1873, p. 324.

18. Delange, 1869, Pl 31, Baron Alphonse de Rothschild Collection.

19. Wallen, 1968, pp. 103-04.

20. There is what appears to be a good colour illustration in Kube, 1976, No. 58.

21. Illustrated by Rackham, 1952, Pl. 70 B.

22. Cartwright, 1903, II, p. 243.

23. Campori, 1879, p. 111.

24. New York, Metropolitan Museum, R.L.C. 1975. 1. 1004.

25. d'Arco, 1845, p. 136; Campori, 1879, pp. 76 and 79-80.

26. Campori, 1879, pp. 79-80.

27. Liverani, 1938, p. 345; reprinted Liverani, 1939, p. 16.

28. Kube, 1976, 54, there dated 1545-50, and attributed to Cafaggiolo. However the painting of the arms and supporters links the Leningrad dish to Cat. 199 and to a dish formerly in the Murray Collection.

29. Chicago, Museum of Fine Arts 37.850, with the subject of Numa Pompilius, to be illustrated by J.V.G. Mallet in *Apollo*, September 1981.

30. Marryat, 1868 edition, pp. 63-64 and fig. 31.

31. Henry Havard, *Dictionnaire d'Ameublement* II, 1887 p. 506; Charles Oman, "Caddinets and a forgotten Version of the Royal Arms", *Burlington Magazine*, C, 1958, p. 431. The resemblance of this piece to later silver *Cadenas* was drawn to my notice by Mr. C.H. Truman.

32. Tjark Hausmann, 1972, Nos. 136 and 137.

33. Kristinkovich, 1962, Pl. XIV.c.

34. Jirina Vydrová, 1955, No. 97, Pl. 40, where the arms are given as those of the Emperor Ferdinand II and Anna Eleonora Gonzaga, a mistake corrected by the same author, 1973, No. 106.

35. Bertolotti, 1890, p. 32.

36. Bertolotti, 1890, p. 35.

37. Campori, 1879, p. 80.

38. Rackham, 1940, No. 882.

39. Bertolotti, 1890, p. 192.

Ceramic tiles for the Gonzaga
by Mariarosa Palvarini Gobio Casali

The Gonzaga used painted tiles to cover floors not only because they liked ceramic art and this was a fashionable form of it, but also to discourage mice, which were infesting the Castello San Giorgio in the 1490's[1]. Earlier than this, in 1473, the Marquis Ludovico's eldest son, Federico Gonzaga, had drawn his parents' attention[2] to a Venetian glass-blower called maestro Marco who was offering to supply rectangular gilded tiles with arms (*quadri da salicare cum arme e dorati*) as a floor covering for Ludovico's *Camera* (*el pavimento de la sua camera*) which presumably means the *Camera Picta* of Mantegna. But it is not clear whether these were ever commissioned (Ludovico was unwell and advised against a sudden decision[3]) and documentation about ceramic tiles does not continue until twenty years later, near in time to the marriages of Elisabetta and Maddalena in 1489, which connected the Gonzaga family with the respective rulers of Urbino and Pesaro, the leading centres of maiolica workshops.

In 1493 Marquis Francesco II, probably urged by his wife Isabella d'Este, tiled a small room (subsequently known as the *camerino della maiolica*) in the villa of Marmirolo[4]. He involved in this scheme his brother-in-law, now a widower, Giovanni Sforza signor of Pesaro, who wrote obligingly to tell him on 5 January 1493 that he had the drawings made; patience was needed because bad weather prevented the tiles from drying out quickly[5]. In March 1494 the tiles were ready and the Marquis' brother, Giovanni Gonzaga, who was with Isabella when she briefly visited Pesaro on her way to Loreto as a pilgrim, wrote on 24 March that he had admired the floor covering (*la saligata*)[6], while Giovanni Sforza professed astonishment to learn that Francesco insisted on paying for it himself[7]. On 1 June 1494 the thirteen cases containing the tiles arrived in Mantua and were unpacked in the castle[8]. Some were then transferred to Marmirolo (fragments were recently discovered in excavations there near the early seventeenth-century villa of Bosco della Fontana) but others were used to pave the *studiolo* of Isabella in the Castello San Giorgio. They were installed there quickly; the secretary Sigismondo Golfo wrote on 9 July[9] to tell Isabella, who was staying at Cavriana, that her infant daughter's governess Violante de Pretis had on the previous day shown him the *studiolo*, which in his opinion could not

be more beautiful on account of the decorative paving (*non porria essere più bello per l'ornamento de la nuova saligata*). In fact on 8 July Violante herself had written[10] to inform Isabella that on that day the *studiolo* had been paved with the tiles showing her husband's devices and commented that this was very necessary because of all the mouse nests found beneath the floorboards (*Hozi si è salicato el studiolo de la Signoria Vostra de li quadri da le divisie del Illustrissimo Signore nostro, quali compare assai bene, et in vero l'è stata una optima provisione et quasi necessaria perché sotto quelle asse se li sono ritrovati de molti nidi de ponteghi…*). Indeed, a few days earlier, according to a letter of 4 July from Tolomeo Spagnuoli, three mice had been caught in Isabella's *studiolo* and another three in her *camera*[11]. The devices referred to on the tiles (Cat. 127-128) included at least eight different examples: the coat of arms quartered with the lions of Bohemia conceded by the Emperor Charles IV to Luigi, the first Gonzaga Capitano of Mantua; the white hound seated on guard, a device of Gianfrancesco the first Marquis[12]; the deer with the motto "Bider Kraft" associated with his father Francesco (1382-1407) and later with Barbara of Brandenburg[13]; the dove on a tree trunk with the words "Vrai amour ne se change" apparently used on coins in 1462[14]; the sun surrounded by a scroll which reads "Per un dexir", adopted by Marquis Ludovico after the military defeat at Caravaggio (1448)[15] and the iron glove with the motto "Buena fè non es mudable", also associated with Ludovico; the island surmounted by a diamond and with the Greek letters ΑΜΩΜΟΣ which was a device of Marquis Federico I and Margherita of Bavaria[16], and finally the muzzle inscribed "Cautius" of the Marquis Francesco himself, already used on a medal dated 1490[17]. These same devices were likewise used to decorate various walls and ceilings of rooms in the Castello, and Francesco's muzzle device was used on the velvet hangings of his room[18]. His well known device of the flaming crucible does not occur on the tiles because it was adopted a few years later[19].

These tiles laid down in the first *studiolo* (of which nothing remains) were probably taken up at the time Isabella moved her *camerini* to new quarters; they may have been relaid in another of her rooms in the *Corte Vecchia*[20] but their ultimate fate is unknown except that examples survive in various collections. Their design has been attributed to Antonio dei Fideli of Pesaro who on 7 May 1496[21] wrote asking Isabella d'Este to be paid for his *quadri da saligare* for which her agent, six months earlier, had promised him ten florins down payment and fifty florins which would follow together with the drawings. Meanwhile Antonio had incurred expenses and refused other work. It is puzzling how he could have set to work if he still needed the drawings, and if the tiles were of the same devices as those delivered in 1494 one might have expected that he already had a copy of the drawings or examples to work from.

However Isabella also commissioned an entirely different set of tiles bearing her own particular devices and painted in white, orange, turquoise and blue (Cat. 129-130) which Antonio dei Fideli may have made for her. It is possible that they were used to pave her first *grotta* in the Castello San Giorgio in 1498, or when the *grotta* was reconstructed between 1506 and 1508, though no documents have come to light which prove this. All that remains in the first *grotta* are some decorative rings painted on the walls and the wooden ceiling carved by the brothers Antonio and Paolo Mola who reported the completion of their work between July and August 1508[22]. Here the devices of the musical pause or silence alternate with the device of lottery tickets. The choice of these motifs for the ceiling may perhaps have been precisely because the rest were represented on the floor. In fact upon the ceiling of the new *grotta*, carved by maestro Sebastiano, all eight of Isabella's devices appear, instead of being distributed in the manner suggested in the old *grotta*. Unfortunately, the documents do not give precise indications about the laying down of the floor tiles in the new *camerini*, though a letter of C. Ghisi dated 30 October 1522 mentions that doors, chimney-pieces, paving (*saligate*) and windows had been completed[23].

Finally it should be mentioned that ceramic floors were also intended for Palazzo Te. In a letter of 3 August 1528 Giulio Romano wrote[24] that a certain Fedele who worked at Pietole wanted him to provide a drawings for the maiolica paving (*Quel Fedele che lavora la maiolica a Piettoli voria che io li facessi un disegno da far la sallegata di maiolica*) and the cost of this maiolica was listed on 31 August[25]. Another letter which he addressed to Duke Federico on 27 October 1531 about works in the Palaz-

zina Paleologa suggests that there was a tiled floor there, too[26], and on 28 October 1536 Giulio Romano wrote concerning further works (*mastro Agostino da Covo ha finito le salegate di sopra di tavelle et la camera et camerini di quadri et messi in opera doi camini*)[27].

Notes

1. See below n. 10, n. 11.

2. ASMAG, b. 2101, c. 326, 25 June 1473.

3. Reply of Barbara of Brandenburg, 26 June 1473, ASMAG, b. 2892 lib. 72 c 36r.

4. Mantua, *Scienza*, 1979, pp. 196-200.

5. ASMAG, b. 1065; Braghirolli, 1878, p. 46.

6. ASMAG, b. 2109, c. 10; Bertolotti, 1977, p. 10; Luzio and Renier, 1893, pp. 73-77.

7. ASMAG, b. 1065, 16 June 1494.

8. ASMAG, b. 2446, c. 260; Bertolotti, 1977, p. 10.

9. ASMAG, b. 2446, c. 56.

10. ASMAG, b. 2446, c. 172; Verheyen, 1971, p. 11.

11. ASMAG, b. 2446, c. 268.

12. Gerola, 1918, p. 103.

13. Portioli, 1879, p. 85 quoting Equicola and an inscription.

14. Letter of Giovanni Striggi to Marquis Ludovico, 11 June 1462, ASMAG, b. 2398.

15. Portioli, 1879, p. 84.

16. Gerola, 1930, pp. 381-402.

17. Magnaguti, 1965, IX p. 92, Tav. vi, nos. 20, 21.

18. ASMAG, b. 2992, Lib. 5 c. 44r.

19. Brown, 1973, pp. 153-159.

20. Gerola, 1929, p. 261.

21. ASMAG, b. 851 (Pesaro); Bertolotti, 1977, p. 11.

22. ASMAG, b. 2472, c. 716, c. 720, c. 723.

23. ASMAG, b. 2503.

24. ASMAG, Autografi b. 7 c. 221.

25. *Ibid.*, c. 223.

26. *Ibid.*, c. 230.

27. *Ibid.*, c. 239.

Antico and the Mantuan Bronze
by Anthony Radcliffe

In the later years of the fifteenth century there evolved in the territory of Mantua under the patronage of the Gonzaga family a unique type of bronze statuette, more directly classicizing, more sumptuously finished and more technically advanced than the bronzes produced in any other part of Italy.

It was to be expected that the genre of the bronze statuette, which had its origin in Florence in the mid-fifteenth century as a re-creation of what was seen as one of the most authoritative art-forms of antiquity, would be taken up in the humanistic milieu of the Mantuan court. It was also to be expected that in that milieu it would to some extent be informed by the influence of Mantegna; and indeed the characteristic type of the Mantuan bronze, with its archaeological correctness, its precision of finish, its clean hard surfaces and firm outlines can be seen as the sculptural counterpart of Mantegna's painting. But, although the determining influence on the form which the bronze statuette was to take in Mantua may well have been Mantegna, the undoubted inventor of the Mantuan bronze, and its chief exponent over many years, was Pier Jacopo Alari Bonacolsi, known appositely by the nickname "Antico". More is known about Antico and his relations with his patrons than is known about any other Renaissance bronzist, thanks to the exemplary documentary research of Umberto Rossi in the archives of Mantua and Parma, the connoisseurship of Wilhelm Bode, and the brilliant synthetic scholarship of H.J. Hermann which formed a sound basis for all later research. Even so, little is known about his early years. We may infer from the fact that his father owned a house there that Antico was a native of Mantua, and from the fact that he was fully active by 1479 that he was born probably around 1460. That he was at first in the service of Marchese Federico I Gonzaga is suggested by the fact that he was granted by him the privilege of a stall in the meat-market in Mantua. His work shows that his training had been that of a goldsmith, and he must have acquired early in his career a special reputation as a classicizing artist, since the earliest documents already refer to him by his nickname, and his first dateable works, two medals, are signed "ANTI".

These medals (Cat. 49, 50) were made for the marriage in 1479 of Gianfrancesco Gonzaga, Count of Ró-digo and Lord of Bozzolo and Sabbioneta, and Antonia del Balzo. Gianfrancesco was the younger brother of Federico I and the third son of Marchese Ludovico, and Antico seems to have entered his service at his residence in the castle of Bozzolo at some time in the 1480s (possibly after the death of Federico in 1484): he is documented as well established at Bozzolo by 1487. For Gianfrancesco and Antonia del Balzo he made the so-called *Gonzaga Vase* (Cat. 51), which bears their personal devices. This is the sole surviving example of a special Mantuan genre of classicizing metal vessels to which we have documentary references. In this genre the leading spirit appears to have been Mantegna. A much-cited document of 1483 refers to the commission by Federico I to the goldsmith Gian Marco Cavalli for the making of urns and vases, probably of silver, in antique style to designs by Mantegna. In the inventory after death of Gianfrancesco Gonzaga of 1496 the first item listed is "two small vases of silver gilt; from the hand of Antico".

In this same inventory appear the first references to bronze statuettes identifiable as being by Antico. Here we find "A figure of metal called the Villanello" (*Meleager*, Cat. 54), "The Hercules with the club" (Cat. 53), one of the *giganti* with one of the horses from the *Dioscuri* at the Quirinale, and the equestrian statue of *Marcus Aurelius*. All of these were bronze reductions after classical statues at that time in Rome, and yet the first record we have of a visit to Rome by Antico dates from the year after Gianfrancesco's death, 1497, when he was sent there by Marchese Francesco to acquire antiques. Whether or not this was Antico's first visit to Rome (and it would seem likely that it was not), it is from this date that we begin to find a series of specific references in the documents to bronze reductions by him of Roman statues. By 1498 Antico was once again resident in Bozzolo, this time in the service of Gianfrancesco's younger brother, Bishop Ludovico Gonzaga. For the Bishop he had completed in that year the wax models for reductions of the *Apollo Belvedere* (Cat. 57) and of "the nude woman kneeling on a tortoise", a marble formerly in Rome and now in the Prado (autograph bronze in the Thyssen-Bornemisza Collection, and an aftercast in Naples). By 1499 he had completed a *Spinario* (examples in the Wrightsman Collection, New York, and

44. *Antico, Meleager (Cat. 54).*

the *Atropos* (Cat. 56) and a *Marcus Aurelius*, of which no example seems to have survived. In 1501 an *Apollo* was cast (probably a second cast from the wax of 1498: see Cat. 57), and yet another *Spinario* was cast, this time to the order of the Marchesa Isabella d'Este.

The first documentation of Isabella's interest in Antico's work dates from the previous year, 1500, when she sent her sculptor Gian Cristoforo Romano to him with a commission for sculptural decoration for a doorcase. Antico was busy preparing moulds for bronzes and had to decline the commission, and the *Spinario* which he cast for her in 1501 is the first of the many works by him which Isabella is known to have owned. She placed it on the cornice above one of the doors in her rooms in the Castello di San Giorgio, and in 1503 she wrote to the Bishop asking him to order Antico to provide a pendant statuette to place above the other door in the same room. This, which was completed and dispatched within the year, is almost certainly to be identified with a seated female figure known as *Andromeda*, the finest example of which was formerly in the collection of Baron Gustave de Rothschild in Paris.

From this point onwards Antico, resident from 1501 in the Gonzaga palace at Gazzuolo, to which Antonia del Balzo had retired after her husband's death, was in almost constant communication with Isabella. In 1504 he made for her a gold statuette of St. John the Baptist and in the following year some small sculptures in silver, and he was increasingly in demand to restore antique sculptures for her and to advise her about their acquisition. In 1506 she consulted him as to whether she should buy the bust of Faustina from the aged and bankrupt Mantegna, and after Mantegna's death later in that year Antico seems to have assumed to a certain extent the painter's former rôle as adviser in general on artistic matters. He became more and more Isabella's intimate: it was to her that he turned for special favours for his family, his wife made perfumed soap for her, and she took into her service Antico's beautiful daughter Delia, whose marriage to a Mantuan gentleman of the court she arranged in 1518.

When after the death of her husband Francesco in 1519 Isabella was planning a new *Studiolo* and *Grotta* in the Corte Vecchia wing of the Palace, she was in touch with Antico with a request for new casts of the bronzes

formerly in the Trivulzio Collection, Milan), a cast of which was ordered by the Bishop in that year from the goldsmith Gian Marco Cavalli, and was working on a *Hercules* (Cat. 53). In the same year there are references by the Bishop to several wax models ready for casting for him and to a *Satyr* (example in Vienna) which was to be the companion to the *Nude of the Tortoise*. Other bronzes positively identifiable as cast for the Bishop during this time are the *Hercules and Antaeus* (Cat. 55),

47

which he had made some twenty years before for Bishop Ludovico. Antico looked out his old models and moulds, and found eight of them still surviving which he proposed to have cast for her by the founder Maestro Iohan, who had formerly worked for the Bishop. This Maestro Iohan, who first appears in the documents in the service of the Bishop in 1501, cannot, as is usually supposed, be Gian Marco Cavalli, who had cast Antico's *Spinario* in 1499, since Cavalli seems to have died soon after 1508.

Several of these statuettes cast for Isabella in 1519 are identifiable in the inventory of her possessions compiled in 1542, three years after her death, and the inventory specifies exactly how they were displayed in her apartments. In her old rooms in the Castello di San Giorgio the *Spinario* and the *Andromeda* had been displayed on the cornices above the doors, and here in her new purpose-built rooms Antico's statuettes were displayed in the *Grotta* on an extensive cornice running around the room. Above this was another cornice on which were displayed bronze busts, some modern, almost certainly by Antico, and others antique.

The replication for Isabella of the bronzes which Antico had made some twenty years before for Bishop Ludovico requires some explanation. We have already seen how, while he was working for the Bishop around 1500, it had been possible for Antico to supply more than one cast of a given model, and indeed most of the bronzes of Antico survive today in more than one example. Radiographical researches initiated by Richard E. Stone of the Metropolitan Museum and pursued by Dr. Jonathan Ashley Smith at the Victoria & Albert Museum have shown that Antico's bronzes were produced by a method very sophisticated for its time which was designed specifically for exact replication. His original wax models were piece-moulded, and hollow wax casts were produced from the moulds. These were filled with a plaster core, and the resulting replica after minimal repair was used in the lost-wax casting process. The end result of this process is a bronze replica which normally differs from its fellows only in the smallest details of repair in the wax and in the degree of sumptuousness of finish in the metal. The original models and piece-moulds could be kept intact for many years and used repeatedly. For a comparable sophistication of replication in Italian bronzes one has to look forward to the statuettes produced by Antonio Susini for Giambologna in the closing years of the sixteenth century.

Five of the eight statuettes which we may presume on the strength of the documents to have been cast for Isabella's new *Grotta* in 1519 are to be identified with bronzes surviving today in the greatest single concentration of works by Antico, in the Kunsthistorisches Museum, Vienna, together with two busts by Antico, which must once have been amongst those on the upper cornice of the *Grotta*. These came to Vienna by a peculiarly circuitous route. Bought in Mantua for King Charles I in 1627-8, they were sold under the Commonwealth to Archduke Leopold Wilhelm von Habsburg, Governor-General of the Spanish Netherlands, and passed by 1659 to the Stallburg in Vienna. Specifically mentioned in Antico's letter of 1519 were a *Hercules and Antaeus*, the *Nude of the Tortoise*, and her companion, the *Satyr*. Of these, the first and last-mentioned are today in Vienna and the *Hercules and Antaeus* (cf. Cat. 55) has under its base an inscription with the name and title of Isabella. The other bronzes in Vienna with this provenance are an *Atropos* (cf. Cat. 56), a *Hercules* (cf. Cat. 53) and a *Mercury*. Curiously enough, a characteristic which all these bronzes share is an absence of the fire-gilding and silver-inlay which is so striking a feature of other bronzes by Antico, and it would therefore appear that the bronzes made for Isabella's *Grotta* were in general less splendid in finish than those made some twenty years earlier for Bishop Ludovico at Boz-

zolo. Of the other known bronzes by Antico only the *Apollo* of the Ca' d'Oro (Cat. 57) has a secure provenance from Mantua itself and this by contrast is one of the most splendidly finished of all.

Antico passed his declining years at Gazzuolo in a house which he was enabled to build for himself by the generosity of Antonia del Balzo. After 1519 there is no further mention in the documents of bronze-casting, but he was commissioned in 1523 by Camilla Bentivoglio Gonzaga, the daughter-in-law of Gianfrancesco and Antonia del Balzo, to take charge of new architectural work at the palace of Gazzuolo, and his sculptural decorations there, now sadly destroyed, were later much admired. He died at Gazzuolo in July, 1528, having served three generations of the Gonzaga family.

Antico's bronzes stand in striking contrast to those of his Paduan contemporary Andrea Riccio. Both were in their own ways classicizing artists deeply influenced by Mantegna, but each exemplifies a different aspect of Mantegna's art; Antico all form and Riccio all expression. If in the end Antico must be accounted the lesser artist, we would be grossly mistaken if we were to go so far as to write him off as a mere copyist of classical sculptures. For one thing we should always bear in mind the fact that the antique marbles on which he based his bronzes were still in his day unrestored, so that his statuettes become interpretations, rather than mere copies. At their most imaginative they amount to brilliant variations on antique sculptural themes.

Just as Riccio embodied in his work the ideas current in the University of Padua in his day, Antico, less intellectual, but the perfect court artist, made his work the direct expression of the humanist taste of the Gonzaga.

PRINCIPAL SOURCES:

See under BIBLIOGRAPHY: Gaye, I, 1839, pp. 337-38; Rossi, 1888; Bode, 1907[2]; Hermann, 1910.

Isabella d'Este, Patron and Collector
by J. M. Fletcher

Isabella d'Este arrived in Mantua as a bride in 1490. She brought thirteen painted chests in her luggage, and Ercole Roberti, the Ferrarese artist who had designed them, travelled with her[1].

Isabella was the first child of Eleonora and Ercole d'Este, Duke and Duchess of Ferrara. She was her mother's favourite daughter and unlike her sister Beatrice who spent much of her childhood in Naples, Isabella grew up in Ferrara. Both her parents were active and discriminating patrons of the arts and Isabella was brought up on the erudite and exotic art of Tura and Cossa at a court where humanists discussed painting[2] and a great scholar, Guarino, had devised the programme for the decoration of her uncle Leonello d'Este's Studiolo[3]. Mantua is not far from Ferrara and throughout her life Isabella maintained close contact with her d'Este relations. Her insistence on fine meanings in her pictures, her musical skills and her faith in astrology, typified by the cryptic reverse of her medal (Cat. 109) can all be attributed to her Ferrarese upbringing[4]. Long after her marriage Isabella employed artists from her home. She sent Mantuan musicians to learn in Ferrara[5], and in 1511 when she wanted an "exotic pavilion" (un casino bizarro) designed for her property at Porto she borrowed the Ferrarese Court architect Biagio Rossetti[6]. Her favourite gem engraver was the Ferrarese Anichino who worked in Venice, and although Costa (the only important painter that she permanently attracted to Mantua) came to her through Bentivoglio relatives in Bologna, he too was originally from Ferrara.

Isabella's marriage started well but soon deteriorated and she and her husband began to lead rather separate lives, which led to the Marchesa developing her own taste (she had no mother-in-law to guide her). Francesco supervised the building and decoration of his palace at San Sebastiano while Isabella devoted herself to the decoration of her private living quarters in the Castle. Francesco, who was not uncivilized, shared Isabella's love of music, plays and dogs but, irritated by her independence and her greed for culture, he exaggerated his martial image and posed as a man of brawn and little brain. In fact Francesco was on good terms with Mantegna, and proved an appreciative and generous patron to Costa.

In almost half a century at Mantua Isabella witnessed an enormous stylistic change in the arts as well as fluctuations in her own political role which meant, paradoxi-

cally, that when she was at her most powerful she had less time and energy to devote to patronage. She acted as regent from 1509-10 during her husband's captivity in Venice and again after his death in 1519, when her son was on military campaigns.

Isabella revelled in patronising the arts. The motto on her medal (Cat. 109) which she distributed amongst her friends and admirers reads Benemerentium Ergo, "for those who deserve well". She was seen as "a tenth Muse" (una decima Musa)[7] and she took her role as the inspirer of poetry, music and art extremely seriously. Not only do the Muses dance in Mantegna's Parnassus (Pl. 89), a selection of them reappear on the marble frame of the doorway in her Grotta[8] (Pl. 60-61). Isabella found painters more difficult to handle than writers who did not keep her waiting and whose flattering dedications cost her nothing[9]. Mantegna showed himself an extremely shrewd judge of her intellectual aspirations and autocratic temperament when, although long established as court painter, he took the most unusual step of securing a letter of recommendation from her old tutor, Battista Guarino, on his return to Mantua in 1490. Isabella treated artists dictatorially or reverentially, depending on their standing. On her own admission she was appetitosa, hungry for art, and the faster a work was delivered the more she enjoyed it. She threatened her painter Liombeni and her marquetry makers the Mola brothers with the dungeons if they did not hurry up with their work[10], but she called Leonardo da Vinci "our friend" despite the fact that he rarely complied with her requests.

Money was a major problem for Isabella[11]. She paid for art out of her income. She was poor compared to her sister Beatrice married to Ludovico Sforza, Duke of Milan, and, dazzled by their treasures, Isabella exclaimed "would to God that we who spend willingly should have so much"[12]. Isabella's jewels were often pawned at times of economic crisis[13] and in 1511 when she was involved in heavy building expenses she stopped her Roman agent from sending classical sculptures on approval lest on seeing them she should succumb to temptation[14]. Shortage of money combined with her fondness for cameos led her to try to obtain a secret recipe for making imitation agate and cornelian[15]. Constant economy seems to have made her rather mean, and her sculptor Gian Cristoforo Romano hits the nail on the head when, writing for her instructions regarding the tomb of the Blessed Osanna, he supposes that she will want it to be honourable but as cheap as possible. Isabella rose to the bait and told him to use up the pieces of jasper that were left over from the making of her *Studiolo* door[16].

Isabella was aware of her own fastidious taste and constantly refers to it in letters when ordering luxury goods for household and personal use and, although she is famous as the patron of painters and sculptors, her influence on the applied arts was greater. She was imitative by nature and having seen something which pleased her on her travels she encouraged local craftsmen to produce something similar. After her return from Rome in 1527 she ordered glassware from Murano "in the style that is used in Rome" (*di la fogia che si usa in Roma*). A bed canopy is rejected because "it is not to our design"[17].

She orders gilt-edged, vellum editions of the Aldine classics and insists that they be specially checked for clear type and printer's errors[18]. The result of her care can be seen in her copy of Petrarch's *Cose Volgari* (Cat. 102). Her exceptional sense of quality was accompanied by a desire for exclusiveness. She was extremely proprietorial and ladies who wanted to wear hats or fabrics that she had either invented or first modelled wisely applied for her permission[19]. She ordered a cousin to whom she had loaned a rare Greek manuscript not to show it to many people lest it be devalued by exposure to the common eye[20].

Isabella's reputation as a patron rests on the pictures that she commissioned to decorate her first *Studiolo* (see plan, Pl. 3). This is a small room in a tower on the first floor of the Castle. Directly under this room is a barrel-vaulted, cavernous space appropriately known as the *Grotta*[21] in which she eventually housed her collection of antiquities (Pl. 57). Soon after her arrival in Mantua, aged only seventeen, Isabella began to plan the decoration of these apartments.

She was familiar with other princes' *studioli* in Ferrara, Urbino and Gubbio, but the idea for the decoration of her own was rather original. She intended to commission paintings from "the most outstanding masters in Italy"[22], in competition with each other (*paragone*, or comparison, was a concept particularly dear to her). But as both Leonardo and Bellini failed to provide her with paintings, she ended up with two pictures by Mantegna (Pl. 30, 89) one by Perugino (Pl. 54), and a pair by Costa (Pl. 55, 62, Cat. 114).

Each artist would work on a similar scale, the direction of the light in the picture being determined by the fall of the natural light in the room. All the paintings were to be on canvas, and the foreground figures in each were to be the same size. These simple conditions were not easy to transmit to artists working outside Mantua, for measurements were not standardized and varied between cities. Isabella complicated matters even further by countermanding her orders on subject matter and sequence, and on at least one occasion she got hopelessly muddled and issued contradictory instructions concerning the fall of light[23]. A more fundamental problem was that not all her artists were used to classical or allegorical themes, and some were inhibited by her repeated insistence on comparison with Mantegna, who excelled in such subjects[24]. Even when invited to choose his own theme Bellini failed to produce a painting, arguing that he was used to following freely his own imagination, and he could do nothing well if he were tied down to detailed specifications[25].

The meaning of her pictures was of paramount importance to Isabella, who tended to subordinate the painting to its literary content, and the subject matter of some scenes was invented by a Mantuan poet, Paride de Ceresara[26].

Isabella's method of commissioning a picture is best followed through the correspondence consisting of over seventy letters about a painting for her *Studiolo* ordered from Perugino in Florence. Perugino was to follow a literary programme which is actually copied into his notarial contract and he also received a drawing to help him visualize the theme. The programme for his *Battle between Love and Chastity* (Pl. 54) is impossibly detailed and although Perugino was allowed to omit some minor episodes in the love lives of the gods he was forbidden to add anything of his own invention. Once he began painting he was harassed by frequent visits from Isabella's advisors. When, contrary to his instructions, he painted Venus nude instead of clothed Isabella protested that if a single figure was altered it would change the whole meaning of her work. On delivery of the picture in 1505 Isabella told Perugino that she would have liked it better if he had used oil although it was on her instructions that he had followed Mantegna and painted in tempera[27]. Perugino worked hard for his 100 ducats.

would have been three had he lived) and two smaller works imitating bronze reliefs[30]. Isabella struggled to obtain a work from Bellini when Giorgione was already painting classical subjects for connoisseurs in Venice. Only after Giorgione's death did she enquire about pictures thought to be in his workshop, but without success[31]. Botticelli was willing to paint for her *Studiolo* but she chose Perugino because he was friendly with her two most trusted advisers, Gian Cristoforo Romano and Lorenzo da Pavia. By borrowing paintings, Isabella educated herself as a connoisseur. In 1502 Bernardo Bembo offered to lend her his Memling Diptych[32]. In 1498 she sent a messenger to Milan to collect Leonardo's portrait of Cecilia Gallerani so that she could compare it with portraits by Giovanni Bellini that she had just seen[33]. It may have been fear of an extended loan or enforced presentation that prompted Castiglione to beg his mother to hide his collection which included a Raphael Madonna when he moved it from Rome to Mantua in 1520[34].

Isabella confessed to an "insatiable desire" for classical art. She was a fashionable woman who wished to be involved in an activity which was both intellectually and socially prestigious; the possession of antique sculpture was a sign of a cultivated mind and a serious attitude to art and life. She seems to have begun by acquiring gems and cameos, and only graduated to collecting sculptures after she had prepared a room to receive them[35]; it was not until her second visit to Rome that she seriously took up coin collecting.

However she faced serious competition when collecting classical art. Impecuniousness forced her to build up her collection piece-meal; often she acquired objects as gifts. Like all collectors she was restricted by the papal embargo on exports of antiquities from Rome. Although the Gonzaga did not own a palace in Rome and consequently could not conduct private excavations on the adjacent land, Isabella visited the city twice, in 1514–15, and again from 1525 to 1527. But through the cooperation of Fra Sabba da Castiglione, an unconventional Knight of Malta, she acquired Greek sculptures from Naxos and Rhodes, fragments from the Mausoleum of Halicarnassus, and a coin wrapped up in a sonnet written in the Temple of Apollo at Delos[36]. Isabella had agents in all major Italian cities informing her on prices, sales, and dealers' stocks; she was able to buy a precious late antique onyx vase from the collection of

The *Studiolo* and *Grotta* became one of the sights of Mantua to be shown to visiting dignitaries. Since the rooms are small, with poor lighting, and without fireplaces they were not suitable for everyday use in winter. They were an obvious security risk and they must often have been kept locked. Even the best bred guest could be light fingered, and valuable silver objects were missed after the Duke of Bourbon's retinue had been allowed to visit the rooms in 1509[28].

After her husband's death Isabella moved to new apartments on the ground floor of the *Corte Vecchia* in order to give her son more space and herself fewer stairs[29]. Here she recreated her *Studiolo* (Pl. 64), and around 1530 added a pair of allegories by Correggio (Pl. 52, 53; see Cat. 115). Her new rooms were all on one floor, and her *Studiolo* was the only means of access to her inner sanctum, the *Grotta* (Pl. 58).

Isabella's taste in painting was somewhat unadventurous; she tended to patronise established artists and did little talent spotting. Mantegna was already old when Isabella arrived in Mantua yet he remained her favourite artist until his death in 1506. He was given the lion's share in her *Studiolo*, painting two large pictures (it

48. *Antico,* Hercules and Antaeus *(Kunsthistorisches Museum, Vienna).*

49. *Giancristoforo Romano, Medal in gold of Isabella d'Este in a frame of diamonds and enamel (Kunsthistorisches Museum, Vienna, Munzkabinett) (see Cat. 109).*

the connoisseur Michele Vianello when it was put up for auction in Venice in 1506 (Cat. 119)[37].

If Isabella lacked money, she had much expert advice. Her view of antiquity was deeply influenced by Mantegna's own nostalgic interpretation of the classical world, and his collection of classical art was famous throughout Italy. Isabella did not see Rome until she was middle-aged, and must surely have imagined it through Mantegna's pictures, for writing in 1507 to the Duchess of Urbino who was about to visit the city, Isabella hoped that she herself could see the ruins so that she might realize "what the Triumph of a Victorious Emperor must have been"[38].

Leonardo inspected classical vases for her which were on offer from the Medici Collection[39]. In 1505 she returned an ivory head to Rome because Mantegna and Gian Cristoforo Romano had judged it to be neither good nor antique[40]. Jacopo Sansovino was one of a panel of experts who found that statuettes sold her by a Roman dealer as ancient were modern fakes[41]. Only the year before her death she interrupted Giulio Romano's work and made him act as intermediary between herself and a jeweller who had cameos for sale.

As a collector Isabella had few scruples, and her methods of acquisition reveal the most unpleasant side of her character. She knowingly received stolen alabaster heads looted from the Bentivoglio Palace in Bologna[42], and she haggled disgracefully with the mortally ill Mantegna when debt forced him to part with one of his most cherished possessions, a bust of the Empress Faustina[43] (Cat. 121-122). She acted with unseemly speed when on hearing that Galeazzo Sforza, who had willed her a part of his collection, was dying she sent off her messenger post-haste to collect her portion long before he was actually dead. One of her greatest treasures was a *Cupid* by the young Michelangelo which had belonged to her sister-in-law's husband Guidobaldo Montefeltro. Isabella acquired it from Cesare Borgia who had driven the Montefeltro from Urbino in 1501, but after their restoration she characteristically refused to return the Cupid[44] (see also Cat. 279).

Several generations of Gonzaga men had collected classical art before Isabella. Federico I had a statue of Bacchus in his *Studiolo*[45] and Cardinal Francesco had built up an important collection of classical gems and cameos[46].

Isabella seems to have been the first Renaissance woman to have been involved seriously in collecting antiquities. Her motivation was aesthetic and social rather than scholarly and antiquarian, and in her letters she makes appreciative, rather than learned comments on them. In 1498 she forced Mantegna to sell her a female bust not because she wanted to make up a set of illustrious Roman women but so that she could send it to her cousin whom it was said to resemble[47].

Isabella was susceptible to rare marbles and semi-precious stones and her collection was exceptionally rich in agate and jasper vases. She had no qualms about mixing antiquities with objects of curiosity or of sentimental value; with gilded cages, corals, clocks and a unicorn's horn[48]. She displayed her medal in the *Grotta*, her profile in gold and her name spelt out in precious stones. (Pl. 49). Like most Renaissance collectors Isabella was no purist and encouraged contemporary artists to paint and sculpt in the antique style. She enjoyed the smooth surfaced bronze reductions of classical masterpieces like the *Hercules and Antaeus* (Pl. 48) which she commissioned from Antico who had earlier worked for Gianfrancesco Gonzaga of Bozzolo[49].

The bulk of Isabella's antiquities were destined to decorate her *Grotta* and their final arrangement in this room can be reconstructed from the inventory compiled in 1542 (Cat. 118). From it we can get some idea of her crowded yet calculated display which suggests that her collecting, like so much of her patronage, was directed by her highly developed sense of interior decoration[50]. She rejected a vase by Caradosso because it was too big[51]. She commissioned balancing bronze statuettes from Antico to stand on ledges above the doors[52]. She juxtaposed her *Cupid* by Michelangelo with a Praxitilean *Cupid* and so invited a direct comparison between a great modern work in the classical style and an antique.

The sarcophagus relief of *Hermes seeking Proserpine in Hades* (Cat. 117) was not placed in the *Grotta* but embedded in the wall beneath the window in her *Studiolo* presumably because this piece unlike most of Isabella's sculptures is a narrative scene. The story told in Virgil's *Georgics* had been carefully explained to her when it was despatched to Mantua. Isabella must have felt that it complemented the *all'antica* paintings. Her belief in the superiority of classical over modern art is exemplified by the fact that she turned down Michelangelo's

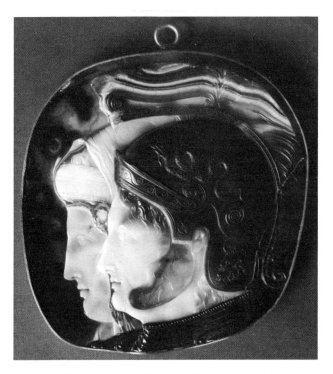

Sleeping Cupid when offered it in 1496 thinking of it merely as a fake antique. Only when she was informed that Michelangelo was the foremost sculptor of his generation did she try to get hold of it[53].

Although Isabella rarely used her sex for special pleading learned men were inclined to make allowances for her. After explaining her personal device of the XXVII (*Vinti sette*) (Pl. 63) Giovio observes that the rules of composition have been broken because the language used in this pun is the mother tongue of its inventor but he adds that this can be tolerated because Isabella is a woman "and such a great lady at that"[54]. And she gained considerable prestige from her abortive attempt to raise a statue to Virgil (Cat. 92). She publicized her intention by involving Pontanus, who had edited Virgil, and Sannazaro, who imitated his arcadian poetry, in the project. Pontanus particularly praised her efforts because Isabella was a woman and "not learned". In fact she made considerable efforts to learn Latin, employing tutors, including Mario Equicola, to coach her. Unlike a male ruler, Isabella had little opportunity to commission buildings; impecuniousness and lack of understanding of the principles of architecture hamper-

ed her. Although her visits to Rome increased her understanding of architecture, she ran into competition with her son Federico for the services of the court builders: Covo, who had designed her *Corte Vecchia* rooms and perhaps her secret garden (Pl. 56) was grudgingly loaned to her just for a week in 1528[55].

Consequently she concentrated on interior decoration. She enjoyed decking out rooms for state visits like that of the recently bereaved Ludovico Sforza when she rejected plain black hangings in favour of a less lugubrious combination of black and purple[56]. On a visit to Urbino she was impressed by the fact that there were enough wall coverings to go round all the apartments and that they did not have to be moved with the guests from room to room as was the case at Mantua[57]. In a letter addressed to the Ambassador in Venice in 1496 she orders *verdure* tapestries to be specially woven and asks that small animals and birds be included so that no-one can mistake them for hired-in pieces[58].

Most Renaissance women patrons, including Isabella's mother, spent their money on religious foundations and altarpieces[59] but Isabella was more interested in the secular decoration of her own living quarters. Although it is true that she commissioned devotional works from Costa and Titian, she tried to get a Nativity from Bellini and a Christ from Leonardo only after her efforts to persuade them to paint pictures for her *Studiolo* had failed. Both in contemporary and antique art she showed a womanly penchant for appealing representations of babies and children. She wanted Leonardo to make a Christ about twelve years old "with that sweetness and softness of atmosphere" (*cum quella dolcezza et suavità de aiere*) which she regarded as one of the most desiderable features of his style[60], and she asked Antico to make her a tiny figure of the Baptist aged three, either nude or with revealing drapery[61].

Isabella was conventionally but not exceptionally pious and her frequent pilgrimages to famous shrines gave her an opportunity to sightsee simply dressed, and without incurring the crippling expense of a formal state visit[62]. Travel prevented her taste from stagnating and she even ordered a picture from Titian "to take on journeys" (*da portar in viaggi*)[63].

Isabella's vanity made her a difficult subject for portrait painters[64]. Her intelligence was more striking than her appearance, and despite courtly eulogies to her beauty it would seem that she was not as good looking as her

two main rivals, her sister-in-law Lucrezia Borgia and her younger sister, Beatrice. To one so visually sensitive an incipient double chin and tendency to run to fat was hard to bear[65]; she must have spent many hours in front of the mirrors which she collected and placed amongst the treasures of her *Grotta*. In 1531 Federico's secretary gave a poignant description of the elderly Isabella resting during her tour of inspection of the new rooms in the Castle, lost in self contemplation before a Venetian mirror[66].

Isabella wanted her portraits to be beautiful yet lifelike. She was highly critical of a portrait that Mantegna produced in 1493 rejecting it on the grounds that it did not resemble her in the least. She ordered another portrait from Raphael's father, Giovanni Santi, to send to the Duchess of Atri who had originally asked for her picture. Later she complained to Ludovico Sforza that the painter Maineri had made her too stout.

Isabella could improve her appearance with cosmetics and by dressing to conceal her corpulence in black but she found it difficult to censor her painted image. Writers were more obliging than painters, since they were willing to rewrite offending passages. She managed to edit Trissino's word picture of herself by insisting that certain details concerning her appearance which he described in his *Ritratti* were changed before it was printed. But she was unable to persuade Francia to lighten her eyes in a portrait, for he argued that if they were altered he would have to change all the shading on her face. It would be interesting to know if the difference

52.	*Correggio,* Allegory of Vice *(Musée du Louvre, Paris).*
(see Cat. 115).

53.	*Correggio,* Allegory of Virtue *(Musée du Louvre, Paris).*

between Bonsignori's sensitive preliminary drawing of Isabella for the Beata Osanna Altarpiece and her younger profile in the painting (Cat. 139, 140) is the result of the artist's discretion or Isabella's personal intervention.

Isabella was portrayed by artists ranging from Tura to Titian. She changed her portrait painters in the way she changed her clothes. In 1499 Leonardo visited Mantua and drew Isabella (Pl. 46). He simultaneously alluded to her physical and intellectual assets by making much of her hair and by placing a book in her hand. Isabella liked this image and when her husband gave the drawing away she wrote to Leonardo asking for another. (Cat. 108).

As a young woman Isabella had been willing to sit for a wide range of artists but by 1516 she declared that she was tired of holding a pose and vowed never to do so again. This made life easier for Isabella but harder for artists like Francia who had to paint her *in absentia* guided only by a mediocre portrait and the description of Lucrezia Bentivoglio. It was this portrait painted when she was thirty-six that Isabella sent as model to Titian who used it as the basis of his portrait.

Titian had already proved his skill as a copyist by painting the portrait of Cornelia Malaspina from another artist's picture. This painting arrived in Mantua in 1530 and must have impressed Isabella. It is clear from her correspondence that she asked Titian to make a retrospective portrait of her face, and not to adjust the earlier picture to her older appearance, although the dress must have been updated. She had every reason to be pleased with the result, for inevitably Titian's portrait (Pl. 47) makes her look far younger than her daughter Eleonora whom he painted from life two years later. Isabella complimented Titian, saying that by his art he had made her more beautiful than she had ever been in life.

We know a lot about what people did with Isabella's portraits. A female friend in Ferrara propped one up on a chair and placed it opposite her during meals. Isabella's brother Ippolito begged for her portrait so that he could hang it at the head of his bed in place of a holy image. Portraits were passed to and fro between Mantua and Ferrara and, when Isabella was an old lady, she sent a picture of herself aged about three so that her relatives could compare it with the features of her great niece who they thought resembled her.

Isabella's contemporaries also projected her likeness into pictures she commissioned. The Queen of France went rather far when she cast Isabella as the Virgin, Francesco as Joseph and the ten year old Federico as the baby Christ in a *Holy Family* by Costa that Isabella had sent her in an attempt to win French support for Francesco's release from his Venetian prison.

Costa's *Woman with a Lap Dog* (Cat. 112) deserves serious consideration, for Isabella doted on her pet dogs, and she had been painted by Costa by 1508; a portrait of her by the same artist was given to the English Ambassador in 1514. However the clothes date the portrait to the late 1490's, when Costa was still in Bologna, and Isabella would not have sat in a costume that was a decade behind the times. She was obsessed with fashion, even commissioning a copy of an old picture of her father specifying that he be reclothed in a modern hat and doublet of the kind that had been fashionable

54.   *Perugino,* Battle of Love and Chastity
(Musée du Louvre, Paris).

56.   *Palazzo Ducale, Mantua: Secret Garden of Isabella d'Este.*

55.   *Lorenzo Costa,* The Reign of Comus
(Musée du Louvre, Paris).

when he died. The Costa portrait is smooth and sweet but it illustrates Isabella's taste, not her face.

The pale lady in Giulio Romano's portrait (Cat. 110) may be how we might like Isabella to look but there is no documentary or physiognomic evidence to prove that this is her. If this is Isabella, then she looks too young and thin for her age and she has managed to turn her dark eyes green. If this is not Isabella then it must be a woman of similar rank also connected with Mantua and deeply influenced by her, for the complicated turban was invented and first modelled by the Marchesa, and the knot pattern on her dress was devised for her by Niccolò da Correggio[67]. This picture does conjure up the *ambiente* of the ladies of the Mantuan Court. It shows us something of the life of a noble woman who rules over her own apartments, spending much of her private life in the company of her ladies-in-waiting, sustained by the counselling of local nuns and relieved from boredom by visits from loyal lady friends.

Isabella arrived in Mantua aged sixteen in 1490 and died there aged sixty-five in 1539. She lived in Mantua for almost half a century so it is surprising that her influence on its art and that of neighbouring courts has never been properly assessed. Isabella operated through a close network of family and loyal followers. Many of her agents and artists were friends and several of her painters were related to each other. Raphael, whom she commissioned to paint Federico's portrait, was the son of Giovanni Santi who had earlier painted her own. Bellini was Mantegna's brother-in-law and Perugino's wife was the daughter of the architect Luca Fancelli who had served Mantua for over forty years.

Isabella's *Studiolo* inspired her younger brother Alfonso d'Este whose famous *Camerino* at Ferrara was decorated with more hedonistic themes by Titian, Dosso, and Bellini. He also borrowed her manuscript translation of

57. *First 'Grotta' of Isabella d'Este, Castello S. Giorgio, Palazzo Ducale, Mantua.*

58. *Second 'Grotta' of Isabella d'Este, Corte Vecchia, Palazzo Ducale, Mantua.*

59. *Marble door frame leading into the second 'Grotta' of Isabella d'Este, Corte Vecchia, Palazzo Ducale, Mantua.*

60-61. *Details of Pl. 59, roundels.*

Philostratus' *Imagines*, a Greek text which described imaginary masterpieces in a make-believe gallery, and used it as a source for the subjects of his own pictures[68]. Given Alfonso's admiration for Isabella's room it is fitting that he was represented in it; she kept an example of his carpentry, a small beechwood cabinet, amongst the treasures of her *Studiolo*[69].

Isabella's family frequently asked for her opinion on artistic matters. Although her husband mocked her excessive fondness for Michelangelo's *Cupid* he was anxious for her approval of his newly decorated rooms in the palace at San Sebastiano. Although she assured him that she found them beautiful she cancelled out her compliment by adding that she particularly liked them because he had imitated her own room[70].

Isabella passed on her passion for the arts to her children. Her eldest son, Federico, was given a humanist education at her insistence, but his taste in the arts was also influenced by the years he spent as a youth in Rome. Her second son Ercole sat to Sebastiano del Piombo remembering his mother's praise for that artist[71] and Ferrante managed to save two Raphael tapestries during the sack of Rome and passed them to his mother for safe keeping[72]. It is hardly surprising that children raised in the *ambiente* of Mantua should in their turn become great patrons of the arts.

The Marchesa was the acknowledged family expert on antique sculpture and her husband freely admitted "that we understand horses and arms better than engraved gems" (*che noi ce intendemo meglio de cavalli et arme che de intagli*)[73]. Isabella fostered her sons' interests in antiquities and throughout their lives they made her presents of classical art[74].

By the 1520's Federico's patronage of the arts superseded that of his mother, but she responded to his new artists, employing Titian, Giulio Romano, and Correggio. The latter injected a disconcertingly sensual note into her *Studiolo* for, although his figure of *Virtue* (Pl. 53) which was originally bare-chested has been covered up[75], his *Vice* (Pl. 52 cf. Cat. 115) is clearly having an erection under his drapery. Despite her troubled relationship with Federico and the development of his grandiose and sensual taste he still respected her judgment. On receiving a *Magdalene* from Titian he told the artist that he should be pleased that his mother had praised it for she had seen so many fine pictures[76]. Federico, like his father before him, was anxious for Isa-

bella's approval and when he built the *Palazzina* to house his bride Margherita Paleologo. Isabella inspected the apartments as far as she was able, but by 1531 she was too stout and stiff to descend a difficult stair, even though a handrest had been specially placed there for her use. She sent her ladies-in-waiting below to report back to her. Isabella praised the new building for its superior amenities, better views, greatly increased privacy and access to fresh air, which compared favourably to her own living quarters[77].

Isabella became nostalgic in old age and, recalling the five triumphal arches constructed for her own bridal entry she asked Giulio Romano to design an arch to stand at the lakeside under which she could welcome

Federico's bride. This project (Pl. 51) was to be her swansong, marking the arrival of Mantua's first duchess and her own official retirement as first lady. But Federico cut down her project and eliminated the painted decoration which he judged too expensive for a temporary structure[78].

Isabella began her marriage in a bed designed by Ercole Roberti[79]. She ended up on a catafalque planned by Giulio Romano[80]. In her last will and testament[81] she disposed of her treasures with that same care and attention to detail that she had displayed while collecting them. To her daughters who were nuns she left ivories from her oratory. To her son Cardinal Ercole, she bequeathed an emerald engraved with the head of Christ which had belonged to her father his namesake. To each of her favourite ladies-in-waiting she left a painting of their choice. To her daughter-in-law Margherita Paleologo she gave her suburban palace and garden at Porto to be held in perpetuity for the recreation of all future duchesses of Mantua. To her son Federico, whose love of art she had fostered and whose patronage outgrew her own, she surrendered her most precious possessions, the contents of her *Grotta* "for his delight and pleasure" (*per suo diletto et piacere*).

62. *Lorenzo Costa,* Allegory *painted for Isabella d'Este (Cat. 114).*

63. *Fragment of ceiling formerly in Isabella d'Este's first Studiolo, in Castello S. Giorgio, now in the second Grotta, Corte Vecchia, Palazzo Ducale, Mantua.*

64. *Second Studiolo of Isabella d'Este, Corte Vecchia. Palazzo Ducale, Mantua.*

Notes

1. Venturi, 1889, p. 349.
2. Baxandall, 1963, pp. 304-26.
3. Baxandall, 1965, pp. 183-204.
4. Luzio, 1887; Lauts, 1956, pp. 135 ff, 212 ff.
5. Luzio and Renier, 1903, p. 49.
6. Luzio, 1914-15, p. 159.
7. Luzio, 1887, p. 25.
8. The best interpretation of the iconography of the roundels of the door is found in C. Elam, 1970.
9. Luzio and Renier, 1903, p. 151.
10. Luzio, 1887, pp. 18-19; Bertolotti, 1889, p. 171.
11. Martindale, 1964, pp. 183-84.
12. Luzio and Renier, 1890, p. 356.
13. Luzio and Renier, 1896, lxiii, p. 464.
14. Brown, 1976, p. 335.
15. Bertolotti, 1889, p. 69.
16. Venturi, 1888, p. 113.
17. Luzio and Renier, 1896, lxv, pp. 278, 282.
18. Cartwright, 1904 (3rd Edition) II, pp. 21-27.
19. Luzio and Renier, 1896, lxiii, p. 462.
20. Luzio and Renier, 1903, p. 25.
21. There has been much speculation concerning the word *grotta*, see Liebenwein 1977, p. 126. Hirschfeld, *Mäzene, die Rolle des Auftraggeber in der Kunst*, Munich 1968, suggests that the room was named after the Grotta in Boiardo's *Orlando innamorato.* I believe that the physical character of the room determined its name.
22. Canuti, 1931, II, p. 209.
23. Canuti, 1931, II, p. 219, Brown, 1968, pp. 321-22.
24. Braghirolli, 1877, p. 377.
25. Cian, 1887, p. 106.
26. Canuti, 1931, II, p. 223.
27. Canuti, 1931, II, pp. 212-13, 224-36.
28. Brown and Lorenzoni, 1977-78, p. 171.
29. Luzio and Renier, 1893, p. 248.
30. These were hung above the doors: Luzio, 1908, p. 423.
31. Richter, 1937, p. 304.
32. Cian, 1887, pp. 84-85.
33. Beltrami, 1919, p. 51.
34. d'Arco, 1857, II, pp. 86-87.
35. Brown, 1976, pp. 324, 331.
36. Luzio, 1886, pp. 91-112.
37. Brown, 1973, pp. 124-28.
38. Cartwright, 1904, I, p. 300.
39. Beltrami, 1919, pp. 70-71.
40. Venturi, 1888, p. 108.
41. Luzio and Renier, 1893, pp. 284-86.
42. d'Arco, 1857, II, p. 73.
43. Kristeller, 1902, pp. 577, 580-82.
44. Brown, 1976, pp. 333, 338-39, 350.
45. Bertolotti, 1890, p. 67.
46. Weiss, 1969, p. 196.
47. Kristeller, 1902, p. 564.
48. These objects are listed in the inventory of the *Grotta* compiled by Stivini in 1542, see Luzio, 1908, p. 413 ff.
49. The *Hercules and Antaeus* is inscribed under the base *D. Isabella M. Mar.*
50. For a reconstruction of the arrangement see Brown and Lorenzoni 1977, p. 156 ff.
51. Venturi, 1888, pp. 116-117.
52. Rossi, 1888, p. 177.
53. Norton, 1957, p. 251 ff.
54. Panofsky, 1961, p. 5.
55. Negri, 1954, pp. 88-89.
56. Luzio, 1890, p. 656.
57. Luzio and Renier, 1893, pp. 75-76.
58. Brown and Lorenzoni, 1972, p. 110.
59. Chiappini, 1956.
60. Beltrami, 1919, p. 90.
61. Rossi, 1888, pp. 179-180.
62. Once a religious vow was made it was necessary to dress in black or white. This point was made by Stephen Kolsky in an unpublished paper *Images of Isabella.* I am most grateful to him for allowing me to read it.
63. Braghirolli, 1881, pp. 104-05.
64. All the following portraits are discussed in Luzio, 1913, pp. 183-238, the references are taken from him.
65. In 1509 Isabella complained to her husband that if she had more to do with running the state she would not have grown so fat.
66. Hartt, 1958, I, p. 266.
67. Luzio and Renier, 1890, p. 382.
68. Fehl, 1974, p. 89 ff.
69. Luzio, 1908, p. 424.
70. Cartwright, I, p. 289.
71. Luzio, 1908, pp. 386-87.
72. Luzio, 1908, p. 89.
73. Luzio and Renier, 1903, p. 315.
74. Brown, 1976, pp. 336, 344.
75. *Pentimenti* revealed by X-rays: see Béguin, 1975[1], pp. 53-54.
76. Gaye, 1839-40, II, p. 224.
77. Hartt, 1958, I, pp. 263-64.
78. Gaye, 1839-40, II, pp. 236, 238.
79. Venturi, 1889, p. 349.
80. Hartt, 1958, I, p. 79.
81. ASMAG, b. 332. The will is dated 22 December 1535.

65-68. *Paolo Giovio*, Dialogo dell'Imprese militari et amorosi *(Lyon, 1574, pp. 53, 122, 123, 124).*

poſto quello,ille ſuo, non volendo dir'altro , che quel
porco,diçēdo ſpeſſo,ille vuol dir pur quello, e ſuo vuol
pur dir porco, come hò imparato à ſcuola à Sebenicco.
La coſa andò in gran riſa, e paſſo fin'à ſua Santità , e
diede auuertimēto à glialtri,che nō debbano ſpezzar
le parole per lettere,per nō cauſare ſimili errori d'An-
fibologia appreſſo de'Goſfi, i quali preſumono d'hauere la lor parte di ſapere, come ſi dice ,fin'al finocchio.

Quella anchora che figurò il Molza à Hippolito
Cardinal de' Medici ,benche fuſſe belliſſima di viſta e
di ſoggetto,hebbe mancamento : perche non fu com-
pitamente inteſa,ſenon da' dotti e prattichi,e ricorde-
uoli del Poema d'Horatio. Percioche volēdo egli iſpri-
mere,che Donna Giulia di Gonzaga riſplendeua di

D 3

Fù anchora vn poco ampulloſa l'impreſa del Signor Luigi Gonzaga chiamato per la brauura Ro-
domōte: il quale il dì che Carlo Quinto Imperatore
fece l'entrata in Mantoua, portò vna ſopraueſta di
raſo turchino fatta à quadretti,i quali alternati di
colore à due à due , l'uno moſtraua vno ſcorpione
ricamato,e'l'altro vn breue, che diceua I Q V I V I-
V E N S L A E D I T, M O R T E M E D E T V R: eſſendo la proprietà dello ſcorpione di medicare il veleno,
quando egli è ammazzato e poſto ſopra la piaga: volendo che s'intendeſſe ,ch'egli hauerebbe ammazzato
chi preſumeſſe d'offenderlo ,riualendoſi del danno
dell'offeſa con la morte del nimico.

Hebbene

Hebbene vn'altra il medeſimo Signer Luigi di
Gonzaga,che fu molta più bella : e ciò fu ,ch'eſſendo
egli venuto cō ſoldati imperiali all'aſſalto di Roma,
& eſſendo entrata la ſua bandiera prima di tutti
ſopra le mura di Roma,tra la porta Aurelia e la Set-
timiana,dopo già preſo il borgo di San Pietro,per l'ar-
dire de'ſoldati di quella bandiera fu preſa, e miſera-
bilmente ſaccheggiata Roma da'Tedeſchi , da'Spagnuoli e da Italiani,ch'adherinano alla parte Ceſarea.
Et egli diceua , ch'il ſoldato debbe hauere per iſcopo
la fama ò buona'ò triſta ch'ella ſi ſia : quaſi dicendo,
che la preſa e la rouina di Roma,anchor che foſſe abomineuole ad ogni buono Italiano,penſaua nondime-
no che gli doueſſe dar fama e riputatione.E per queſto
s'in

s'inuēto l'impreſa del tempio di Diana Efeſia,il quale eſſendo abbruciato da vn'huomo deſideroſo di fama , nè curandoſi ch'ella fuſſe peſſima & empia per
hauer diſtrutto la più bella coſa del mondo,gli fu fatto da'Greci vn decreto , che non ſi nominaſſe mai il
nome di lui, come ſceleratiſſimo & abomineuole : il
motto ſuo diceua,

A L T E R V T R A C L A R E S C E R E F A M A:
il qual motto gli fu poi meſſo da me, e fu pronato e
lodato da lui e da altri:hauendone eſſo poſto vn'altro,
che non ci pareua coſì viuo:ciò è, S I V E B O N V M,
S I V E M A L V M F A M A E S T.

Ne feci anchor'io vna,ch'aueua dell'altiero ,al Signor Marcheſe del Vaſto , anchorche fuſſe d'honeſto
propo

The Gonzaga devices

by Mario Praz

At the very beginning of Gabriele d'Annunzio's novel *Forse che sì forse che no* the hero Paolo Tarsis on his way back from the airfield visits the desolate Ducal Palace of Mantua with Isabella Inghirami and her brothers Aldo and Vana, and they remain fascinated by the azure and gold of the ceiling representing a labyrinth with the meandering inscription which supplies the title of the novel and the illustration of its frontispiece. The motto of Isabella d'Este's device appeals particularly to her modern namesake, Isabella: "She had turned her face to the gold and azure, and her very soul was spread over her head, rich and inextricable, mirrored in its thousand meanderings. She was reading with troubled eyes the terrific word inserted numberless times in the daedalean causeways, in the ultramarine fields". Later, her adolescent brother pronounces the fatal words with a spleen-veiled voice, and asks: "Why, Isa, between one Forse and the next there is a little twig and not a wing, not your wing, Tarsis? Daedalus' wing or else Ariadne's thread. Why then a little twig?" Even more puzzling to the visitors, side by side with the name of the Duchess are the Alpha and Omega, the enigmatic number XXVII, the musical score, the triangular candelabrum, the sheaf of white tickets, and the motto *Nec spe nec metu* ("but I hope what I fear and I fear what I hope"). "Whatever does the figure XXVII mean?", asked Vana, who in the confusion of her soul was moved to guess and foresee with superstitious anxiety.

The astonishment and superstitious awe of these modern readers of sibylline inscriptions contrasts with the spirit in which they were conceived, a spirit so described by Baldassarre Castiglione in his *Cortegiano* (XXX): "If the words used by a writer bear with them a little, I will not say difficulty, but recondite wit (*acutezza recondita*) [...] they give a somewhat greater authority to the writing, and cause the reader to be more wary and attentive, and to ponder more, and to delight in the ingenuity and learning of the writer"; and by Balthasar Gracián's *Agudeza y arte de ingenio*: "Emblems, Hieroglyphs, Apologues and Devices are like precious stones to the gold of elegant discourse" – a passage noteworthy for its connexion with the taste for the artifacts of *pietre dure* which prevailed in Florence and elsewhere in the seventeenth century. The sixteenth and seventeenth centuries witnessed not uni-

formly courteous battles over the definition and properties of that new-fangled wonder which was the perfect device. Great merit was accrued to the literary men who achieved distinction in the invention of devices. Alcibiade Lucarini wrote in 1629: "The good fortune of our times has brought it about that in this age there should live and flourish men whose perfect genius, sovereign intellect, and sound judgment, together with the excellence of their learning, and the surpassing quality of their knowledge, were sufficient to achieve the utmost limit of perfection in the making of DE-VICES". In *Il Rota, overo dell'Imprese* (Naples 1562) by Scipione Ammirato, the Bishop of Potenza defined the device as "a philosophy of the knight (*una filosofia del cavaliere*), as poetry is the philosophy of the philosopher"; when asked to explain these oracular words, he alluded to the theory according to which the ancient sages were said to have evolved fables in order to conceal the secrets of the speculative sciences from the vulgar herd. No wonder, then, that so many state apartments in Italy and Germany (and monasteries in Southern Germany and Austria) were ornamented with devices and emblems, and the members of the Gonzaga family did not lag behind in this widespread fashion. Devices were symbolical representations of a purpose, of a wish, a line of conduct (*impresa* is what one intends to *intraprendere*, i.e. to undertake) by means of a motto and a picture which reciprocally interpret each other. But if the thing in itself dwindles to so little, the scaffolding of ideas that grew around it is somewhat fantastic, and would figure better in one of Swift's satires than in the actual history of culture.

The invention of the Labyrinth device of Isabella d'Este (wife of Francesco Gonzaga) is easy enough to interpret, but the XXVII and the devices which puzzled d'Annunzio's characters need a historical explanation. After the death of her husband (1519), most courtiers deserted Isabella and honoured the lady loved by her son Federico, and she expressed her appreciation for the loyalty of those who remained in her retinue by means of the triangular candelabrum, a device she had used as early as 1512 (Luzio and Renier, 1896, p. 451). In the Holy Week office priests extinguish its candles one by one until the one on the top of the triangle only remains: the motto was now added SUFFICIT UNUM IN TENE-

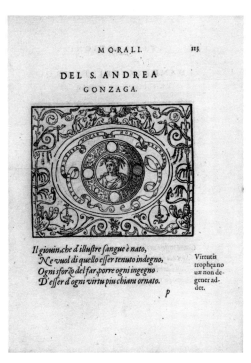

MORALI.   113

DEL S. ANDREA
GONZAGA.

Il giouin,che d'illuftre fangue è nato,
Ne vuol di quello effer tenuto indegno,
Ogni sforzo del far,porre ogni ingegno
D'effer d'ogni virtu piu chiara ornato.

Virtutis
trophæano
ux non de-
gener ad-
det.

p

69.   *Gabriele Simeoni,* Le Sentenziose Imprese, et Dialogo
del Symeone *(Lyon, 1560, p. 113).*

symbol of the eagle whose keen eyesight was prover-
bial; so was the device of the hind which, growing old,
becomes more wary and is able to detect dangers from
a distance (from Ovid, *De arte amatoria,* I, 766). GLO-
RIA IN ALTISSIMIS DEO ET IN TERRA PAX HO-
MINIBUS was a motto common to the Orengo and
Gonzaga families; another religious motto is AD
MONTEM DUC NOS ("Lead us to the mountain"),
related to the red cross of St George charged with four
eagles of the Gonzaga coat of arms, but was especially
employed to animate the device of Mount Olympus
surmounted by an altar bearing the motto FIDES.
This last one was included in the thirty-six Gonzaga
devices given by Jacobus Typotius in his *Symbola varia
diversorum Principum* (third part of the *Symbola Divina et
Humana*). Typotius associates this device with Guglielmo Gonzaga Duke of Mantua (1550-1587) to whom
Ruscelli dedicated his *Imprese illustri,* but it was conferred, supposedly, by the Emperor Charles V in 1522 on
Federico, on account of his valiant defence of Pavia
against the French. Mount Olympus was considered to
be never troubled by storms and winds. Other Gonzaga devices illustrated by Typotius are: SOLUS INDE-
FICIENS ("Alone unfailing") with the figure of the
sun, pertaining to Federico II, Marchese and then Duke
of Mantua (d. 1540). He also used the older device – it
goes back to the Marchese Ludovico (Gerola, 1930) – of
the diamond on the top of a mountain flanked by four
torches and the motto in Greek letters AMΩMOΣ (*Blameless*) to stress irreproachability. Another love device
associated with Federico represents a green lizard
(which was thought never to be in love) with the motto
QUOD HUIC DEEST ME TORQUET ("What this
creature lacks, torments me"). Typotius ascribes this
device to Francesco Gonzaga, the second Duke. The
second Gonzaga device illustrated by Typotius on pl.
70 (the plates are not regularly arranged) is well-
known: Francesco Gonzaga when employed as *condot-
tiero* by Venice, at the Battle of Fornovo (1495) failed to
follow up his success and did not pursue the defeated
French; he was suspected, being the brother-in-law of
Ludovico il Moro, to have been induced to spare the
French army for fear that the Venetians should become
too powerful. He was however cleared of this imputa-
tion, the fault lying with another commander. Hence

BRIS which explains the conceit: only one light is sufficient to keep her faith alive. Later she adopted the device of the white tickets, which are drawn from the urn
of the lottery, to show that she had tried several remedies to obtain the peace of her soul. Lastly the Roman
figure for twenty-seven, by itself, without a picture, as
Silvestro Pietrasanta remarks in his *De Symbolis Heroicis*
(Lib. VI, cap. V, p. 176) repeating Giovio's explanation: the Italian for twenty-seven sounds like *vinti sète,*
that is "you are defeated", meaning her adversaries (the
explanation offered by Gelli, that *sette* stands for the
"sects" she had defeated, is not correct). As for NEC
SPE NEC METU (her most famous motto, about
which Equicola wrote a treatise in 1505) with the picture of the magnet, worn by Isabella when she became
Marchesa, the meaning would seem to combine a reference to the equanimity to which she aspired, together
with a belief in her own powers of attraction.
The Gonzaga family surpassed other Italian dynasties in
their fondness for devices. Several of these devices are
not attached to any particular member, others are common to other families. TENTANDA VIA [EST] ("A
way must be tried", from Virgil, *Georg.,* III, 8) is common to the Gonzagas and Cesare Borgia. The hack-
neyed FRANGAR NON FLECTAR ("I will break,
not bend") is common to a number of families, including the Colonna (the figure being a column), and the
Gonzaga. DIVINUM DARE, HUMANUM ACCI-
PERE ("To give is divine, to receive is human"), with
the figure of Charity, was used by the Gonzaga for a
long time, as well as ALTA E LONGE COGNOSCE-
RE ("To know sublime things from afar"), with the

66

the device of the crucible filled with gold bars and enveloped in fire, with the motto (from Psalm 139, 1) PROBASTI ME DOMINE ET COGNOVISTI ME ("O Lord, thou hast tried and known me"). Carlo Emanuele I of Savoy accompanied the same motto with the image of a column surrounded by flames, the intention of the sovereign being to show that he had been severely tried by private and public misfortunes. Another device of Francesco Gonzaga pictured a roebuck (a symbol of gratitude) on the top of a mountain, implying that the way to virtue is arduous, the motto being AD NOS LAUDIS AMOR ("For us the love of praise [glory]"). The fourth Gonzaga device illustrated by Typotius on pl. 70 is that of Isabella d'Este, the triangular candelabrum we have already seen. The sixth device, IN AETERNUM (already mentioned above) shows two clasped hands; it is associated with Margherita Paleologo, wife of Duke Federico, to signify a pact of eternal fidelity. The first Gonzaga device on pl. 75, in Typotius' volume is Francesco's love device of the green lizard already mentioned; the second, VIAS TUAS DOMINE DEMONSTRA MIHI ("Make known your ways unto me o Lord"), a device used also by Baccio Bandinelli, has Tobias and the angel Raphael: it is connected with Francesco, the fifth duke, for according to Typotius his widow adopted the laurel tree struck by the thunderbolt, with the motto SPOLIAT MORS MUNERA NOSTRA ("Death despoils us of rewards"). This device is however associated by

other writers on devices with Bona of Savoy for the premature death of Galeazzo Maria Sforza, and with Margherita of Austria who was twice widowed. OLYMPUS, the fourth Typotian device on pl. 75 has been discussed above; the fifth device COSÌ MORIR MI PIACE ("I like to die thus") is given to Eleonora of Austria, Duke Guglielmo's wife, with the ivy which does not survive the tree to which it clings (i.e. her husband); she was wasting away after her husband's death. SEMPER VIVA ("Alive for ever") with the moon partially lit by the sun is Typotius' sixth symbol on pl. 75, connected with Duke Vincenzo I Gonzaga (the moon is always lit by the sun, even when it is not visible to the inhabitants of the earth). The Duke's love for his first wife persisted even after the marriage had been dissolved because of her sterility. The same Duke used also other devices: SESSIONEM MEAM ("Here I find my seat") with the furnace instead of the crucible (Typotius reports it with the motto PROBASTI DOMINE), meaning to warn that his spirit felt at home in trials of his loyalty. Other devices are reported under the name of Duke Vincenzo: the crescent surrounding the word SIC, meaning "Sic illustrior crescam" ("Thus I grow ever brighter"): he wished to grow more illustrious in process of time like the waxing of the moon; AETERNUMQUE TENET (he holds on to the eternal) a green lizard clings to a camomile plant, to infer that his house came victorious out of trials as the lizard healed its wounds through that plant: FLATUS (or the

74-77.   *Jacobus Typotius*, Symbola Divina et Humana...
(Prague, 1601-03, Pl. 70, 75, 99, 103).

corresponding Greek word φνσα: Typotius' first device on pl. 79), from the quotation "Dum prospero flatu fortunae utimur, nec adverso affligimur"("While we are enjoying fortune's prosperous breath and are not afflicted by adversity") with the image of the sun surrounded by a garland, over the water. Duke Vincenzo I fought in Hungary against the Turks, and on the occasion of the marriage of his son Francesco with Margherita, daughter of Carlo Emanuele I of Savoy, founded the Order of the Redeemer; he bore also the device of the eagle with the eaglets in the nest protected by stones which have the virtue of keeping snakes at bay. The mottoes VENENOSIS UT OBSISTAT ("To withstand poisonous creatures") and MUNIT ("He defends") accompany this image. A coin of the same Duke, the *ducatone*, had the image of St. George killing the dragon, with the motto PROTECTOR NOSTER, ASPICE ("Behold our Protector") a motto used also by other families, the della Porta, Aldobrandini, Piccolomini: the latter added ET RESPICE IN FACIEM CHRISTI TUI ("And look upon the face of your Christ"). It would be hard to guess the personality of Vincenzo I Gonzaga, the fourth Duke of Mantua, from these heroical and devout devices.

Another Vincenzo Gonzaga, the son of Ferrante I, lord of Guastalla, was a general in command of the galleys of the Hospitaller Order of St. John at the defence of Malta in 1565; on that occasion he adopted the device of a column surmounted by three stars with the words SIC IMMORTALIS SUM, ("Thus I am immortal") to mean that with the assistance of the Holy Trinity he hoped to become immortal through his defence of Malta (the same device had been used by Doge Tommaso Mocenigo in 1413).

The sense of a device is not uniformly easy to gauge, because the intent was deliberately mysterious so that the vulgar might not apprehend it. A bear leaning against an astrolabe with the signs of the Zodiac and the motto SICUT IN COELIS ("As in heaven") perhaps conveys a maxim of sound family education in the device of Alessandro Gonzaga: the bear was a model of education, because it was thought to lick its young into shape. Alfonso, the son of Alessandro, before becoming count of Novellara, was secretary to the Conclave of 1550 when Julius III was elected pope; the Pope

made Alfonso secretary to the Congregation of Briefs. When he published the code of rules to be observed by the servants of the Papal Court, he took the device of three mountains placed on top of each other by the Giants with the motto SIC ITUR AD ASTRA ("Thus one reaches the stars") intimating that one reaches great altitudes only through hard work (this device was common to other families, Liguori, Sforza, etc.).

Andrea Gonzaga, the son of Ferrante I Lord of Guastalla, distinguished himself in the Battle of Djerba (1560) as commander of troops of the Spanish army, and in order to show that he meant to emulate the exploits of his forbears, he adopted as a device a blank shield surrounded by a laurel frieze in which were inserted four small circles showing the devices of four members of his family: the crucible of Francesco Gonzaga, the Mount Olympus of Federico, the bundle of halberds of Andrea da Capua, his grandfather on his mother's side, the scroll with the motto NEC SPE NEC METU of his grandmother Isabella and his father Ferrante. The motto runs VIRTUTIS TROPHAEA HAEC NOVAE NON DEGENER ADDET ("True to his stock he will add these trophies of new gallantry"). Another device composed by Giovio for Andrea Gonzaga shows a church steeple and a cog-wheel like the one connected with the martyrdom of Saint Catherine, with the scroll QUUM CREPITAT SONORA SILENT ("When it creaks, noises are stilled"). The

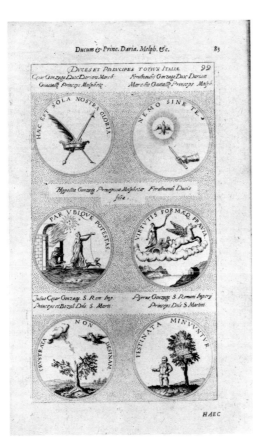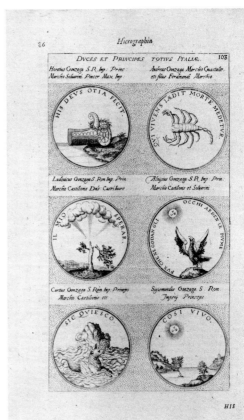

cog-wheel is in this case the instrument used during the Holy Week when the bells are silent; the device was directed against evil tongues which spread calumnies against valiant people (the device was originally composed for the Marchese del Vasto).

Ruscelli illustrates a device composed for Annibale Gonzaga, (a rock beaten by the waves with a motto meaning steadfastness, SEMPER IDEM). A plant which inspired many authors of devices is the sunflower in the case of Carlo Gonzaga (1417-56), second son of the first Marchese Gianfrancesco I; it expresses the fact that Carlo owed everything to his father (the sun): restless and disloyal, he served in succession as *condottiere* Filippo Maria Visconti, Sforza, and the Venetian republic: the Spanish motto runs SYN SUS RAYOS MYS DESMAYOS ("Without his beams I am lost").

Another Carlo, Duke of Nevers and Rethel, and then Duke of Mantua (1627-37), in succession to Vincenzo II, had the sun in the Zodiac with the motto NEC DEVIO NEC RETROGRADIOR ("I neither swerve nor turn back"). His grandson, Carlo II, who sold the dukedom of Nevers and Rethel to Mazarin after falling out with the French court, adopted as his device a genius who dictates the principles of justice, with the motto DISCITE IUSTITIAM MONITI ("Be warned, learn justice").

Curzio Gonzaga, one of the minor poets of the Cinquecento, the son of Luigi Gonzaga (a descendant of Corrado Gonzaga) and of Elisabetta Lampugnani, was a poet, a soldier and a diplomat; in the poem *Il fido amante* he celebrated the glories of the Gonzaga family.

He had several devices: ET SOLE ALTRO NON HAGGIO ("And I have no other sun") the eagle looking at the Great Bear (Orsa Maggiore), an allusion to his love for a lady of the Orsini family; SIC QUIESCO ("Thus I rest") with the seal which was supposed to lie quiet on its rock during the worst storms, and not to be harmed by thunderbolts. This device appears in many places in the palaces of Mantua and Borgoforte: the seal in the picture is represented fantastically as a combination of a calf or a bull and a fish. The motto runs also NEC RUMPITUR QUIES ("And the silence is not broken"). Another of Curzio Gonzaga's devices accompanied a pine tree struck by a thunderbolt with the words IL MIO SPERAR CHE TROPPO ALTO MONTAVA ("My hope which soared too high"). Another shows, an arm brandishing a sword in front of the Hydra, with the Petrarchan line E S'IO L'UCCIDO PIÚ PRESTO RINASCE ("And if I kill it, it rises all the sooner") for the vain attempt to forget the lady who had forsaken him; another of his amorous devices represents Love blindfolded, holding out two wings with the motto CON QUESTE ("With these"), words of another line of Petrarca, meaning that he trusted to persuade the beloved one with the wings of a constant love; as this faithfulness little availed, he had to be content with the sight of his love, hence the image of an eagle which soars toward the sun: PUR CHE NE GO-DAN GLI OCCHI ARDAN LE PENNE ("For the eyes to enjoy it, the feathers burn"). Battista Pittoni illustrates this device with the sun represented by Apollo in his chariot.

Cardinal Ercole Gonzaga (1505-63) a president of the Council of Trent in 1561, used the image of two swans fighting an eagle and overcoming it (according to Aristotle and Aelianus) to intimate that a peaceful nature, provoked, defeats the adversary: this image appears under two mottoes: SIC REPUGNANT ("Thus they fight back") and TANTUM LACESSITUS ET VINCIT ("He wins even if only provoked"), or only LACESSITUS.

Ferdinando, Cardinal and then Duke of Mantua (1612-26) had as a device an eagle about to take flight from the top of a rock, with the words VIVA AUT MORTA ("Alive or dead") to signify that he was prepared to face any enterprise. Later he chose NEMO SINE TE ("No one without you") with the figure, representing God, of a dove surrounded by a halo. His last device was the moon facing the sun with the words NON MUTUA-TA LUCE ("Not with borrowed light"), hinting at the light reflected from his ancestors, and denying that his own glory was only due to this reflection (another, probably unreliable, version gives NON MUTATA LUCE ("With unchanged light") to signify that his virtues as a cardinal had not lost their splendour when he had become a duke).

ALIAS DEVORAT UNA MEA (or SIC ALIAS, etc.) ("Only one of mine devours the other ones"), the device of Ferrante I Lord of Guastalla (d. 1557), *generalissimo* of Charles V, shows an eagle's feather in the midst of feathers of other birds. The feather stands for the eagle which devours other birds. If instead of MEA one reads (as Pietrasanta does) MEAS, the meaning is that the glory conferred upon him by the king of birds, i.e. the Emperor, surpasses all his other titles of honour). Another *impresa* of the eagle fighting with lions, and the motto (from Horace, *Od.*, IV, 4, 29) FORTES CREANTUR FORTIBUS ("The strong generate the strong") belongs to Ferrante Gonzaga Marchese di Gazzuolo who took part in the battle of Lepanto; he adopted also the device of the magnet (NEC SPE NEC METU) associated with Isabella d'Este, Philip II, Alberto della Rovere, and others.

Ovid (*Her.*, 13, 84) is the source of the device BELLA GERANT ALII ("Let others wage wars") with the eagle perched on an olive branch, worn by Cardinal Francesco Gonzaga (1538-66) son of Ferrante I Lord of Guastalla.

Horace's MICAT INTER OMNES ("He shines among them all"), referred to the brilliant comet which appeared in the northern part of the Roman sky a few days after the death of Julius Caesar, supplied the motto INTER OMNES for the device, invented by Francesco Molza for Cardinal Ippolito de' Medici, to signify that Giulia Gonzaga surpassed in beauty all the women of the time. Bargagli accompanied the same motto with the crescent outshining the surrounding stars (another image from Horace), and says that the device had been applied to a lady called Luna; the comet was retained in the case of Giulia Gonzaga, because her name was reminiscent of Julius Caesar.

The undying amaranth, a symbol of immortality as well as of love, was the flower joined with the motto NON MORITURA in the device adopted by Giulia daughter of Ludovico Gonzaga lord of Sabbioneta, when her husband, Vespasiano Colonna, died; but she, being proud of her own beauty, also used the device of the comet with the INTER OMNES. She was however even more distinguished intellectually, so much so that Pope Pius V suspected that heretical ideas inspired her warm support for the reform of ecclesiastical discipline.

In 1571 Giulio Cesare, son of Carlo Gonzaga, Marchese of Gazzuolo, obtained from the emperor Rudolph II the title of count of Pomponesco, and provided the little town with buildings and a fortress. He had taken part in the battle of Lepanto; his motto FRUSTRATA NON DESINAM ("Frustrated, I shall not desist") shows a tree split by a thunderbolt; an eagle, which perched on it, hovers nearby in admiration.

Duke Guglielmo (1550-1587) had the device of Justice with her attributes (the sword and the scales) with the words CUIQUE SUUM ("To every one his own". Ruscelli opens his Fourth Book with a full-page illustration of this device and a long dissertation and a short poem in praise of Guglielmo.

DI FRANCESCO CARDINALE GONZAGA.

Guerreggi pur, cui 'l guerreggiar è dato,
E dimoſtri nel'arme alto ualore:
Queſto ſaggio e magnanimo Signore
Solo a la pace e a le uirtuti è nato.
Seco la cortesia, seco il beato
Secol ritorna; ou'hebbe 'l primo honore
La ſanta Palla; e 'l chiare almo ſplendore
D'ogni raro coſtume, e piu lodato.

Viua dunque fra noi l'etate in terra
Del buon Neſtore, e ognihor gli tēga dietro
La sua ſi glorioſa inclita ſchiera.
E dal mondo fuggendo il uitio tetro,
Ottenga alfin, com'otterrà, l'altera
E Santa, a noſtro ben, ſedia di Pietro.

DELLA S. LVCRETIA GONZAGA.

Candida Cerua al ſuo bel collo intorno
Neſſun mi tocchi, ha in lettre d'oro impreſſo:
Cio di LVCRETIA hà 'l bel theſoro eſpreſſo;
Che le fa' l petto immortalmente adorno

Coſi, mentre n'apporti Apollo il giorno,
E ſplenderà la Luna;
In coſtei non haurà potenza alcuna
Mai ne tempo, ne morte, ne Fortuna.

The daughter of Ferrante, first lord of Guastalla, Ippolita, had the device PAR UBIQUE POTESTAS ("An equal power everywhere") with the figure of the Moon and Diana, a hunting-horn at her lips, with two dogs on the leash, Cerberus issuing out of the gates of Hell. Ippolita was successively married to Fabrizio Colonna and Antonio Carafa; she was greatly praised by the Italian men of letters for her talents (see Cat. 148-149). A bronze medal coined by Pisanello for Marchese Ludovico Gonzaga (Cat. 15) the husband of Barbara of Brandenburg, had on the reverse the image of an armoured knight on horseback; a sunflower appears above the horse's head, and the sun high up in the sky.

On the day of Charles V's solemn entry into Mantua, Luigi Gonzaga, nicknamed Rodomonte for his bravery, donned a coat-armour of blue satin quartered alternatively with an embroidered scorpion and the motto QUI VIVENS LAEDIT MORTE MEDETUR ("Who wounds when alive, heals when dead"): it was accounted a property of the scorpion to heal the venom of its sting with the oil obtained from its dead body: the innuendo was that Rodomonte would kill an offender. Pietrasanta ascribes this device to Andrea Gonzaga. The temple of Diana set on fire by Heratostratos is the figure of the motto ALTERUTRA FAMA ("Any sort of fame"), or else, SIVE BONUM AUT MALUM FAMA EST ("Whether it's good or bad it's fame"),

adopted by Luigi (Rodomonte) Gonzaga after having taken part with the Imperial troops in the sack of Rome. Ludovico Gonzaga, son of Gianfrancesco Count of Rodigo who served under Emperor Maximilian against the Venetians during the League of Cambrai war, and took part in the siege of Padua (1509), had a device representing a big block of crystal hanging from a rock with the motto EX GLACIE CRISTALLUS EVASI ("From ice I turned to crystal"), to hint at his own precious quality. This device was also used by the sculptor Baccio Bandinelli to indicate his indebtedness to Cosimo de' Medici for his own preferment.

Virgil's HAEC DEUS NOBIS OTIA FECIT (*Georg.*, I, 6) ("God made these idle pleasures for us") was the inscription beneath a wheel and a portion of a ship surmounted by a crown in the device of Orazio, son of Federico Gonzaga of Bozzolo, to commemorate the service rendered by land and sea to the Emperor from whom he had obtained the coronet.

TU NE CEDE MALIS ("Don't yeld to adversities" with Hercules killing the Hydra with his club (Virgil, *Aen.*, IV, 95) is, according to Pietrasanta, the device of Cardinal Pirro Gonzaga; conscious of his modest qualities, he used also the device with a dwarf next to an old tree and the words FESTINATA MINUUNTUR ("Things done in haste do not turn out well").

POTIUS, (or PRIUS) MORI QUAM FIDEM FAL-

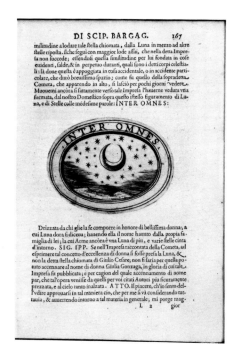

LERE ("Better to die than break faith"), with the device of a small cross held out by an arm, was used by Scipione Gonzaga, the son of Carlo, Marchese of Gazzuolo, who protected Torquato Tasso, and founded the Paduan *Accademia degli Eterei*. The same motto, illustrated by an iron collar, is attributed by Giovio to a member of the Orsini family. When Cardinal Ercole Gonzaga died (1563), Scipione Gonzaga, who had benefited by his protection, adopted the device of the ship being rowed with lowered sails to signify PROPRIIS NITAR i.e. he would try to get on by his own strength; hence in the *Accademia degli Eterei* he had taken the name of *L'Affannato* (the Breathless one).

Another Gonzaga cardinal, Sigismondo (1469-1525) after signing the surrender of Bologna to the Papacy (June 1512) on condition that the citizens could retain their ancient republican privileges, adopted the device of the weeping crocodile (CROCODILI LACRYMAE) because Pope Leo X, whose election he had promoted, did not respect the terms of the surrender; the device was intended to blame those who conceal evil intentions under appearances of love. Typotius (who connects Alessandro Gonzaga with the device of the croco-

dile) records another device of Sigismondo indicating his debt to God: SIC VIVO ("Thus I live"): plants in a landscape which owe their life to the sun.

Vespasiano, son of Luigi Gonzaga (Rodomonte) was appointed commander in chief of the Italian infantry in the Spanish army in 1544; he was the first Duke of Sabbioneta, and, irked by his dependence on the Emperor, adopted the device of a muzzled dog with the words E IN LIBERTÀ MI GODO ("And I take pleasure in liberty"). He also adopted the Horatian motto (*Od.*, III, 10, 11-12) FERIUNT SUMMOS ("They hit the high"): the thunderbolt hitting the top of a mountain, to intimate that only God could curb him; another interpretation is that the thunderbolt hits only those who hold high office and enjoy great fortunes, and leaves the humble in peace (this device is found in most of the treatises). Vespasiano's warlike character is also illustrated by the device of the hedgehog with the motto DECUS ET TUTAMEN IN ARMIS ("Arms are my glory and my protection"): when the hedgehog is attacked by dogs, it contracts itself into a spiky ball. Another device was more aggressive: three thunderbolts with the motto HIS IMPII TERRENTUR ("The ungodly are terrified by these"). Vespasiano illustrated yet another device IUVAT EMPTA LABORE GLORIA ("Glory bought by struggle helps"), with the image of a camel, a hard-working animal.

PRINCIPAL SOURCES

P. Giovio, *Dialogo dell'Imprese militari et amorose*, Lyon 1574; Gabriele Simeoni, *Le Sentenziose Imprese, et Dialogo del Symeone*, Lyon 1560; Girolamo Ruscelli, *Le Imprese illustri*, Venice 1583; Scipione Bargagli, *Dell'Imprese*, Venice 1594; Camillo Camilli, *Imprese illustri di diversi*, Venice 1586; Silvestro Pietrasanta, *De Symbolis Heroicis Libri IX*, Antwerp 1634; B. Pittoni, *Imprese di diversi Prencipi, Duchi, etc.*, Venice 1566; Jacobus Typotius, *Symbola Divina et Humana… Symbola varia diversorum principum*, Prague 1601-03; Jacopo Gelli, *Motti, Divise, Imprese di famiglie e personaggi italiani*, Milan 1916.

For earlier but longlasting Gonzaga devices not recorded by the above authors of books on devices, see essays above for their use on ceramics, also Cat. 127-138, and for their use on medals etc. see Cat. 13-16, 40, 46, 62, 83-91 etc. Under BIBLIOGRAPHY see Gerola, 1918, 1930; Meroni, 1966; Mumford, 1979.

Federico II Gonzaga as a Patron of Painting
by Charles Hope

As a patron of painting Federico, fifth Marquis and first Duke of Mantua, was probably more enthusiastic and certainly more influential than any other member of the Gonzaga family. In recent times his activity has been somewhat overshadowed by that of his mother Isabella d'Este, but by comparison her commissions were insignificant in scale or importance. Although she may well have played some part in awakening his interest in painting as a child, Federico's later taste for large decorative projects without any strongly moralistic content owes much more to the example of the earlier marquises, notably to Ludovico and to his own father Francesco, who certainly promoted even if he did not necessarily commission the *Triumphs of Caesar*, or to the recent d'Este dukes of Ferrara.

In his childhood Federico spent several years in Rome at a time when Michelangelo was painting the ceiling of the Sistine Chapel and Raphael the *Stanza della Segnatura* and the *Galatea*. These masterpieces, more than anything available in Mantua, formed his taste. In the first years after he succeeded to the title in 1519 he had to rely on Costa and Leonbruno, the old-fashioned artists favoured by Isabella, but already in 1521 he tried to recruit Raphael's best pupil, Giulio Romano. Giulio was finally induced to move to Mantua in 1524, thanks to the efforts of Federico's ambassador Baldassare Castiglione and of Pietro Aretino, who had just achieved a certain notoriety by publishing a series of very obscene sonnets to which Giulio had provided equally pornographic illustrations. In the same year Aretino acted as Federico's agent in his attempts to acquire Raphael's celebrated portrait of Leo X and to commission a picture from Sebastiano del Piombo, which the marquis specified should not be "to do with saints, but something pleasant and beautiful to look at". Three years later, Aretino, by this time living in Venice, was urging on Federico the claims of yet another outstanding artist, Titian. These episodes are all indicative of Federico's attitudes as a patron, for Aretino not only took an openly hedonistic delight in painting and sculpture, he was also to become the most sophisticated writer on art of his generation, and the first unreservedly to accord it a status equal to that of literature.

From the time of his arrival in Mantua until his death there in 1546 Giulio Romano dominated the artistic life of the city even more completely than Mantegna had done two generations before. His role as Federico's principal painter, architect and designer was to create a total environment which would proclaim the wealth and sophistication of his patron. Two major projects still bear witness to the success of his efforts, the Palazzo del Te, a lavish villa just outside the city constructed and decorated in two stages between 1527 and 1534, and the *Appartamento di Troia* in the old Palazzo Ducale, with its equally elaborate decoration executed between 1536 and 1538. Both have been much restored, but the quality of the paintings must always have been uneven, since the scale of these undertakings forced Giulio to rely extensively on pupils. This was not only normal practice at the period, it also fitted with his own inclinations as a painter. His talent, as Vasari recognized, lay primarily in the fertility of his invention rather than in the sustained labour needed to realize his ideas in perfectly executed pictures.

Today we value the latter quality more highly than the former, and in the case of Giulio's work it is our loss. The label of mannerism which is so often applied to his paintings is itself a further obstacle, implying as it does that his style was just a stereotyped and "mannered" distortion of Raphael's. Even the more positive connotation of virtuosity is suspect. This quality was, however, central to Giulio's achievement, and it was in his mastery of draughtsmanship, and particularly of its most difficult aspect, foreshortening, that he made his greatest contribution to the figurative vocabulary of European painting. His style too, a subtle and faithful interpretation of ancient Roman models, now seems affected only because Raphael's equally selective but different version of the antique has become canonical. In his own day Giulio's classicism, which Aretino aptly described as "anciently modern and modernly ancient", certainly possessed an authenticity which we can recognize only by a conscious effort.

As befitted its function as a villa, the themes of the frescoes in the Palazzo del Te were taken predominantly from classical mythology. The two most elaborate rooms were the *Sala di Psiche*, with explicitly erotic subjects, and the *Sala dei Giganti*, designed simply to overwhelm visitors with the brilliance of its illusionism. In the Palazzo Ducale, by contrast, more serious

74

81. *Titian,* Federico Gonzaga, Fifth Marquis and First
Duke of Mantua *(Museo del Prado, Madrid).*

themes from ancient history were preferred. Attempts
have recently been made to find subtle allusions to Federico and his political ambitions even in the mythological frescoes of the Palazzo del Te, but these are surely
misguided. It was his role as patron that was emphasized here, and made explicit by means of inscriptions
and personal devices. Federico's fame was thus to be
assured by the fact that he employed an artist of the
stature of Giulio and provided him with an unparalleled
opportunity to display his genius. In this his hopes
were fulfilled, for these paintings soon became a model
for palace decoration throughout Italy, and even in
France and Germany.

Federico's patronage of Giulio, or his purchase in 1535
of no less than a hundred and twenty Flemish landscapes, does not mean that in art he was only interested
in lavish schemes of decoration or was indifferent to
excellence of technique. His efforts to obtain individual
works by Raphael, Sebastiano and, on several later
occasions, Michelangelo demonstrate his desire for
masterpieces by the outstanding artists of his day; the
same is true of his contacts with two other great painters, Correggio and Titian. The only pictures by Correggio certainly acquired by him were four canvases showing the amorous adventures of Jupiter, now distributed
between Rome, Berlin and Vienna. These were apparently intended to decorate a room in one of Federico's
residences, but they were soon given to the Emperor
Charles V, presumably in 1530 or 1532. Isabella d'Este
had also commissioned two pictures from Correggio;
but it is significant that these obscure moral allegories,
clearly painted to her precise specifications and now in
Paris (Pl. 52, 53), were altogether less suited to the
artist's talents than the straightforward erotic themes
preferred by her son.

With Titian too Federico was careful to choose subjects
which accorded with the painter's own inclinations.
This sensible attitude enabled him to acquire the largest
collection of pictures by the Venetian artist anywhere
in Italy, at a time when Titian could afford to take his
pick of available commissions. Federico first employed
Titian in 1523, for a portrait, but on a regular basis only
from about 1528. Over the next twelve years he acquired some thirty works from the artist, only a handful of
which still survive. Most were portraits, among them

the marvellous one of Federico himself (Pl. 81), now in
Madrid, and the eleven *Roman Emperors* (Cat. 168-179);
there were also a number of devotional compositions,
such as the *Madonna and Child with St. Catherine and a
rabbit* (Cat. 155), and at least one mythological subject.
A few of these pictures were sent by Federico as gifts to
important political figures, but most were for his own
pleasure. His relationship with Titian, which was marked by exceptional cordiality on both sides, was of the
greatest importance to the artist in bringing his work to
the notice of Charles V and his court.

Federico was a major patron of painting for little more
than fifteen years. His activity during this period was
matched by none of his predecessors or successors in
Mantua, indeed by none of his contemporaries elsewhere in Italy. Although the duchy had no native artists
of any significance, through his personal initiative alone
he made it into one of the major artistic centres of his
day.

PRINCIPAL SOURCES:
See under BIBLIOGRAPHY: Golzio, 1936; Gould, 1976; Hartt, 1958; Luzio,
1913; Marani and Perina, 1961; Verheyen, 1977; Wethey, 1969-75.

82.   *Castello and Ponte San Giorgio, showing former Palazzina Paleologa, Mantua.*

83.   *Former Palazzina Paleologa, Mantua.*

"That rare Italian Master…"
Giulio Romano, Court Architect, Painter and Impresario
by E. H. Gombrich

Thanks to the copiousness of the Gonzaga archives more is known about the day-to-day activities of Giulio Romano during the fifteen years he served Federico Gonzaga than about those of any other Renaissance master[1]. The appendix to Frederick Hartt's standard monograph on the artist[2] (here abbreviated as H.) lists and summarises 247 documents the large majority of which refer to this period. Some ninety of them, dealing with the construction and decoration of the Palazzo del Te – the best preserved and most conspicuous of Giulio's works – have also been listed and supplemented in the more recent book by Egon Verheyen[3] on that building. Further archival gleanings relating to other enterprises were published in a volume commemorating the four hundred and fiftieth anniversary of the artist's arrival in Mantua[4]. Thus it would be a work of supererogation to review this evidence once more; all that is intended here is to convey an impression to the reader of the outer circumstances of the life of an artist who enjoyed an extraordinary fame among his contemporaries and received the final accolade of the mention in Shakespeare's *The Winter's Tale* quoted in the title of this essay and discussed in its conclusion.

There are several earlier witnesses to this fame, most of all Giulio's biography which Vasari included in the first edition of his *Vite* of 1550, an invaluable source, since Vasari had been the guest of the artist in his house in Mantua in 1541 and thus speaks as an eye witness. We also find several reflections of Giulio's high reputation in the letters of Pietro Aretino and in one of his plays, in the architectural writings of Sebastiano Serlio and in Benvenuto Cellini's autobiography[5].

Giulio certainly had a splendid start in life as an assistant, and probably the favourite helpmate of Raphael in Rome. Vasari, who was reckless about dates but more reliable about other matters, says that Giulio was born in 1492 and came to Raphael's workshop *da putto*, as a little boy. Since Raphael's activities in the *Stanze* of the Vatican only began around 1509 Giulio would on Vasari's reckoning have been seventeen at the time, surely not a "little boy". Luckily we need not bother our heads over this contradiction since Giulio's age at the time of his death in 1546 is given in Mantua as forty-seven, which means that he was born in 1499 and was no more than ten at the time when Raphael started to

work in Rome. These were also the years when young Federico Gonzaga was at the court of Julius II as a hostage and it is tempting to speculate whether the two might have met when Raphael painted the prince[6]. They were roughly of the same age. It so happens that the question of Giulio's age during the years of his apprenticeship is of more than biographical relevance. The knowledge that he – like most painters – started work as a boy is relevant also to the assessment of Raphael's own development. Too many critics and art historians of the past who relied on Vasari's information blamed Giulio for any feature of Raphael's *œuvre* which did not fit in with their pre-conceived idea of the divine Urbinate. However precocious Giulio may have been, he cannot have taken such an active part in the workshop before the very last years of Raphael's career. In any case Giulio's name only turns up in the documents after Raphael's death at Easter 1520 when the fights, intrigues and squabbles for the succession began. Raphael seems to have been able to hold his large team together – and Giulio was to show later that he had profited from this lesson – but as early as 17 June 1520 we hear that Giulio and Giovanni da Udine quarrelled "like madmen" over the completion of the Villa Madama in Rome (H. 23). At the same time Sebastiano del Piombo, backed by Michelangelo, tried to secure the main commission, the decoration of the *Sala di Costantino*, but Giulio and Penni won in the end, claiming – possibly correctly – that they were in possession of drawings by Raphael for this project.

No doubt Giulio had a right to claim a special relationship with Raphael who had made him his heir. The document recording the marriage between Lorenzetto (a sculptor from Raphael's circle) and Giulio's sister Girolama, mentions that this union had been Raphael's wish (H. 34, 35).

What was decisive for Giulio's future, however, was the fact that Raphael's patron and friend Baldassare Castiglione took an interest in the master's successors. He saw to it that the sum still owing for Raphael's last commission, the *Transfiguration*, was paid out to Giulio and his companion Francesco Penni (H. 30). As early as 1521 he also reported to Federico Gonzaga that the two would like to enter his service after the work in the *Sala di Costantino* was completed (H. 29). Some fifteen months later Giulio was paid for a model he had sent to Mantua at the Marchese's request for a new wing of the castle of Marmirolo (now vanished) (H. 36), and the contacts never broke off. It is unlikely, however, that the further delay in making the move to Mantua was to Giulio's detriment. He must have used his time to good purpose to continue Raphael's activities in recording the ancient treasures of Rome. He himself had a sizeable collection which he gave to Federico; he was also consulted as an authority on ancient sculpture and engraved stones, and his subsequent work in Mantua amply testifies to the degree to which he had mastered and assimilated the idiom of Roman art.

There is a pleasing glimpse of Giulio's life in Rome in Cellini's autobiography[7], where we are told of a banquet to which all members of a circle of artists were asked on condition that they brought a beautiful courtesan with them; the prize went to Cellini who had dressed up a young man as a girl. Giulio, who was of the party, is recorded to have been deep in conversation with Michelangelo da Siena on serious and profound topics. There is no reason to doubt the fact that Giulio's existence in Rome was imperilled by a notorious scandal. He had made a series of pornographic drawings representing various forms of sexual intercourse which had been engraved by Marc Antonio Raimondi and published together with a sequence of descriptive sonnets by Pietro Aretino who was probably the initiator, though he later claimed that he had merely commented on Giulio's inventions[8]. According to Vasari[9] it was only the engraver who got it in the neck, but Giulio might have found it prudent to remove himself from the scene, having been promised for some time a safe haven in Mantua.

When he arrived there in 1524, aged twenty-five, Lorenzo Leonbruno held the position of principal artist of the Gonzaga court. It was he who directed the building and decoration of the castle of Marmirolo over which the Marchese had consulted the Roman artist. There is a pathetic letter of Leonbruno's which shows that he had reason to fear such a rival[10]. Asking Federico humbly for a favour, he writes that receiving it would "give me new life and would so illuminate my intellect that I shall create new marvels (*bizarrie*) such as have never been seen before". Alas, when it came to the invention of *bizarrie* for the pleasure and entertainment of the court nobody was likely to be a match to Giulio Romano. The documents do not tell us, however, how Giulio was employed during the first years of his stay. The first record, dating from more than a year after his arrival (22 November 1525) mentions a design for a *saliera* of silver (H. 58). A few months later (23 January 1526) we hear of three drawings made by Giulio for Isabella d'Este (H. 63). In February of that year we hear for the first time of work being carried out for the Palazzo del Te (H. 65).

On March 16 of that year Federico Gonzaga, in a letter only recently published[11], asks *Julio Romano, Vicario della corte nostra* jointly with another official to attend to the repairs of the ruined walls of the castle of Bigarello. But only on the 5 June of that year did he receive the letter patent by the Marchese making him a citizen of Mantua (H. 68). We may thus assume that the designs Giulio had submitted for the Palazzo del Te and the aptitude he had shown in organising the building works were responsible for his rapid rise. One week after his appointment as a citizen he is allocated a house, the document describing him as a famous painter (H. 69). On August 31, that is some two years after his arrival, Federico signed a letter patent conferring on Giulio the vacant office of Vicar of the Court and Superior General of all the Gonzaga buildings inside and outside Mantua because "We have had ample experience of the ability and integrity of our most beloved citizen and painter" (H. 70). Soon afterwards Giulio was also given the income from the state sawmill, and other privileges followed. On November 20 he was also made "Superior of the Streets of Mantua" in other words city architect, stating that he has shown himself no less worthy in architecture than in painting (H. 73). About that time (15 October 1526) the Marchese sent a note to Giulio: "Messer Giulio, one of my bitches has died when having litter and we want to have her buried in a beautiful marble tomb with an epitaph. We thus wish you to make two designs which should be beautiful to be executed in marble and once you have made them send them or bring them to me as quickly as you can. *Bene valete*" (H. 72).

It is the first note in that voluminous correspondence

which gives us such a perfect picture of the master's position and of the character and expectations of his employer. However much the Marchese may have been fond of art and of splendour this was only one of his interests or passions. Not that he was an aristocratic barbarian. As is shown in another essay in this catalogue he was a discerning and exacting patron of painting who always insisted on receiving the best that was available. Even so it is likely that for him the chase and all that went with it meant even more than art. His famous stud, his innumerable splendid hounds and dogs, his hunting hawks, among which he had as many favourites as among his horses and dogs, were immensely important to him. To record these favourites for posterity, to paint their portraits on the walls of his castles, to design tombs for them seemed to him a worthy use of art. Nor is it an accident that the Palazzo del Te, which now began to occupy the mind of this impatient prince, started as a monumentalized stable. In Giulio, Federico had found an artist to whom (in Vasari's words) "one only had to mention an idea for him to understand and draw it".

When Benvenuto Cellini came to Mantua after the sack of Rome "through a world full of war and pestilence" he found Giulio there living like a lord and building a splendid work for his master[12]. A large team of artists, craftsmen and workmen had been assembled under Giulio's direction who carried out his plans and ideas

and were payed out by him. The documents explain in detail the division of labour between the various assistants, builders like Maestro Battista (who was later to succeed Giulio in office), the painters Rinaldo Mantuano (who gave Giulio a good deal of trouble), Benedetto Pagni, Fermo da Caravaggio, Primaticcio (who earned his spurs in stucco work at Mantua and later acquired fame in France), and Recanati (the gilder); gilding was an expensive enterprise since genuine gold leaf was used, and the Marchese's treasurers were not always happy to supply it. In 1528 Gianfrancesco Penni, Giulio's erstwhile partner in Rome, also appears in the documents (H. 95) but he does not seem to have enjoyed his subordinate position and soon left.

But this large team, although kept at work continuously, never satisfied the Marchese's impatience. The way he urged and pressed the painter to complete the work testifies to his interest. Most of the many letters we have from Giulio's hand are responses to these constant threats and cajolings. They show him as the perfect courtier always compliant and resourceful in finding excuses and making fresh promises. "If it pleases you, make them lock me in that hall till it is finished" he writes on one occasion, "but I cannot do anything against God's will". (31 August 1528) (H. 108).

The conditions under which the artist had to work can be seen to get worse with the number of commissions he received. The visit of Charles V to Mantua in 1530 necessitated designs for sumptuous pageants[13], and when in 1531 Federico, having been made a Duke, was to marry Margherita Paleologo from Casale her reception again demanded an enormous expenditure of effort and money which must have strained the resources of the court to the utmost. The officials responsible for these multifarious enterprises frequently express their despair and pessimism to their absent Lord. "I cannot do anything but to urge and to hurry and I also urge Messer Giulio Romano" writes the majordomo Calandra on 3 October "but truly I see a chaos"[14]. He suggests that the Duke should write fierce letters to Giulio. He should enlist more workers and pay them better for otherwise the work would not be finished in time. "Giulio Romano replies to me it will be done, it will be well finished in time, he can say so in his position but I see very little order" (6 October 1531, H. 117). Giulio in his turn has to find new ways of reassuring his master. "Her Excellency the Marchesa" – Isabella d'Este – had inspected it all and had liked it, he himself would not be found wanting, but he was short of money, of lime, of workmen, of timber, of carts and most of all of dry weather.

Even so the little *Palazzina* (Pl. 82-83), specially erected next to the Castello for the new Duchess and linked to it by a covered bridge, somehow was ready in time, richly decorated with armorial bearings and frescoes. Maybe the haste with which it was completed also accounts for its ultimate demolition; the derelict building was considered unsafe and pulled down in 1899[15]. The only surviving record of the pretty interiors which were prepared under such pressure are a few inadequate photographs taken at the time (Pl. 84-85), some of the better preserved rooms – not all dating from Giulio's time – were taken down and subsequently reconstructed within the Palace. Fredrick Hartt only illustrated one of them, and they have been neglected in the literature. No major claim can be made for their artistic merit, but like everything Giulio touched, they testify to his fertile imagination and to the skill with which he directed such enterprises.

Meanwhile, of course, work on the Palazzo del Te had to go on, indeed it was only a year or two later that it reached its grizzly culmination in the famous or notorious *Sala dei Giganti* (Pl. 88). Around 1536 new plans were put in train for transforming various suites in the Palace, notably the *Appartamento di Troia*, which was, amongst other things, to house the series of *Caesars* commissioned from Titian. The documents tell the same story of frustrations and delays but also of ultimate achievement. Giulio did not only have to cope with the whims and ambitions of his exacting employer but also with the hardships of the climate. Placed between lakes and swamps as a fortress guarding the Po Valley, Mantua had to pay for its relative security by endemic malaria.

When Benvenuto Cellini had contracted the fever shortly after his arrival he cursed "Mantua, its Lord and anyone who felt like staying there", an outburst which was not well received[16]. Giulio, who seems to have constantly fallen ill, and whose assistants and servants also suffered from fever, stayed on. He had to fight the wearying battles with the Duke's treasurers to finance more gilding, he had to direct untrained and unwilling work-forces during floods and incessant rain, while assistants sometimes stole his drawings or carried out his ideas so badly that he lost all pleasure in his work. Nevertheless he never tired of suggesting new ideas, of preparing new rooms for the Duke's residences inside and outside Mantua, of making designs for castles, gardens, tapestries, majolica, tableware, costumes, stage sets and pageants for festivals and funerals, still finding time to work on his paintings and to make drawings for engravers and sculptors.

At least one of his letters referring to work in the Castello may here be quoted *in extenso* to illustrate his trials and triumphs as an impresario[17].

"Most illustrious and excellent Lord,

Count Brunoro has reproached me for being negligent in informing your Excellency about the progress of the building works. So far I have left this to Messer Zaffardo who told me that your Excellency had commissioned him to advise you from time to time how the works proceeded. It is quite true that I was unwilling, because things did not go as I would have wished, for in the first week I was short of the gold from coins and of lime and the captain would not lend me any. Still in the end he gave me a little and so I put the Castello in good order: Messer Agostino will have vaulted the two rooms in the next week, that is the first floor and he will also have finished the garden wall and I promised him to pay him from my own money so that he could hurry and your Excellency could be satisfied and find the garden green within two weeks.

Underneath I was not able to work on the moat because of the height of the water level, even so they began vaulting and the work will go on.

As to the painted room, Anselmo will have finished painting within ten days and then the gilding will proceed using five hundred pieces of gold every week, for Messer Carlo has promised me not to fail supplying the coins for so large a sum. The little room next to the room is gilded but the falcons have not been painted. Six are still outstanding and as soon as I have them I shall have them done. I have given instruction to begin work on the wainscot of walnut wood to the marquet-

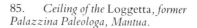
ry workers the de la Mola and other masters who deal with wooden panelling. The two cornices to go into the room are finished as far as the woodwork is concerned and I have completed one and this is where I shall put the horses which are being done, for there are still three of them missing which will go into the smaller places and I have already prepared the frames and the canvas.

And if it pleases your Excellency to advise and instruct which horses and which falcons should be painted, they will be made immediately, but I would think it should be horses which are not too large and should be brightly coloured, if there is no shortage of the necessary.

There is nothing, however, which will make me delay except the quantity of gold which will go on to the vault and further down to match the beauty of the vault.

I have also made two places ready to accommodate the lights so that they should not smoke and I have commissioned them to begin work on the mantlepiece of stone which will be the most beautiful so far made.

That other white little room will be finished within ten days and then they will immediately go to the next. As to the storage shed, it will be finished within a week but it will be necessary to spend a little on the chimney or else the rats would use it as a ladder to get into the dovecote. However I have found a good remedy and it would have been finished earlier if it had not been for the rain and for being unable to get the timber.

As to Marmirolo, more could already have been done if the foreman had not left; and since there was nobody to do the plastering and erecting the scaffolding Maestro Luca spent a few days there in vain; then I made the foreman return and Maestro Luca has finished two beautiful landscapes, and I have tidied up things well there for there is another painter there who is mean-

while doing the cornices and the decorations and I have given him instructions to paint the War in Tunis according to the account of that man from Cyprus.

As to the new rooms between the two gardens, they will be begun on Monday and there is a clear instruction to complete the fireplaces, to construct them and to do two ceilings above to the mezzanine, to make the doors and windows and the frames for the glass; Messer Carlo had begun to give me the money for this and on that Monday I shall send Anselmo to have the panelling varnished in the rooms and in the hall. I have done my very best to satisfy your Excellency with more zeal than has in fact been apparent. It seemed to me better to be able to make my apologies and I only will say so much that if I am short of money for the job I shall freely spend my own, little as I have of it. I do so for the favour of your Excellency to whom I humbly recommend myself and kiss your hands.

Mantua, 10th June 1536.

Your Excellency's humble servant,

Giulio Romano".

A modern reader of this letter would hardly guess that its humble writer was by that time a very celebrated artist. The Duke of Ferrara asked for his services to learn of "certain of his ideas" (7 April 1537, H. 195), but the Duke only reluctantly gave him leave. Pietro Aretino invited him to Venice (H. 239), the Directors of the Works of San Petronio in Bologna commissioned him to design a façade for the still unfinished church (H. 241 b), the Congregation of the Church of the Steccata, Parma, approached him (H. 224-233) and so did the Bishop of Verona for whom he designed the frescoes for the apse of the cathedral in 1534. He also served his master on these journeys. He purchased Indian peacocks and took over the busts Federico had commissioned from the sculptor Alfonso Lombardo (H. 202).

He had meanwhile married (2 June 1529), and had three children, two girls Criseide and Virginia and a boy called Raffaello, after his master; he lived in a splendid house which he had built himself and which is still partly preserved. It was there that he entertained Vasari on his visit and showed him his rich collection some of which – like Dürer's self-portrait – he had inherited from Raphael. Even the tone of the Duke's letters chang-

ed markedly in the last few years; *Maestro Julio nostro charissimo* (our dearest Master Giulio) is now the form of address (H. 222).

Federico's sudden death in 1540, at a time when further ambitious projects were in train, must have been a shattering blow. The Duke's widow, Margherita Paleologo does not seem to have had either the means or the wish to continue her husband's patronage. The only letter we have from her in which Giulio's activities are mentioned is a negative one. She writes, on 12 October 1541, from Casale to her Majordomo, Carlo Nuvoloni: "I do not remember well if I have talked to you about the plan of fitting out the chapel which I discussed with Messer Giulio; I herewith tell you not to let him put his hand to this work on the interior before I have given you further instructions" (H. 234).

Frederick Hartt, who mentions this letter in his monograph, suggests that it may refer to a *Chiesa del Crocifisso* mentioned elsewhere in the documents but the answer from Nuvoloni, dated 16 October (H. 235) rules this out. He speaks of the "Chapel of the Castello" and reports that he had never heard of it from the Duchess but Giulio had asked whether she had left any instructions for money to be given to the workers for this purpose. Messer Ferdinando also had told him that he was very surprised that Giulio had been given this instruction, if this were the case he would certainly have the money ready. But since he had heard nothing, Giulio would not be allowed to proceed.

As it stands this exchange of letters leaves us guessing whether the work in question was ever carried out. Even so it draws attention to the existence of a chapel in the Castello which was ready for fitting out (*acconciare*) suggesting that the actual structure had been completed. There is in fact a chapel in the Castello which bears all the marks of Giulio's late style but which has never to my knowledge been described or illustrated (Pl. 86). Though small in dimension (6.70 × 3.45 m.), it has an elaborately articulated interior with Corinthian pilasters and rich entablatures skilfully adjusted to an irregular shape, suggesting that here, as in other of his ecclesiastical commissions, Giulio had to adapt his design to an existing structure.

It was in fact as a church architect that Giulio now rose to fame during the last six years of his life when the

Duke's brother, Cardinal Ercole Gonzaga, took over the direction of the state. He commissioned Giulio to remodel the church of the monastery San Benedetto al Polirone and what is left of it inspires much respect for Giulio's architectural skill and tact[18]. Early in 1545 Giulio was also asked to submit a detailed plan for the renovation of the Duomo of Mantua. We do not know how much of this plan was carried out in the few remaining months of Giulio's life, but there can be little doubt that the highly original and successful transformation of a Romanesque interior into a splendid Renaissance building still bears the mark of his genius. It was at this juncture that Giulio received the invitation to take over the building of Saint Peter's in Rome after the death of Antonio da Sangallo[19]. Who knows whether it would have been crowned with Michelangelo's cupola if he had accepted? That he hesitated to shoulder such a burden is understandable. Maybe his health played a part in this decision. As early as 24 December 1537 (H. 199) he complained in a letter that his eyesight suffered so much from endless bleedings and drugs that he could only work with difficulty by candlelight. In February 1545 according to Aretino rumour had spread that he was dead. In the summer of the next year we hear that he suffered from fever and stomach-ache but there was no need for worry (H. 242). However, on 15 September 1546 he writes to Ferrante Gonzaga in a

letter published by Jane Martineau below (introduction to Cat. 188-192), that he expects his illness to get worse. Six weeks laters on 1 November 1546, the Register of Deaths shows the entry "Died today, Messer Giulio Romano di Pippi, Overseer of the Ducal Buildings... of fever... aged 47" (H. 244).

The letter from the Cardinal, dated 7 November, to his brother Ferrante (H. 245) merits reprinting in full as a fitting memorial.

"The most grievous loss of our Giulio Romano hurts me so much that I seem to have lost my right hand. I would not have cared to inform your Excellency so quickly if I did not think that the later one hears of such a loss the less there was to be done, particularly since he was engaged in the purification of the water.

Like those who seek always to extract something good from any evil, I tell myself that the death of that rare man will at least have helped me by ridding me of the appetite for building, for silverware, for paintings, etc., for in fact I would not have the heart to commission anything of this kind without the designs of that fine mind; hence as soon as a few things, for which I possess his designs, have been finished I want to bury all my desires with him; as I said. May God give him peace, which I hope he certainly will, for I knew him as a good and very pure man, as far as the world is concerned and I hope also in the eyes of God. With tears in my eyes I can never have enough of speaking of his achievements, and yet I must stop since it has pleased Him who governs all to put an end to his life".

It is well known that Giulio Romano is the only artist of the Renaissance whose name occurs in Shakespeare's works. The passage from Act V. Scene 2 of *The Winter's Tale* may here be reproduced in the spelling of the First Folio:

"The Princesse hearing of her Mothers Statue (which is in the keeping of *Paulina*) a Peece many yeeres in doing, and now newly perform'd, by that rare Italian Master, *Iulio Romano*, who (had he himselfe Eternitie, and could put Breath into his Worke) would beguile Nature of her Custome, so perfectly he is her Ape: He so neere to *Hermione*, hath done *Hermione*, that they say one would speake to her, and stand in hope of answer".

It has long been observed that the eulogy here applied

to Giulio as a rival of nature may well derive from the use which was made of this formula by one of Vasari's humanist helpers who supplied him with a ficticious epitaph of the master at the end of his *Vita* of 1550[20]: "Jupiter saw sculpted and painted bodies breathe and the dwellings of mortals equal heaven through the skill of Giulio Romano. Hence he was angered and having summoned a council of all the Gods carried him off from the earth, since he could not tolerate being vanquished or equalled by an earthborn man..."

Whoever wrote these lines, skilfully fused two motives appropriate to the artist. The first stems from the real epitaph of Giulio's master Raphael in the Pantheon in Rome, penned by Bembo: "This is Raphael's tomb, when he lived it was mother nature's fear to be vanquished by him, and when he died, to die too". The second, of course, alludes to Giulio's most famous work, the *Sala dei Giganti*, which, after all, represents the theme of Jove calling the council of the Gods to punish the giants for attempting to rival heaven.

If Shakespeare had seen the poem, moreover, he might well have inferred from it that Giulio was a sculptor whose statues deceptively resembled life (*Videbat Iuppiter corpora sculpta pictaque spirare*).

There is no need, therefore, to fall in with Frederick Hartt's ingenious proposal to link Shakespeare's reference to a Bolognese master of painted stucco reliefs men-

tioned in a document, who may merely have been a namesake of our Giulio Romano[21].

What appears not to have been noticed in any case is the fact that *The Winter's Tale* is not the first play in which high praise is lavished on Giulio Romano[22]. A precedent was set by Pietro Aretino's comedy *Il Marescalco* which was published in Giulio's lifetime in 1533[23]. Aretino was fond of boosting the reputation of his friends by having them mentioned on the stage. *Il Marescalco* is set in Mantua and features among its *dramatis personae* a comic pedant somewhat reminiscent of Holofernes in *Love's Labours Lost*. In Act. IV, Scene 5 of the comedy one Messer Jacopo addresses the Pedant thus: "Master,

let us walk as far as San Bastiano, in other words to the Te, to see if Giulio Romano will have unveiled some divine painting". *Pedant*: "Let us proceed. Oh what fine structure is that palace which has issued from the architecture of his exquisite model: he has imitated Vitruvius, the ancient perspectivist". (*Jacopo*: "*Andiamo, maestro, in fine a San Bastiano, volli dire al Te, che forse Julio Romano averà scoperto qualche istoria divina*". *Pedante*: "*Eamus: o che bella macchina è il palazzio che da la architettura del suo modelliculo è uscito: Vitruvio prospettivo prisco ha imitato*". Clearly the passage served Aretino in two ways. He praised his friend for the work that was in progress at the time, and he made ample fun of the

88a.   *Giulio Romano, Drawing of a giant (Cat. 167).*

affected jargon used by the pedant in pretending to be a connoisseur of architecture.

In Act V Scene 3 the Pedant also wishes to show off his knowledge of painters and painting and again includes Giulio: "If (we refer to) painters there is Titian, the rival of nature and indeed her master, and certainly there will be the most divine Fra Sebastiano of Venice (Sebastiano del Piombo). And maybe Julio Romano nursling of the court and of the Urbinate Raphael. (*Pedante: Si pictoribus, un Tiziano emulus naturae immo magister, sarà certo fra Sebastiano de Venetia divinissimo. E forse Julio Romano curiae, e de lo Urbinate Rafaello alumno*). The conventional praise Shakespeare was to use later is here applied to Titian rather than Giulio.

What makes these precedents particularly suggestive is the fact that *Il Marescalco* was reprinted in London in 1588, together with three other comedies by Aretino, by that busy Elizabethan printer John Wolf[24]. Thus not more than twenty-three years separate that edition and the first performance of Shakespeare's play in around 1609/10. Any member of the theatrical world whose curiosity was aroused by Aretino's references might have come across the eulogy in Vasari's edition of 1550 and combined them into the image of "that rare Italian Master" – or could it have been Shakespeare himself?

Notes

1.   This essay is based on the introductory chapter of my doctoral thesis *Giulio Romano als Architekt* submitted to the University of Vienna in the spring of 1933. The chapter dealing with the Palazzo del Te and other extracts were published under the title "Zum Werke Giulio Romanos" in the *Jahrbuch der Kunsthistorischen Sammlungen in Wien*, N.F. VIII, 1934, and IX, 1935.

2.   F. Hartt, *Giulio Romano*, New Haven, 1958, henceforward abbreviated as H.

3.   E. Verheyen, *The Palazzo del Te in Mantua, Images of Love and Politics*, Baltimore, 1977. See also my review in the *Burlington Magazine* CXXII, January 1980.

4.   *Studi su Giulio Romano, Omaggio all'Artista nel 450' della venuta a Mantova, (1524-1974)*, Accademia Polironiana, San Benedetto Po, 1975.

5.   For a survey of these testimonials see P. Carpeggiani, "La fortuna critica di Giulio Romano architetto" in *Studi su Giulio Romano...*, 1975, op. cit.

6.   J. Cartwright, *Isabella d'Este*, London, 1903, II, pp. 53, 72-74.

7.   B. Cellini, *La vita scritta da lui medesimo*, Chapter XXX.

8.   P. Aretino, *Il Primo libro delle lettere*, 1537, Nos. IX, CCCXXI.

9.   Vasari, ed. Milanesi, V, p. 395 ff; Life of Marcantonio Bolognese.

10.   P. Carpi, "Giulio Romano ai servigi di Federico II Gonzaga", *Atti e Memorie della R. Accademia Virgiliana di Mantova*, Mantua, 1920, Doc. I.

11.   *Studi su Giulio Romano...* 1975, op. cit., p. 44.

12.   B. Cellini, *La vita*, op. cit., Chapter XL.

13.   A contemporary description of the decorations on the processional road, designed by Giulio, is translated in F. Hartt, op. cit., pp. 269-70.

14.   C. d'Arco, *Delle Arti e degli Artefici di Mantova*, Mantua, 1857, No. 147; this letter is not listed in Hartt.

15.   The only detailed account is in the reports on the restoration carried out under the direction of Clinio Cottafavi, *Bollettino d'Arte*, IX, 1929/30, pp. 276 ff.

16.   See above note 12.

17.   The full text is printed in the article by P. Carpi, 1920, op. cit. I should like to thank Dr David Chambers and Dr Laura Lepschy for help in the elucidation of some obscure terms.

18.   P. Piva, "Giulio Romano e la Chiesa Abbaziale di Polirone", an important paper printed in *Studi su Giulio Romano...*, 1975, op. cit.

19.   We only have Vasari's word for this, but since he reported it in his first edition of 1550 less than four years after the event (which must have been public knowledge) there is no reason to doubt it.

20.   See the second of my articles, E.H. Gombrich, 1935 op. cit., p. 126, note 1.

21.   F. Hartt, 1958, op. cit., p. 194, note 1.

22.   The latest discussion of the passage known to me is G. Bullough, *Narrative and Dramatic Sources of Shakespeare*, London, 1975, VIII, p. 150.

23.   P. Aretino, *Tutte le Commedie*, a cura di G.B. de Sanctis, Milan, 1968.

24.   *Quattro Comedia del Divieno Pietro Aretino*, printed in London by John Wolf, 1588. On this printer see M. Bellorini, "Le pubblicazioni italiane dell'editore londinese John Wolf, 1580-1591", *Miscellanea 1* 1971, pp. 17-65. The author argues (p. 41) that these editions were not only intended for the Italian market.

The Gonzaga and Music
by Iain Fenlon

Among the other arts cultivated at the Gonzaga court, music had an honoured place, indeed an exceptional one, for members of the ruling family might themselves perform or even compose it. This essay will trace the musical heyday of Gonzaga Mantua from the arrival of Isabella d'Este[1] in 1490 to the accession of Duke Ferdinando (1612): both of them enthusiastic music lovers.

Isabella d'Este's upbringing and education at Ferrara had included music and dancing, for which she clearly had a natural aptitude. At Mantua she learnt the cittern, studied the lute about 1495 with Angelo Testagrossa, and later still took up the *lira da braccio*, an instrument primarily associated with improvised song. Evidently she could also play keyboard instruments. This is a remarkable list of skills even in a courtly society which valued musicianship. Moreover Isabella's role as a musically literate patron who understood technical aspects of musical language, and so could communicate her own preferences in precise technical terms, makes her own patronage of music unusually interesting[2]. Shaped by her tastes, Mantuan court music not only took on a particularly distinctive character during the years 1490-1520, but is also of considerable importance in the history of Italian song. In the first place Isabella enlarged the court establishment beyond the requirements of the *alta cappella* (a band of *pifferi* and *tromboni* used on ceremonial and other occasions), and it is noticeable that the majority of these new recruits were native Italians rather than the Northerners who had traditionally provided the backbone of Italian musical institutions throughout the fifteenth century. Secondly, from shortly after Isabella's arrival at Mantua new musical instruments were commissioned in considerable numbers. For some twenty years, from 1496 until his death in 1517, Lorenzo Gusnasco (Lorenzo da Pavia) in Venice acted in the double capacity of Isabella's principal instrument-maker as well as her agent in dealings with Bellini, Perugino, and other artists. Both these developments underline Isabella's preoccupation with secular music, and particularly with the sponsorship of settings of vernacular poetry. By contrast, the musical interests of her husband Francesco Gonzaga seem to have been concentrated on the foundation of a permanent Gonzaga *cappella*, not in the palace itself but in the chapel of Santa Maria dei Voti in the cathedral of San Pietro; this was carried out in 1510, facilitated by Alfonso I d'Este's temporary disbanding of the Este *cappella*[3]. With Isabella's encouragement, sponsorship and sometimes even collaboration, (particularly in the selection of poetic texts), composers such as Bartolomeo Tromboncino and Marchetto Cara, who worked at Mantua, raised the *frottola*, settings of Italian texts cast in traditional poetic schemes, to a new level of achievement[4].

While Isabella's humanistically inspired encouragement of music reflects her own genuine interests, it must also be viewed in part as a political usage of culture, a task for which music, a traditional medium for the expression of status and authority, was peculiarly fitted. Encouragement of the performing arts, and the ownership of paintings and antiquities, were thought of as ways of emphasizing the regal virtues of magnificence, liberality, and erudition. The place of music within this tradition is obvious in the decorative schemes and contents of Isabella's *grotta* and *studiolo*[5].

Nearly all the paintings acquired for Isabella's *studiolo* rely on some sort of musical imagery, if only on the ubiquitous opposition of stringed and wind instruments as symbols of good and evil respectively. This *topos* is most clearly seen in Correggio's two canvases; in one Vice is associated with a recorder (Pl. 52-53; cf. Cat. 115), while in the other Virtue is serenaded by a lyre. More complicated allusions to the power of music are evident in Mantegna's *Parnassus* (Pl. 89) and in one of the later paintings in the group, Lorenzo Costa's *Coronation of a Lady* (Cat. 114; Pl. 62). In the *Parnassus*[6], the centre of the stage is occupied by the nine Muses, (some singing but all dancing), while to the left is the lyre playing Apollo, and to the right Mercury (inventor of the lyre and the syrinx) and Pegasus (the horse of the Muses). In the middle plane to the left, Vulcan, (who can be equated with Tubal Cain who participated in Jubal's discovery of the laws of harmony), is stimulated by Amor who according to Plato was "a composer so accomplished that he is the cause of composing in others". In this way it is possible to relate all the mythological characters to the theme of musical activity or invention. Finally, Amor in his more well-known role unites Mars and Venus who stand above the scene, thus ensuring the peace in which the arts (and particularly the art of music) symbolized beneath may flourish. Mars and Venus have also been interpreted as allusions to Isabella and Francesco, which may imply musical harmony being equated with earthly harmony. The same overall intention maybe is evident in Costa's *Coronation of a Lady*, which shows scenes of brutality and vice in the middle of which is a separate area fenced off and guarded by Cadmus and Diana (Pl. 62). This is the Garden of Harmony where it may be Isabella herself, surrounded by musicians and other artists, who is about to be crowned as Queen. Here again the Garden might be a symbol for Mantua where, isolated from earthly afflictions and failings, the arts flourish and harmony reigns under Isabella's protection[7].

Isabella's patronage of music, testified to so eloquently in the cycle of paintings for the *studiolo*, is evident in other aspects of her decorative schemes. Little remains of the decorations of the first *grotta* in the Castello di San Giorgio except for the barrel vaulted ceiling, but this is covered with repetitions of her favourite musical *devisa*, a clef illustrating the contralto (Isabella's voice), nine rests of varying length and a repeat sign (Pl. 57). The same motif is used elsewhere in her rooms, including on the walls and ceiling of the second *grotta* in the *Corte Vecchia*, as well as on some pieces from a set of maiolica plates (Cat. 131-138). Intarsia decorations line the lower half of the walls of the second *grotta* in the manner of a dado; two of the panels show contemporary musical instruments (Pl. 91-92) while a third (Pl. 90) is worked with the three-voiced canonic chanson "*Prenez sur moi*" of Jean de Ockeghem (c. 1410-97). An inventory of the *studiolo* and the *grotta* was made in 1542, three years after Isabella's death, and among the books are a number of musical interest including two volumes of French chansons and a manuscript devoted to the work of the theorist and composer Gafurius. One of the chansonniers was almost certainly a manuscript now in the Biblioteca Casanatense in Rome (Cat. 105) most probably copied for Isabella's betrothal to Francesco in 1480 and added to later. The repertory is, not surprisingly, a Ferrarese one. Given Isabella's strong interest in practical music, it seems likely that private musical performances, involving not more than three or four performers, took place in these rooms. Throughout her career Isabella commissioned new mu-

sical instruments some of them (such as the famous alabastar organ) of considerable elaboration and beauty. For a brief period of some thirty years Mantua flourished, under Isabella's guidance, as one of the most important musical centres in Italy. But with the death of Francesco Gonzaga in 1519, and certainly by the time of Isabella's distressing experiences during the Sack of Rome some eight years later, her interest in music seems to have declined, while the *frottola* song forms which she so actively encouraged had passed out of fashion. Within Italy, other centres became more important for musical activity; in Mantua power within the ruling family moved in the direction of Isabella's sons, Federico and Ercole. The succession passed to Federico, named captain-general of the church by Leo X in 1521 and created first Duke of Mantua by Charles V in 1530.

Federico's sponsorship of the arts was principally directed towards painting, palace-building and decoration. Meanwhile the force of his brother Ercole's influence, fuelled by ideas of the reform movement within the Church, gradually impressed itself upon Mantuan artistic life. Ercole (b. 1505) had by 1520 succeeded his uncle Sigismondo as Bishop of Mantua, and then at his mother's instigation was sent to further his education at the University of Bologna. He became a Cardinal in 1527 thanks to her influence upon Clement VII. Federico's death in 1540 placed Ercole in a powerful position as co-regent for the seven year-old heir Francesco, and he became regent again in 1550 upon Francesco's death and until Guglielmo came of age[8].

Ercole's overlapping roles as prince, prelate, and private individual make his patronage of music and the arts complex. In general, his priorities as an influential member of the reform movement within the Church found firm expression after 1540 in many aspects of Mantuan life, both at court and elsewhere. Interest in secular music, already less marked during Federico's period than it had been during previous decades, declined further.

A number of madrigalists dedicated publications to Ercole, and his household accounts show payments to singers and instrumentalists, but this is slight compared to the wealth of surviving evidence that relates to Gonzaga interest in church music. This shift in emphasis is

symbolized by the works of Jacques Colebault (Jacquet of Mantua), the most important composer at Mantua during the middle decades of the century and a figure of considerable international significance, who wrote little except liturgical works and state motets. In fact, the key to Ercole's interest in music lies in his realization of the possibilities of the arts in the service of a reforming Church. The first practical demonstrations of his interest in reformist ideas were the pastoral visits which took place in the Mantuan diocese in 1535 and 1538; later he played a distinctive role in the group of reform-minded cardinals that gathered around the layman Gasparo Contarini after his elevation to the college of cardinals. In Mantua, the aims of the reformers were pursued with increasing vigour after 1540, but Ercole's vision of reform was not confined to the spiritual. His own position as a patron of the arts at personal, Church, and State levels makes his patronage of considerable interest as an example of emerging ideas about the function of the arts in the service of the Catholic Reformation. Not surprisingly, the focal point of Ercole's artistic patronage was the local cathedral, and the most prominent result of his interest the reconstruction of the building (see Cat. 203).

According to Giorgio Vasari, one of the Cardinal's main reasons for retaining Giulio Romano in Gonzaga service after the death of Federico was so that he could be employed on the cathedral project[9]. It is tempting to view some details of the remodelling of San Pietro (started in 1545) as the product of reformist thinking applied to ecclesiastical architecture and decoration. Although the Council of Trent's deliberately vague view of the reform of sacred art was not finally published until 1564, those decrees were the product of much thinking and writing about the subject since the end of the fifteenth century. In its emphasis on a large interior space which would not impede observation of the liturgy, and in the arrangement of the High Altar, Giulio's designs do seem to reflect reformist thinking, and it is interesting that Vasari's account emphasizes that Ercole took a strong interest in the renovation, required since the old building was "so badly constructed that very few people can hear, let alone see, when the divine offices are celebrated" (see essay by Burns, above, and Cat. 203).

Musical life in Mantua during Ercole's regency reflects similar priorities[10]. Shortly after his return from Bologna in 1525, cathedral music (which seems to have gone into decline after Marchese Francesco's death in 1519), was re-vitalized - presumably at Ercole's instigation. The establishment was expanded, from 18 men in 1528 to a total of 32 choir clergy in 1565, and from documents it appears that Ercole took a personal interest in some of the details involved in attracting new singers to Mantua. The major figure to arrive was Jacquet of Mantua, who is recorded there for the first time in 1527 and remained until 1559. The employment of a composer of Jacquet's abilities and reputation is further indication of a keen interest in polyphonic music, and the fact that the composer was paid directly by the Cardinal rather than by the Cathedral chapter underlines his personal involvement.

While at Mantua, Jacquet's efforts were almost overwhelmingly directed towards the composition of liturgical works; this is suggestive of Ercole's priorities, but San Pietro was also the dynastic church of the ruling family and a number of Jacquet's motets underline the political aspects of the Cardinal's career. Thus in their reflection of Ercole's varied but inseparable roles as ruler, reforming churchman, and diplomatist, Jacquet's music explores the potential of the art in the pursuit of policy. Outside Mantua, objectives similar to Ercole's were later pursued partly through musical means by Carlo Borromeo; inside the city Ercole's truest disciple proved to be the third Duke, Guglielmo.

As with Ercole, Guglielmo's interest in artistic projects was primarily directed towards ecclesiastical building. More than any other project carried out during his rule, the construction, decoration and liturgical operations of the Palatine Basilica of Santa Barbara occupied Guglielmo almost to the point of obsession. A number of previous Gonzaga chapels were still in existence when he assumed power, though probably not all of them were in use; they included two small chapels in the Castello di San Giorgio, Marchese Francesco's chapel of Santa Maria dei Voti in the cathedral, and the small church of Santa Croce in Piazza in the more recent part of the palace complex. But by early 1560's the demands of court ceremonial had outgrown these facilities, and in 1561 a new church was constructed. This too proved inadequate, and shortly after the new building had been completed, Guglielmo ordered the overseer of the ducal fabric, Giovanni Battista Bertani, to draw up plans for a larger structure to replace it. This chapel (or, more correctly, Palatine Basilica,) was dedicated to Santa Barbara and constructed during the years 1564-72 (Pl. 40, 93-94; Cat. 209)[11].

Guglielmo's foundation of the Basilica and his subsequent interest in the minutiae of its operations may have been motivated by genuine piety; at the same time it provided a useful opportunity for the Gonzaga to convince the Papacy, if not the rest of Christian Europe, of loyalty at a particularly difficult moment in the Church's history. In addition, by constructing the Basilica on a grand scale and acquiring for it extraordinary special privileges from Rome, Guglielmo founded an institution which became the envy of other Italian princes; in this sense the whole enterprise was merely another aspect of the *questione di precedenza*, the battle for status and priority which was such a prominent feature of the relations between the Italian states. Indeed, the foundation Bull of Pius IV conferred a quite special status upon Santa Barbara, establishing a separate rite with its own missal and breviary, and raising the higher clergy of the institution to the elevated rank of Apostolic Protonotary. According to its constitution, the new Basilica employed at full strength, some sixty-four people presided over by an abbot and six dignitaries. These arrangements are exceptional, well justifying Pius IV's reported remark "*Su via, facciamo un Papa di Santa Barbara*".

The Santa Barbara project was to a considerable extent Guglielmo's own, and it is clear from documents that he took a detailed interest in many aspects of the arrangements, particularly in the formulation of the Santa Barbara liturgy. The importance which the Gonzaga attached to the Basilica, and its role as a dynastic building, are reflected in the high quality of the furnishings and relics (see Cat. 210-214). This extravagance also encompassed music; interestingly, the Mantuan ecclesiastical historian Ippolito Donesmondi gives the lack of adequate space for musicians as one of the reasons for the construction of the new church, and certainly the arrangements for polyphony within it were an important aspect of the Duke's conception. A gallery running along the west wall was evidently designed to take "*i musici a cantare le feste solenni*"; it is even conceivable that the alternating chant and polyphonic sections of *alternatim* works would have been performed from the east and west ends of the building respectively. Small galleries high up on the north and south walls accommodated members of the court and, in one of them, a fine

organ by the distinguished Brescian builder Graziadio Antegnati. The occasions on which polyphony was required, and on which the organ should sound, are carefully laid down in the constitution. The repertory of the Basilica, much of it specially commissioned and written to conform with the Santa Barbara rite, has been preserved in a large series of printed books and manuscripts now in Milan[12] (Cat. 215-217).

The major composer concerned with these elaborate arrangements for music at Santa Barbara was the northern composer Giaches de Wert. Probably born near Antwerp about 1535, he had been brought to Italy as a child and had been employed at various minor Italian courts before arriving in Mantua, perhaps in 1564, but certainly by 1565, some five months after the Basilica had become operational. It is clear that Wert rapidly assumed a position of overall responsibility for the ducal music, a position which he effectively retained until his death in 1596. Although most of his compositional efforts were concerned with madrigal writing, he also wrote a good deal of sacred music. Some of the contents of his first motet book (1566), dedicated to Guglielmo, may well have been written for the Ducal Basilica, and his two later books of sacred music, published in 1581, almost certainly reflect Santa Barbara practice. But much of Wert's sacred music remained unpublished, as did that of some of the other, less distinguished composers who wrote for the institution[13]. The same is true of the cycle of Mantuan masses (Cat. 215) by Wert's highly distinguished contemporary Giovanni Pierluigi da Palestrina (c. 1525/6-1594). Connections between Palestrina, *maestro* of the Cappella Giulia in Rome and Duke Guglielmo (who was also a composer), began in 1568, and a series of letters from Palestrina to Guglielmo has survived[14]. From these it appears that both men exchanged ideas and informa-

tion about musical matters, and that over a period of some years Palestrina who never lived in Mantua, wrote a series of masses for the Basilica preserved in the Santa Barbara manuscripts. As with much of Wert's music for Santa Barbara, Palestrina's settings remained unpublished, with the exception of one mass printed in a collection of ordinary settings by Mantuan composers. As a repertory which remained distinct, and which was not transmitted beyond Santa Barbara, (and in a small number of instances other Gonzaga churches), the specially composed music for the Basilica is symptomatic of a conception in which the arts are seen, at least partly, as yet a further way of projecting the power, authority, and status of the prince.

This sense of exclusiveness lies at the heart of the Santa Barbara project. Planned as a dynastic temple on an imposing scale, the Basilica functioned partly as a private chapel, and partly as a state church. Within its walls a specially constituted liturgy fused and confused celestial and earthly deities, God and the Gonzaga, in a convenient projection of the image of the God-fearing prince. And since the institution was to a considerable extent the conception of Duke Guglielmo, a composer and musical enthusiast, the recruitment of singers and the composition of polyphony for Santa Barbara retained much of his attention. Certainly other kinds of musical activity took place at court, and *feste* on a grand scale must have required large musical force, but it is the Santa Barbara project which provides the key to Guglielmo's own artistic temperament and which remained the focal point of the Duke's patronage. There are signs that during the 1580's the more adventurous composers working in Mantua, including Wert, were becoming dissatisfied with the predominantly conservative artistic atmosphere at court; that situation changed radically after 1587 when, with the coming to power of

Veduta del Alter Maggiore della Chiesa Ducal di S.ta Barbara Con l'apparato e Funtioni Funebri Celebrate ali VII genaro 1666 per la morte del Ser.mo CARLO II. Duca di Mantua Monferato &.

Vincenzo Gonzaga in September of that year, different tendencies were encouraged.

In fact there could hardly be a greater contrast in personality, temperament and style of government than that between father and son. The careful husbanding of resources which had characterized Guglielmo's attitudes towards financial matters now gave way to an extravagance and indulgence which effectively laid the foundations for the collapse of the Gonzaga fortunes that took place in the early seventeenth century. Initially it seemed as though Vincenzo would emulate his father's caution and avoidance of conflict in external relations, but when Emperor Rudolph II appealed to the Italian princes for aid against the Turks, Vincenzo accepted. The three campaigns of 1595, 1597 and 1601 were of little military significance and great expense; on the first expedition Vincenzo's elaborate retinue even included five musicians headed by Monteverdi. Supported by Guglielmo's carefully accumulated reserves, Vincenzo's ambition and vanity combined to pursue a vision of the Mantuan state which recognized its strategic importance but underestimated its capabilities[15].

There were marked changes in the character of Gonzaga patronage after 1587. Although Guglielmo had commissioned some works of art from elsewhere, including Tintoretto's eight Gonzaga history paintings (Alte Pinacothek, Munich) in 1579, the major artistic projects carried out during his reign (for instance the altarpieces of Santa Barbara) were the work of local men, mostly followers of Giulio Romano - Lorenzo Costa the younger, Ippolito Costa, Fermo Ghisoni and Ippolito Andreasi. Vincenzo was more adventurous: he employed, after 1600, northern painters such as Frans Pourbus the younger and Rubens; Anton Maria Viani, his principal architect, had been born in Cremona but his style was largely formed in Munich: his main task was to design and supervise alterations and additions to the Ducal Palace[16].

Similarly there were striking changes in the court music establishment. Among the new arrivals was Claudio Monteverdi, who was employed in ducal service by 1590. At Santa Barbara the number of musicians also increased, and the range of the Basilica's activities as a dynastic and state church were broadened. By this time Vincenzo's reputation as a ruler with strong musical interests must have been considerable, and the quantity of new publications both by Mantuans and composers working elsewhere that now appeared with dedications to him is impressive. In general terms three fresh interests are discernible in the works of Mantuan composers during these years: an enthusiasm for the lighter secular forms influenced by Marenzio's *villanelle* (most obviously apparent in Gastoldi's popular three-voice *balletti*), explorations of the possibilities of the new styles of virtuoso singing already established at Ferrara and Florence, and cultivation of new theatrical forms with music (including early opera). The quantity of secular music produced by court composers during Vincenzo's period stands in contrast to the predominant interest in sacred music which characterizes his father's rule.

These tastes were largely shaped by Vincenzo's contacts with the Ferrarese and Florentine courts during the 1580's. Musical life at Ferrara had been dominated during that decade by the *concerto delle dame*, an ensemble of female virtuoso singers frequently supplemented by male performers, who had acquired a legendary rep-

94.   *Santa Barbara, Mantua: view of interior.*

95.   *Letter of Giaches de Wert, 15 November 1584 (Archivio di Stato, Mantua, Autografi, b. 10 c. 303).*

and Christine of Lorraine. The possibilities of the new ensemble were exploited by a number of Mantuan composers including Alessandro Striggio the elder, Benedetto Pallavicino, Giaches de Wert, and most noticeably by Claudio Monteverdi in his *Il Terzo libro de madrigali a cinque voci* (Venice, 1592).

The courts of Florence and Ferrara also fashioned Mantuan enthusiasm for theatrical displays during Vincenzo's period. During Duke Guglielmo's years, the traditions of court theatre centred on the visits of travelling companies, and on the activities of the ghetto whose sponsorship of productions was an important aspect of theatrical life. There is some evidence that both these were discouraged during Guglielmo's latter years. By contrast, Vincenzo's taste for the theatre, nurtured on Ferrarese cultivation of the new pastoral and the Florentine tradition of extravagant *intermedi*, produced a noticeable change after 1587. The influence of Ferrara was strong until 1597, when, with the death of Alfonso II d'Este the territory reverted to Papal control and the

utation for brilliantly executed florid singing. The group was imitated a little later at the Medici court in Florence. Vincenzo Gonzaga, who spent much of his time at Ferrara after the marriage of his sister Margherita to Alfonso II d'Este in 1579, clearly preferring the atmosphere there to the counter-reformation gloom of his father's court, evidently heard and admired the ensemble. So did Giaches de Wert, whose *Il Settimo libro de madrigali a cinque voci* (Venice, 1581) included pieces reflecting the abilities and vocal style of the *concerto*. Equally Vincenzo may have been influenced by Florentine adoption of the style; Mantuan contacts with Florence became closer than hitherto with the marriage of Vincenzo to Eleonora de' Medici in 1584. There is some evidence of Duke Guglielmo's distaste for these new fashions, but shortly after Vincenzo's assumption of power a similar group was established at Mantua consisting of singers brought from Vicenza; they were a regular attraction at court by April 1589, and later that year may have performed in the famous *intermedi* for *La Pellegrina*, a play by Bargagli given at Florence in celebration of the marriage of Ferdinando de' Medici

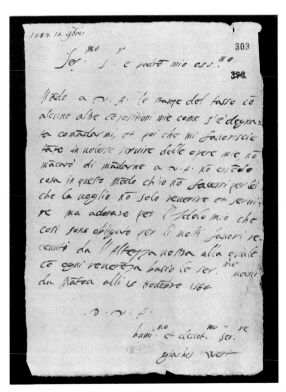

Este moved to Modena. The most obvious example of this influence is the unsuccessful attempt to stage Guarini's controversial pastoral drama *Il Pastor Fido* at the Palazzo Te in 1591-92; the attempt was made with Guarini's collaboration and under the patronage of Vincenzo Gonzaga's mistress Agnese Argotta, Marchesa di Grana. Florentine traits are certainly evident in the Mantuan production of 1598, particularly in a balletic scene which owes much to the example of Emilio de' Cavalieri's sixth *intermedio* from the set devised for the Florentine performance of *La Pellegrina* in 1589. This is symbolic of the shifting relative importance of Ferrara and Florence for Mantuan court theatre, a point which is underlined by the extravagant Mantuan spectacles of 1607-08[17]. The performance of Monteverdi's *l'Orfeo* (Cat. 253) during the carnival season of 1607 were at the instigation of the *Accademia degli Invaghiti*, but the organization was largely in the hands of Prince Francesco Gonzaga who, through contacts with his brother Ferdinando then in Pisa, relied to a considerable extent on Florentine performers. Florentine involvement is even more noticeable one year later when, in celebration of Francesco's marriage to Margherita of Savoy, performances were given of Monteverdi's now-lost opera *Arianna* and his *Il ballo delle ingrate* (Cat. 255-256).

The death of Vincenzo Gonzaga in 1612 marks the end of the most effective period of Gonzaga patronage of music. Monteverdi, the most talented composer working at the court, moved to Venice in that year. Apart from Frescobaldi, who spent a few months at Mantua in 1615, no composer of any consequence was employed by the Gonzaga during the succeeding decades.

Notes

1. See essay above by J.M. Fletcher.

2. For music at Mantua during Isabella's period and later see Bertolotti, 1890, Canal, 1881, and Fenlon, 1980.

3. Prizer, 1978.

4. Further details in Einstein, 1949, pp. 34-107, and Rubsamen, 1943.

5. See Verheyen, 1971, for the history of these rooms and their contents.

6. This interpretation is based on that in Lehmann, 1973.

7. See in general Verheyen, 1971, also Cat. 114 below.

8. Ercole's career requires a detailed study. There is basic information in Pastor, *History of the Popes*, IX, 1891; see also Montesinos, 1931, pp. xxi-liv.

9. See the accounts of the last works of Giulio Romano in Vasari-Milanesi, 1878-85, Vol. V, pp. 522ff., and Hartt, 1958.

10. Further details of musical life at the Cathedral during Ercole's time are given in Tagmann, 1967 and Fenlon, 1980, pp. 62ff.

11. The fullest account of the building history of the Basilica is that in Gozzi, 1974.

12. For music at Santa Barbara see Tagmann, 1970, and Fenlon, 1980, pp. 95ff. The latter presents a good deal of documentation including the portions of the Constitution relating to the performance of music. The music and liturgical books from Santa Barbara are now divided between the Conservatorio di musica in Milan and the Archivio Storico Diocesano in Mantua. The former collection is described in Barblan, 1972, the latter in Fenlon, 1980, Appendix III.

13. Wert and his music are discussed at length in MacClintock, 1966.

14. The relationships between Palestrina and Duke Guglielmo are treated in Jeppesen, 1950 and Jeppesen, 1953, and in Strunk, 1947. Guglielmo's own career as a composer is dealt with in Gallico, 1977, and in Sherr, 1978. For his contacts with other composers and other aspects of his patronage see Fenlon, 1980, pp. 85ff.

15. Coniglio, 1967, pp. 363-78, Mazzoldi, 1960, II, pp. 37ff.; Errante, 1915.

16. See Moro and Mattioli in Mantua, *Rubens*, 1977.

17. Further details of musical life at the Mantuan court during the first decade of Vincenzo's period are given in Fenlon, 1980.

'Mantua Peeces': Charles I and the Gonzaga Collections
by David Howarth

Charles I was attracted by the grand gesture: the magical entrance at Court Masques to impress all with the magnificence of his person; the dismissal of Parliament and attempt to rule without it; the disastrous descent upon Westminster to arrest the Five Members. Frequently ill-timed and ill-conceived, such actions served only to compound the difficulties which gathered about him. But if his quixotic gestures usually failed, the most splendid was the shining exception. During the early years of his reign he acquired for just over £ 30,000 the best part of the Gonzaga collections, the finest in Italy; an achievement which created a sensation throughout Europe.

By the end of the 16th century the Dukedom of Mantua was in grave financial difficulties. These had become so serious by the 1620's that Duke Ferdinand had to consider radical action. By then the passion for collecting at the English Court was well enough known in Italy for the Duke to cast a line in that direction. The first tentative enquiries were made through the agency of the Countess of Arundel, one of the most formidable ladies at the English Court. The grand-daughter of Bess of Hardwick, Lady Arundel had developed into a colourful personality. After marrying the great connoisseur Thomas Howard, Earl of Arundel in 1606, she became quite as enthusiastic a collector as her more celebrated husband. When he took Inigo Jones to Italy in 1613, she accompanied them to incarcerate herself in a monastery in Siena, there to master Italian at its purest source. Six years later she was in Venice with the young Van Dyck and her sons whom she installed in a palace on the Grand Canal to learn "polite accomplishments". It was on her return home in 1623 with two blackamoors, a gondola and a box of "prodigious edible snails" which she wished to add to the English cuisine, that approaches were made by Count Alessandro Striggi, the Grand Chancellor of Mantua. In July she replied and requested a model of il *Palazzo del Serenissimo Duca di Mantova detto del Te* to be made as quickly as possible, together with a clear and detailed description of the contents of the rooms, adding with the instincts of the collector she had become, that it would be better still if Giulio Romano's own model could be provided. The documents tell us nothing more, but we may assume that the *bon bouche* arrived because more people now became involved.

Through Lady Arundel's auspices, the treasures of Mantua eventually came to London though it was to be nearly a decade before this was accomplished; a successful outcome certainly, though one marred by bitterness in all quarters and credit in none. The chief protagonists were Alessandro Striggi, Daniel Nys and Nicholas Lanier. Nys was a French merchant long settled in Venice whose respectable position as Swedish Consul was belied by a dubious reputation as one of the most unscrupulous art dealers on the Italian market. Charles's interests were represented by his master of music Nicholas Lanier who had recommended himself to the King by combining an unrivalled eye for drawings with a virtuoso's skills upon the lute and viola da gamba.

In 1625, two years after Lady Arundel's overtures, Lanier was sent to Venice to discuss the strategy for the impending sale with Nys who was brought in because of his unrivalled experience of the market. From Venice, Lanier went on to Mantua arriving to inspect the prospective purchases in the worst of the summer heat. A few days sufficed for this before a brief return to Venice and then a journey to Rome to take part in what remained of the Holy Year, and to buy pictures for Charles. In a few months in Italy, Lanier had his own portrait painted – possibly the one by Van Dyck in Vienna – and acquired contemporary works by Guercino and Albano in addition to one of the versions of the portrait of *Giulia Gonzaga* by Sebastiano del Piombo. By the spring of 1626 he was back in London to report on the current state of negotiations which he had left in the capable if slippery hands of Nys. As letters passed between Nys in Venice and Striggi in Mantua, complications began to arise. At a delicate stage Duke Ferdinand died, to be succeeded by his vacillating and decadent brother Vincenzo II whose desperate need for money was tempered by fear of the reaction such a sale might provoke. Nys was winning the duke round when Vincenzo was informed by a third party that the paintings were not destined for England but either for the Farnese or the Medici. Prior to this unwelcome news, Vincenzo had consoled himself with the thought that they were to leave Italy and would not, therefore, add to the lustre of rivals nearer home. After Nys had

96. *Nicholas Lanier,* Self-portrait *(Cat. 274).*

97. *Sustermans,* Vincenzo II Gonzaga *(Cat. 258).*

protested that he had no intention of selling this collection to another Italian family, matters progressed slowly and Nys was forced to agree on a price of fifty thousand *scudi* (the previous estimate had been thirty-eight thousand *scudi*) for the collection which included eleven *Caesars* by Titian, *The Madonna della Perla* by Raphael for which it was alleged Vincenzo I had given a marquisate in Monferrato, worth fifty thousand *scudi*, and the controversial *Death of the Virgin* by Caravaggio, a painting that had caused such an outcry when unveiled in Rome in 1606 because of the stark realism of the Virgin. It had been rejected by the authorities, and was snapped up for Mantua by Rubens, acting in his capacity as Keeper of the Ducal collections.

Just as it appeared that matters could be settled to the satisfaction of all parties more trouble suddenly appeared. Furtively the pictures were transported up the Brenta to be secreted far from the curious eyes of Venetian connoisseurs in Nys's house on the island of Murano. But as the cases were unpacked it became obvious that all the paintings had not left Mantua. Whether this was an oversight or a clumsy attempt at fraud as was common in many sales of the time is not clear. As if there had not been enough complications already, the news of the sale then became public. Vincenzo's advisers had braced themselves for a hostile reaction but they were astonished at what happened. Mantua could talk of nothing else. Diego Crestino, an adviser to Striggi, sought an audience with Vincenzo to inform him that his subjects were prepared to subscribe twice the amount he had received for them rather than lose their patrimony. But it was to no purpose, Vincenzo wanted to talk only of a dwarf with whom he was infatuated. The deed was done. Nys was the first to inform England in a letter to Endymion Porter: "Since I came into the world, I have made various contracts, but never a more difficult one than this and which has succeeded so happily. In the first place, the City of Mantua, and then all the Princes of Christendom, both great and small, were struck with astonishment that we could induce the Duke to dispose of them. The people of Mantua made so much noise about it".

Nys and Lanier, who had recently returned to Venice from London to take part in the last stages of the sale, now turned to the services of Sir Isaac Wake, sometime

98. *Correggio,* Education of Cupid *(National Gallery, London).*

Public Orator of Oxford University, then serving as Ambassador in Venice before returning to become Secretary of State. Wake had a healthy contempt for Nys's world. Recently he had been asked to buy pictures for Lord Conway. Knowing he was ill-qualified to do this he nevertheless objected to the patronizing attitude of: "Some in England who have taken unto themselves a monopolye of passing their verdict upon all things of this nature, so that if a man do not baptise his picture or statue at the font of their censure he cannot be admitted into the Church". However, all had to work together if they were to send the collection safely to England. Accordingly Wake went to the Doge's Palace to obtain exemption from customs dues for the cargo valued at one hundred tunnes and on 28 April 1628 wrote to Lord Conway of how Lanier had taken every possible care in seeing the pictures well stowed "uppon ye Margaret of London, whereof Thomas Browne is Master, who did set sayle and goe out of this port of Malamocco upon Saturday morning ye 15th April st° n° and is (as wee hope) by this halfe waye out of ye Gulfe".

The voyage began auspiciously but when only three days out of Venice the *Margaret* hit "a furious storme". Wake did his best to soothe the anxieties of those waiting in London by writing that since Lanier and he had heard "nothing of misadventure, wee do presume shee was got over into Istria or Dalmatia, before ye storme fell, and that by consequence she was out of danger, being indeed a tall ship, very strong and well manned with 37 mariners".

All might have been as Wake hoped if only Lanier had indeed been careful. But instead of having the pictures stowed where they could come to no harm, he had allowed them to be packed against a cargo of mercury; carelessness which had disastrous consequences. As the ship strained against the heavy seas, the jars broke, spilling the lethal substance against some of the canvases. Some time after the cargo had reached London those pictures that had been affected were described as "utterly spoiled and defaced by quicksilver".

Lanier himself did not sail in the *Margaret* but slipped away from Venice the day before she left harbour with "an intention to passe through Helvetia, Lorrain and so to Bruxelles". Armed with Wake's safe-conducts he completed the first stage of his journey by using the Ambassador's gondola to take him to Padua where he was accompanied to Bergamo by a guide proven to be a "diligent and faithfull man". At the foot of the Alps Lanier was joined by five horsemen because "He doth cary w^h him ye best pieces of paintings, namely those of Correggio, wch were in grotta at Mantova, in regard of being in water-colours, they would not have brooked ye sea".

Magnificent though the undamaged pictures were, others still remained in Mantua with which Vincenzo had refused to part. However, quite suddenly in December 1627 he died and in the spring of 1628 as the last arrangements were being made with Thomas Browne of the *Margaret*, Nys and Lanier made an agreement to buy

97

99.   *Titian*, Entombment *(Musée du Louvre, Paris)*.

100.   *Raphael*, Madonna della Perla *(Museo del Prado, Madrid)*.

Mantegna's nine canvases of the *Triumphs of Caesar*, in addition to the large collection of antique busts and statues which Vincenzo's successor Charles of Nevers regarded with indifference.

Yet this successful culmination of all Nys's efforts prov-ed to be his undoing. The prospect of acquiring the Mantegnas was too tempting. Knowing that they were the envy of the great collectors of Europe he began to play one interested party off against another expecting to take a considerable profit on the way. Problems arose when he gave £ 10,500 for the pictures and statues without securing Charles's agreement who saw Nys's precipitate action as an excuse to avoid paying for what he could not afford. Because of Charles's devious behaviour Nys decided to offer them secretly to Marie de Medicis and Cardinal Richelieu while emphasizing in all the letters he wrote to England that his sole aim was the honour of the English crown. His protestations however served merely to alert rather than convince the King's advisers. Threatened by his creditors, Nys went on to make a serious error of judgement in despatching the worst of the statues to England still hoping the King would reimburse him the sum he had paid for the entire collection; those pieces remaining in his own house were to be disposed of to other collectors when the dust had settled. Unfortunately he had not reckoned upon the presence in London of Lord Dorchester and Sir Peter Paul Rubens. Dorchester had become well acquainted with the snares of the Venetian art market during his time as Ambassador in Venice when he had himself collected a fine group of "heads and statues" which he later sold to Rubens. Rubens, a man with a profound knowledge of classical sculpture and the former Keeper of the Mantuan collections, was in a unique position to expose Nys. When Dorchester duly confronted him with evidence of his double dealing in a letter, Nys hurriedly sent a servant to London with an elaborate excuse. He claimed that the public

101. *Van Honthorst*, Charles I *(Cat. 276)*.

102. *Van Dyck*, Portrait of Lord Dorchester *(National Portrait Gallery, London)*.

exhibition of statues was creating so much interest among the Venetians all of which redounded to the credit of Charles that he had thought it a pity to send them away so soon.

Such arguments convinced no one, merely encouraging Charles to continue to ignore the outstanding bill of £ 10,500. At last in October 1630, Wake's successor Thomas Rowlandson managed to extract from Nys what he hoped were the last Mantuan pieces. When though it came to encasing the statues and remaining paintings, Rowlandson's worries, though of a different nature to those Wake had endured two years earlier, were no less pressing. Then it had been the storms of the Adriatic, now it was the plague.

> "I must confesse I doe longe to see them aboard, for this towne is heavily afflicted with a great mortalitye... I doubt I shall be forced to shutt myselfe up in my house not knowing where to save my selfe and my familye; since the passages are all guarded very strictlye, but before I take any resolution I will see his M^tyes statue sent away".

Away they duly went in the *Roebuck, London, Industrye* and *Peter Bonaventura*, with a promise from Rowlandson that he would inform those in London precisely how Nys had been trying to double-cross them. But if Rowlandson thought he had the measure of his man, he was mistaken. There were further revelations to come. Still owed more than £ 10,000 in the summer of 1631 Nys was forced to open his house to his creditors inviting them to take all "even to the last farthing". In the

general turn-out Nys was "astonished" and "delighted" to find three Titians, a Raphael and statues by Praxiteles, Michelangelo and Sansovino all originally bought for the King, somehow forgotten and now discovered by a servant rummaging in the back part of the house. Disingenuous though he was, Nys must have realized the full story would now emerge.

Finally Charles took possession of all that was due to him. By no means all the "Mantuan peeces" were first class and some of the more modest canvases were given away or exchanged; nonetheless it was a collection which, when combined with his other treasures, equalled anything in Europe. But he paid a heavy price for the pleasure of owning Titian's *Entombment* or the *Education of Cupid* by Correggio; both Gonzaga pictures. Filippo Burlamachi the King's money lender explained that as a result of paying £ 15,000 for the paintings which had come over on the *Margaret*, he was now

103. *Caravaggio,* Death of the Virgin *(Musée du Louvre, Paris)*.

regarded the purchase as betraying a fundamental lack of priorities. Consequently this act of magnificence contributed to the King's isolation by alienating many men of influence and power.

Sadly the king was to enjoy the Mantuan collection for all too short a time. He left London in 1642 and once the Royal Palaces were occupied by Parliament the careful arrangement of pictures and sculpture was disrupted, never to be restored. After Charles's execution in 1649 the treasures were sold, some going abroad, others remaining in England. Yet a permanent tribute to the most spectacular collection ever to be brought to this country was made by none other than Cromwell himself who, perhaps appreciating the martial spirit of Mantegna's canvases of the *Triumphs of Caesar,* reserved them for the nation. Today they hang not in the Palace of Whitehall, long since destroyed, but at Hampton Court, the former residence of Henry VIII, another royal patron of the arts.

PRINCIPAL SOURCES

See under BIBLIOGRAPHY: Noel Sainsbury, 1859; Luzio, 1913; Millar, 1960; Millar, 1972.

unable to equip the army Buckingham was taking to the relief of the French Protestants at La Rochelle. Charles's role as collector and connoisseur cannot be divorced from the more serious issues of politics; often this private pursuit impinged upon matters of state with unfortunate results. The sheer cost of the purchase seriously affected the Exchequer: the money finally disbursed represented more than the King could expect from his annual land rents. At a time when he was trying to rule without Parliament such extravagance was improvident. Furthermore, although collecting became fashionable within the King's immediate circle, the majority of courtiers did not share this taste and

Catalogue

I   Foundations

1

Photograph: **A bird's eye view of Mantua in 1628**
Gabriele Bertazzolo, VRBIS MANTVAE DESCRIPTIO
Engraving; original, 77 x 110.5 cm
Biblioteca Comunale, Mantua

An earlier view of Mantua, showing it among the lakes of the
river Mincio, was published in 1575, but in 1596 a much
more detailed topographical panorama, with a numbered key
to principal locations, appeared by the hand of Gabriele Bertazzolo (1570-1626), who later earned fame as a hydraulic
engineer and festival designer (Cat. 254, 272). He dedicated it
to Duke Vincenzo Gonzaga's Florentine wife Eleonora de'
Medici, with an allusion to the city's supposed Etruscan origins. The view was republished, with some alterations, two
years after his death. From the bottom (east) the eye travels
over the bridge of S. Giorgio to the site of the early medieval
city, which remained under the Gonzaga regime the seat of
princely and spiritual power (the Ducal Palace complex of
buildings and the cathedral; detail Pl. 2), then into the civic
and commercial centre dominated by the church of Sant'Andrea, the Palazzo of the Commune and the market place, and
continues towards the third line of walls in the west to which
Mantua had expanded in the century before the Gonzaga obtained control of it (1328). Bertazzolo indicates the sixteenth-
century fortifications and nearby Gonzaga villas and in the
1628 version some recent buildings (e.g. the church of Sant'
Orsola) were added. Dedicated to Duke Carlo I of the line
of Nevers, the map portrays Mantua in the troubled time of
his succession, on the eve of the catastrophic siege (1629-30).

D.S.C.

BIBLIOGRAPHY: DBI; Paccagnini, 1960; Marani and Perina, 1965.
ADDITIONAL BIBLIOGRAPHY: C. Berselli, "La pianta di Mantova di Gabriele
Bertazzolo", *Civiltà mantovana*, ii, 1967, pp. 278-97; G. Pecorari, "La
pianta di Mantova disegnata e incisa dal Bertazzolo nel 1596", *Civiltà
Mantovana*, xi, 1977, pp. 325-48.

1

2

The Expulsion of the Bonacolsi in 1328

Domenico Morone (c. 1442-after 1517); painted in 1494
Oil on Canvas, 165 x 315 cm. Inscribed: DOMINICUS MORONUS
VERONENSIS PINXIT MCCCCLXXXXIIII
Museo del Palazzo Ducale, Mantua (Inv. Sta. n. 235; Cat. 58)

On 16 August 1328, Luigi Gonzaga (c. 1268-1360), together
with his sons and troops supplied by Can Grande della Scala
of Verona, entered Mantua and, after a battle in the Piazza S.
Pietro, killed Rinaldo (Passerino) Bonacolsi, Capitano of
Mantua, on the steps of his house. Later that month Luigi
swore an oath of fealty to the people of Mantua before the
Cathedral of S. Pietro when he was appointed *Capitano e
Signore* of Mantua, and the Emperor Louis of Bavaria recognized him as Imperial Vicar in 1329. This was the beginning of Gonzaga rule in Mantua.

This painting by the Veronese Domenico Morone, made for
Marchese Francesco Gonzaga (1484-1519) demonstrated the
importance for the family of these events which took place
over a hundred and sixty years earlier. Several separate incidents are incorporated: on the left, the conspirators are seen
entering the city through the Porta Mulina (which leads to the
road for Verona); the ensuing fight between the Bonacolsi
and Gonzaga factions occupies the foreground, and Passerino
Bonacolsi, lanced in the back, falls from his horse before the
Palazzo del Capitano on the right. In the background Luigi
Gonzaga swears fidelity to the citizens on the steps of the
cathedral. The majority of the shields in the foreground, and
the red banners in the oath scene, display the old Gonzaga
arms of black and white stripes but some soldiers in the skirmish (one defending Passerino) have shields emblazoned with
the red and yellow stripes of the Bonacolsi (Gerola, 1918;
Meroni, 1966; pl. 30, 41).

The picture is also of great topographical interest. Morone set
the events of 1328 in Mantua of the 1490's (the armour and
costumes would appear to be of the late fifteenth century as

well) and gives a visual record of buildings which have since
been destroyed. On the left the Porta Mulina, one of the principal gates of the city, is shown (destroyed in 1902); the large
palace on the right with Ghibelline crenellations (both the
Bonacolsi and the Gonzaga supported the Emperor) is the
Palazzo del Capitano. It was built in the mid-thirteenth century, and made over to Guido Bonacolsi in 1308 when he was
created Capitano of Mantua. The lower palace with Venetian
chimneys is the Domus Magna, built as the residence of the
Bonacolsi at the beginning of the fourteenth century. In the
background is the Venetian gothic façade of the cathedral,
designed by the the the delle Masegne brothers and built between
1395 and 1403. Flanked by brick side-aisles, the central section is faced in marble and surmounted by five aediculae, each
holding a statue (Marani, 1960, pp. 72-104). The façade was
demolished in 1761. Just behind the Cathedral is the church of
S. Agata, and the low villa between the cathedral and the
Domus Magna is the *Ca' Zoiosa*, built by Francesco Gonzaga
in 1388 for his amorous pursuits, but taken over in the 1420's
by Vittorino da Feltre for his school also known as the *Casa
Giocosa*.

Although the painting came from the palace at S. Sebastiano,
there is no evidence that it was painted for that setting as has
been frequently asserted. The palace was only begun in the
early years of the sixteenth century, and was initially decorated with paintings (including Mantegna's *Triumphs of Caesar*
cycle) not intended for it. It may be that Francesco planned a
series of Gonzaga "triumphs" either for the Villa at Marmirolo, or the Castle at Gonzaga, both of which were being refurbished in the 1490's. In July 1495, after his "victory" at the
Battle of Fornovo, Francesco sent Bonsignori to the site of
the battle to make topographical studies for a painting of his
great triumph; it is possible this was the final scene in a series
which started with the *Expulsion of the Bonacolsi*.

Domenico Morone was a conservative artist who worked
most of his life in Verona his native town. However he appears to have been travelling in the 1490's (there is a dated
painting of 1496 in a church near Arco, Trentino), and this

painting with its touches of genre (the muleteer on the left) and its careful topography is reminiscent of Gentile Bellini's and Carpaccio's great canvas paintings made for the various charitable schools of Venice. Francesco Gonzaga, as commander of the Venetian forces, often visited Venice and would probably have seen these; the battle scene he ordered from Morone is only in keeping with his career as a *condottiere*.

J.T.M.

PROVENANCE: Palazzo di S. Sebastiano (di Porta Pusterla) Mantua; possibly in Palazzo Ducale, Mantua in 1627 (Luzio, 1913, p. 93); in 1707 left by the last Duke, Ferdinando, to Silvio Gonzaga, thereafter in the collection of various Mantuan families. Galleria Crespi, Milan; bought for Palazzo Ducale, Mantua by the State in 1913.
BIBLIOGRAPHY: Gerola, 1918, p. 98; Mantua, *Mostra Iconog.*, 1937, no. 2; Ozzòla, 1949, no. 58, p. 10; Paccagnini, 1960, pp. 50, 58, 74, 81-82, 150-51, 158, 242-44; Marani and Perina, 1961, p. 333; Mantua, *Mostra Mantegna*, 1961, p. 118, no. 82 with bibliography; Meroni, 1966, pl. 30, 41; Mantua, 1972, no. 27.
ADDITIONAL BIBLIOGRAPHY: R. Brenzoni, *Domenico Morone*, Florence, 1956, pp. 13, 16-17.

3

Luigi Gonzaga appointed first Capitano of Mantua in 1328

Anon. Mantuan, (*c.* 1570-90)
Pen, brown ink, and wash over chalk, cut at base, vertical central fold, 25.5 x 68.5 cm. Inscribed *Rymsdyk à M* (Crossed out) in left-hand corner.
British Museum, Department of Prints and Drawings (Cat. 291)

This drawing, together with its companion Cat. 4, probably by the same artist of the circle of Ippolito Andreasi (*c.* 1548-1608), presumably served as the finished design, or *modello* for one in a series of Gonzaga triumphs made to decorate a palace or villa belonging to the family. The scale of the *modelli* and the fact that Cat. 4 is squared up suggest that the decorations had reached an advanced stage of preparation. Tintoretto had painted eight scenes of Gonzaga triumphs for the Palazzo Ducale, including a version of this scene in 1579-80 (Eikemeier, 1969). Andreasi, together with Francesco Borgani (*c.* 1557-1624) and a large number of assistants were decorating the villa at Goito in 1586-87 which had been built for Duke Guglielmo between 1584-87. The Duke's apartments included a *Camera della Vittoria* decorated with elaborate Gonzaga triumphs by Ghisi, Borgani, and Andreasi (whose *Battle of Fornovo* included fifty main figures and thirty-six horses) but there is no mention of earlier scenes of Gonzaga history. The adjacent *Camera dei Frutti*, besides vegetable decoration, contained the portraits of the entire dynasty as well as some triumphs. Historical accuracy was important: Stefano Sanviti sent for Titian's portrait of Duke Federico and that of Francesco by Costa il Vecchio so that he might copy them. By 6 March 1587 Sanviti "had finished the two triumphs and two portraits, he is working on the third, beginning with Luigi I" (*ha fato le due fame et doi retrati, è drieto al terzo, cominciando a Luigio primo*; Intra, 1888, pp. 44-45). The annex (*Monasterolo*) also had a *Sala delle Istorie*.

Luigi Gonzaga's appointment as Capitano of Mantua in 1328 marked the foundation of the family's rule in the city, and was an obvious subject for Gonzaga Triumphs. It forms the background of Cat. 2 and there is a fresco of the same subject in the Palazzo Ducale dated 1496. The artist has made considerable efforts to be historically accurate: he views the Cathedral square from a different angle to that chosen by Morone, showing the Cathedral, still with the gothic delle Masegne façade on the right. The pages in the centre hold the old Gonzaga arms (black and white stripes) and a helmet surmounted by the Gonzaga eagle. The arms on the large banner and those decorating the trumpets are those of the city of Mantua, (St George Cross with the head of Virgil in one quarter), while the shield of one of the soldiers on the cathedral steps is emblazoned with the arms of the della Scala (a ladder): the della Scala of Verona had helped the Gonzaga to seize power in Mantua. Two contemporary characters mentioned by Mantuan chroniclers are included in the scene: the giant Guglielmo di Drafignana, six braccia tall (nearly four metres) was a favourite of Luigi's son Filippino, as was the dwarf Trambaldo, who measured *quattro palmi* (about eighty-five centimetres), and who always led cavalcades, as Equicola, one of Duke Guglielmo's favourite historians, relates in *Dell'Istoria di Mantova*.

J.T.M.

PROVENANCE: W. Ottley, J. van Rymsdyk, Sir T. Lawrence, S. Woodburn, Phillipps-Fenwick.
BIBLIOGRAPHY: Equicola, 1607, p. 83; Intra, 1888, pp. 23-48; Pouncey and Gere, 1962, pp. 174-75; Mazzoldi etc., 1963, pp. 77, 87, 367-77; DBI (Andreasi); Eikemeier, 1969, p. 75.

3

4

Soldiers Boarding a Ship by Night

Anon. Mantuan, (*c.* 1570-90)
Pen and brown ink and wash over traces of black chalk, squared up in black chalk; cut on both sides, 26.1 x 53.2 cm
British Museum, Department of Prints and Drawings, (Cat. 292)

This *modello*, closely related to Cat. 3, shows Gonzaga forces (identified by their striped shields) repulsing an attack by the della Scala (whose arms, a ladder, are visible on the shields of the soldiers in the boats). The artist has made some attempt to set the scene in the past by equipping the soldiers with longbows and archaic swords, and the castle is evidently of the date of the Castello S. Giorgio. Lit by the flares held by soldiers, the fire on the boats, and beacons on the ramparts, this design would have made a dramatic night scene. It is difficult to reconcile the subject with the Tintoretto naval *Battle of Legnago* included in the Palazzo Ducale series commemorating Ludovico Gonzaga's triumph of 1439. More plausible would be an event taken from the fourteenth century, when the della Scala of Verona were at the zenith of their power. Although they had actively supported the Gonzaga coup for 1328, relations between the two families were particularly strained by 1332 over the della Scala enforcement of customs duties on river traffic; sporadic outbreaks of fighting occured from then on. One possible subject for this scene is the attack by the della Scala in 1348 when the "enemy army... infested the Mantuan territory by water and land and intended to besiege the town". Luigi's son, Filippino, died defending Mantua, "it was a great and memorable victory for the Gonzaga" (Equicola). Another naval attack involving Bernardo della Scala took place at Borgoforte in 1368.

J.T.M.

PROVENANCE: P. Sandby,l W. Ottley (?), Sir T. Lawrence, S. Woodburn, Phillips-Fenwick.
BIBLIOGRAPHY: Pouncey and Gere, 1962, p. 175; Equicola, 1607, pp. 85, 100.

SS collars and swans: Links between Lancastrian England and Gonzaga Mantua

Two livery emblems used by the Lancastrian Kings (Henry IV to Henry VI, 1399-1471) were highly favoured in the Gonzaga Court: the "S" device, of uncertain meaning, used by Henry IV's father John of Gaunt, and the swan which, although also found elsewhere, was the emblem of the family of Henry IV's wife (de Bohun). How they first came to be introduced to Mantua is not clear. It is possible that Francesco Gonzaga visited England in 1389 (see essay by Toesca, above) and Henry Bolingbroke as Earl of Derby had visited the north of Italy on his way to and from Jerusalem in 1392-3. He arrived back in Venice about 20 March 1393, and in late April and early May travelled to Milan with his retinue, passing through Padua, Verona and Pavia. A book of payments shows that in both Venice and Milan silver gilt and gold collars were purchased or made to order at this date.

ADDITIONAL BIBLIOGRAPHY: L. Toulmin-Smith, *Expeditions to Prussia and the Holy Land made by Henry Earl of Derby... in the years 1390-1 and 1392-3...*, London, 1894, pp. 286-87.

5

Henry VI

English School, (*c.* 1540)
Oil on panel, 25.4 x 31.8 cm (panel inset into frame which is inscribed HENRICVS VI
National Portrait Gallery, London (Cat. 2457)

Henry VI (1421-71), the last of the Lancastrian line, was in correspondence with Gianfrancesco Gonzaga, first Marchese of Mantua, in 1436 (see Cat. 6). This portrait, one of a set of copies of earlier kings and queens of England produced in a studio active at the end of Henry VIII's reign, shows Henry VI wearing a gold collar decorated with the "S" device; in this case the pendant is a jewelled crucifix, not the swan badge (see Cat. 8-11). No contemporary likeness of Henry has survived, but the inscription of the frame, of the same date as the painting, makes it virtually certain that this copy was taken from an *ad vivum* likeness.

J.T.M.

PROVENANCE: Purchased from F. Yates, 1930. Previously either from Bostock Hall, Rushton Hall, or Bladen Castle.
ADDITIONAL BIBLIOGRAPHY: R. Strong, *National Portrait Gallery, Tudor and Jacobean Portraits*, London, 1969, pp. 146-47.

6

Photograph: **Letter of Henry VI to Marquis Gianfrancesco Gonzaga, Westminster, 19 October 1436**
Manuscript in Latin on vellum with wax seal
Archivio di Stato, Mantua (Archivio Gonzaga, b. 387)

The King expresses thanks for the reception in Mantua of his councillor John Le Scrope, who had been making a pilgrimage to Jerusalem, and gives permission for the Marquis to distribute gold livery collars to fifty persons (... *licentiam dedi-*

5

aureum laboratam ad S a divisam regis Anglie*, or another made by a Mantuan goldsmith for Marchesa Paola Malatesta in 1417-18). It would have been intended for presentation to a relatively unimportant recipient as indeed were the fifty collars which Henry VI licensed Marchese Gianfrancesco Gonzaga to distribute (Cat. 6).

D.S.C.

BIBLIOGRAPHY: Toesca, 1977, pp. 351-52,359.
ADDITIONAL BIBLIOGRAPHY: J.B. Trapp and H. Herbruggen, *Sir Thomas More*, National Portrait Gallery, London, 1977, p. 31, with bibliography.

8

The Dunstable Swan Jewel, *c.* 1400

Unknown artist (French)
Gold jewel decorated with white enamel; chain of 30 links ending in a ring; 3.2 cm x 2.5 cm; chain 8.2 cm
British Museum, Department of Medieval and Later Antiquities (Inv. 1966 7-3, 1)

Although this rare object, intended as a brooch, was certainly not a pendant for a Lancastrian SS collar, and the enamelling technique is more closely associated with Paris than England, it provides various points of reference. It reminds us that the swan badge was not confined to the Bohun-Lancaster dynasty but was used by a number of leading European nobles such as the Duke of Berry, the Duke of Cleves and the Margrave of Brandenburg. It also suggests the appearance of a jewel that must have been much more costly, described in a Gonzaga inventory of 1416: "the gold jewel with a white swan in the form of a device of the King of England with a large ruby and large diamond on its breast and with a jewel on the swan's chain with a beautiful pearl set in five diamonds".

D.S.C.

PROVENANCE: Found in excavation at Dunstable (1965); purchased 1966.
BIBLIOGRAPHY: Cherry, 1969; Toesca, 1973, p. 368; 1977, p. 351.

9

Fragment from the frieze decorating the upper border of a tournament scene, showing an SS collar, with a swan pendant jewel, intertwined with marigold flowers

Antonio Pisanello (*c.* 1390-*c.*1455)
Detached fresco on masonite, dark brown preparatory underpaint over whitewash. 80 x 81 cm
Museo del Palazzo Ducale, Mantua (Inv. no. 2087)

This section of the frescoes (see essay by Toesca; Pl. 5-6, and below Cat. 12) was never actually finished, only outlined on the *intonaco* by means of a perforated pattern (*spolvero*) and emphasized by a brown colour wash applied around the contours of the decoration; so details which were to be painted in colour or modelled in *pastiglia* and later gilded are missing. The collar has been identified by the present writer as the Lancastrian SS livery. A real collar was delivered to Gianfrancesco Gonzaga by the Archbishop of Cologne, Dietrich von

---

mus eidem consanguineo nostro conferendi liberatas colerae nostrae aut devisamenti quinquaginta personis) provided they were of sufficiently noble blood. The letter implies that although a livery collar was sent as a present (see below Cat. 9) replicas would need to be made in Mantua. Another letter, dated 31 October, confirmed the permission, thanking the Marquis for his zeal in wishing to honour the Lancastrian livery collar and clarifying that it could be bestowed upon friends of knightly status.

D.S.C.

BIBLIOGRAPHY: Toesca, 1973, pp. 361-77, text on p. 366 also in Toesca, 1974, p. 213. The letter is mentioned by Luzio, 1913, p. 63; Luzio, 1917-18, p. 178; Luzio, 1922, p. 124, and listed in *Cal. Pat. Rolls H. VI 1436-41* (1907) p. 27.

7

7

Collar of SS

Silver gilt, length 80.7 cm, width of links 1.3 cm; 15th-16th century
Victoria & Albert Museum, Department of Metalwork (1022-1926)

An example of the type of SS Livery collar which consisted of a metal chain to which (though missing in this example) a pendant with a swan or some other device might be attached. Although it is not the type illustrated in the Pisanello fresco in Mantua, it may be a less prestigious and costly equivalent of some of the collars in Gonzaga possession listed in earlier documents (for instance in the 1416 inventory *unam collariam*

Mörs, in 1436, as we gather from a letter in the Archivio Gonzaga. Another letter to Gianfrancesco Gonzaga signed by Henry VI of 19 October 1436 granted the Marchese of Mantua permission to distribute fifty SS collars to fifty noblemen of sufficiently high rank (Cat. 6).

The Lancastrian livery provides a *terminus post quem* for Pisanello's work (although the Gonzaga already owned such collars, previously they had not been entitled to distribute them).

The fresco was certainly not started before the end of 1436, but we should like to emphasize that it was probably not begun after the death of Gianfrancesco (September 1444).

I.T.

BIBLIOGRAPHY: Cherry, 1969, pp. 38-53; Toesca, 1973, p. 361; Id., 1974, p. 210 (with previous bibliog.); Id., 1976, p. 622; Id., 1977, p. 349.
ADDITIONAL BIBLIOGRAPHY: I. Toesca, "Postilla a proposito di un fiore", *Civiltà Mantovana*, XII, 1978, p. 233 (about the probable heraldic colours of the Gonzaga *calendula*, or marigold).

9

10

Photograph: **John Gower's SS collar**
Engraving of detail (before restoration) of tomb in Southwark Cathedral, London

This SS collar, apparently made of leather with SS stamped on it, and a pendant with the device of the swan, is probably the nearest illustration of the sort of Lancastrian collar depicted in Pisanello's fresco (see Cat. 9). The poet Gower was presented with a collar by Henry Earl of Derby, the future Henry IV, in *c*. 1393-94; his tomb dates from *c*. 1408-09; it therefore predates by only a few years the first references to SS collars and swan pendants in Mantuan documents.

D.S.C.

BIBLIOGRAPHY: Wagner, 1959; Cherry, 1969, p. 48.

11

A swan holding in its mouth an SS collar
Bronze roundel, formerly enamelled, in black, blue, red and torquoise (damaged by bombing in Second World War); diam. 8.4 cm, fifteenth century.
British Museum, Department of Medieval and Later Antiquities (82, 10-11, 22)

This pendant, probably a harness ornament, combines the devices of the swan (associated in England with the Bohun family and thus by marriage with Henry of Lancaster and his heirs) and the collar of SS (associated with John of Gaunt and so with the Lancastrian dynasty). The swan holds in its beak what appears to be a type of SS collar made of leather with buckle and belt tag for wearing on armour or horse trappings

as in the Pisanello frieze at Mantua; the esses are in angular Gothic lettering, which weakens a theory that the "S" itself was intended to represent the swan by shape and as a misspelling of *cygnus*.

D.S.C.

PROVENANCE: Unknown.
BIBLIOGRAPHY: Cherry, 1969, pp. 48, 53.

12

Study for a Virgin and Child, Gonzaga coat-of-arms, two studies of a Youth in court dress, and other decorative devices
Antonio Pisanello (*c*. 1390-*c*. 1455)
27.7 x 19.7 cm, bistre ink on rough beige paper, traces of black chalk beneath the interlinked rings, an obliterated chalk drawing beneath the Virgin and Child
Verso: traces of red chalk
Musée du Louvre, Cabinet des Dessins (no. 2278)

The inclusion of the old Gonzaga arms on this sheet connects it with Pisanello's work for Mantua; its close relationship to other Louvre drawings (e.g. Vallardi, 2277) suggests that it is contemporary with the *Giostra* fresco cycle uncovered just

over a decade ago in the *Corte Vecchia*. The date of both frescoes and drawings is contentious; Fossi Todorow dated the drawings *c.* 1446-47, Paccagnini accepted this date for the frescoes and assumed that Ludovico Gonzaga commissioned them. Others, on the grounds of style and iconography, date the frescoes (and consequently the drawings) in the late 1430's, certainly before the death of Gianfrancesco Gonzaga in 1444. (See Toesca's article in this catalogue and Cat. 9). Pisanello was resident in Mantua as early as 1422 and was working for the Gonzaga between 1439-42; although he corresponded with Gianfrancesco in 1443 there is no firm evidence that he visited Mantua again.

This sheet containing designs for a variety of projects is typical of Pisanello's working method (paper was still comparatively expensive). In the top left-hand corner is a sketch for an altar of a Virgin of Humility (she sits on the ground) in a mandorla, with cherubim and possibly angels either holding back curtains or supporting a crest. Paccagnini (1973) connected the sketch with the *Virgin & Child with St Anthony Abbot and St. George* (National Gallery, London) but this appears to be a design for an independent altar, possibly on a small scale. To the right seraphim support the Gonzaga arms (1 and 4 Lion of Bohemia *arg.* crowned *or*, 2 and 3 *or* 3 bars sable) used from 1365 to 1433, but even after that date they served as an escutcheon of pretence, so this does not provide a *terminus ante quem* (Hill, 1965, p. 30) as Amadei believed (1968, p. 296). Hill suggested these arms were designed for a medal, of which the obverse was to be the *impresa* of a muzzled dog first used by Gianfrancesco (Gerola, 1918) and drawn on another Louvre sheet, no. 2277. But the larger study of the dog on the same drawing is so close to the *sinopia* of the dog (reversed) on the hangings of the ladies' pavilion in the *Giostra* frescoes that both designs may have been for this fictive brocade (Mantua, 1972, p. 73). Beneath the arms is a rapid sketch of a winged seraphim, below are two complex designs of interlinked rings (a ring was a Gonzaga symbol especially used by Gianfrancesco) possibly also intended for brocade decoration. Pisanello's interest in dress and fabric designs may stem from the fact that both his father and one of his step-fathers were drapers by trade. The final two sketches may be both for the same figure seen from two viewpoints. Paccagnini suggested they were studies for courtiers to be shown in the foreground of the *Giostra* fresco, but Zanoli (1973) observed the similarity between this figure and that of a youthful saint in another Louvre drawing (no. 2300) which appears to be for a three-dimensional object rather than a painting, possibly a design for a silversmith for a *pax* in the form of an elaborately framed Virgin & Child flanked by saints.

J.T.M.

PROVENANCE: Vallardi.
BIBLIOGRAPHY: Gerola, 1918, p. 98; Hill, 1965 (Reprint), p. 29 no. 9.; Fossi Todorow, 1966, p. 36 ff., p. 86, no. 69 (with bibliography); Amadei, 1968, p. 278-320; Mantua, 1972, p. 98 no. 49; Paccagnini, 1973, pp. 219-20; Zanoli, 1973, pp. 23-44; Toesca, 1973, p. 361 ff., and 1976, p. 622 ff.

Pisanello's portrait medals of the Gonzaga

Antonio Pisano called Pisanello (*c.* 1390-*c.* 1455) was not only famous as a painter but also because "he virtually invented the art of the portrait medal" cast in lead or bronze; these fine objects commemorating individuals or events, suitable as gifts or mementoes and inspired by the ancient Roman medallion, clearly had a strong appeal for patrons already under the influence of humanist learning and values.

His first such medal represented the last Byzantine Emperor John VIII Paleologo, when he came to Ferrara in 1438 for the Church Council there; Pisanello thereafter designed medals for various patrons including a series for the Gonzaga, one of which is dated 1447, though it is uncertain where he made these medals.

13

Gianfrancesco Gonzaga (1395-1444), **first Marchese of Mantua**
Medal; lead; diam. 100 mm; *c.* 1447 (?)
Antonio Pisanello (*c.* 1390-*c.* 1455)
British Museum, Department of Coins and Medals (Inv. 1912-3-6-1; Hill, *Corpus*, no. 20e, 20f.)

The obverse commemorates Gianfrancesco's role as a military captain, principally in Venetian service, as well as his political status as Marquis of Mantua, conferred by the Emperor Sigismund in 1433. The reverse, signed OPVS. PISANI PICTORIS, shows Gianfrancesco on horseback bearing a commander's baton, and behind him the rearview of a dwarf-like page also on horseback; just in front of his head appears to be a stylized version of the device of the sunflower or heliotrope. The design is related to Pisanello's drawing of riders in a rocky landscape (Louvre, Inv. 2595). Although this medal may have been made *c.* 1439 in Gianfrancesco's lifetime, the possibility is great that Marchese Ludovico commissioned it later as a commemorative portrait of his father.

D.S.C.

BIBLIOGRAPHY: Hill and Pollard, 1967, no. 2, p. 7; Paccagnini, 1972, no. 76, p. 114; Hill rev. Pollard, 1978, p. 37; Jones, 1979, p. 23.

14

virtues with an understanding of scholarship and the arts.

D.S.C.

BIBLIOGRAPHY: Hill and Pollard, 1967, no. 18 p. 10; Paccagnini, 1972, no. 79, p. 116; Hill rev. Pollard, 1978, p. 41; Jones, 1979, p. 23; Woodward, 1897, pp. 7-8; Garin, 1958, pp. 596, 640; Signorini, 1979, pp. 9-19.
ADDITIONAL BIBLIOGRAPHY: R. van Broek, *The Myth of the Phoenix*, Leyden, 1972, pp. 197, 358.

14

Vittorino da Feltre (1378-1446), **humanist educator at the Gonzaga Court**
Antonio Pisanello (*c*. 1390-*c*. 1455)
Medal; lead; diam. 67 mm; *c*. 1447
British Museum, Department of Coins and Medals (Inv. 1906-11-3-237; Hill, *Corpus* no. 38d)
Victoria & Albert Museum, Department of Sculpture (Inv. 504-1864; not listed by Hill).

Pisanello's medal provides a characterization of the revered schoolmaster (cf. Cat. 16-17), who had brought from Padua (where he studied and taught from 1396 to 1416) many new influences in learning including the educational precepts of Pier Paolo Vergerio which combined ancient moral virtues, acquired through the study of literature, with christian duty. The naturalistic portrait on the obverse corresponds in facial expression to accounts of his amiable manner combined with gravity, although he is wearing a tall cap rather than the small hood (*cappuccio piccolo*) described in the short biography of him by Vespasiano da Bisticci, the Florentine bookseller. The inscription, continuing from obverse to reverse sides of the medal, reads: VICTORINVS. FELTRENSIS. SVMMVS/MATHEMATICVS ET. OMNIS HVMANITATIS. PATER. OPVS. PISANI. PICTORIS.
Vittorino's distinction not only as a scholar of Latin and Greek (humanity) but as a mathematician also goes back to his Paduan days. A bird, usually assumed to be a pelican appears on the reverse (Hill and Pollard), shedding blood for the sake of its young, and symbolizing Christ. But the bird does not look like a pelican, and Vittorino's pupil and biographer Francesco Prendilacqua (known *c*. 1422-*c*. 1483) states that Pisanello painted a portrait of Vittorino among the ancient philosophers with a phoenix at his feet and also depicted it in bronze, drawing its own blood to raise its young. The phoenix, he explained, represented Vittorino's self-sacrifice as a teacher. It seems unlikely that Prendilacqua had simply made a mistake (Signorini, 1979).
One version of the phoenix legend (Horapollo, *Hieroglyphica*, II. 57) tells that it was from the blood of its parent's self-inflicted wound that the single young phoenix was born. The bird shown here does, moreover, seem to be standing above something which could be the nest of precious spices on which it will die or the flames on which it will be sacrificed. On the other hand the presence of two chicks and the parent still alive nourishing them is more suggestive of the pelican. The date 1447 for the medal, corresponding to that of Vittorino's pupil Cecilia (Cat. 16) is convincing; Marchese Ludovico had every reason, as another former pupil at the *Casa Giocosa* (see Cat. 2) to commemorate gratefully the teacher who had recently died. Prendilacqua mentions that Ludovico as a boy was fat and clumsy and Vittorino had made him diet and listen to music; thanks to his education Ludovico became an example of the new style of prince, combining military

15

Ludovico Gonzaga (1412-78), **second Marchese of Mantua**
Medal; bronze; diam. 102 mm; *c*. 1447 (?)
Antonio Pisanello (*c*. 1390-*c*. 1455)
Victoria & Albert Museum, Department of Sculpture (Inv. A 166-1910; Hill, *Corpus* no. 36e)

Ludovico, bareheaded on the obverse, is described as CAPITANEVS. ARMIGERORVM. MARCHIO. MANTVE. ET. CET (the etc. refers presumably to the lesser lordships, e.g. the castle of Borgoforte, which he received in the division with his brothers of

15

Gianfrancesco's inheritance). The reverse shows him on horseback in armour and closed helmet with crest; the Gonzaga devices of the sun and the sunflower accompany him and the signature is given OPVS. PISANI. PICTORIS. Because the medal of Cecilia (Cat. 16) is dated 1447, it has been inferred that her brother also commissioned among others this medal of himself in his father's image (Cat. 13) to commemorate his appointment in January 1447 as Captain in the service of Florence. Previously he had had a protective alliance with Duke Filippo Maria Visconti of Milan and had been involved in the defeat of the latter's troops at Casalmaggiore (September 1446); he now committed himself to the league of Venice and other powers against Milan, which started a successful offensive under his leadership in April-June 1447, only cut short by Visconti's death.

D.S.C.

BIBLIOGRAPHY: Hill and Pollard, 1967, no. 16, p. 10; Paccagnini, 1972, no. 78, p. 116; Hill rev. Pollard, 1978, p. 47; Jones, 1979, p. 23; Mazzoldi, 1960, pp. 3-6.

Cecilia Gonzaga (1426-51), **a prodigy of learning and model of chastity**
Antonio Pisanello (*c.* 1390-*c.* 1455)
Medal; bronze; diam. 87 mm; dated 1447
Victoria & Albert Museum, Department of Sculpture (Inv. 7131-1860; Hill, *Corpus* no. 37d)

Cecilia Gonzaga, one of the cleverest of Vittorino's pupils (Cat. 14, 17) astonished Ambrogio Traversari by her progress in Greek at the age of seven. Tall and beautiful according to Francesco Prendilacqua, she refused marriage to the disreputable Oddantonio di Montefeltro Duke of Urbino (murdered in 1444) in defiance of her father but with the support of Vittorino. After Gianfrancesco's death she became a Clarissan nun at Santa Paola, the convent attached to the church of Corpus Domini in Mantua much favoured by her mother Paola Malatesta, who herself entered it as a widow. Three of her brothers and a large crowd escorted her there through the streets of Mantua in February 1445. This portrait medal, commemorating her example, is inscribed on the obverse CICILIA. VIRGO. FILIA. IOHANNIS FRANCISCI. PRIMI. MARCHIONIS. MANTVE; it shows her nevertheless in secular court dress with her hair tied back with ribbon which suggests that Pisanello was not in Mantua in 1447 and used an earlier drawing. The reverse shows the mythical unicorn, symbol of chastity, being tamed by the prescribed method, the touch of a virgin girl alone in the moonlight; a tablet is inscribed OPVS. PISANI. PICTORIS. MCCCCXLVII, providing the only date on any of Pisanello's Gonzaga medals.

D.S.C.

BIBLIOGRAPHY: Woodward, 1897, pp. 50, 60; Garin, 1958, p. 648; Hill and Pollard, 1967, no. 17, p. 10; Mantua, 1972, no. 77, p. 115; Zanoli, 1973, pp. 31-32; Hill rev. Pollard, 1978, pp. 40-41; Signorini, 1979, pp. 17-18; Jones, 1979, p. 23, Letts, 1980, pp. 26-31.

16

Humanist education at the Mantuan court and Gonzaga book collecting

The Gonzaga were already collecting books in the fourteenth century and an inventory of 1407 lists 392 titles, many of them works of theology and piety and French romances, though including some copies of Latin classics and literary works in Italian, particularly of Petrarch and Boccaccio. But in the fifteenth century Gonzaga book collecting expanded greatly, owing to humanist influence and particularly that of Vittorino da Feltre, court schoolmaster from 1423 to 1446, who was put in charge of Marchese Gianfrancesco's library. Ludovico Gonzaga, Marchese of Mantua from 1444 to 1478, a former pupil of Vittorino, deeply respected humanist values; he kept in touch with many scholars, employed a variety of scribes and illuminators and in addition to buying books widely (including Greek texts) received numerous dedications. His sons, particularly Francesco, appointed a Cardinal in 1461, followed this tradition of literary patronage and collecting, which continued well into the age of printing.

17

Photograph: **Letter of Vittorino da Feltre to Marchesa Paola Malatesta, Borgoforte, 2 February 1439**
Manuscript in Latin on paper; autograph
Archivio di Stato, Mantua (Autografi, b. 9, c. 161)

Vittorino Ramboldini da Feltre (1378-1446), famous as a humanist and educational pioneer, who influenced a generation of Italian princes and scholars, wrote no books and few of his letters survive. Most of what is known about him and his teaching methods in the court school of Mantua, over which he presided from *c.* 1423, depends on the writings of grateful pupils and admirers. This note to his patroness addressed from Borgoforte, a castle on the Po, gives a good report on the Gonzaga children, praising in particular the youngest son (Alessandro). A complaint against a certain woman to whom the celibate Vittorino refers wryly as his Xantippe (Socrates' wife) has not been explained; she was perhaps a housekeeper or governess for Cecilia and Margherita.

D.S.C.

BIBLIOGRAPHY: Luzio, 1888, p. 333; Woodward, 1897, p. 75; Garin, 1958, p. 715; Signorini, 1979, pp. 62-63; Letts, 1980.

18

Speeches of Cicero copied for Marchese Gianfrancesco Gonzaga
M. Tullii Ciceronis, *Orationes*
Manuscript in Latin on paper, 230 fols, 25.5 x 14.5 cm; unknown scribe and illuminator of initials, probably Venetian; Gonzaga arms of 1433
British Library (Burney MS 159)

As models for the practice of rhetoric Cicero's works were indispensable to humanist studies. The present selection of eighteen speeches is in a humanistic style of handwriting found in Venice from the early 1420's and the border decora-

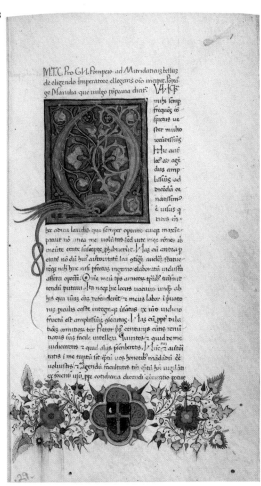

18

Lionardo Bruni of Arezzo (1370?-1444) the eminent humanist scholar, who in 1427 became Chancellor of Florence, writes in his preface to this work, which he composed about 1419, that owing to the loss of the section of Livy's Roman history which covered the first Punic war, he had been "moved... to compose a commentary on the war", basing himself on what he "could learn... from Polybius and other Greeks". The *De bello punico* is, in fact, primarily a free and condensed version of books I to II, 35, of Polybius' *Histories*, which he supplements with material derived from other historians and his own additions. It nevertheless constitutes the first Latin version of any part of Polybius' work made in the Renaissance; it was to be followed, in 1454, by Niccolò Perotti's translation of the first five books of the *Histories*. In the *Histories*, Bruni "had discovered a missing chapter of Republican Roman history and had suddenly presented Polybius as an authority on Republican Rome" (Momigliano).

The scribe of this manuscript is unidentified, but the interlaced decoration of the opening initial shown here is clearly by the same Mantuan illuminator who decorated initials in some other Gonzaga books e.g. Cat. 20 and British Library, Harley MS. 3691, text of Josephus; (information from Dr. A. de la Mare who has also identified the library stamp on fol. 1r as that of the convent of the Santissima Annunziata, Florence).

N.R.

BIBLIOGRAPHY: Meroni, 1966, p. 36, pl. 95.
ADDITIONAL BIBLIOGRAPHY: B. Reynolds, "Bruni and Perotti present a Greek historian", *Bibliothèque d'humanisme et de Renaissance*, xvi, 1954, pp. 108-114; A. Momigliano, "Polybius' reappearance in Western Europe", in *Entretiens sur l'antiquité classique*, xx, Geneva, 1973, pp. 352-57.

19

tions can be compared to the work there of Cristoforo Cortese (information from Dr. A. de la Mare). Other works of Cicero copied for the Gonzaga library in about the same period are the *Philippics* (Burney, MS 154) and *Tusculan Disputations* with *On the Greatest Degree of Good and Evil* (*De Finibus*) (Burney MS 153). The treatise *On Duties* (*De Officiis*) is known to have been written for Marchese Ludovico in 1463 by the scribe Matteo Contugi (Meroni, 1966, pp. 57-58) and Ludovico also had a copy of the *Dream of Scipio* with two other texts (Meroni, 1966, p. 79; pl. 90) which – judging from the arms with the letters LU – must have been made for him before his accession in 1444.

D.S.C.

BIBLIOGRAPHY: Meroni, 1966, p. 37; pl. 93 (wrongly labelled as MS Burney 154).
ADDITIONAL BIBLIOGRAPHY: *Cat. of MSS in the British Museum, The Burney MSS*, London, 1842, p. 52.

19

Roman Republican history in the Gonzaga library
Lionardo Bruni, *De bello punico libri tres* (1421)
Manuscript in Latin on vellum; 89 fols; 21 cm x 14 cm; third quarter of fifteenth century; decorated (fol. 1r) with Gonzaga arms of 1433 and crest
British Library (Additional MS 14777)

A de luxe edition of a work by Boccaccio copied for Marchese Ludovico Gonzaga

Giovanni Boccaccio, *Il Filocolo*
Manuscript in Italian on vellum, 35.5 x 23 cm; II +240 +2 fols.; written 1463-64 by Andrea de Laude (Lodi); illuminations by (?) Pietro Guindaleri of Cremona and another hand; first title page with Gonzaga arms
Bodleian Library, Oxford (MS Canonici Italiani 85)

A recently discovered letter (ASMAG b. 2401) identifies Andrea de Laude (Lodi) as the scribe of this manuscript; he wrote to remind the Marquis on 30 January 1464 that (for the third time of asking) his needs – six florins and four sacks of corn – should be satisfied, and "I will deliver within a month a Filocolo which I have begun, which will be the most accurate and correct of any I have ever written" (*Fornirò uno philocolo che ho principiato, il quale sarà el più iusto et più correcto de quanti ne ho mai scripto*). In 1458 he had been paid for copying two other books. Pietro Guindaleri of Cremona, who is known to have been in Gonzaga service by 1464 (see Cat. 24) has been identified as the probable illuminator. Boccaccio's story *Il Filocolo*, written *c.* 1336-38, is about a King's son, Filocolo, who searches for his childhood love Biancifiore who had been sent away. At the beginning of Book IV (shown here) he and his companions pass by Mantua "the marshy place where Manto [the legendary foundress] laid her bones". At last Filocolo traces her to Alexandria where he narrowly escapes death, but the story ends happily as her noble origins are revealed and the Moslems become Christians. Boccaccio's works were well represented in the Gonzaga library and the local printer Pietro Adamo de Michaeli asked Marchese Ludovico in September 1471 to lend him a manuscript of the *Decamarone* from which he produced one of the earliest books printed in Mantua.

D.S.C.

BIBLIOGRAPHY: Wardrop, 1963, p. 51; Meroni, 1966, pp. 37, 53, 56-57; Pescasio, 1972, pp. 45-51; 101; Pächt and Alexander, 1970, p. 40.
ADDITIONAL BIBLIOGRAPHY: *Mostra, VI Centenario della morte di Giovanni Boccaccio*, Florence, 1975, no. 9, 31-32; J. Alexander, "The scribe of the Boccaccio Filocolo identified", *Bodleian Library Record*, ix, 1977, pp. 303-04.

21

Latin grammar of Francesco (later Cardinal) Gonzaga, 1457

Tractatus grammaticalis
Latin manuscript on vellum written by Giuliano da Viterbo; fols. 17.2 x 12.5 cm; illuminator unknown
Biblioteca Estense, Modena (MS Lat. 1101)

This elementary grammar book was written for the protonotary Francesco Gonzaga, according to a note dated 30 May 1457 on fol. 39, by Giuliano da Viterbo, the same scribe who wrote a text of Josephus for Guidone Gonzaga (British Library, Harley MS 3691) and was described by Francesco as *un mio scritore* in a letter to his mother, 17 May 1460 (ASMAG b. 1621). That the text was composed by Francesco himself is suggested on the title page (*editus a puero per me Franciscum Gonzagam*) and at the end (fol. 22v) but this can hardly be the whole truth. The title page bears portraits of the thirteen year-old Francesco and of his tutor, probably Bartolomeo Marasca who claimed in a letter of 31 October 1458 (ASMAG b. 2393) to have taught Francesco more in two years than he

20

21

had learned in five at school (*ho fato in due ani che seranno a nove di de novembre quello zia facea in cinque in la scola generale*). The tutor declared he had used many teaching tricks (*astutie e arte*) and meant perhaps among these the pretence of writing a special grammar with his pupil (the treatise does contain various exercises which refer to the noun *protonotarius*). However slow in his lessons as a boy, Francesco as a Cardinal (1461-83) was to be a notable patron and book collector. The unpublished inventory drawn up after his death includes (fol. 17r) an item which may be this book (*la grammatica dal quondam Monsignore*) with a marginal note that it had been given to a *magnifico domino Francesco*, probably the Cardinal's infant son known in Mantua as the *Cardinalino*.

D.S.C.

BIBLIOGRAPHY: Meroni, 1966, pp. 181-82; pl. 109.
ADDITIONAL BIBLIOGRAPHY: On the inventory, G. Frasso, "Oggetti d'arte e libri nell'inventario del Cardinale Francesco Gonzaga", Mantova, Gonzaga Convegno, 1978, pp. 141-44; on the *Cardinalino*, Chambers, 1980.

22

A Latin grammar for Federico Gonzaga, later third Marchese of Mantua

Ognibene Bonisoli da Lonigo (Omnibonus Leonicenus), *Liber de octo partibus Orationis sive Grammaticae libellus ad Fredericum de Gonzaga*, Venice, Jacobus Rubeus, 1473
British Library (C 2 a.3)

Ognibene (*c.* 1412-74) was formerly a pupil in Mantua of Vittorino da Feltre and from 1449 to 1453 himself taught there; but most of his active life as humanist teacher, translator and commentator was spent at Vicenza. He had taught Marchese Ludovico's eldest son Federico who was not the

22

brightest of pupils according to Francesco Filelfo – and in a letter (ASMAG b. 2101, *c.* 36) of 1 September 1473 to his mother Barbara of Brandenburg Federico recalled that Ognibene had composed an elementary Latin grammar for him (cf. Cat. 21) of which he could no longer find a copy. Ognibene, however, had said that he could easily rewrite it, and the new version was brought by his nephew, a former schoolmate of

Federico's (*Ugnabene, che fu mio maistro a schola, me fece altra volta regole per insignar a putti: e me ne lassò copia la quale è persa: e per haverne de nova copia scrissi piú dì fa a decto Ugnabene che volesse farmela havere: e me rispose non se trovaria haverne copia alcuna ma che ben le haveva a memoria e pigliaria il tempo di metterle in scritto e me le mandaria. E cussì adesso me le manda per el nepote che fumi compagno el qual vene per visitarme e per darme dicte regole*).

It may be presumed that either Ognibene or Federico immediately had the work printed in this rare early edition (which was intended to have initial letters painted in by hand), and that it was used for the instruction of Federico's children, including Francesco the future Marquis and Sigismondo the future Cardinal. The preface by Ognibene refers to Vittorino as the master of Federico's father (*magister... simul et vivendi praeceptor*) and recalls his own appointment to Vittorino's place; he exhorts Federico to take good care of the education of his own children (*... ut liberi tui bonis moribus et optimis disciplinis imbuantur*). Federico in fact appointed Mario Filelfo (Filippo's son) as his children's tutor and bought Mario's books from his widow in 1480 (Meroni).

D.S.C.

BIBLIOGRAPHY: Davari, 1876, pp. 8-9; Luzio and Renier, 1890[2], pp. 140-42; DBI; Meroni, 1966, p. 62.

23

Dedication copy to Federico Gonzaga of the treatise *On the Prince* by Platina (1421-81)

B. Platina, *De principe*, 1471?
Manuscript in Latin on vellum, 107 fols. 18.3 x 12.4 cm; scribe (and illuminator?) Bartolomeo Sanvito (1438-1511)
Biblioteca Comunale, Mantua (MS A.I. 13)

Bartolomeo Sacchi called "Platina" (from his birthplace Piadena near Cremona) was educated at Mantua by Vittorino, a *Life* of whom he wrote, and was briefly a tutor of Marchese Ludovico's children before joining in 1457 the group of humanists round Cosimo de' Medici and Ficino in Florence. Sometime after 1461 he entered the household in Rome of Cardinal Francesco Gonzaga who protected him when he was imprisoned with other humanists for alleged conspiracy against Paul II; in 1475 Sixtus IV appointed him head of the new Vatican Library.

Author of the first humanist history of the Popes, he also composed numerous Latin treatises. Two of these, the *De principe* and the *De optimo cive*, are different versions of the same text. Platina dedicated the former to Federico Gonzaga, son and heir of Ludovico, the latter to Lorenzo de' Medici, grandson of Cosimo; the former is a treatise on princely virtues for an autocratic Italian ruler, the latter a eulogy of civic virtues in the person of Cosimo, first citizen and virtual ruler of Florence, who was posthumously awarded the title of *pater patriae*. Accordingly the two versions often provide different, and at times contradictory, lessons to the ideal ruler for whom they are designed; and in the *De principe* an additional third book deals with matters such as war and hunting that were considered to be more appropriate to a prince than to a citizen. The chronological relationship between the two treatises can be reconstructed from the following evidence. Another manuscript of the *De principe* was copied in Rome in 1470, and in a letter dated, from Rome, 22 October and probably written in 1471 (ed. Luzio and Renier, 1889, p. 439) Platina announced to Marchese Ludovico the gift of the treatise. In April 1474 Lorenzo de' Medici thanked Platina for the *De optimo cive* which, as Donato Acciaiuoli wrote to Platina in the

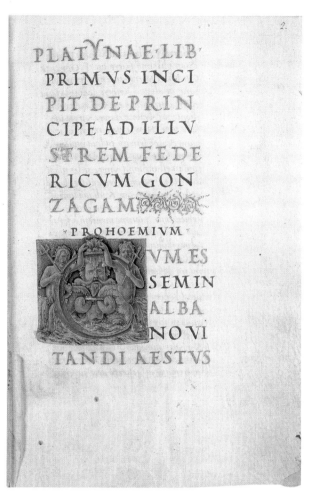

23

24

following month, he had greatly enjoyed reading. Since it is unlikely that Platina dedicated to Lorenzo in 1474 a work written before 1470 (even, as has been assumed, before 1461) it can be safely assumed that the *De principe* antedates the *De optimo cive*, although the existence of an earlier draft of this work cannot be excluded.

N.R.

BIBLIOGRAPHY: Luzio and Renier, 1889; Wardrop, 1963; Meroni, 1966, p. 83 Tav. 119
ADDITIONAL BIBLIOGRAPHY: The *De principe* was printed in Frankfurt in 1608 and in Genoa in 1637; critical ed. by G. Ferraù, Palermo 1979. Cf. *ibid.*, introduction (with bibliography); F. Gilbert, "The Prince of Machiavelli", in *History, Choice and Commitment*, Cambridge, Mass., 1977, pp. 99, 107; H. Lutz, "Bemerkungen zu dem Traktat 'De optimo cive' des Bartolomeo Platina", *Mitteilungen des Instituts für Österreichische Geschichtsforschung*, LXXVII, 1970, pp. 372-85; N. Rubinstein, "Le dottrine politiche nel Rinascimento", in *Il Rinascimento. Interpretazione e problemi*, Bari 1979, pp. 213-14.

24

Petrarch's "Canzoniere" for Cardinal Francesco Gonzaga

Manuscript in Italian on vellum, *c.* 1463-83; 299 fols; 26 x 17.5 cm
British Library (Harley MS 3567)

The Gonzaga arms, though partially erased, surmounted by a

Cardinal's hat on the title page (fol. 9r) – which also has a faded miniature showing Petrarch and Laura with Cupid aiming an arrow at them – indicate clearly the owner of this manuscript was Cardinal Francesco. Among other works of Petrarch in his library a second copy of the *Canzoniere* certainly belonged to him (Vatican Library, MS. Vat. Urb. 681) and possibly a third (see Cat. 25); maybe this example was the one bound in green velvet (*Un Petrarcha coperto de veluto verde*) which is mentioned (fol. 16r) in the inventory drawn up after his death (1483). A note in the inventory margin by the hand of Giovanni Pietro Arrivabene, the Cardinal's former secretary and executor, states that it had passed to the protonotary Ludovico Gonzaga (the Cardinal's younger brother). The scribe Matteo Contugi of Volterra, who worked for the Gonzaga in Mantua at least as early as August 1463 and until 1486, signed the manuscript as the work of his hand (fol. 189r) though there are also rubrics and commentary in a hand identified as that of Bartolomeo Sanvito.

The illumination (shown here is the Triumph of Time, fol. 184r) is thought to be by the hand of Pietro Guindaleri of Cremona, also identified as the illuminator of the *Filocolo* (Cat. 20) who in a letter of 30 November 1489 to Marchese Francesco stated that he had entered Marchese Ludovico's service twenty-five years previously (ASMAG b. 2438, c. 16). Although Guindaleri had also since 1479 been doing some illumination for Sigismondo Gonzaga, the latter (then only ten) did not become a Cardinal until 1505 and the evidence above does not suggest that this manuscript was his.

D.S.C.

BIBLIOGRAPHY: Wardrop, 1963, p. 51; Meroni, 1966, pp. 28, 57, 60; Pächt and Alexander, 1970, II, p. 40; Mann, 1975, pp. 296-8; information from Dr. G. Frasso.
ADDITIONAL BIBLIOGRAPHY: C.E. Wright, *Fontes Harleiani*, London, 1972, p. 167.

Laura and an inscription below providing the title. Facing it is Francesco dei Russi's decoration of the first page of the *Rime*.

D.S.C.

PROVENANCE : Dyson Perrins. Acquired by purchase, Sotheby's 1946.
BIBLIOGRAPHY: Wardrop, 1963, pp. 34, 51; Ruysschaert, 1969, pp. 363-74; Alexander, 1970, pp. 27-40; Mann, 1975, pp. 329-31.
ADDITIONAL BIBLIOGRAPHY: J. I. Whalley and V.C. Kaden, *The Universal Penman*, Exhibition Catalogue, Victoria & Albert Museum, 1980, no. 48, p. 28.

25

26

25

Petrarch's "Canzoniere": another copy for Cardinal Francesco Gonzaga

Manuscript in Italian on vellum, written by Bartolomeo Sanvito *c.* 1462-75; 23 x 14 cm; 197 + 1 fols; illuminations by Francesco dei Russi and another
Victoria & Albert Museum, Library (L 101-1947)

Although the coat of arms beneath the Cardinal's hat on the frontispiece has been rubbed out, the likeliest owner of this manuscript is thought to have been Cardinal Francesco Gonzaga. The text is agreed to be in the hand of Bartolomeo Sanvito of Padua (1438-1511) who copied other manuscripts for him, though he was no means the only patron of this prodigiously active scribe. Of the two artists who decorated it, one has been identified as Francesco dei Russi, who was born in Mantua but had worked at Ferrara on Borso d'Este's Bible (finished 1461) and the other, remaining anonymous, expresses the influence of Mantegna or at least of the archaeologizing classicism the latter brought from Padua. These two artists also collaborated with Sanvito on a Book of Hours now in the Biblioteca Ambrosiana, Milan.

Their work can be contrasted here on a pair of facing pages, (fols. 9v-10r). The anonymous artist's tinted yellow frontispiece has a figure on the left of Apollo, or possibly Orpheus, holding a lyre. There is a tomb, flanked by winged genii bearing torches, with a niche containing busts of Petrarch and

26

Greek Gospels for Cardinal Francesco Gonzaga

Manuscript in Greek on vellum; 299+II fols; 31 x 21.5 cm; written by Johannes Rhosos, 1478; illuminator unknown
British Library (Harley MS 5790)

Although it is most unlikely that Cardinal Francesco Gonzaga knew any Greek, it is clear from a note on fol. 299 that this manuscript was written for him in 1478 by the Cretan scribe Johannes Rhosos as were in 1477 copies of the *Iliad* and the *Odyssey* now in the Vatican Library (MSS Vat. Gr. 1626-27). Rhosos was very productive and 124 manuscripts in his hand (1457-97) are known; among other patrons in Rome he had worked for was Cardinal Bessarion (d. 1472). Maybe the commission was thanks to Cardinal Francesco's scholarly secretary Giovanni Pietro Arrivabene who later possessed the Gospels (his signature appears on fol. 1r); it is also notable that neither this nor any other Greek manuscript books are listed in the inventory of the Cardinal's books and chattels drawn up after his death in 1483. The title page of each Gospel is decorated and all except Matthew have facing full page illustrations of the respective Evangelist at work in architectural settings. It is suggested by Professor R. Nelson that the illuminator, probably Italian, for the headpieces of each Gospel may have been following a late eleventh century Greek Gospel book (Bib. Vat. MS Rossianus 135-38) which could arguably have been in a Roman library in the 1470's. In the

27

opening shown here of the beginning of St John's Gospel (fol. 232v - 233r) the headpieces showing Christ and archangels correspond to the prototype, as does the tiny figure of St John the Baptist beside the bottom of the text column, although he is no longer beside the appropriate verse because Rhosos' script was so large that he only reached verse 6 on the second page.

D.S.C.

BIBLIOGRAPHY: Meroni, 1966, pp. 37, 59-60; Alexander and de la Mare, 1969, pp. 107, 109; Alexander, 1970.
ADDITIONAL BIBLIOGRAPHY: M. Vogel and G. Gardthausen, *Die griechischen Schreiber des Mittelalters und der Renaissance*, Leipzig, 1909; unpublished information from forthcoming works by Dr. G. Frasso and Professor Robert Nelson.

27

A Herbal Treatise from Cardinal Francesco Gonzaga's library
Apulei Platonici *Herbarium*; manuscript in Latin on vellum, 25 x 16 cm; 50 fols. 1481-83
British Library (Additional MS. 21115)

In the unedited inventory of Cardinal Francesco Gonzaga's goods and chattels after his death (1483) there is an entry (fol. 17r) among his other books of *un Apuleio de herbis cun le picture*

which is to be identified with this book. Not only is it decorated (fol. 2r) with the Gonzaga arms and (fols. 5v-6r) with the sun device and motto "Per un desir sub [sole] O[mni]A tempus habe[n]t" but it also contains a dedicatory letter to him written by Giovanni Filippo La Legname (de Lignamine) pointing out that the *Herbarium* (a practical and widely used prescription book based on Dioscorides, which was known since the fourth century A.D.) might be useful if he was ill. This was a fair conjecture, seeing that Cardinal Francesco, like others of the Gonzaga family, was much concerned about his own and others' health, and his letters are full of details about sickness and remedies. Giovanni Filippo was a physician in papal service and also an editor of early printed texts; in fact this manuscript appears to have been copied from his printed edition of the *Herbarium* which likewise contains the dedication to Cardinal Francesco and was published in *c.* 1481-82, though there is no reason to infer that the Cardinal had any prejudice against printed books, others of which were dedicated to him.

Giovanni Filippo kept up longstanding contacts with the Gonzaga and in 1477 had been sent to Mantua as papal ambassador, bringing the honorific gift of the Golden Rose to Marchese Ludovico.

ADDITIONAL BIBLIOGRAPHY: ed. F. Hunger, *The Herbal of Pseudo-Apuleius*, Leyden, 1935; unpublished information from Dr. G. Frasso.

II   The arts of peace and war

While the Gonzaga remained professional soldiers, commanders who hired out their services, they also equipped themselves for peaceful pursuits: physically as keen horsemen and hunters, intellectually as patrons of the arts, stimulated by their humanist educators and contacts throughout Italy. Under Ludovico Gonzaga (Marchese 1444–78) and his successors, Mantua became an outstanding centre of artistic achievement, notably from *c.* 1460 when the painter Andrea Mantegna had moved there and Alberti was advising Ludovico on architectural matters. The idea that princes and their courtiers should combine military skills with knowledge of all the arts owes much to the Gonzaga.

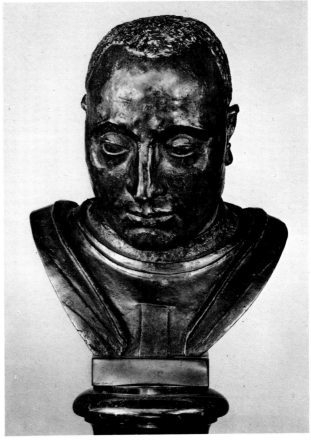

28

Ludovico Gonzaga, second Marquis of Mantua (1412–1478)
Ascribed to Leon Battista Alberti (1404–72)
Bronze bust; h. 34 cm; third quarter of the 15th century
Staatliche Museen, Berlin-Dahlem (52)

Two versions of the bust are known, the other being in the Musée Jacquemart-André, Paris (Inv. no. 1937).
The identification of the subject as Ludovico Gonzaga was made by Grimm in 1883. It is clearly correct, and has received general acceptance. Until 1958, when the current ascription to Alberti was proposed by Badt, the bust was almost universally accepted as a work by, or after Donatello, who was in Mantua in 1450-51 (although a few writers preferred Niccolò Baroncelli). Comparisons adduced with the head of Erasmo de' Narni (*Gattamelata*) in Donatello's equestrian monument at Padua serve, however, only to emphasize the disparity between the structure and handling of the bust and that of Donatello. The argument for Alberti's authorship rests on compelling analogies in handling with Alberti's two self-portrait medallions respectively in the National Gallery of Art, Washington and the Louvre, and it is persuasively demonstrated by Badt that the bust is not the work of a professional sculptor: a view which has recently received powerful support from Middeldorf.
While some writers have seen the version in Paris as a simple aftercast of the present version, several discrepancies make it clear that it is cast from a free and separate model. It is argued by Gavoty that the Paris bust shows Ludovico at a more advanced age than the present bust. Alberti is recorded in Mantua in 1463 and again in 1470, and Gavoty proposes that the present bust was modelled in the former year and that in Paris in the latter: that is, shortly before Mantegna's portraits of Ludovico in the *Camera degli Sposi*.

28

A free variant of the head alone, also in Berlin (Inv. no. 172), appears to show Ludovico at a yet more advanced age. This, while it is apparently loosely based on the same model, is wholly different in facture from the present bronze, highly finished and with the eyes inlaid with silver. A laurel wreath seems to indicate that this head is posthumous. The facture is close to that of Antico's classicizing heads in the Seminario Vescovile, Mantua (see Cat. 123), and this head may well be a Mantuan production of the late fifteenth century. Bode notes a second version of the head alone formerly in the Stroganoff collection, St. Petersburg.
The problems posed by the two busts and their critical history are fully discussed by Gavoty with an exhaustive citation of the extensive earlier literature.

A.F.R.

PROVENANCE: purchased in Paris in 1877 from Frédéric Spitzer.
ADDITIONAL BIBLIOGRAPHY: W. Bode, "Ludovico III Gonzaga in Bronzebüsten und Medaillen", *Jahrbuch der königlich preussischen Kunstsammlungen*,

117

X, 1889, pp. 49-53; W. v. Bode, Staatliche Museen zu Berlin, *Bildwerke des Kaiser-Friedrich-Museums, Die italienischen Bildwerke der Renaissance und des Barock*, II, *Bronzestatuetten, Büsten and Gebrauchsgegenständ*, 4 ed., Berlin/Leipzig, 1930, no. 1; K. Badt, "Drei plastische Arbeiten von Leone Battista Alberti", *Mitteilungen des Kunsthistorischen Institutes in Florenz*, VIII, 1958, pp. 78-87; F. de la Moureyre-Gavoty, *Inventaire des Collections Publiques Françaises*, 19, *Institut de France: Musée Jacquemart-André: Sculpture Italienne*, Paris, 1975, no. 44; U. Middeldorf, "On the dilettante sculptor", *Apollo*, CVII, 1978, p. 314.

29

Half size photographic replica: **The Camera Picta (Painted Room, so-called Camera degli Sposi)** 1465-74
Andrea Mantegna (1431-1506)
Dimensions: original 8.1 sq. m; height 7 m
Castello di S. Giorgio, Palazzo Ducale, Mantua

Despite its apparent unity, Mantegna's most famous exercise in perspectival illusionism took nine years to complete (see essay by Elam, above). He must have started with the ceiling, moved on to the "Court Scene" on the right hand wall and finished with the "Meeting" wall in 1474.
The real architecture of the square audience chamber (see diagram) has had to be simplified for the purposes of this half-size reproduction. A simple curve replaces the complex lunette vault, and none of the real architectural elements (door, window, fireplace, bracket capitals) appear in three dimensions here. In the original, Mantegna extends the archi-

tecture into a more elaborate two-dimensional illusionistic setting, with an open oculus in the ceiling, vault ribs with mouldings and bosses, and decorated pilasters resting on a continuous dado. On the two walls not shown here the curtains are painted as drawn; on these two they are "pulled back" to reveal the scenes of Ludovico Gonzaga and his court. The figures on the left wall are placed under what appears to be an open loggia against a landscape background; they stand on the "dado", while those on the right wall are placed higher up above the (real) fireplace, in front of a coloured marble screen. The physical obstructions of door and fireplace are exploited as platforms for painted figures. To obtain the correct viewpoint in the half-size reproduction, the walls have in this model been raised so that the spectator's eyes should be on a level with the mantelpiece, looking up at the legs of the figures on the right wall, but down at those on the left wall.

The Ceiling
At the centre of the ceiling is simulated an open oculus surrounded by a marble balustrade. Ladies of the court and a moorish slave look down on us, while ten winged putti play around. The illusion succeeds above all through the foreshortening of the parapet and of the putti.
The remainder of the ceiling is painted as monochrome stucco relief set against a background of gold mosaic. In the lozenge shaped divisions around the oculus, reliefs of the first eight Caesars in garlanded roundels are "supported" by putti in apparent three-quarter relief on the curved pendentives.

'Meeting scene': Identification of figures

1 Marquis Ludovico Gonzaga.
2 Cardinal Francesco Gonzaga.
3 Frederick III, Holy Roman Emperor.
4 Christian I, King of Denmark.
5 Federico Gonzaga, future Marquis.
6 Francesco Gonzaga, future Marquis.
7 Sigismondo Gonzaga, future Cardinal.
8 Ludovico Gonzaga, Protonotary, future Bishop
  of Mantua.

'Court scene': Identification of figures.

1 Marquis Ludovico Gonzaga.
2 Barbara of Brandenburg.
3 Either Gianfrancesco or Federico Gonzaga.
4 Either Rodolfo or Gianfrancesco Gonzaga.
5 Protonotary Ludovico Gonzaga, later Bishop of Mantua.
6 Paola Gonzaga (1463-97) youngest daughter of Ludovico
  and Barbara, m. Leonhard Count of Gorizia (1477).
7 Barbara ("Barbarina") Gonzaga, (1455-1505) m. Eberhard
  Duke of Württemberg (1474).
8 Rubino.

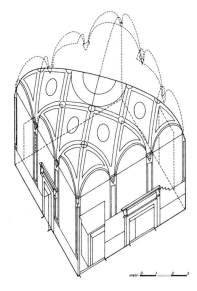

Axonometric projection of the Camera Picta without Mantegna's painted decoration. After drawing by G. Alessi in Coletti and Camesasca, 1959.

The series begins in the north west corner and follows the historical sequence of the Caesars anti-clockwise round the vault: Julius Caesar, Augustus, Tiberius, Caligula, Claudius, Nero, Galba and Otho. Some emperors (e.g. Nero, Galba) are close to their known likenesses; others are more freely invented. Augustus wears the radiate crown of a deified emperor, which in this context may be a reference to the Holy Roman Empire. The supporting putti below Tiberius and Galba are particularly beautiful (cf. Pl. 24).

The twelve curved triangular vault sections above the lunettes contain scenes (also in fictive relief) from classical mythology showing stories of Orpheus, Arion and Hercules: (1) (above window and proceeding anti-clockwise) Orpheus enchanting all nature with his lyre-playing; (2) Orpheus taming Cerberus at the mouth of hell; (3) Maenads killing Orpheus; (4) Arion, poet and musician of the 7th century B.C., cast away by sailors, attracts a dolphin by his song; (5) Arion on the dolphin's back; (6) The sailors accused by Arion before Periander, ruler of Corinth; (7) Hercules, having shot his bow at – (8) the Centaur Nessus, who carries off Deianeira, wife of Hercules; (9) Hercules killing the Nemean lion; (10) Hercules and the Hydra (ruined state); (11) Hercules and Antaeus (see Antico, Cat. 55, for use of antique pose); (12) Hercules captures Cerberus. Iconographically, Orpheus is linked to Arion by the power of music, and to Hercules by having also conquered Cerberus. (In the first scene Orpheus looks back at Hercules in the last). Thus the stories could be said to show the power of the liberal arts to overcome evil, compared with that of heroic physical force, an appropriate theme for a cultured general like Ludovico.

Lunettes

Swags of fruit and flowers hanging from rings decorate each lunette. Two out of the three arches on each wall contain Gonzaga emblems: (1) (starting from above window and proceeding anti-clockwise). Dove and log with motto (*Vrai amour ne se cange*) (ruined state); (2) Sun. This device, with its motto *par un desir* was granted to Mantegna in 1459; (3) Hind with motto *Bider Craft* (against force) (ruined state); (4) Tower; (5) Mount Olympus (ruined state); (6) Wolf hound; (7) Winged talons grasping a ring; (8) Hydra.

The Walls
"Court Scene" (Right wall)

Marquis Ludovico and his wife, Barbara of Brandenburg, are shown seated among courtiers and family, including a favourite dog and one of the court dwarves. The figures appear to encroach on the real space of the room: Ludovico turns away to discuss a letter with a courtier who appears in front of the painted architecture on the left; and on the right of the main group some turn to look at the bustle of young men on the fictive staircase which "leads up" to the level of the mantelpiece.

Five of the Gonzaga can be identified with certainty (see diagram). The absence of Ludovico and Barbara's daughter Dorotea (d. 1468) and the presence of the youngest daughters, (identified from a letter recently discovered by A. Tissoni-Benvenuti) Barbarina (b. 1455) and Paola (b. 1463) demonstrate that Mantegna must have painted this wall between 1468 and 1474, probably in 1471-72, to judge from the children's ages. Costume and livery may provide clues to the status of other figures; those in hose of red and white are probably courtiers; the youth on the extreme right has red, green and white stockings, also Gonzaga colours.

The condition of this wall is poor, and figures in the right half are largely repainted. Arguments that the wall was painted by Mantegna at two different periods (Camesasca) are based on figures ruined by restoration and may be discounted.

The "Meeting" (Left wall)

The three scenes, divided by painted pilasters, are set against a landscape. The hills and rocks are unlikely to represent a particular topography, whether of Verona (Kristeller) or Rome and Tivoli (Signorini), but demonstrate both Mantegna's enjoyment of complex rock formations, and his skilful compensation for the low perspectival viewpoint (if the landscape were flat, like that around Mantua, only sky would be visible). His knowledge of antiquity is evident in the cityscape on the right. Despite references to Roman and Veronese monuments, this is an imaginary city with Gonzaga arms over the gate. [Detail on front-cover]

Reading from left to right the three scenes show: (1) Servants attending to hounds and a horse; (2) More servants (one carrying a letter) with hounds. Mantegna's dedicatory inscription (see essay) appears above the doorway, surrounded by putti with butterfly wings; (3) A "meeting" between Marquis Ludovico and his son Cardinal Francesco, attended by members of the family, courtiers, the Holy Roman Emperor Frederick III and the King of Denmark (see diagram and essay by Elam for identity of figures; for details see Pl. 25 and cover). To the left of the scene Mantegna has inserted his own portrait into the foliage decorating the pilaster (Signorini, 1976). Two different liveries, one perhaps the Cardinal's, appear among the servants on the left. All three non-clerical Gonzaga heirs wear distinctive hose of red white and blue, while the Emperor's stockings are white with a blue flash.

Several attempts have been made to identify exact historical events represented on the two walls. Most recently, Rodolfo Signorini has argued forcefully for a link with events of December 1461 to January 1462, after the news of Francesco's elevation to the cardinalate. But the letter Ludovico holds in the "Court scene" would then be not the announcement of this good news (for the court looks grave), but a summons to Ludovico from Milan, where Duke Francesco Sforza lay seriously ill. The "Meeting" would be that between Ludovico (on his way to Milan) and Francesco (on his way from Milan to Mantua) at Bozzolo, about fifteen miles from Mantua, on 1 January 1462. There are drawbacks to this hypothesis, however. The ages of the figures depicted are of the years when the two scenes were painted (*c.* 1470-74), not of 1461-62; three of the Gonzaga children (Paola, Sigismondo and Francesco, later Marquis) were not born in 1462; and the Emperor and the King of Denmark were never present together in Italy, let alone at such an encounter. Signorini explains these anomalies by suggesting that the subject to be depicted was chosen in 1465, but that Mantegna's slowness meant that the portraits had to be updated (Ludovico complained in 1470 that less than half the room had been completed) and more portraits, having nothing to do with the original event, were added. Others have concluded that no specific moment is represented (Martindale, Gilbert); certainly the reference to 1462 (or to Cardinal Francesco's other visits to Mantua in 1463 and 1472) could be at most a generalized one. It is worth asking how clear an idea Ludovico and Mantegna can have had of what would be painted on the walls at the time the ceiling was started in 1465; the decision to have group portraits at all may not have been an immediate one. The prominent role assigned to letters in the frescoes is an accurate reflection of Gonzaga life; the obsessive writing and preserving of letters in Mantua accounts for our unique knowledge of that court.

Mantegna used both linseed and nut oil to "temper the colours" of the Camera, which cannot therefore be entirely in true fresco. That parts of the paint surface had peeled off "like a skin" in 1901 (Kristeller) also suggests extensive work *a secco* (i.e. on dry rather than wet plaster). *Giornate* (sections of a true fresco painted in one day) have, however, been discerned on the left wall, which Mantegna was hurrying to finish in 1474. Restoration, by Mantegna's sons, was already necessary in the year he died, and the Camera has been restored many times since then, most recently in 1938-41.

C.E.

BIBLIOGRAPHY: Kristeller, 1901, pp. 236-60; Blum, 1930, pp. 69-73; Coletti and Camesasca, 1959; Mantua, *Mostra Mantegna*, 1961, pp. 38-41; Paccagnini, 1961[2]; Marani and Perina, II, 1961, pp. 272-76; Martindale and Garavaglia, 1967, pp. 100-08; Brown, 1972, pp. 861-63; Signorini, 1972, 1974, 1975, 1976, 1977; Mulazzani, 1979; Gilbert, 1980, pp. 129-31.
ADDITIONAL BIBLIOGRAPHY: Forthcoming article by A. Tissoni-Benvenuti in *Italia Medioevale e Umanistica*.

30

Andrea Mantegna (1431-1506); late 15th, or early 16th century
After an original bronze by Andrea Mantegna
Modern coloured plaster cast of the bronze bust set in a roundel of porphyry and Istrian stone in the memorial chapel of Andrea Mantegna in the Basilica of S. Andrea, Mantua
h. of bust 47 cm; diam. of roundel 70 cm
Victoria & Albert Museum

The original is set on the wall near the entrance to the first chapel in the left-hand aisle of S. Andrea. In his will of 1 March, 1504 Mantegna set aside a sum of 200 ducats for his mausoleum, and in August of the same year the canons of S. Andrea granted him this chapel which was at that time undecorated. Announcing his father's death to Marquis Francesco on 2 October, 1506, Ludovico Mantegna stated that his father had left 200 ducats for the memorial chapel, which was to be finished in a year. Work on the decoration on the chapel must have been begun soon after Mantegna's death, but, as an inscription on the chapel records, it was not finished until 1516. No contemporary document relating to the modelling, the casting or the installation of the bust has been discovered, and its origins have been the subject of considerable speculation.

It is to be presumed that the bust was installed in its present position between 1506 and 1516. It was removed in 1797 by Vivant Denon and taken to Paris, but was returned to Mantua

30

and re-installed in its original location in 1814-16.

In the eighteenth century, and for most of the nineteenth, the bust was generally ascribed to Sperandio, sometimes confused with Bartolomeo Melioli. However, in 1888 Rossi speculatively suggested the goldsmith and medallist Gian Marco Cavalli, a friend of Mantegna and a witness to his will, and this ascription for long received general acceptance. On the strength of it Bode ascribed also to Cavalli the similar bronze bust of Giovanni Battista Spagnoli now in the Berlin Museum (Inv. no. 1555). The Spagnoli bust had been removed by Denon from Mantua along with the Mantegna bust, but passed in 1814 into Denon's own collection, and is stated in Denon's catalogue to have been originally mounted in a roundel of porphyry and Istrian stone similar to that of the Mantegna bust. From this point the argument for Cavalli's authorship of the Mantegna bust becomes circular, each ascription being made to reinforce the other. The two busts are however quite clearly by different artists, that of Spagnoli, although less impressive as a portrait, being more plastic in character. The bust of Spagnoli is almost certainly referred to in a letter of 9 June, 1519, in which Spagnoli's brother Fra Tolomeo petitioned Francesco II Gonzaga for permission to have a bronze of his late brother, destined for Spagnoli's tomb, cast in the Marquis' ordinance foundry (permission which Francesco granted the same day). If this is the case, the bust dates from some time after the death of Cavalli, who is last recorded active in 1508.

As regards the origin of the Mantegna bust an important indication is provided by Scardeone, who wrote in 1560 of Mantegna "... *sepultus est humi in phano divi Andreae, ubi aeneum capitis eius simulacrum visitur, quod suis sibi conflaverat manibus*" ("... he is buried in the church of S. Andrea, where the bronze portrait of his head can be seen, which he cast for himself with his own hands"). At the least this statement must record a strong early local tradition. It is argued by Tietze-Conrat that the statement refers only to the casting process (as the word *conflaverat* would in its strictest sense imply), and that the bust was cast by Mantegna from a lifemask of himself taken a some time in the early 1480's. However, as observed by Paccagnini, the bust does not have the

121

character of a life-mask, and Scardeone's statement should be read as referring to the entire creative process. This view has recently received support from Middeldorf, who argues that the bust, in contrast to that of Spagnoli in Berlin, is clearly not the work of a professional sculptor.

The bust was possibly modelled in the 1480's, well in advance of the practical arrangements for the memorial chapel, for which we know some paintings were already prepared some time before Mantegna's death.

A.F.R.

BIBLIOGRAPHY: Bertolotti, 1890[1], pp. 51-52; Venturi, VIII, 3, 1914, p. 252; Fiocco, 1937, pp. 102-03; Fiocco, 1940, pp. 224-28; Tietze-Conrat, 1955, pp. 19, 248; Paccagnini, 1961, p. 74; Marani and Perina, II, 1961, pp. 518-19; Signorini, 1976, pp. 205-12.
ADDITIONAL BIBLIOGRAPHY: B. Scardeone, *De antiquitate urbis Patavii*, Basel, 1560, p. 372; C. de Fabriczy, "Il busto in rilievo di Mantegna attribuito allo Sperandio", *Archivio Storico dell'Arte*, 1888, pp. 428-29; U. Rossi, "I medaglisti del rinascimento alla corte di Mantova, III, Gian Marco Cavalli", *Rivista italiana di numismatica*, I, 1888, pp. 453-564; W. v. Bode, "Die Bronzebüste des Battista Spagnoli in Königlichen Museum zu Berlin, ein Werk mutmasslich des Gian Marco Cavalli", *Jahrbuch der königlich preussischen Kunstsammlungen*, X, 1889, pp. 211-16; U. Rossi, "Gian Marco e Gian Battista Cavalli", *Rivista italiana di numismatica*, V, 1892, p. 483; W.v.Bode, Staatliche Museen zu Berlin, *Bildwerke des Kaiser-Friedrich-Museums, Die italienischen Bildwerke der Renaissance und des Barock*, II, *Bronzestatuetten, Büsten und Gebrauchsgegenständ*, 4th ed., Berlin/Leipzig, 1930, no. 4; W. Prinz, "Die Darstellung Christi im Tempel und die Bildnisse des Andrea Mantegna", *Berliner Museen*, XII, 1962, pp. 52-54; U. Middeldorf, "On the dilettante sculptor", *Apollo*, CVII, 1978, p. 314.

31

Risen Christ between St Andrew and St Longinus
(*c.* 1470-80)
Andrea Mantegna (1431-1506)
Engraving; 32.9 x 30.6 cm
Victoria & Albert Museum (Dyce 991)

This is a late impression of one of the seven engravings generally assigned to Mantegna's own hand. The subject can be firmly connected with the church of Sant'Andrea in Mantua, whose patron saint appears with St Longinus, the centurion at the Crucifixion traditionally believed to have collected Christ's Blood in a chalice, which he brought to Mantua before his martyrdom, and which was rediscovered centuries later and preserved in Sant'Andrea. Versions of the three figures in the engraving were frescoed on the atrium of the new church by members of Mantegna's workshop.

The first known reference to Mantegna in the context of engraving is his drastic action against pirating competitors in 1475 (see essay by Elam, above). A letter of 1491 shows that he used prints (by himself or his workshop) to keep a record of compositions he might want to repeat, but the seven accepted engravings are assumed to have been produced as independent works of art. Early impressions of the engravings are extremely rare (only two exist of this composition) perhaps because Mantegna's technique was closer to drypoint than to engraving with a burin (Landau).

The dating of Mantegna's engravings is controversial, and dates given for this example range from the late 1450's (Landau) to Mantegna's last years (Hind). The Sant'Andrea connexion makes a date after 1460 certain (after Mantegna's arrival and initial proposals to rebuild the church) and suggests a date after 1472. Stylistic criteria would support a date in the 1470's. St Andrew and St Longinus may be contrasted with the same saints in the *Madonna della Vittoria* (1495) (Pl. 29).

C.E.

BIBLIOGRAPHY: Kristeller, 1901, pp. 400-02; Hind, 1938-43, vol. 5, pp. 6-7; Tietze-Conrat, 1955, p. 242; Mantua, *Mostra Mantegna*, 1961, p. 197,

31

n. 148; Levenson and others, 1973, pp. 178-80; Chambers, 1977; Landau, in Alston and others, 1979.

32

Adoration of the Magi (*c.* 1495-1505)
Andrea Mantegna (1431-1506)
Tempera on canvas; 54.5 x 71 cm
Collection of the Marquess of Northampton, Castle Ashby
(on loan to the National Museum of Wales)

Those few writers on Mantegna who have seen this work have not doubted its autograph quality. It is an example of the kind of devotional painting suitable for a private bedroom or chapel, which Mantegna produced on demand for his own friends and those of his Gonzaga patrons. Such small canvases could be easily rolled up for despatch, although Mantegna's persistence in using tempera rather than the more resilient oil medium meant that the painted surfaces of these pictures have, as here, suffered considerably. At least seven inferior copies ascribed to other artists are known of this composition, which was evidently celebrated in its day. This type of religious narrative with half-length figures was apparently Mantegna's invention, first found in the much earlier *Presentation of the Christ Child* in Berlin. Here the composition is both more complex and more assured, with a high degree of psychological intensity and interaction. The use of colour, restricted to a warm and tonally unified range, is reminiscent of the *Madonna della Vittoria* (Pl. 29), where St. Elizabeth wears a turban of the same shape and golden yellow colour as that of this Madonna. Such turbans recur in the *Holy Family* in Mantegna's funerary chapel (Mantua, S. Andrea) and would support a date for this picture in the last decade of the artist's life.

C.E.

BIBLIOGRAPHY: Kristeller, 1901, pp. 143-45, 438-39; Tietze Conrat, 1955, p. 192; Cipriani, 1963, p. 100; Martindale and Garavaglia, 1967, p. 121.
ADDITIONAL BIBLIOGRAPHY: S. Ringbon, *From Icon to Narrative*, Åbo, 1965, pp. 90 ff.

Dead Christ (*c.* 1475-85)
Andrea Mantegna (1431-1506)
Tempera on canvas; 66 x 81 cm
Pinacoteca di Brera, Milan

Left in Mantegna's studio at his death, the *Cristo in scurto* ("foreshortened Christ") was immediately claimed by Cardinal Sigismondo Gonzaga, but was back in the main Gonzaga collections in time to be hung in Margherita Palaeologo's newly furnished apartments in 1531 (see introductory essays by Gombrich and Fletcher).

We know nothing of a commission for the painting, and it has been suggested (Kristeller, 1901) that Mantegna made it as a private exercise in perspective at the time of the *Camera Picta* (Cat. 29). In fact it belongs quite recognizably to the category of Mantegna's devotional works with half-length figures, although the virtuoso foreshortening of Christ's body makes it unique within that genre. The three mourning figures, especially the weeping Madonna, exhibit an almost Flemish emotional intensity (cf. Hugo van der Goes, fragment of a *Lamentation* at the Picture Gallery, Christ Church, Oxford). These Flemish echoes, and the robust figure style, suggest a date in Mantegna's middle years, although the painting is sometimes considered to be a late work (e.g. Mantua,

Mostra Mantegna, 1961) because of its provenance from the artist's estate.

The strange inconsistency in the perspective may puzzle modern observers. The degree of recession in the marble table suggests a viewing point relatively close to the picture plane; but we should expect in that case to find Christ's feet larger than his head. Without this optically correct distortion the body appears as if seen from a distance, as it were through a telephoto lens. Since eye and brain compensate for such distortions of scale, they were less evident before the invention of photography. Renaissance perspective was in any case based on theoretical constructions rather than empirical observation, and no rules for the perspectival scaling of a figure are given in contemporary treatises (Smith, 1974). Religious decorum also might have deterred Mantegna from achieving perspective truthfulness at the cost of disrespect to a sacred figure.

C.E.

PROVENANCE: In the *Camerino delle Dame* in Mantua in 1627 (Luzio, 1912, p. 115). Offered to Louis XIV by Camillo Pamfili in 1665; Bernini saw it in France (Rose, p. 263 f.). Described by Félibien (1669-79) as in Cardinal Mazarin's collection, Rome. To Brera in 1824 from collection of Giuseppe Bossi. No clear chain links these appearances together, and the possibility of two versions cannot be ruled out, although the canvas with Christ alone discussed by the Tietzes (1948 & 1955) must be a copy.
BIBLIOGRAPHY: Kristeller, 1901, pp. 230-234; Mantua, *Mostra Mantegna*,

32

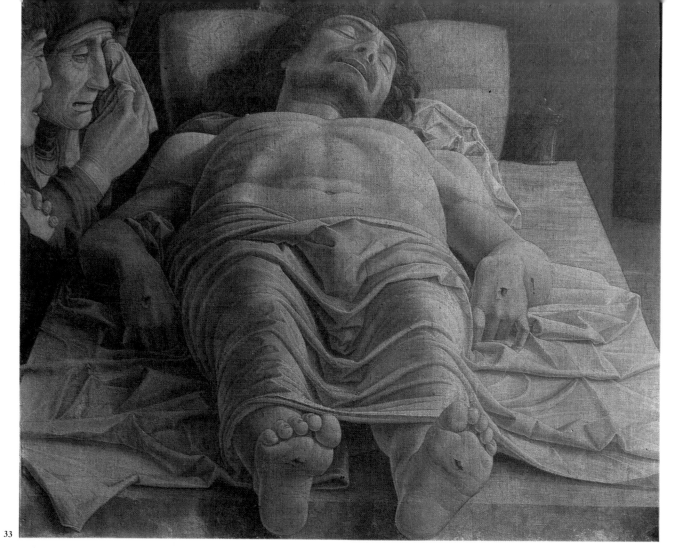

33

1961, pp. 60-61; Luzio, 1913, p. 115; Tietze, 1948, Tietze, 1955, p. 188; Martindale and Garavaglia 1967 no. 57 (with colour plate)

ADDITIONAL BIBLIOGRAPHY: A. Félibien, *Entretiens sur les Vies des Peintres*, Paris 1669-79, I. p. 196; H. Rose, *Tagebuch des Herrn von Chantelou über die Reise des Cavalier Bernini nach Frankreich*, Munich, 1919, pp. 265 f; R. Smith, "Natural versus scientific vision: the foreshortened figure in the Renaissance", *Gazette des Beaux-Arts*, 84, 1974, pp. 239-47.

34

Photograph: **Ludovico Gonzaga's Palace at Revere**

Revere lies south of the river Po, just below its confluence with the Mincio; it was a convenient crossing place, a strategic point for the regulation of land and river traffic and although only a small fortified settlement, an administrative centre for the region. Marquis Ludovico Gonzaga made his authority felt throughout Mantuan territory by his frequent journeys and he made use of many different residences. The Palace at Revere was his first substantial building project.

As such, it is a stylistic hybrid. The façade, towered and decoratively crenellated in conformity with local artisan practice, has windows and a front door in the *all'antica* style (see essay by Burns, Pl. 35). These details were provided by the Florentine Luca Fancelli, between 1451 and 1458 (Ludovico was quick to adopt a Tuscan classicizing style). The courtyard also demonstrates a grafting of two distinct styles (Pl. 36). Columns are of Lombard craftsmanship; archivolts, corbel

capitals and windows follow Tuscan practice. The creation of the three-sided courtyard – to be associated with the *logge* vaulting and the spaces above, notably the commodity of the large *salone* at the north – suggests a Tuscan planner, perhaps Antonio Manetti.

However, the original military purpose of the building is evident in the towers and crenellations of thoroughly Lombard

34

124

flavour. They were painted with heraldic devices (as may still be seen under the north roof), including the muzzled dog, which also appears on the front door jambs. Local building practice was yet to form a true partnership with the imported classicizing style.

J.L.

ADDITIONAL BIBLIOGRAPHY: P. Carpeggiani, *Il Palazzo Gonzaghesco di Revere*, Mantua 1974; J. Lawson, *The Palace at Revere and the Earlier Architectural Patronage of Lodovico Gonzaga, Marquis of Mantua (1444-78)*, Ph. D. Thesis, University of Edinburgh, 1979.

35

Photograph: **The Church of San Sebastiano, Mantua**
Partly executed after designs by Leon Battista Alberti (1404-72)

San Sebastiano was already an enigma to Cardinal Francesco Gonzaga in 1473, the year after Alberti's death: "as that building is made after the ancient fashion not very dissimilar from that fantastic vision of messer Baptista di Alberti, I could not understand whether it was meant to turn out as a church, a mosque or a synagogue" (Lamoureux, 1979, Doc. XLVII). The church was not finished in Alberti's lifetime or according to his original scheme. It fell into neglect in the eighteenth and nineteenth century, and the restoration of 1924-25 introduced various arbitrary changes, and destroyed evidence about the fifteenth century structure. Modern scholars by over confident readings of ambiguous documents have possibly further confused its history (Wittkower, 1952, pp. 41-46 is particularly misleading).
A contemporary chronicler records that Marchese Ludovico decided to build the church "because of a dream which he dreamt one night" (Vasić Vatovec, 1979, p. 83, n. 1). St. Sebastian was a popular saint, painted three times by Mantegna, much appealed to in times of plague (cf. Lamoureux p. 184). Ludovico's chronic worries about outbreaks of plague in his city were probably intensified in 1459-60 by the fact that he was acting as host to Pius II and the Papal court, and could well have led him to dream that he should build a church in this unhealthy area (Ibid., pp. 125-34). He may also have intended it as his burial place: two fifteenth century burial churches, San Bernardino in Urbino, intended as a mausoleum for Federico di Montefeltro, and the church of the Grazie in Milan, built by Ludovico Sforza il Moro, also have domed central spaces flanked by apsidal chapels (Ibid., pp. 134-47).
There is no written indication as there is for Sant'Andrea (Cat. 36) as to what Alberti (or Ludovico) had in mind when he designed the church. The decision to build a crypt with its floor at ground level was a way of raising the main church off the ground, which Alberti recommends, and a sensible decision in an area prone to flooding (Alberti, ed. 1966, II, p. 558).
The crypt with its forest of twenty-four stocky piers and its portico and apses embellished with niches is a notable creation in itself, and would have been intended to serve as a place of devotion during the many years needed to complete the church proper. Masses were already being said there in 1478 (Lamoureux, Doc. LVI). The piers, which are crowned with an entablature and carry arches are very similar to the equally Roman arches along the flank of Alberti's Tempio Malatestiano, and their use may have been suggested by the interior of large vaulted Roman reservoirs, like the reservoir near the Baths of Diocletian (Serlio, 1540, p. XCIX).
There are many antique and medieval precedents for the

35

Greek cross plan (Lamoureux, pp. 109-14). None that have been cited, however, is as close to the scheme of Alberti's church as one of the seven churches of the Apocalypse painted by Giusto de' Menabuoi (fig.) in the Baptistery, Padua (Bettini, 1944, pl. 110). This too consists of a central domed square, surrounded on three sides by rectangular chapels each adorned with a small apse. The resemblance is so striking that it suggests that this painted church, which both Alberti and Ludovico (could it have figured in his dream?) had probably seen was the point of departure for the design. A mid sixteenth century sketch by Labacco appears to be copied after a preliminary outline project for San Sebastiano (Lamoureux, pp. 109-14). The general scheme is close to the executed building and the dimensions, in Mantuan feet, either agree with or are only slightly different from the actual ones; no stairs are shown. In accordance with Alberti's precepts the dimensions are interrelated; they mostly belong to an *ad quadratum* series, as well as generating basic "musical" proportions, or their derivates, like the 3:5 ratio of width to height which governs the elevation (Burns, 1979, pp. 105-13). The notes and a little elevation sketch make it clear that Alberti intended the building to be covered by a dome, and not by the cross vault which was begun about 1499 (Lamoureux, Doc. LXI).
Alberti consigned *modoni*, drawings to be used by the builders, to Ludovico on 27 February 1460 (Ibid., Doc. III). Work went ahead rapidly on the foundations and the construction of the crypt, which seems to have been vaulted by the end of 1462 (Ibid. Doc. XIX). The walls of the upper church and the portico of the crypt were then begun and building went on throughout most of 1463 under Alberti's direction (Ibid., Doc. XXI, XXII). Thereafter, because of plague and lack of money, the pace seems to slow, and effort to be concentrated on the stonework of the portico of the crypt (Ibid., pp. 42-44); there is some doubt as to whether the letters refer to the crypt portico or the upper level). In October 1470 Alberti gained Ludovico's approval for "the diminishing of those piers of the portico etc." and in November Ludovico wrote to Alberti about the latter's readiness to provide "those measurements and directions for execution" of the portico, and added that "we truly greatly desire that the portico should be formed before anything else is done" (Ibid., Doc. XXXVII. The phrase *in anti* must mean "before" and not *in antis* as Lamoureux suggests). It is clear that priority was now to be given to the upper portico (an essential part of a "temple" according to Alberti) and that Alberti had modified his design; though it is very unlikely that this involved reducing the number of pilasters on the façade from six to four as Wittkower suggested (pp. 42-46). In June 1475 Fancelli announced that "two arches are built, the middle one and another; that on the right on entering still has to be built, and it lacks two pieces of vault, or rather stone arch" (Lamoureux, Doc. XLVIII). This reference too is probably to the portico, as the mention of stone arches seems to rule out the interior. The vault of which Fancelli writes in March 1478 as containing 15,000 bricks

125

probably is that of the portico, and could not be the vault of the central square as Calzona suggests; a vault of this many bricks, four bricks thick, would have a surface area of about 90 sq. m. of the portico vault (Ibid., Doc. LII and p. 50 n. 40; cf. Calzona, pp. 85-86). In 1479 Fancelli wrote to the Marchese that the "big cornices" of the portico had been put in place, presumably those above the central doors (Lamoureux, Doc. LVII); this could not refer to the main facade entablature (Wittkower, p. 49) which is of brick. The contract for raising and building the walls and constructing the cross vault was finally made in 1499, and the side stairs covered by a *loggia* were probably also constructed about this time (Lamoureux, Doc. LXI).

The present stairs in front of the church were added by Schiavi in 1925, on the basis of evidence (including foundations) for the original presence of a structure of this sort at the southern end of the façade. There is no reason to doubt Schiavi's findings, though unfortunately he did not fully record them (Lamoureux, pp. 878-89). A letter of May 1460 refers to stairs "at the head" of the portico, but it does not make clear whether these were to lead up to the ends of the portico, or to the ends of the façade, or both (Ibid., Doc. X). One obvious precedent would have been the arrangement of stairs in San Miniato in Florence, and a similar scheme appears in Leonardo's *Adoration of the Magi* and in Mansueti's *Mark healing Anias* in the Scuola di San Marco in Venice (Ibid., pp. 115-18). A near-classical precedent for a church with a centrally placed crypt entrance and a raised portico is the Tempietto di Clitunno, probably referred to by Alberti, 1966, p. 59 (I owe this suggestion to Dr. S. Lang). It is not known when the upper part of the façade was built, with its over heavy entablature and an arch in the pediment, or whether it follows Alberti's design (1966, II p., 549).

San Sebastiano, then, is still as mysterious as it was to Cardinal Francesco. The crypt is entirely Alberti's, and so too is probably the idea of the portico, with its *all'antica* portals which are grander versions of those of the Palazzo Rucellai and the *Camera degli Sposi*. The façade is puzzling, and the interior has lost its pilasters and its *serliane* (replaced by round windows) and never received the intended dome. But one can still see how the apses lead up to the four great barrel vaulted arms, and imagine how these in turn would have supported the commanding form of the cupola, creating above all in the interior, an effect of sombre Roman grandeur completely different from the delicacy and luminosity of Brunelleschi's Pazzi chapel, where barrel vaults also support a dome. With all its alterations San Sebastiano still embodies "that fantastic wisdom of messer Baptista", and remains one of his most impressive and original conceptions.

H.B.

BIBLIOGRAPHY: Authors cited in general Bibliography.

36

Photograph: **Letter of Leon Battista Alberti to Marchese Ludovico about rebuilding the church of Sant'Andrea,** 21-22 October 1470
Archivio di Stato, Mantua (Autografi, b.7)

Sant'Andrea is Alberti's greatest and most influential architectural work. It is also the clearest practical demonstration of the architectural principles which Alberti set out in his *De re aedificatoria* (Cat. 38), above all of his sense of the need to design a building which should simultaneously be beautiful, functional and structurally sound, as well as built of local

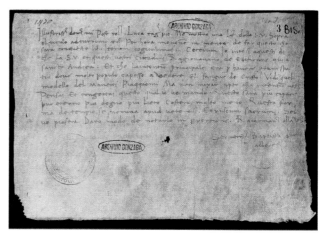

materials, and not excessively expensive. Alberti makes all this clear, for instance, in his appreciative description of the ancient citadel of Alatri (Alberti, 1966, I, p. 60) but expresses it even more succinctly in his letter to Ludovico about Sant' Andrea:

"Luca the stonemason shows me a letter of Your Lordship about the inscription of the tower etc. For the moment it came to me to do this which will be with these letters. I shall think about it again. I have also learned in these days that Your Lordship and these citizens of yours have been discussing building here at Sant'Andrea. And that the chief aim was to have a larger space where many people could see the Blood of Christ. I saw that design of Manetti. I liked it. But to me it does not seem suitable for your purpose. I thought up and imagined this, which I send you. It will be more capacious, more eternal, more worthy, more cheerful. It will cost much less. This type of temple was called Sacred Etruscan by the ancients. If you like it I will see to drawing it out in proportion. Your servant,

Baptista de Albertis

The letter was probably written on 21 or 22 October 1470, as Ludovico's reply is dated 23 October (Chambers, 1977, p. 111): "We have also seen the design which you have sent of that temple, which in principal pleases us; but as we cannot properly understand it for ourselves, we shall wait till we are in Mantua, and then when we have spoken with you and explained our idea (*fantasia*) and understood yours, we will do what seems to you best" (Vasić Vatovec, p. 120).

Ludovico Gonzaga had had his eye on the ancient Benedictine Abbey of Sant'Andrea (and its revenues) for more than a decade. It stood right at the centre of the city, its relic of the Holy Blood, displayed on Ascension Day was a source of prestige and tourist income, and Ludovico wanted to rebuild the shops it owned as part of his plan for a general renovation of the city centre (Dall'Acqua, 1974; Johnson, 1975; Chambers, 1977). To Ludovico the architecture of the church would have been unworthy and outmoded, and the balcony or two storey loggia (the *pozo* which does not mean "well") from which the relic was displayed to the crowd in the piazza was on the point of collapse (Chambers, Doc. 22). But although, as Alberti indicates, Ludovico had already obtained a design from the Florentine architect Antonio Manetti (d. November 1469; Chambers, p. 104) his schemes had been blocked by the Abbot Nuvoloni, who did not die until March 1470. In 1470 the Abbey was put under the direct control of Ludovico's son, Cardinal Francesco, and in 1472 was transformed into a collegiate church with the Cardinal as its head (Chambers, *passim*). The foundation stone of the new church was laid by Ludovico on 12 June 1472 (Johnson, p. 10).

There is no indication of how Alberti's ideas for the church may have changed between 1470 and 1472 (the year of his death) but the portico and nave of the church (finished by 1494 or soon after: Johnson, p. 18) embody the approach set out in the letter. The capacious nave is uncluttered by columns and side aisles, and so permits an unimpeded view towards the altar. Manetti's design was probably a derivative of Brunelleschi's San Lorenzo, with stone columns and side aisles: by dispensing with columns in stoneless Mantua, Alberti saved money, gained space, and achieved a more magnificent effect, which to him, with his very strong response to the beautiful was *lieto*, cheerful. The great central space was made possible by using a barrel vault, buttressed by the walls between the chapels. This solution has parallels in medieval Italian architecture (the cathedral in Vicenza), in recent Florentine architecture (the Badia at Fiesole, of the early 1460's, where Alberti could have acted as a consultant) and of course in ancient architecture, in a vast vaulted building like the Basilica of Maxentius, which has been shown to be the model for Alberti's idea of the Etruscan Temple (Krautheimer, 1969). Alberti's version of his model is full of personal and original touches. Though there are, as in the Basilica of Maxentius, three great barrel vaulted chapels on either side of the nave, these alternate with smaller, enclosed domed chapels (the first on the left belonged to Mantegna). The paired pilasters set up a wide narrow rhythm, which was to become popular in the next century. The barrel vault has a grandeur distinct from that of the great cross-vaulted halls of the Roman baths. Alberti's sources were not exclusively antique; the elevation of the interior, with pilasters framing a flat topped door and a round opening, closely resembles the building on the left of Ghiberti's *Joseph* panel on the Florentine Baptistery, and the façade echoes in its central arch works by Brunelleschi, and in the niches above the doors Michelozzo's niches above the doors in the Novitiate Chapel in Santa Croce (until they were closed up in a recent restoration). The light is controlled: it penetrates indirectly to the round nave windows, and the round window at the end of the nave is shaded by the arch built out over the portico. The portico is the most striking feature of the city's central area and the culmination of Ludovico's efforts to embellish it by rebuilding shops and porticoes, and by remodelling the exterior of the Palazzo del Podestà. The portico reflects the scheme of the interior and covers the width of the nave (it could not be any wider because of the pre-existing campanile). Again for reasons of economy, Alberti uses pilasters, not columns (which he had used on the facade of Santa Maria Novella in Florence). Though the pediment of the portico resembles a temple front its internal arrangement derives from Roman triumphal arches.

Alberti's entire scheme for Sant'Andrea is not known. It seems unlikely that he intended only to build the nave and to terminate it with an apse, creating a direct replica of his "Etruscan temple", as such an apse would certainly have been built together with the nave; and Johnson has noted that the crossing piers toward the north, subsequently strengthened by thickening the pilasters, originally had the same elevation as the nave piers on both its faces (Johnson, pp. 16-17). Inspection of the exterior brickwork on the west side of the north transept does not support Johnson's view that this was, at the lower level, built during the first campaign, which ended about 1494 (Johnson, pp. 17-18). What Johnson read as a building line in fact is merely a difference in pointing between one level and another, on a wall which has suffered many insertions and repairs and once had a house built against it (Forster, 1977). Although the porch on this side was finished by 1550, it is more likely that Alberti conceived the

transepts as less deep than the present ones, in fact as in the case of the Badia at Fiesole no deeper than the nave chapels. The completion of the transepts and choir took place in 1597-1600 and 1697-1704. Juvara's dome was constructed between 1733 and 1785, and Paolo Pozzo redecorated the interior *c.* 1780 (Johnson, p. 2). The present crossing and transepts, spatially and in terms of illumination, are completely different from the nave, as presumably they would not have been had Alberti's design been followed. The nave, however, *bellissima et ornatissima* as Razzi noted in 1572, when this was the only completed part of the church, is in no way spoiled by these later additions, and stands as the most notable testimony to Alberti's genius as an architect.

H.B.

BIBLIOGRAPHY: Authors cited in general Bibliography.

37

Photograph: **Sant'Andrea, Mantua**

37

38

De re aedificatoria
L.B. Alberti (1404-1472)
Manuscript in Latin, on paper; 32 x 21.5 cm
Eton College Library (MS 128)

Alberti's great work on architecture was probably written between 1444 and 1452, that is after his important books on painting and on the family, but before he designed his known architectural works in Florence and Mantua (Grayson, 1960). By 1450 (the year of his project for the Tempio Malatestiano) he had clearly reflected deeply on all aspects of architecture, read innumerable ancient authors on the subject and acquired much direct experience both of constructional matters and of design. The principles which he set out in his book were those he followed in practice (cf. Burns, 1979) and are implict in his designs and in his compactly expressed comments on them (Cat. 36).

Only six fifteenth century manuscripts of the *De re aedificatoria* are known: Alberti probably did not seek to diffuse the work, and after 1485, manuscripts were no longer needed as it was printed, under the direct auspices of Lorenzo de' Medici, who was so interested in the book that he had it read to him, fascicule by fascicule as it came off the press, without waiting for the whole volume to be printed and bound (Martelli, 1966). Of the early manuscripts Eton College Library, Ms. 128 (James, 1895; Ker, 1977) is probably the most interesting. It was almost certainly bought in Venice by Sir Henry Wooton when he was ambassador there, and left to Eton at his death in 1639. It belonged originally to the cultivated Venetian patrician, diplomat and statesman Bernardo Bembo (his arms are on the title page), a friend of Lorenzo de' Medici and Poliziano, and father of the famous Pietro Bembo (Clough, 1971). The copy was certainly made for Bernardo, probably when he was ambassador in Florence in the late 1470's (f. 70 v. is in fact written in his hand) and contains (f. 208) a long note describing the visit he made together with his son Pietro to the Lago di Nemi in 1489, when he was Venetian ambassador to Rome, and had presumably taken the manuscript with him as appropriate reading (James, p. 59; Grayson, 1956).

The volume in addition to the complete text of Alberti's treatise contains the text of Bk. IX from the middle of ch. 6 to the end (ff. 229-235) written in another hand from the rest of the manuscript, and with corrections added here and there by Alberti himself. Thus on f. 231 v. Alberti adds that he does not praise Deoces, King of the Medes who surrounded the city of Ecbatana with seven walls, each of a different colour – a piece of information which Alberti would have found in Herodotus (Alberti, 1966, II, p. 846).

The presence in the volume of a small section of the text corrected by Alberti himself could be explained by the hypothesis that Bembo when he was in Florence, through his contacts, with Lorenzo de' Medici and Poliziano was able to borrow the manuscript which was published in 1485, and a fragment of it remained in his hands (Grayson, 1956 and 1960; cf. Orlandi, in Alberti, 1966, II, pp. 1005-1013).

H.B.

ADDITIONAL BIBLIOGRAPHY: M. R. James, *A Descriptive Catalogue of the Manuscripts in the Library of Eton College*, Cambridge, 1895; N.R. Ker, *Medieval Manuscripts in British Libraries*, ii, Oxford, 1977.

38

39

the latter's uncles or by the Marchese himself, reached a peak in 1491 when a lengthy indictment for seditious conspiracy was issued (ASMAG, b. 3453). He died fighting on the French side at the Battle of Fornovo (1495). Originally there was a frieze beneath a coffered ceiling in the castle consisting of a large series of similarly painted panels, each with a profile bust set within a Mantegnesque arch decorated with two swags of leaves; the painter has not been identified with any success, not have the persons portrayed, whether intended to represent illustrious figures of the past or prominent contemporaries. In *c*. 1881 a private collector bought 44 of them and they have become widely dispersed; there are two more in the Victoria & Albert Museum, and twelve in the Metropolitan Museum, New York, one of which portrays a Venetian Doge; a number have unidentified monograms on their hats or clothing and some wear military helmets; a few are profiles of women.

D.S.C.

BIBLIOGRAPHY: Secco d'Aragona, 1956; Mazzoldi, 1960, II, pp. 77-90; Marani and Perina, II, 1961, pp. 80, 342.
ADDITIONAL BIBLIOGRAPHY: A.J. Koope and H.F. Cook, "The Bramantino Portraits from San Martino di Gusnago", *Burlington Magazine*, VIII, 1905-06, pp. 135-41; C.M. Kauffmann, *Catalogue of Foreign Paintings before 1800 in the Victoria and Albert Museum*, London, 1973, no. 219, pp. 177-79, with further bibliography.

40

Ludovico Gonzaga, second Marchese of Mantua (1412-78)

Pietro da Fano (documented 1452-64)
Medal; lead; diam. 95 mm; *c*. 1452-57
British Museum, Department of Coins and Medals (Inv. G III, R. Mant. M.4., Hill, *Corpus*, 407a)

This medal, inscribed on the obverse LVDOVICVS DE GONZAGA MARCHIO MANTVAE AC DVCALIS LOCVMTENENS GENERALIS. FR[ANCISCI] SFORZIA, has been dated by Hill to between 1452 and 1457; in fact Ludovico's first military contract (*condotta*) with Francesco Sforza, the new Duke of Milan, was already made in November 1450 (Mazzoldi, II, 1961, p. 11). The reverse (lacking on this example) has a not very naturalistic hedgehog shown with a wingless Cupid or genius sitting on a rock and the inscription NOLI ME TANGERE. Little is known about the medallist (signature on the reverse OPVS. PETRI. DOMO. FANI.) except that he made a medal of Doge Pasquale Malipiero of Venice (1457-62) and in 1464 was again in Marchese Ludovico's service.

D.S.C.

BIBLIOGRAPHY: Hill rev. Pollard, 1978, p. 57.

41

Half "grosso" of Marchese Ludovico

Silver coin; diam. 22 mm; weight 1.72 g.

39

Four profile busts from a frieze in a Gonzaga castle, *c*. 1480

Unknown painter; tempera on spruce; av. 46 x 44.5 cm
Victoria & Albert Museum, Department of Prints and Drawings (Inv. 664-667/1904)

The castle from which these panels came is at San Martino di Gusnago (near Ceresara, about twenty miles north west of Mantua); it was built for Marchese Ludovico Gonzaga by Luca Fancelli *c*. 1460 but was granted to Francesco Secco (1423-96) a prominent courtier and military figure who married Ludovico's illegitimate daughter Caterina (Cat. 45). In 1477 King Ferrante of Naples granted Secco the right to use the arms of Aragon which also appear in the decoration. Secco apparently lived magnificently and was a collector, but the house was sacked after his flight in disgrace; he had continued to enjoy great power and favour under Marchese Federico I and following the succession of the young Marchese Francesco in 1484, but accusations against him, whether inspired by

British Museum, Department of Coins and Medals (55.6.12.202; *CNI* IV p. 233, no. 32 var.)

The vessel containing the Precious Blood of Christ, Mantua's celebrated relic preserved in the church of Sant'Andrea, is shown on the reverse of this coin, and the Gonzaga arms, with the quartering of imperial eagles, on the obverse. Both these types were first used on the silver *grosso* struck in 1436 for Gianfrancesco, whose creation as Marquis in 1433 included the right to have coins minted bearing his head. The Precious Blood also appears on the first Mantuan gold ducat (*zecchino* or *marchesano d'oro*) minted for Ludovico in 1460; it became a much favoured type on Gonzaga coins.

D.S.C.

BIBLIOGRAPHY: Magnaguti, I, 1913, pp. 14-15, 20-21.

42

Ludovico Gonzaga, second Marchese of Mantua (1412-78)
Bartolomeo Melioli (1448-1514)
Medal; bronze; diam. 80 mm; dated 1475
Victoria & Albert Museum, Department of Sculpture (Inv. A. 209-1910; Hill, *Corpus*, no. 194a)

Two late portraits of Ludovico appear on this medal; in both he is wearing armour although his fighting days were long over, on account of age and ill health. The bust on the obverse shows him in a cap but below is a helmet bearing the device of a bird on a tree stock; he is wearing a breastplate decorated with a hydra (a helmet crest of a hydra – possibly Ludovico's – was formerly in the Figdor Collection, Vienna: Mann, 1943, pp. 22, 37). The inscription LVDOVICVS. II. MARCHIO MANTVAE. QVAM. PRECIOSVS. XRI. SANGVIS. ILLVSTRAT refers to the famous relic of the Precious Blood in Sant'Andrea, which church, thanks to the Marchese, was currently under reconstruction (Cat. 37) On the reverse Ludovico is seated (the device of a leashed hound is beneath his chair) and in *all' antica* armour, with a laurel wreath upon his helmet. He is confronted by personifications of Faith and Learning (Pallas Athene) – a proper characterization of so devoted a pupil of Vittorino da Feltre – as the inscription explains: FIDO. ET. SAPIENTI. PRINCIPI. FIDES. ET. PALLAS. ASSISTVNT. Melioli, a Mantuan goldsmith and coin-engraver, made five other Gonzaga medals, and another also dated 1475 (Hill, *Corpus*, no. 193) commemorates King Christian I of Denmark who had visited Mantua on his way to and from Rome in 1474. Comparisons can be made with the portraits by Mantegna (Cat. 29) by whom in general Melioli seems to have been influenced.

D.S.C.

BIBLIOGRAPHY: Hill and Pollard, 1967, no. 68 p. 17; Hill rev. Pollard, 1978, pp. 48-49.

43

Federico Gonzaga, third Marchese of Mantua (1441-84)
Bartolo Talpa (active *c.* 1494)
Medal; bronze; diam. 81.5 mm; signed on reverse BARTVLVS TALPA
British Museum, Department of Coins and Medals (1886-10-5-1; Hill, *Corpus*, 204b)

The medal inscribed FREDERICVS GON MAN MAR III is one of two signed by this artist, believed to be identical with Bartolino Topino, nicknamed the philosopher; a pupil of Mantegna

40

41

42

43

44

45

46

who was painting at the palace of Marmirolo in 1494 (d'Arco, 1857, II, p. 32). The other medal depicts Federico's son Francesco, describes him as fourth Marchese, and has on the reverse an image of Curtius on horseback riding into flames; the inscription VNIVERSAE ITALIAE LIBERATOR presumably alluding to Francesco's exploits at Fornovo (1495) (*Corpus*, 205). Since it seems very likely that the two medals are a pair, presumably that of Federico is posthumous; this raises the possibility that the portrait was based on Mantegna's fresco of Federico in the "Meeting" scene in the *Camera Picta* of some twenty years earlier: both hats and hairstyle, as well as the facial features are very close. The reverse shows two branches of laurel crossed passing through the handles of a tablet inscribed EPO: interpreted as E(picorum) P(oetarum) O(ptimus) also found on the reverse of anonymous Mantuan coins with Virgil's portrait, and also on a shield in the battle scene on the reverse of Ruberti's medal of Francesco, fourth Marchese (Cat. 85). Presumably it had been adopted by the two Gonzaga as a symbol of Mantua, home of Virgil, rather than alluding to any poetic skills of their own.

J.T.M.

BIBLIOGRAPHY: d'Arco, 1857; Hill and Pollard, 1978, pp. 48-49.

44

Cardinal Francesco Gonzaga (1444-83)
Sperandio Savelli (*c*. 1425-*c*. 1504)
Medal; bronze; diam. 91 mm; *c*. 1483
Victoria & Albert Museum, Department of Sculpture (Inv. 6803 - 1860; Hill, *Corpus* no. 390e)

Sperandio, a prolific medallist if an inferior imitator of Pisanello, was born in Mantua but worked mainly at Ferrara; from 1478 to *c*. 1490, however, he worked at Bologna where Cardinal Francesco Gonzaga, who had been appointed Papal Legate there in 1471, was resident for long periods and eventually died. The obverse, which portrays the Cardinal at a later age than the famous image of him by Mantegna (Cat. 29) celebrates his generous patronage: FRAN[CISCVS]. GONZAGA. CAR[DINALIS]. MANT[VE]. LIBERALITATIS. AC. ROMANE. ECC[LES]IE. IVBAR. ("splendour of liberality and of the Roman Church"). The reverse, inscribed OPVS. SPERANDEI. shows a lynx (?) sitting beside a pyramid labelled ENIGMATA and surrounded by pieces of martial equipment (a cuirass, shield, bow and arrows) also reflected in the sky. The pyramid has been related (by Gerola) to Marchese Ludovico's emblem of a pyramid-shaped diamond above a rocky island. Possibly the design refers to the uncertain outcome of the war with Venice over Ferrara; Cardinal Francesco had been sent from Bologna as the Pope's special Legate to Ferrara in the winter of 1482-83.
A silver copy of this medal was owned by Gianfrancesco Gonzaga, the Cardinal's brother (inventory of 1496).

D.S.C.

BIBLIOGRAPHY: Gerola, 1930, p. 396; Mazzoldi, II, 1960, p. 41; Meroni, 1966, Tav. 62; Hill rev. Pollard, 1978, p. 52; Jones, 1979, p. 33.

45

Caterina, natural daughter of Marchese Ludovico Gonzaga
Unknown medallist
Medal, lead; uniface; diam. 41 mm; probably 18th century from late 15th century original

British Museum, Department of Coins and Medals (Inv. 1925-3-10-14; Hill, *Corpus*, no. 240a)

Caterina was one of the many bastard children Ludovico fathered in spite of his almost patriarchal moral propriety. According to the Mantuan chronicle of Andrea Schivenoglia she was hunchbacked or one-eyed "... *Madona Chatelina, fiolla bastarda del Marchexo Lodovigo; ley si è goba e si non ha sona uno hochio*" (Biblioteca Comunale, Mantua, MS I. I. 2 (1019), fol. 53r) in which case the medal does her credit. Moreover she married a leading figure of Ludovico's court, the successful military captain Francesco Secco (Cat. 39) who inherited the lordship of Calcio, hence she is designated as CO[N]TI[SS]A. Their daughter married Marsilio Torelli, a Mantuan noble.

D.S.C.

BIBLIOGRAPHY: Secco d'Aragona, 1956.

46

Paola Gonzaga, Countess of Gorizia (1463-97)
Unknown medallist
Medal, bronze; diam. 62 mm
British Museum, Department of Coins and Medals, (Inv. M 0011; Hill, *Corpus*, no. 257c)

Paola, the youngest child of Marchese Ludovico Gonzaga, and deformed like her elder sisters Susanna and Dorotea, married Leonhard Count of Gorizia in 1477 taking with her a large dowry in four marriage chests (see Cat. 81); however, on account of his cruelty she returned home for four months in 1480. Chronically ill, she visited the baths of Abano (near Padua) in 1495, but died two years later. Hill comments that the portrait, inscribed PAVLA GONZAGA COMIT[ISSA] GORICIE shows her wearing a widow's veil, which is puzzling since her husband did not die until April 1500. The reverse of the medal (lacking on this example) shows two women working at a loom – signifying wifely patience? – and (in the Berlin example, Hill, 257a) the inscription VOI VOLET[E] IL TVTTO IO VOGLIO SCVDI VENTI (you want everything, I only want twenty *scudi*). Since Giovanni Gonzaga attempted to recover her dowry, it might be that this medal was intended to commemorate her and publicize her husband's infamy.

D.S.C.

ADDITIONAL BIBLIOGRAPHY: F. Babinger, "Le estreme vicende di Paola di Gonzaga, ultima contessa di Gorizia", *Studi Goriziani*, XX, 1956, pp. 7-19.

47

Gianfrancesco Gonzaga (?)
Francesco Bonsignori (*c*. 1460 (?)-1519)
Black chalk with white highlights, cut all round 30.5 x 23.5 cm
Gabinetto Disegni e Stampe degli Uffizi, Florence (1702 F)

Although it has been suggested that this drawing is a posthumous portrait of Gianfrancesco's elder brother, Marchese Federico (d. 1484), possibly copied by Bonsignori from a Mantegna painting (Schmitt), the face is close to that of the man in a red cap and gold brocade tunic immediately behind Marchese Ludovico in the court scene of the *Camera degli Sposi*, traditionally identified as Gianfrancesco (1445-96). He was founder of the Bozzolo and Sabbioneta line of Gonzaga, a condottiere by profession and a collector and conoisseur by inclination. Obviously the face in the drawing is considerably

47

48

older than that in the fresco, and until the identity of those portrayed by Mantegna is established it will be open to doubt which brother this drawing represents. An argument in favour of it being Federico is that it would appear to have been used by Tintoretto as a model for the Marchese in *The Battle of Legnago*, in the series of *Gonzaga Triumphs* painted in 1579 for the Palazzo Ducale and now in the Alte Pinakothek, Munich. Portraits of the Marchesi Federico and Francesco (prominent in the *Battle of Fornovo*) were despatched to Venice in October 1579 to aid the artist (Eikemeier, 1969). Bonsignori, first documented in Mantua in 1492, cannot have drawn Federico from life, and this portrait has an immediacy which would be surprising to find in a copy. But the artist made several portraits of Gianfrancesco, one in 1492 on the orders of his nephew Marchese Francesco. Bonsignori wrote to Francesco of having "to go to portray his Excellency Signor Zuan Francesco and also all the other people that Your Excellency wants included in the triumph of fame" (*dovendo andar a retrar la eccelentia del Signor Zuan Francesco et etiam li altri i quali vole la S. Vostra gli finza nel trionfo della fame*) (Schmitt, 1961, Doc. XIII). Presumably Bonsignori made portrait drawings which served as a basis for the decoration seen by Vasari at Marmirolo "Francesco painted… some triumphs and many portraits of gentlemen of the court" (Vasari ed. Milanesi, V, p. 300).

This drawing may be unconnected with the Marmirolo paintings, although the date would accord with the sitter's age (if it is he). Bonsignori painted and drew the *signori di casa Gonzaga* frequently, some were sent as diplomatic presents to other courts, although Vasari saw a portrait *del signor Giovanfrancesco* in Mantua (Vasari ed. Milanesi, V, p. 301).

It is extremely unlikely that this drawing served as a preparatory study for the painting of Gianfrancesco at Bergamo; apart from the different orientation, the style, dress, and Gianfrancesco's appearance date the painting to an earlier period, possibly from the time of this marriage in 1479: the pendant of two entwined A's may refer to his wife Antonia del Balzo.

J.T.M.

BIBLIOGRAPHY: Vasari ed. Milanesi, 1878, V, p. 300 ff; Mayer, 1929, pp. 345-55; Mantua, *Mostra Iconog.* 1937, p. 55, no. 245; Mazzoldi, 1960, II, pp. 35-38, 112, 118, 144; Schmitt, 1961, pp. 92, 122, no. 22; Eikemeier, 1969, p. 75 ff.

48

Gianfrancesco Gonzaga (1446-96) on horseback
Unknown (? Venetian) woodcarver;
Horse and rider separately carved in willow and poplar, *c.* 1587; polychrome repainting (18th century); 2.52 m x 2.18 m x 1.10 m
Palazzo Ducale, Sabbioneta

Gianfrancesco's great-grandson, Vespasiano Gonzaga Duke of Sabbioneta (1531-91), ordered twelve wooden figures on horseback of his antecedents (starting with Luigi, First Capitano of Mantua) and culminating with himself (Cat. 202). The statue of Gianfrancesco, Lord of Ródigo, is one of the four which still survive; through him, the third son of Marchese Ludovico and Barbara of Brandenburg, the line of Gonzaga lords of Bozzolo and Sabbioneta diverged from the ruling line of Mantua. The other three surviving are of Ludovico, third Capitano of Mantua (ruling from 1369 to 1382), Vespasiano's father Luigi Rodomonte, Lord of Sabbioneta, and Vespasiano himself. Virtually the only information is in a letter of 4 July 1587 from Paolo Moro in Venice (cited by Affò, 1780, p. 103; original untraced) which stated that a

Venetian sculptor had been given the commission. The motive for such a display of his noble lineage, with its emphasis on military bearing, may have had something to do with Vespasiano's honorary admission into the Venetian patriciate the previous year and wish to demonstrate parity with Vincenzo the young heir to the Dukedom of Mantua. However as early as January 1556 he had allegedly instructed his secretary Muzio Capilupi to collect portraits of his ancestors, and they were also represented in stucco (the work of Alberto Cavalli, c. 1575) in the *Sala degli Antenati* in the Ducal Palace at Sabbioneta: Gianfrancesco's image there could have been used as a model for this naive portrait on horseback.

D.S.C.

BIBLIOGRAPHY: Affò, 1780, pp. 91-92, 103; Marani and Perina, 1965, pp. 402, 416, n. 8; Mantua, 1972, p. 127 with earlier bibliography.

49-50

Gianfrancesco Gonzaga, Count of Ródigo, lord of Bozzolo, Sabbioneta, etc., (1443-1496), and his wife Antonia del Balzo (1441-1538)

Four bronze medals by Pier Jacopo Alari-Bonacolsi, called Antico (c. 1460-1528).

A. *Obv.* Gianfrancesco Gonzaga, insc: IOHANNES FRANCISCVS GONZ.
Rev. Fortune standing on a sphere on a ship's prow, with Mars to the left and Minerva to the right. Insc: FOR. VICTRICI, and signed ANTI in the exergue.
Diam. 40 mm
British Museum (Hill, *Corpus* no. 206c)
PROVENANCE: King George III.

B. *Obv.* Gianfrancesco Gonzaga, insc: IOHANNES FRANCISCVS GONZ.
Rev. A blazing hearth, with below on a scroll the motto PROBITAS LAVDATVR. Insc: MARCHIO COMES ROTI
Diam. 39 mm
Victoria & Albert Museum (739-1865; *Corpus* no. 210c)
PROVENANCE: Soulages Collection, 1865.

C. *Obv.* Gianfrancesco Gonzaga, insc: IOHANNES FRANCISCVS GONZ.
Rev. Antonia del Balzo, insc: DIVA ANTONIA BAVTIA DE GONZ. MAR.
Diam. 40 mm
British Museum (*Corpus* no. 211c)
PROVENANCE: Bank of England Collection.

D. *Obv.* Antonia del Balzo, insc: DIVA ANTONIA BAVTIA DE GONZ. MAR
Rev. Hope standing on the prow of a ship drawn over the sea by two pegasi, over which flies an Amor. On the side of the ship the motto MAIPIV.
Insc: SVPEREST. M. SPES, and signed ANTI in the exergue.
Diam. 40.5 mm
Victoria & Albert Museum (740-1865; *Corpus* no. 212g)
PROVENANCE: Soulages Collections 1865.

Gianfrancesco Gonzaga di Ródigo was the third son of Ludovico Gonzaga, second Marchese of Mantua. An able military commander, he passed much of his early life as a soldier in the service of Ferrante, King of Naples. It was in Naples that he met his future wife, the cultivated Antonia del Balzo, daughter of Pirro, Prince of Altamura, of the Provençal family des Baux settled in Naples since the reign of Charles of Anjou in the thirteenth century. They were married in 1479, and in that year Gianfrancesco was made Count of Ródigo, and

49 [A]

49 [B]

50 [D]

Lord of Bozzolo, Sabbioneta, Viadana and Gazzuolo in the territory of Mantua. They made their seat in the *rocca* of Bozzolo, where until Gianfrancesco's death in 1496 they kept a brilliant court. After the death of Gianfrancesco Antonia retired to the *rocca* of Gazzuolo, where she lived until her death in 1538 at the age of ninety-seven, known to the Gonzaga family as the "mother of all". She shared the literary and musical interests of Isabella d'Este, and the two became close friends, constantly corresponding, visiting each other and exchanging books. Her three sons Pirro, Lodovico and Federico followed their father in becoming distinguished soldiers, as did her favourite grandson, the famous Luigi Rodomonte, whose death at Vicovaro in 1532 is said to have at last robbed her of her seemingly eternal youth. The court at Gazzuolo, presided over in her later years by her son Pirro, Lord of Bozzolo, and his wife Camilla Bentivoglio, was as brilliant as that which she had held earlier at Bozzolo with her husband Gianfrancesco.

Antico's medals of Gianfrancesco and Antonia, which number eight in all, are probably his earliest surviving works, produced in the early 1480's soon after their marriage. At some time in the 1480's (probably after the death of Federico I in 1484) he entered their service and settled at Bozzolo. The personal devices of Gianfrancesco and Antonia which appear on the reverses of some of these medals, the winged thunderbolt on the shield of Mars in medal *A*, which also appears on the reverse of another medal (Hill, *Corpus*, 208), the blazing hearth on the reverse of medal *B* and the motto *Mai piu* on the reverse of medal *D*, serve to establish that Antico also made for them at about the same time the *Gonzaga Vase* (Cat. 51),

132

since this bears these same devices on little shields on its flanks. Antico's earliest known statuettes were also made for Gianfrancesco (see Cat. 52, 53, 54).

In 1501 Antico, after a short period of service with Bishop Ludovico Gonzaga at Bozzolo, followed Antonia to Gazzuolo, where he was to build himself a house with materials given to him by Antonia. He remained resident there in her service and that of her daughter-in-law Camilla Bentivoglio until his death in 1528.

A.F.R.

BIBLIOGRAPHY: A. Litta, *Famiglie celebre italiane*, I, *Gonzaga*, pl. XIV; Rossi, 1888, pp. 433-38; Hermann, 1910, pp. 222-32; Hill and Pollard, 1967, nos 71 b, 72.

51

The Gonzaga Vase; late 15th century
Pier Jacopo Alari-Bonacolsi called Antico (*c*. 1460-1528)
Bronze; h. 30 cm
Galleria Estense, Modena

The vase bears a frieze in relief depicting a triumphal procession of Neptune in a boat drawn by horses accompanied by marine deities. Above this, depending from classicizing masks, are four ansate shields, which bear the following charges: 1. a winged thunderbolt; 2. a burning hearth above a scroll with the motto PROBITAS LAVDATVR; 3. the motto MAI-PIV, 4. a sun. Of these, the first two are devices of Gianfrancesco Gonzaga di Ródigo, and appear in identical form on the reverses of two of his medals by Antico (Hill, *Corpus*, nos. 208, 210: for the latter see Cat. 49), while the third is a motto of his wife Antonia del Balzo, and appears on the reverse of her signed medal by Antico (Hill, *Corpus*, no. 212: see Cat. 50). The fourth, the sun, is a device of Gianfrancesco's father, Marchese Ludovico. The motif of the boat drawn by a pair of horses also appears in closely similar form on the reverse of the medal of Antonia del Balzo. The relief style of the frieze is analogous to that of Antico's set of roundels with *Labours of Hercules* (see Cat. 58-61).

The medals in question must date from soon after the marriage of Gianfrancesco and Antonia del Balzo in 1479, and it should seem to follow that the vase is an early work by Antico, made for Gianfrancesco probably in the early 1480's. The vase itself does not appear in the inventory after the death of Gianfrancesco in 1496, but it is to be noted that the first item in this inventory is "*Duo vaseti de argento dorati; de man de lo Anticho*".

A letter of 1483 in the Mantuan archives refers to the transfer of a commission by the Marquis Federico for the making of classicizing silver vases to designs by Mantegna from Gian Marco Cavalli to Giovanni Francesco Ruberti. Although this commission must be roughly contemporary with the probable date of production of the present vase, it is clear that the design of the vase cannot be due to Mantegna. The difference in approach between the frieze on the vase and the two engravings by Mantegna of the *Battle of Marine Deities* is discussed by Heikamp.

An old photograph published by Planiscig shows standing on the knop an incongruous statuette of a nude boy, since removed.

A.F.R.

PROVENANCE: Gianfrancesco Gonzaga di Ródigo and Antonia del Balzo, Bozzolo; Medagliere Estense, Modena; Liceo Modenese, 1797; acquired in 1877 for the Museo Estense.
BIBLIOGRAPHY: Rossi, 1888, pp. 433-38, 441-42; Bode, 1907[1], I, p. 35, pl. LXXI; Bode, 1907[2], p. 303; Hermann, 1910, pp. 233-34; Hill, *Corpus*,

51

nos. 208, 210, 212; Planiscig, 1930, p. 23, pl. CI, fig. 172; London, 1961, Arts Council, no. 30; Pope-Hennessy, 1961, no. 30; Florence, *Bronzetti*, 1962, no. 29; Heikamp, 1966, pp. 3-4.

52

Cupid late 15th century [Pl. 45]
Pier Jacopo Alari-Bonacolsi, called Antico (*c*. 1460-1528)
Bronze statuette, parcel-gilt and inlaid with silver; h. 29 cm
Museo Nazionale del Bargello, Florence (coll. Carrand, 218)

The hair, the wings, the quiver and the strap of the quiver are fire-gilt, and the eyes are inlaid with silver. The bow and arrow are missing. The bronze is associated by Hermann and others with an item in the inventory after the death (1496) of Gianfrancesco Gonzaga: *Un dio damor di metalo cum el carchasso* (i.e. *turcasso*); "a god of love in metal with the quiver". A second version of the statuette, now in the Rijksmuseum, Amsterdam, lacks the fire-gilding and the silver inlay, but retains its original circular moulded bronze base. In its general facture and in the form of its base this is associable with bronzes with a Mantuan provenance today in the Kunsthistorisches Museum, Vienna, which are almost certainly to be identified as coming from a set of eight bronzes cast in or soon after 1519 for Isabella d'Este from earlier models by

133

Antico (see Cat. 55). By contrast, the present bronze is identical in facture to the reduction of the *Meleager* (Cat. 54), also identifiable with an item in the inventory of 1496 of Gianfrancesco Gonzaga. It is therefore likely that this is one of the earliest known bronze statuettes by Antico, made at Bozzolo for Gianfrancesco Gonzaga before 1496.

Unlike many of the statuettes of Antico, the bronze has no single recognizable antique source. A relationship to Donatello in style has been remarked upon by several writers, and indeed it was exhibited in Florence in 1887 with an ascription to Donatello.

A.F.R.

PROVENANCE: (?) Gianfrancesco Gonzaga di Ródigo, Bozzolo, before 1496; Louis Carrand, bequeathed to the Comune of Florence in 1888.
BIBLIOGRAPHY: Bode, 1907[1], I, p. 35, pl. LXIX; Bode, 1907[2], p. 302; Hermann, 1910, pp. 215, 244-46; London, 1913, Burlington Catalogue, p. 73, no. 47, pl. XLVII; Heikamp, 1966, p. 4.
ADDITIONAL BIBLIOGRAPHY: U. Rossi, "La Collezione Carrand nel Museo Nazionale di Firenze", *Archivio storico dell'arte*, III, 1890, p. 27, n. 11; O. Supino, *Catalogo del R. Museo Nazionale di Firenze*, Florence, 1898, p. 82, no. 218; W. Bode, *Collection of J. Pierpont Morgan: bronzes of the Renaissance and subsequent periods*, Paris, 1910, I, no. 79, pl. XLVIII; J. Leeuwenberg & W. Halsema-Kubes, *Beeldhouwkunst in het Rijksmuseum*, Amsterdam, 1973, no. 663.

53

Hercules; late 15th century
By Pier Jacopo Alari-Bonacolsi, called Antico (*c.* 1460-1528)
Bronze statuette, parcel-gilt and inlaid with silver; h. with base, 38 cm; figure alone, 34 cm
Museo Arqueológico Nacional, Madrid (52.991)

The lion-skin and the wreath in the hair are fire-gilt, and the eyes are inlaid with silver. The statuette stands on an original circular moulded bronze base.

The bronze is one of three known versions which may be ascribed to Antico, all of which retain their original circular moulded bronze bases, which differ somewhat in form in each case. One of these, presented to the Frick Collection in 1970, has silver eyes like the present version, and is more extensively gilded, the gilding covering also the hair and beard. It has a shallower and more restricted base, on which the club (now missing) would have been fixed at its lower end inside, instead of outside the right foot. The other, in the Kunsthistorisches Museum, Vienna, has neither gilding nor silver inlay, and is set on a higher bronze base with more generous mouldings and a more pronounced waist. A fourth cast from the model in the Louvre (OA9134) is comparatively crude in execution, and must be a later aftercast.

The Vienna version was identified by Schlosser with an item in the inventory after death of 1496 of Gianfrancesco Gonzaga: "*Lo Hercules dal bastono, de bronzo*". However, as noted by Hermann, it corresponds precisely in facture with a *Hercules and Antaeus*, also in Vienna, which is inscribed under the base with the name and title of Isabella d'Este, and which is therefore presumably to be indentified with a *Hercules and Antaeus* documented as to be cast for Isabella in 1519 together with seven other bronzes, all from models produced around 1500 for Bishop Ludovico Gonzaga (see Cat. 55; Pl. 48). The two bronzes, which are recorded as being together in the inventory of the collection of Archduke Leopold Wilhelm (1659), and are almost certainly identifiable as together in the Mantuan inventory of 1627, must be presumed to have been purchased for King Charles I in Mantua in 1627-28, and it would seem that the Vienna *Hercules*, like the Vienna *Hercules and Antaeus*, must have been one of the bronzes cast for Isabella in, or soon after, 1519 from older models.

The casting of a bronze *Hercules* by Antico for Bishop Ludovico Gonzaga between February and May 1499 is referred to in letters preserved in the Parma Archives, and it is thus possible that of the two other versions of the *Hercules*, that in the Frick Collection and the present bronze, one is the version recorded there, while the other is that recorded in the 1496 inventory of Gianfrancesco.

Of the two, that in the Frick Collection appears to be closer in model to the Vienna version. It resembles closely in facture the sumptuously-finished version of the *Apollo Belvedere* from the Ca' d'Oro (Cat. 57) while the present version compares closely with a signed version of the *Apollo* in Frankfurt, with which it shares an identical type of bronze base, with delicate, tight mouldings and a straight-sided waist. It is persuasively argued by Legner that the signed *Apollo* in Frankfurt is the earliest of three known versions of this model, and it would indeed appear to be an extremely early bronze by Antico.

For the reasons advanced by Legner in the case of the *Apollo*, it would seen likely that the present bronze is the earliest of the extant versions of the *Hercules*, and it may therefore be proposed that it is possibly the version which belonged to Gianfrancesco Gonzaga, while the version in the Frick Collection is that made for Bishop Ludovico in 1499, and that now in Vienna is a copy of the Frick version made twenty years later for Isabella. The bronze has a provenance from the Spanish Royal Collections, and it is possible that it was presented to the Emperor Charles V on one of his two visits to Mantua.

The figure would originally have held in the left hand the Apples of the Hesperides, now missing in all three versions. It has been suggested that the model is based on the classical type of one of the two statues of *Hercules* in the stair hall of the Palazzo Pitti, formerly at the Villa Medici in Rome. However, the connexion is extremely tenuous and the figure must be a free variation by Antico on a generalized antique theme.

A.F.R.

PROVENANCE: (?) Gianfrancesco Gonzaga di Ródigo, Bozzolo, before 1496; (?) presented to the Emperor Charles V by Federico II Gonzaga in 1530 or 1532; Spanish Royal Collections; old inventory number 80 painted on front of base; given by King Carlos III to the Biblioteca Real, later Nacional; transferred to the Museo Arqueológico Nacional, 1867.
BIBLIOGRAPHY: Rossi, 1888, pp. 172-73; Hermann, 1910, pp. 208, 214, 219, 240-41; 266-67; Bode, 1912, III, pl. CCXXXV; Planiscig, 1930, pl. CI fig. 173; Pope-Hennessy, 1961, no. 27; London, Arts Council, 1961, no. 27; Florence, *Bronzetti*, 1962, no. 26.
ADDITIONAL BIBLIOGRAPHY: A. Berger, "Inventar des Kunstsammlung des Erzherzogs Leopold Wilhelm von Oesterreich...", *Jahrbuch der Kunsthistorischen Sammlungen des Allerhöchsten Kaiserhauses*, I, 1883, 2, p. CLXIX, no. 128; H. Zimerman, "Franz v. Stamparts und Anton v. Prenners Prodromus zum Theatrum Artis Pictoriae...", *Jahrbuch der Kunsthistorischen Sammlungen des Allerhöchsten Kaiserhauses*, VII, 1888, 2, pl. 30; E. Molinier, *Collection Charles Mannheim: objets d'art*, Paris, 1898, no. 136. J. v. Schlosser, *Werke der Kleinplastik in der Skulpturensammlung des A.H. Kaiserhauses*, I, Vienna, 1910, p. 3; W. Bode, *Collection of J. Pierpont Morgan: bronzes of the Renaissance and subsequent periods*, I, Paris, 1910, p. XXIV, 26, no. 92; L. Planiscig, Kunsthistorisches Museum in Wien, *Die Bronzeplastiken*, Vienna, 1924, no. 99; *Carlos V y su ambiente*, Toledo, 1958, no. 287; *Guía del Museo Arqueológico Nacional*, Madrid, 1965, p. 227; A. Legner, "Anticos Apoll vom Belvedere", *Städel-Jahrbuch*, N.F. I, 1967, pp. 103-18; J. Pope-Hennessy, "Cataloguing the Frick bronzes", *Apollo*, XCIII, 1971, p. 21.

54

Meleager late 15th century [Pl. 44]
Pier Jacopo Alari-Bonacolsi, called Antico (*c.* 1460-1528)
Bronze statuette, parcel-gilt and inlaid with silver; h., with base, 32.1, figure alone 30.7 cm
Victoria & Albert Museum (A 27-1960)

tion that the present model is referred to here, and that the item in question may actually have been the present bronze is suggested by the fact that it is notably close in facture to the *Cupid* of the Bargello (Cat. 52), which is also probably to be identified with an item in the same inventory.

There is no further reference to the model in the published documentation of Antico, and this is the only version which has so far appeared, but an item in the inventory of the *Guardaroba* of Alfonso II d'Este, Duke of Ferrara, of 1584 may possibly refer to the present bronze or to a second version: *Uno Villanello gia donato all'Ill. mo sig. Don Francesco* (Francesco d'Este, Marquis of Massa, 1516-1578, uncle of Alfonso II). If the engraving of the marble *Meleager* published by Gori in 1740 can be believed to be reasonably accurate, the statue may at the time at which it was known to Antico have been lacking the head and arms, since the bronze differs somewhat from the engraving in these respects, while corresponding closely with in it all others.

A.F.R.

PROVENANCE: (?) Gianfrancesco Gonzaga di Ródigo, Bozzolo, before 1496; purchased by the Victoria & Albert Museum on the London art

55

53

The bronze is fire-gilt on the hair, the moustache, beard and teeth, the tunic and the sandals. The eyes are inlaid with silver. The figure stands on an original oval bronze base without mouldings identical to that of the version of the *Hercules and Antaeus* in the Victoria & Albert Museum (Cat. 35).

As observed by Keutner, the model derives from a classical marble statue of *Meleager* which was for some time in the Uffizi, Florence before it was destroyed in the fire of 1762. The marble is first recorded in the Uffizi in the inventory of 1638, and was apparently earlier in the Belvedere in Rome. The earlier history of the marble is obscure. In the Uffizi it was associated with the marble of the boar, the famous *Florentine Boar*, which still survives in the Uffizi, although much damaged in the fire. The boar, which was presented to Cosimo I by Pope Pius IV, and was in the Uffizi at an earlier date than the *Meleager*, was excavated at an unknown date in a *vigna* belonging to the Ponti family on the Esquiline, part of a group, according to Pirro Ligorio, representing Meleager hunting the Calydonian Boar. In spite of this, there is no evidence that the two statues were actually excavated together, and indeed this appears to be unlikely. It is also open to question that the marble original of Antico's bronze actually represents Meleager.

The marble was popularly known when it was in the Uffizi as the *contadino* or the *villano* both of which mean "peasant". Amongst the bronzes in the inventory after death of Gianfrancesco Gonzaga di Ródigo compiled at Bozzolo in 1496 is listed *Una figura di mettale ghiamata il villanello*: "a figure of metal called the little peasant". There is thus a strong supposi-

135

market in 1960 with the help of a contribution from the National Art-Collections Fund

BIBLIOGRAPHY: Hermann, 1910, p. 24; London, Arts Council, 1967, no. 29; Pope-Hennessy, 1961, no. 29; Florence, *Bronzetti*, 1962, no. 28.
ADDITIONAL BIBLIOGRAPHY: U. Aldovrandini, *Delle statue antiche che per tutta Roma, in diversi luoghi e case si veggono* 2nd ed., Venice 1558, pp. 193-94; A. Gori, *Museum Florentinum*, III, Florence, 1740, pl. LXXVIII; *Documenti inediti per servire alla storia dei Musei d'Italia*, III, *Monumenti Estensi*, Florence/Rome, 1880, p. 8; R. Lanciani, *Storia degli scavi di Roma*, III, Rome, 1907, p. 160; G. Mansuelli, *Galleria degli Uffizi: le sculture*, I, Rome, 1958, pp. 78, 79, no. 50, p. 264, no. 4; H. Keutner, "Italienische Kleinbronzen", *Kunstchronik*, XV, 1962, p. 172.

55

Hercules and Antaeus *c.* 1500
Pier Jacopo Alari-Bonacolsi called Antico (*c.* 1460-1528)
Bronze group, inlaid with silver; h. with base, 40.7 cm; figures alone, 39.1 cm
Victoria & Albert Museum (A. 37-1956)

The eyes of both figures are inlaid with silver. The group is fixed to an original oval bronze base without mouldings, identical to that of the *Meleager* (Cat. 54). It has been totally re-patinated, probably in France in the late 17th century at the time at which it was mounted on a *boulle* socle of that date. The bronze is one of two casts of the model which can be ascribed to Antico, the second being in the Kunsthistorisches Museum, Vienna (Pl. 48). A third version, in the Museum of Fine Arts, Houston, Texas (Straus Collection), is apparently a late aftercast.

There is no specific documentation for the model in the earlier part of Antico's career. However *l'Ercule che amaza Anteo, che la piú bella antiquita che li fusse* is specifically mentioned in a letter of 1519 from Antico to Isabella d'Este as one of the models which he had cast some twenty years earlier at Bozzolo for Bishop Ludovico Gonzaga, and which he proposes to have re-cast for her by Maestro Iohan. The Vienna version, which lacks the silver inlay, and is mounted on a bronze base with heavy mouldings, has inscribed under the base "D(omina)/ISABEL/LA/M(antua)E/MAR(chionissa)". The inscription was made in the wax before casting, and the bronze must therefore have been made specially for Isabella. The model is identifiable amongst the bronzes in the inventory of Isabella's collections compiled in Mantua in 1542, and again in the inventory of 1627, where it appears together with a *Hercules*. The Vienna *Hercules and Antaeus* and the version of the *Hercules* now in Vienna (see Cat. 53). appear together in the inventory of 1659 of Archduke Leopold Wilhelm, and would thus have both had a direct provenance from Mantua, having been acquired there for King Charles I in 1627/8 before being sold to the Archduke in about 1650 under the Commonwealth.

If it may thus be assumed that the version now in Vienna is that which Antico proposed to have cast for Isabella in 1519, it is possible that the present version is that which we may deduce from the letter of 1519 Antico had made for Bishop Ludovico Gonzaga at Bozzolo some twenty years earlier, of which Isabella's version was to be a copy. In favour of its being an early cast by Antico is the fact that it is identical in facture, apart from the absence of fire-gilding, to the *Meleager* (Cat. 54), which is likely to be one of the earliest known statuettes by Antico.

The model derives from the classical marble of *Hercules and Antaeus* which is today in the courtyard of the Palazzo Pitti in Florence presented to Cosimo I by Pius IV in 1560. Before this, it had been in Rome in the Belvedere, where it was installed by Julius II. Although its date of discovery is not known, it was known before 1474 to Mantegna, who adapted

it for a scene on the vault of the *Camera degli Sposi*, completed in that year. Before its arrival in Florence, where it was restored, it was a fragment, consisting only of the two conjoined torsoes and the head of Hercules. The head of Antaeus, the lower legs of both figures and the right arm of Antaeus are supplied by Antico for his small bronze, and these features consequently differ from the corresponding features in the marble as it appears today.

A.F.R.

PROVENANCE: (?) Bishop Ludovico Gonzaga, Bozzolo, about 1500; Dr. W. L. Hildburgh, purchased on the London art market in 1934 and placed on loan at the Victoria & Albert Museum; bequeathed to the Museum in 1956.
BIBLIOGRAPHY: Rossi, 1888, pp. 190-91; Hermann, 1910, pp. 212, 216, 219, 239-41; 264-66; Bode, 1912, pl. CCXXXV.
ADDITIONAL BIBLIOGRAPHY: A. Berger, "Inventar des Kunstsammlung des Erzherzogs Leopold Wilhelm von Oesterreich...", *Jahrbuch der Kunsthistorischen Sammlungen des Allerhöchsten Kaiserhauses*, I, 183, 2, p. CLXIX, no. 130; H. Zimerman, "Franz v. Stamparts und Anton v. Prenners Prodromus zum Theatrum Artis Pictoriae...", *Jahrbuch der Kunsthistorischen Sammlungen des Allerhöchsten Kaiserhauses*, VII, 1888, 2, pl. 27; L. Planiscig, Kunsthistorisches Museum in Wien, *Die Bronzeplastiken*, Vienna, 1924, no. 98; H. Mobius, "Vier hellenistische Skulpturen", *Antike Plastik*, X, 1979, pp. 39-47.

56

Atropos; *c.* 1500
Pier Jacopo Alari-Bonacolsi called Antico (*c.* 1460-1528)
Bronze statuette; h. 29.6 cm
Victoria & Albert Museum (A. 16-1931)

The figure has suffered damage to the left arm, which has been bent downwards, and has been re-patinated at a later date. She wears a string of pearls across her forehead, and holds in her right hand the remains of a pair of scissors and in her raised left hand a small object recently identified by Richard E. Stone (personal communication) as a silk cocoon. As noted by Pope-Hennessy, the statuette must represent *Atropos*, and not *Venus*, as was thought by earlier writers. A second version, in the Kunsthistorisches Museum, Vienna, lacks the string of pearls, the scissors and the cocoon, but retains its original circular moulded bronze base.

It has been observed by Stone that the Italian for cocoon is *bozzolo*, and it may therefore be deduced that the statuette was made for Gianfrancesco Gonzaga di Ródigo, Lord of Bozzolo, before his death in 1496, for his widow Antonia del Balzo or his son Pirro, also Lord of Bozzolo, thereafter, or for Bishop Ludovico Gonzaga during his residence at Bozzolo around 1500.

The subject is not identifiable in the 1496 inventory. The version in Vienna is identifiable with an item in the 1659 inventory of Archduke Leopold Wilhelm collection and it may be assumed that it is one of the bronzes acquired from Mantua for King Charles I in 1627-28 and sold to the Archduke under the Commonwealth. These are almost certainly casts made in or soon after 1519 for Isabella d'Este from models made by Antico for Bishop Ludovico some twenty years earlier (see Cat. 55). The model may be compared with that of the kneeling *Nude of the Tortoise* ("*La nuta che inenochata in su la bisa schudelara*": versions in the Thyssen-Bornemisza Collection and in Naples) with which it shares the motif of a thread apparently stretched between the hands. This is recorded as having been made for Bishop Ludovico at Bozzolo by 1498, and is specifically cited in 1519 as one of the old models to be re-cast for Isabella. It would seem to be significant that the symbolic cocoon is omitted in the Vienna version of the

56

of the arms in the marble *Venus Victrix* in the Museo Naziona-le, Naples.

A.F.R.

PROVENANCE: (?) Bishop Ludovico Gonzaga, Bozzolo, about 1500; Sir Otto Beit, Bart., bequeathed to the Victoria & Albert Museum in 1931. BIBLIOGRAPHY: Berger (as Additional Bibliography above) I, 183, 2 p. CLXIX, no. 29; Rossi, 1888, pp. 170-1, 174, 190-91; Bode, 1907¹, I, p. 35, pl. LXIX; Bode, 1907², V, p. 303; Hermann, 1910, pp. 251-53; 261-63; London, 1913, Burlington Catalogue, pp. 72-73, no. 46, pl. XLVI; London, 1961, Arts Council, no. 31; Pope-Hennessy, 1961, no. 31; Florence, *Bronzetti*, 1962, no. 30.
ADDITIONAL BIBLIOGRAPHY: W. Bode, *Catalogue of the collection of pictures and bronzes in the possession of Mr Otto Beit*, London 1913, p. 60, no. 281; L. Planiscig, Kunsthistorisches Museum in Wien, *Die Bronzeplastiken*, Vienna, 1924, no. 101; M. Leith-Jasper, National Museum of Western Arts, *Italienische Kleinbronzen und Handzeichnungen der Renaissance und des Manierismus aus Oesterreichischen Staatsbesitz*, Tokyo, 1973, no. 4.

57

Apollo; late 15th or early 16th century
Pier Jacopo Alari-Bonacolsi; called Antico (*c.* 1460-1528)
Bronze statuette, parcel-gilt and inlaid with silver; h. with base 40 cm
Galleria Giorgio Franchetti alla Ca' d'Oro, Venice.

The hair, the *chlamys*, the strap for the quiver, the sandals and the mouldings on the base are fire-gilt, and the eyes are inlaid with silver. The circular moulded bronze base is original. The quiver is missing.

The bronze is a free reduction from the marble known as the *Apollo Belvedere*, today in the Vatican. In about 1500 the marble was in the garden of S. Pietro in Vincoli, belonging to Cardinal Giuliano della Rovere, and it must have been there that Antico saw it on his recorded visit to Rome in 1497, or possibly earlier. Some time after the Cardinal became Pope as Julius II in 1503 the statue was removed to the Vatican, and is recorded in the Belvedere by 1511. Until its restoration by Montorsoli in 1532-33 the marble lacked the left hand, together with much of the left forearm, and the greater part of the right hand. It is recorded in this state in the earliest drawings and engravings, such as that in the *Codex Escurialensis*. The missing parts are supplied in the bronze by Antico in a form which differs from the restorations by Montorsoli.

This is one of three known versions acceptable as the work of Antico, all of which differ in details of model, facture and finish to a degree which is rather greater than is usual in versions of the same model by Antico. One of these, in the Liebieghaus in Frankfurt-am-Main, is the only known signed statuette by Antico, inscribed "ANT" on the strap for the quiver. Like the present bronze, it is partially fire-gilt, with the eyes inlaid with silver, and stands on a circular moulded base, although the mouldings on the base are less heavy and its waist staight-sided. Unlike the present version, it retains the quiver. The third version, formerly in the collection of Sir Otto Beit, and more recently that of the late Lt. Col. M. T. Boscawen, to be bequeathed to the Fitzwilliam Museum, Cambridge, lacks the silver inlay and has oil, instead of fire, gilding. This version has lost its original bronze base. Two further versions referred to by earlier writers, one formerly in the Morgan Collection, now in the Huntington Library, San Marino, California, and the other in the Victoria & Albert Museum, are not acceptable as works by Antico.

Antico's *Apollo* is referred to three times in early documents. The first occasion is on 29 November 1498, when there is mention in a letter of Bishop Ludovico Gonzaga of a model or mould of the *Apollo* prepared by Antico for the Bishop,

Atropos, and it is likely that, while this is a late cast made for Isabella, the present bronze is an original version made for Bishop Ludovico at Bozzolo in about 1500.

References to a third version, supposedly in the Ashmolean Museum at Oxford, which originate with Bode and are repeated by subsequent writers, are erroneous. The photographs purporting to show a version at Oxford in fact show the present version, and there is no third version.

The model depends from no single identifiable classical original, but a comparison is drawn by Leithe-Jasper with the pose

57

Boscawen collections was not directly known to Hermann and has been generally unavailable for study for many years, with the result that its status has been subject to uncertainty. Interest has therefore been concentrated on the present bronze. The present bronze has a direct provenance from the Ducal collections in Mantua, and this might at first sight suggest that it is the version which is recorded in the inventory of 1542. However, as was tentatively suggested by Hermann, the version owned by Isabella would have been likely to have been one of the eight casts made in 1519 or soon after from models made some twenty years earlier for Bishop Ludovico. The character of these late casts is established by the version today in Vienna of the *Hercules and Antaeus* (see Cat. 55) and of other bronzes of comparable facture also in Vienna, which were acquired from Mantua in 1627-28 by King Charles I. The present bronze, with its fire-gilding and silver inlay is quite distinct in finish from these, and is rather to be associated with bronzes by Antico which appear to be productions of around 1500.

Of the three known versions, it is in fact the Beit/Boscawen bronze which is directly comparable with the late casts in Vienna. In its general facture and its oil-gilding it precisely matches the *Mercury* in Vienna, which is recorded in the inventory of 1542 together with the *Apollo* on the cornice in the *Grotta*. If it may be assumed, therefore, that it is one of the eight casts made in 1519, it would have been made from a mould produced for Bishop Ludovico in about 1500. Comparing it with the other two versions, it is clear that it follows very closely the model of the Frankfurt version.

It is persuasively argued by Legner that the Frankfurt version is the earliest of the three. With its comparatively restrained use of gilding, its fine punched working on the *chlamys*, and its base with delicate mouldings and a straight-sided waist, it is precisely analogous to the Madrid version of the *Hercules* (Cat. 53), which appears to be the earliest known version of that model, while the present bronze with its more opulent finish and its base with more generous mouldings and concave waist, is precisely comparable with the more developed version of the *Hercules* in the Frick Collection. A comparison of the three bronzes with the original marble shows that the Frankfurt version and the Beit/Boscawen version, which small adjustments in the repair of the model have made the most elegant of the three, follow the marble more closely than does the present bronze, which is elaborated in certain respects, for instance by the addition of a simulated lead weight to the falling end of the *chlamys*.

While the evidence does not permit a positive identification of each of the three known versions with one of the three documentary references to the *Apollo*, it may at least be proposed that the signed version in Frankfurt is the earliest of the three, probably made around, or shortly before 1500, that the present version was produced not very long after, and that the Beit/Boscawen bronze is a late cast of about 1519 from the moulds originally prepared for the Frankfurt bronze.

A.F.R.

which has been borrowed without authority by Ludovico's chaplain. The second is on 7 December 1501, when the Bishop refers in a letter to an *Apollo* which Antico has completed for him. The third reference occurs in the inventory of the possessions of Isabella d'Este compiled in 1542, in which amongst other bronzes by Antico on the cornice in the *Grotta* is listed *E piú un Apollo simil a quello di Roma*.

Some writers have assumed that all three documents refer to the present bronze, which would have been prepared as a wax model for Bishop Ludovico by late 1498, cast and finished as a bronze for him by late 1501, and subsequently acquired by Isabella. However, Hermann is more cautious, and admits the possibility that the three documents may refer to three different versions. It should be noted in this connection that of the other two versions that in Frankfurt was unknown until its publication by Legner in 1967, following identification by Cyril Humphris, while that formerly in the Beit and

PROVENANCE: Ferdinando Carlo Gonzaga, last Duke of Mantua (b. 1652, d. 1708); purchased after his death from his estate by Domenico Pasqualigo, who presented it to the Museo Archeologico, Palazzo Ducale, Venice; transferred to the Galleria Giorgio Franchetti, Ca' d'Oro.
BIBLIOGRAPHY: Rossi, 1888, pp. 171, 187; Bode, 1907[1], I p. 35, pl. LXVI; Bode, 1907[2], p. 302; Hermann, 1910, pp. 212, 216, 36-38, 41-43; London, *Burlington Catalogue,* 1913, pp. 70, 1, no. 42, pl. XLIII; Planiscig, 1930, pl. XCVIII; London, 1961 Arts Council, no. 28; Pope-Hennessy, 1961, no. 28; Florence, *Bronzetti,* 1962, no. 27.
ADDITIONAL BIBLIOGRAPHY: Bode, *Catalogue of the collection of pictures and bronzes in the possession of Mr Otto Beit,* London, 1914, p. 59, no. 280; A. Legner, "Anticos Apoll vom Belvedere", *Städel-Jahrbuch,* N.F. I, 1967, pp. 103-18.

The Labours of Hercules late 15th/early 16th century
Pier Jacopo Alari-Bonacolsi, called Antico (*c.* 1460-1528)

A. The infant Hercules and the Serpents
 Bronze roundel; diam. 32.7 cm
 Victoria & Albert Museum (58-1881)

B. Hercules and the Erymanthian Boar
 Bronze roundel; diam. 32.7 cm
 Victoria & Albert Museum (149-1882)

C. Hercules and the Nemean Lion
 Bronze roundel. parcel-gilt; diam. 32.7 cm
 Museo Nazionale del Bargello, Florence

D. Hercules and the Lernaean Hydra
 Bronze roundel. parcel-gilt; diam. 32.7 cm
 Museo Nazionale del Bargello, Florence

58 [A]   59 [B]

A fifth roundel with the subject of *Hercules and the Ceryneian Stag* in the same style as *B, C* and *D*, of identical facture and finish to *A* and *B* and with the same dimensions, is in the Kunsthistorisches Museum, Vienna (Inv. no. 5993). The Victoria & Albert Museum also possesses replicas of *C* and *D*, ungilt of somewhat inferior finish, although of the same general facture, and of slightly smaller dimensions (diam 32.1 cm). These, formerly in the collection of Eugène Piot, Paris, were acquired separately from *A* and *B*.
All five roundels were ascribed by Hermann to Antico, and the ascription has not been questioned. The roundels representing the mature Hercules, *B, C* and *D*, together with that in Vienna, are directly relatable in style to Antico's bronze statuettes. Roundel *A, The infant Hercules and the serpents*, with its complex narrative composition, is distinct in conception from the other four. It was, however, clearly designed and modelled by the same hand as the frieze on the *Gonzaga Vase* (Cat. 51), which is generally accepted as a work by Antico.
References to bronze roundels in the inventory after death of 1496 of Gianfrancesco Gonzaga di Ródigo (*due tondi cum certe figure suso, una figura in su uno tondo*) and in that of Isabella d'Este of 1542 (*duoi tondi di bronzo di basso relievo*) are not sufficiently specific to permit identification with Antico's Hercules roundels. However, an entry in the inventory after death of Duke Ferdinando Gonzaga in 1627 specifying three bronze roundels with Labours of Hercules (*Tre tondi di bronzo con le forze d'Ercole*) is likely refer to a set of three from Antico's series.
Roundels *C* and *D*, today belonging to the Bargello, have a provenance from the Ducal collections of the Este family at Modena. That now in Vienna is identifiable in the inventory of Archduke Leopold Wilhelm compiled in Vienna in 1659 (*120. Ein rondes Stuckh von Metal, warin der Hercules einen Hierschen zu Boden wirfft.*), and may therefore be assumed, like other bronzes by Antico now in Vienna and recorded in the same inventory (see Cat. 55), to have been acquired in Mantua for King Charles I in 1627-28 and later sold to the Archduke under the Commonwealth. Roundels *A* and *B* have an old provenance from collections in the Veneto, and the replicas of *C* and *D* in the Victoria & Albert Museum are unrecorded before their appearance in the Piot Collection in the late 19th century.
The two roundels from the Bargello are clearly distinguished by their partial gilding and their notably fine chasing, and must have been made at a different date from the other roun-

dels. On the analogy of Antico's statuettes their finish would seem to indicate that they are early productions, while the ungilt roundels are later. However, on the analogy of the frieze on the *Gonzaga Vase*, which is probably one of Antico's earliest known productions (see Cat. 51), the design of the roundel of the *Infant Hercules (A)* would appear to be early. It therefore seems possible that roundels *C* and *D* are survivors from an early complete series which included an earlier example of roundel *A*. It was suggested by Pope-Hennessy that the surviving reliefs form part of two separate series, one composed of the parcel-gilt roundels *C* and *D*, and the other composed of roundels *A* and *B*, the roundel now in Vienna and the replicas of *C* and *D* in the Victoria & Albert Museum. However, the two replicas of *C* and *D*, besides being of slightly smaller dimensions than all the other roundels, are of inferior quality in finish to the other three ungilt roundels, and must be the product of yet a third casting.
Assuming that there were in fact three separate castings, although it is possible that roundels *C* and *D* are survivors from an early, more comprehensive, set, it does not necessarily follow that subsequently cast sets comprised all five known models. That they possibly did not is suggested by the appearance in Duke Ferdinando's inventory compiled just before the great Mantuan sales of a set of only three roundels.
It was tentatively proposed by Hermann that the set of three Hercules roundels listed in the inventory of 1627 were to be identified with roundels *A* and *B* and the roundel now in Vienna. In view of the fact that these three roundels are identical in facture and finish (it is noteworthy also that, in distinction from the other four roundels, these three have had their suspension rings removed) and that the roundel in Vienna has a probable provenance direct from Mantua in 1627-28, this proposal seems likely to be correct. It was further suggested by Hermann that, in view of the old provenance from the Veneto of roundels *A* and *B*, these might, on the analogy of the version of Antico's *Apollo*, which was bought by the Venetian Domenico Pasqualigo from the estate of Duke Ferdinando Carlo in the early 18th century, have survived the sales and the sack, and remained in the Gonzaga collections in

60 [C]   61 [D]

Mantua until the extinction of the Ducal line in 1708, to be bought by a local collector (see Cat. 57).

A suggestion by Hermann that the roundels were commissioned by Isabella d'Este for insertion in a marble doorcase in honour of her father Ercole I d'Este is unlikely to be correct, since the two roundels of the Bargello and the two replicas in London have suspension rings, and the other three roundels have slots at the top for the fitting of rings of the same type. However, in view of the provenance of roundels C and D from the Este collections and the appropriateness of the subject to Ercole, it does seem possible that the series was initially commissioned for him. The facture and finish of roundels C and D would in any case, on the analogy of Antico's early statuettes made for Gianfrancesco Gonzaga di Ródigo before 1496 and for Bishop Ludovico Gonzaga around 1500, indicate a date of production for these before the death of Ercole I in 1505.

A.F.R.

PROVENANCE: *A, B:* Remondini collection, Bassano; by inheritance to Conte Rigoni, Vicenza; purchased from him by the South Kensington Museum (later Victoria & Albert) through Raffaello Pinti in 1881 and 1882 respectively; *C, D:* Este collections, Ferrara, and later Modena; removed to Vienna in 1868; returned to Italy as war reparations in 1921 and installed in the Palazzo Venezia, Rome; later transferred to the Museo Nazionale, Florence.

BIBLIOGRAPHY: Hermann, 1910, pp. 219, 269-76; Venturi, X (1), 1935, p. 229; Mantua, *Mantegna*, 1961, nos. 116-117.

ADDITIONAL BIBLIOGRAPHY: A. Berger, "Inventar der Kunstsammlung des Erzherzogs Leopold Wilhelm von Oesterreich...", *Jahrbuch der Kunsthistorischen Sammlungen des Allerhöchsten Kaiserhauses*, I, 1883, 2, p, CLXIX, no. 120; E. Molinier, *Les plaquettes*, Paris, 1886, II, pp. 82-83, nos. 486-89; L. Planiscig, Kunsthistorisches Museum in Wien, *Die Estensische Kunstsammlung*, Vienna, 1919, nos. 183-84; L. Planiscig, Kunsthistorisches Museum in Wien, *Die Bronzeplastiken*, Vienna, 1924, no. 106; Royal Academy of Arts, *Exhibition of Italian art*, London, 1930, pp. 403-004; J. Pope-Hennessy, assisted by R. Lightbown, *Catalogue of Italian sculpture in the Victoria and Albert Museum*, London 1964, I, nos. 354-57.

62

62

Francesco Gonzaga, fourth Marquis of Mantua (1466-1519); *c.* 1498
Gian Cristoforo Romano (*c.* 1465-1512)
Terracotta bust; h. 69 cm
Museo del Palazzo Ducale, Mantua (11696)

Francesco is represented in contemporary armour with elaborate symbolic decorations in shallow relief. On the upper part of his breastplate is a crucible containing gold bars heated in a fire upon a vase-shaped brazier. This is a representation of the *impresa del cimento*, or *del crogiuolo*, the device of the trial of the crucible, illustrating the motto *Probasti me Domine et cognovisti*, which was adopted by Francesco in 1495-96. Below this is an eagle with spread wings with a ring in its beak standing on top of a pile of classical arms and armour. On his right pauldron is a caduceus, and on his left pauldron a warrior in classical armour (Mars?) holding up a model of the temple of Janus, inscribed IANI TEMPLVM.

This haunting portrait, which represents the self-styled victor of Fornovo in a way which justifies his nickname of *Il Turco*, came to light in the mid-nineteenth century, when it was presented to the new Museo Civico of Mantua by Pasquale Coddé, secretary of the Accademia Virgiliana, who ascribed it to Andrea Mantegna. This ascription was supported by Carlo d'Arco, and for long enjoyed general currency, largely because of the correspondence of the portrait of Francesco with that in Mantegna's *Madonna della Vittoria* of 1495/6 in the Louvre (Pl. 29).

The name of Gian Cristoforo Romano was first proposed as author of the bust by Adolfo Venturi in 1888 on the grounds of close stylistic correspondences with the effigy of Gian Galeazzo Visconti on his tomb of 1491-97 in the Certosa at Pavia and with the marble bust of Beatrice d'Este, now in the Louvre, carved at the time of, or just before, her marriage to Ludovico Sforza in January, 1491. Isabella d'Este, wife of Francesco Gonzaga, wrote to her sister Beatrice in 1491 requesting work by Gian Cristoforo, who, she knew, had just carved Beatrice's bust in marble, and in 1497, after the completion of his work at Pavia, Gian Cristoforo at last came to Mantua to enter the service of Francesco and Isabella as their official sculptor. He was to remain in their service until 1505. The comparison of the bust of Francesco with that of Beatrice d'Este is highly persuasive. Both have the same sharp objectivity in portraiture, combined with a clear, metallic rendering of symbolic motifs in low relief which is directly relatable to Gian Cristoforo's medal reverses.

As further circumstantial evidence for Gian Cristoforo's authorship of the bust Venturi cited in 1907 a letter in the Mantuan archive, first published by Gaye, from Federico Calandra, master of the Mantuan ordnance foundry, to Marquis Francesco dated 2 December, 1498. The letter concerns a cannon to be cast by Calandra which Francesco had ordered should bear his device of the *cimento*. Calandra has requested Gian Cristoforo Romano to provide a wax model of the device for casting, but there has been some question as to whether the crucible should be shown heated upon a vase, or, in a more realistic way, in a furnace. He therefore encloses two

140

sketches prepared by Gian Cristoforo and himself with alternative renderings of the device for Francesco's consideration. The drawings survive in the archive along with the letter, and it was claimed by Venturi, who was followed in this by other writers, that one of these drawings, which was selected by Francesco, shows the device almost exactly as it is rendered in relief on the bust.

However, C. M. Brown recently published for the first time Francesco's reply of the following day, 3 December, in which he decisively rejected both sketches, and ordered that an earlier approved design for the device should be followed, which pleased him more than either of the new designs. Brown also for the first time reproduced the sheet with the two drawings, and both of these show, albeit in different ways, the crucible heated in a furnace, and not, as on the breastplate of the bust, in a vase. It seems clear from this correspondence that Francesco's preference was for the vase design, however unrealistic this may have been.

Although what Venturi presented as his conclusive argument for Gian Cristoforo's authorship of the bust is thus discredited, the bust itself remains wholly explicable in terms of the known sculptural and medallic work of Gian Cristoforo Romano, and there seems to be no good reason for supposing, with Paccagnini, that Mantegna was in any way involved in its design or execution.

A.F.R.

PROVENANCE: Given by Dr. Pasquale Coddè to the Museo Civico, Mantua, before 1857.
BIBLIOGRAPHY: Gaye, I, 1839, pp. 341-42; d'Arco, 1857, I, pp. 71-72, II, p. 42; Venturi, 1888, pp. 49-59, 107-18, 148-58; Venturi, VI, 1908, p. 1137; Luzio 1913, p. 193; Fiocco, 1937, p. 103; Fiocco, 1940, p. 224; Ozzòla, 1951, no. 60; Paccagnini, 1961, p. 74; Mantua, *Mostra Mantegna*, 1961, no. 108; Marani and Perina, II, 1961, pp. 539-40; Brown, 1973.
ADDITIONAL BIBLIOGRAPHY: A. Venturi, "Il busto di Francesco Gonzaga, opera di Cristoforo Romano", *L'Arte*, X, 1907, pp. 448-49.

63

Francesco Gonzaga (1466-1519), *c.* 1492-1500
Attributed to Francesco Bonsignori (*c.* 1460 (?)-1519)
Black chalk with some wash and white highlights on greenish paper; 34.7 x 23.8 cm
National Gallery of Ireland Dublin (no. 2019)

The identification of the sitter as Francesco II Gonzaga was made by Byam Shaw (1928, pp. 50-54), comparing it to his portraits on the Sperandio medallion of 1495 (Hill, 1930, no. 400), and in Mantegna's *Madonna della Vittoria* of 1496 (Pl. 29); the drawing probably dates from the same decade. Both Byam Shaw and Pouncey (Wildenstein, 1967, p. 6) believed it to be by the same hand as the drawing of an elderly man at Christ Church (below, Cat. 64), but ascribed them to different artists: Shaw to Giovanni Bellini, Pouncey to Mantegna. Schmitt reverted to the traditional attribution to Bonsignori, but accepted Pouncey's attribution for the Christ Church drawing.

It seems probable that both drawings are the work of the same artist; the strong diagonal hatching, the use of white highlights and the scale are all similar, comparable to a signed and dated portrait study of Bonsignori's (drawing of a Venetian Senator, 1487, Albertina, Vienna). It is possible that they formed part of a series: both are nearly life size in scale (although Francesco's portrait had been more severely cut, especially at the top), both show the torso frontally; and the elaborate, bejewelled tunics which both men wear (possibly court dress) are to some extent uniform. It is tempting to

63   64

connect them to the paintings seen by Vasari at Marmirolo: "In 1499 Francesco (Bonsignori) painted some triumphs and many portraits of court gentlemen" (Vasari ed. Milanesi, V, p. 300). For this work, perhaps a series of *Uomini Famosi* (famous men), the Marchese rewarded Bonsignori with land and a house, so evidently it was a large undertaking. In a letter of 1492 to the Marchese, Bonsignori writes that he is working on the portraits for a Triumph of Fame (Schmitt, 1961, p. 141). Whether these portraits were eventually frescoed, or painted on panel or canvas, and how they fitted into the overall decoration is unknown. Marchese Francesco greatly esteemed Bonsignori's work, addressed him as *Carissime Noster, Dilecte noster*. He was famous as a portrait and kept chiaroscuro copies (*copia... in carte chiaroscuro*) of those sent abroad; some were still in the possession of his heirs when Vasari visited Mantua (Vasari ed. Milanesi, V, p. 301). Bonsignori viewed his subjects objectively, yet not unsympathetically in a similar spirit to Hans Holbein the Younger. This drawing from life of the condottiere husband of Isabella d'Este, shows him in a more humane light than any other surviving portrait.

J.T.M.

PROVENANCE: R. Cosway.
BIBLIOGRAPHY: Vasari ed. Milanesi, 18, V, pp. 300-01; A. Schmitt, 1961, pp. 92, 122, no. 20.
ADDITIONAL BIBLIOGRAPHY: J. Byam Shaw, *Old Master* Drawings, II, 1928, pp. 50-54; *Drawings from the National Gallery of Ireland*, Wildenstein, London, May-July, 1967, p. 6, no. 2.

64

Portrait study of an Elderly Man, *c.* 1492-1500
Attributed to Francesco Bonsignori (*c.* 1460 (?)-1519)
Black chalk, washed over on paper 39.1 x 28 cm. Cut all round; scroll inscribed "IM NV"
The Picture Gallery, Christ Church Oxford (no. 702)

Berenson first ascribed this drawing to Alvise Vivarini; Colvin, agreeing with him, suggested it was a portrait of Gentile Bellini, an identification which has been generally accepted. Byam Shaw gave both this drawing and the Dublin portrait (Cat. 63) to Giovanni Bellini. Only Popham conditionally accepted the traditional attribution to Francesco Bonsignori

(1931, p. 49). The similarity between this portrait and that of Marchese Francesco, and the possibility that it belonged to a series of portraits, makes the identification of the sitter as Gentile Bellini unlikely; it may well represent a Mantuan courtier or a Gonzaga relation. The interpretation of the letters on the scroll IM NV as part of a German motto used by Bona of Savoy "*Mit Zait*" (Schmitt 1961) is not properly explained: the drawing is cut on the right and a central letter may have been obliterated by damage, so it is likely that the inscription is fragmentary. The decorative quality of the scroll, and the fact that it does not seem to relate to the portrait head in any obvious way, gives the impression that the inscription was originally longer, possibly running across several portraits.

J.T.M.

PROVENANCE: General J. Guise.
BIBLIOGRAPHY: Mantua, *Mostra Mantegna*, 1961, p. 164, no. 131; U. Schmitt, 1961, p. 139, no. 105.
ADDITIONAL BIBLIOGRAPHY: S. Colvin, *Drawings of the Old Masters in the University Galleries and in the Library of Christ Church Oxford*, Oxford, 1907, II. no. 32; J. Byam Shaw, 1928, (see Cat. 63); A.E. Popham, *Italian Drawings Exhibited at the Royal Academy*, (London, 1930), Oxford, 1931, p. 49.

65

65

Short sword (so-called cinquedea) of Marquis Francesco Gonzaga

Maker and etcher unknown
Iron, ivory and horn; lenght 72 cm
Musée du Louvre, Paris, Département des Objets d'Art (OA 3242)

The upper half of the richly gilded blade of this weapon is etched in four compartments on either side. One face bears the Gonzaga and Este arms, thus identifying it with Marquis Francesco; the Gonzaga sun device appears with a nude figure below and two armed figures (Mars and Hercules ?). The fuller is inscribed ANIMVS TELO PRESTANCIOR OMINI ("the soul excels over every weapon"). The other face shows the Gonzaga devices of the deer with the motto BID CRAF (Bider Kraft) and muzzle with the motto CHAVCIUS, also a page arming a warrior and two nude men, one with a sieve (?), the other with a cornucopia. The fuller is inscribed with a line from Ovid (*Fasti* I, 493) OMENES SOLUM FORTI PATRIA EST ("every piece of earth is the home of the brave") which also occurs on a cinquedea in the Ashmolean Museum, Oxford, signed on the hilt by the maker, Alessandro Coltelli of Bologna. The etching was formerly attributed to Ercole de' Fideli, a goldsmith who worked in Ferrara, but there is no real evidence to suggest he decorated even one of the many blades with which his name has been associated.
The hilt, covered in ivory framed by horn, also has an iscription stamped upon the copper-gilt edges: NVNQVAM POTEST NON ESSE VIRTV LOCOS ("everywhere can be the place for bravery"). The cinquedea – this term is defined by Florio in his *New World of Words* (1611) as "a weapon but five fingers long used in Venice" – cannot be identified from the 1542 inventory of the Gonzaga armoury though at least one item sounds not dissimilar, *una cortella alla damaschina longa un brazzo lavorada la lama col manicho de avolio* (Mann, 1938, pp. 316-17).

D.S.C.

PROVENANCE: Early history unknown; acquired from Baron de Rentz by the Louvre in 1890.
BIBLIOGRAPHY: Mann, 1938, pp. 244-45, with previous bibliography.
ADDITIONAL BIBLIOGRAPHY: C. Blair, "Cesare Borgia's sword scabbard", *Victoria and Albert Museum Bulletin*, II, 4, 1966, pp. 125-36.

66

Photograph: **The Triumphs of Caesar** [Detail, Pl. 28]
Andrea Mantegna (1431-1506)
Tempera on twilled canvas. The original canvas, cut down to the area of the painting is now mounted on heavier canvas and wooden stretchers dating from the restoration of 1931-34; 268 x 278 cm (average size)
Her Majesty the Queen

The *Triumphs of Caesar* have been in England since the seventeenth century and were the crowning glory of that part of the Gonzaga collection purchased for Charles I by Daniel Nys. From about 1508 until the year of their despatch (1629) it is known that they were displayed for most of the time in the *sala* of the Palazzo di S. Sebastiano in Mantua. Their early history is, however, still a matter of argument, made more complicated by the generally accepted observation that the series is in some sense unfinished (see Cat. 67-69). Nor is it clear where the canvases were originally displayed, though it was certainly within the Palazzo Ducale complex.
The recent cleaning by John Brealey (1962-74) has revealed the survival of more of Mantegna's painting than had previously been expected. Currently scholarly opinion is in a state of flux. However, three main lines of thought may be briefly stated. Documentary evidence reveals little more than that the *Triumphs* were already being painted in 1486 and were still being painted in 1492. Traditionally it has been held that these are the years in which the canvases were executed and that it was Marchese Francesco Gonzaga who commissioned the cycle. But six to eight years (broken in the middle by a lengthy visit to Rome, 1489-91) is almost certainly too short a time for the completion of nine extremely large and complicated canvases by an artist working with Mantegna's laborious, minute and time-consuming technique. Martindale suggested that the series was begun under Ludovico Gonzaga (before 1478) as a continuation of the decoration of the palace, following the completion of the *Camera degli Sposi* in 1474. Hope has proposed an alternative hypothesis: that the *Triumphs* were a commission of Francesco Gonzaga (after his accession in 1484) but were worked on until Mantegna's death in 1506. Whereas the second of these hypotheses offers the *Triumphs* as a link between the *Camera* and Mantegna's late work, the third sees the series as an extended piece of "late" work, not begun until Mantegna was already about fifty-five years old. Other interpretations will certainly follow and the question has yet to be settled.

The detailed programme of the paintings, which represent, according to an inscription on the second canvas, the Gallic Triumph of Julius Caesar, is based principally on a combination of the account of the Triumphs of Aemilius Paulus given by Plutarch, and that of Scipio Africanus given by Appian. Whatever the date of the paintings, they offer Mantegna's most complete statement on the appearance of the Roman world. The extensive archaeological observation reflects a wide knowledge of the sculpted monuments of Rome itself. Much of the detail is not new in Mantegna's work; indeed a sort of learned archaeological perception can be seen in his very earliest paintings. The most startling feature of the *Triumphs* is the vivid sense of life and the immediacy with which Mantegna has imbued his depiction of a long distant event.

When the paintings arrived in England (probably in 1630) it seems likely that they were sent straight to Hampton Court where they were certainly to be found in 1649. Until about 1689 they were hung in the old King's Gallery of the Tudor Palace. Following the rebuilding under William III, the *Triumphs* have been housed in a variety of places in the palace. They have been in the Lower Orangery since 1921. Since the paintings had already been moved several times in Mantua, it is likely that their condition had already deteriorated when they arrived in England. Indeed, in the 1660's *The Captives*, now the most seriously damaged canvas, was already singled out as "much spoyled". Two attempts to preserve the *Triumphs* were responsible for their sad appearance until the latest restoration. The first series of "restorationes", carried out between 1693 and 1717, amounted substantially to repainting all the figures. The chief painter in this operation was probably Laguerre who worked on the *Triumphs* between about 1694-1702. A second attempt to preserve the canvases within a thick layer of paraffin wax was carried out between 1931-34. The disastrous results of both these episodes have now been ameliorated (excepting *The Captives*, see Cat. no. 71).

In Mantua itself the *Camera degli Sposi* alone survives to testify to the genius which Mantegna placed at the disposal of the Gonzaga. It is worth emphasising that late fifteenth century sightseers were also taken to see the *Triumphs*; and that in the sixteenth century it was considered that the *Triumphs of Caesar* constituted Mantegna's greatest achievement for the Gonzaga. Daniel Nys reported during the negotiations for the sale of the collection "that, not having the Triumphs of Caesar, I had nothing at all".

A.M.

PROVENANCE: Mantua, until 1629, thereafter Hampton Court.
BIBLIOGRAPHY: A. Martindale, 1979, with full bibliography; C. Hope, 1980 (review of Martindale).

67-68-69-70-71

The Triumphs of Caesar: Associated Drawings and Engravings

67. Trophy-Bearers: copy of a preliminary study for the sixth canvas
After Mantegna
Pen and brown ink; 26 x 26 cm
National Gallery of Ireland, Dublin (Inv. no. 2187)

68. The Triumphal Chariot: Unfinished copy of a preliminary copy of a preliminary study for the ninth canvas
After Mantegna
Pen and brown ink and some red chalk washed with brown,

67

yellow, and green heightened with white; 26.2 x 27.3 cm
British Museum, Department of Prints and Drawings (cat. no. 169)

69. The Elephants: engraving after a preliminary study for the fifth canvas
After a lost drawing by Mantegna (engraving attributed by Oberhuber and Sheehan, to Zoan Andrea)
27 x 26 cm
British Museum, (Bartsch XIII, 235, 12; Hind: Mantegna 14). A good drawn version of this composition exists in a private collection in Paris (illustrated in Martindale, no. 52).

Apart perhaps from a single study (Louvre; Pl. 27) for the

68

first canvas, none of Mantegna's autograph preparatory drawings for the *Triumphs* survives. But a number of copies, drawings and engravings, exist which give some insight into the planning of the series (For extended comment and full catalogue see Martindale, 1979). Cat. 67-69 all record preliminary thoughts for their respective canvases. It will be noted, for instance, that *The Elephants* was originally conceived with a far more elaborately wrought candelabra and without a landscape background; the *Trophy Bearers* was without the arched structure and column found in the background of the finished painting; and the *Triumphal Chariot* was pulled by four horses instead of the pair in the final version. Engraved versions of these preliminary drawings, of the sort represented by Cat. 69 exist for the *Trophy-Bearers* and the *Senators* (see below) and were undoubtedly influential in spreading a somewhat imperfect impression of Mantegna's achievement outside Mantua. It is unlikely however that any of them was produced under Mantegna's supervision since none of them is of sufficiently high quality. There is no evidence that the entire series was engraved during Mantegna's lifetime and the first complete "printed edition" is the publication of Andreani (see below no. Cat. 71) dating from the end of the sixteenth century.

BIBLIOGRAPHY: Hind, 1948; Levenson, and others, 1973; Alston, and others, 1979.

69

70

interplay of figures and architecture. Indications of Mantegna's archaeological interests are evident in the face of the grotesque double-chinned man based on a coin of the Emperor Vespasian, and the round tower which must be derived from the tomb of Caecilia Metella, Rome. The *Senators* and the *Captives* share the distinctive formation of the procession: a dignified, closely packed congregation of adults and children. This is similar to certain relief carvings of the Lombardo brothers (in the Santo, Padua), and both the Santo carvings and Mantegna's designs are close to the reliefs of the Ara Pacis, Rome. There is no evidence that any part of the Ara Pacis was excavated before 1568; but these compositions raise the possibility that sections of it were already known in the late fifteenth century.

71

70. The Senators: engraving after a study for a composition never apparently painted
After a lost drawing by Mantegna; 27 x 26 cm
British Museum (Bartsch XIII, 234, 11; Hind, Mantegna 16)

A good drawn version of this composition exists in the Albertina, Vienna (Inv. no. 2585). Unlike the engraving, the composition of the drawing proceeds correctly from right to left (illustrated Martindale no. 56).
The *Senators* composition was already circulating at some stage in the second half of the 1490's when it was plagiarised by Liberale da Verona for a panel of *Dido's Suicide* (National Gallery, London, No. 1136). The *Senators'* composition is clearly related to that of the *Captives* (see below Cat. 71) in its

71. The Captives, from *Tabulae Triumphi Caesaris...* published at Mantua in 1598-99
Andrea Andreani (active 1584-1610) after Mantegna
Chiaroscuro woodcut, 37 x 37 cm
Victoria & Albert Museum, Department of Prints and Drawings (Dyce, 1369)

The title-page of this publication records that Andreani, a Mantuan himself, was recalled from Siena by Duke Vincenzo Gonzaga specifically to create these woodcuts. In the first place they confirm that the nine paintings now at Hampton Court are those which were displayed in the Palace of S. Sebastiano from 1508 and provide almost certain evidence that Mantegna had painted only nine canvases when he died in 1506.

The *Captives* composition is unique in that it was never totally completed. The blank area in the top left-hand corner of the woodcut reflects a *lacuna* both in the painting itself and in all the known copies (see Martindale, 1979). Therefore it seems likely that it was the last painting of the series on which Mantegna worked.

Today the *Captives* canvas is almost totally illegible, the colour and forms being obscured by the dirty coating of paraffin which was applied in 1930-34. It was the most heavily overpainted in the restoration of *c.* 1700 and it was decided early in the recent restoration not to attempt to bring it back to life. Its original quality can now only be imagined with the aid of copies like Andreani's, and a number of others apparently made in *c.* 1590-1630 (the spirited pastiche by Rubens now in the National Gallery, London, is the most distinguished representative of these).

Andreani decorated the title page with a representation of the bronze bust of Mantegna which is still in his funerary chapel in S. Andrea, Mantua (see Cat. no. 30). In a long dedicatory inscription, Andreani related that for more than a century writers from all parts of the world had been coming to see the *Triumphs*. The publication itself celebrates the pride which the Gonzaga family still felt in the paintings and is a reminder of the unwillingness of Duke Vincenzo II in 1626-27 to sell this part of the family collection. Up to their last moments in Mantua they were a vital part of the "Gonzaga splendour".

BIBLIOGRAPHY: Martindale, 1979; Brown, 1970, 1980.
ADDITIONAL BIBLIOGRAPHY: A. Reichel, *Die Clair-Obscur-Schnitte des XVI, XVII, und XVIII Jahrhunderts*, Zurich, Leipzig, Vienna, 1929.

Postscript
Andrea Andreani's dates, not previously known, were *c.* 1558/9-1629. He died on 15 February 1629, when his age was recorded as seventy (ASM, Reg. Necrologici n. 32 c. 10r n. 78). The note of a payment to him on 17 September 1595 of 30 *schudi* to print engravings of the *Triumphs* has recently been published by C.M. Brown, "The *Triumphs of Caesar* of Andrea Mantegna and Francesco II Gonzaga's supposed trip to Germany in 1486", *Atti e Memorie dell'Accademia Virgiliana di Mantova*, XLVIII, 1980, pp. 114-15. However two corrections (confirmed by Professor Brown) should be noted: for *Adi 17 Zenaro* read *A dì 17 settembre*, and for the payment given as *Libre 1, soldi 80* read *lire 180*.

R.S.

72

Pattern book of Pageant costume, Armour, Arms and Horse bits, also including a **view of Mantua**
Filippo Orsoni, *Liber Philippi Ursonis Manu, Pictoris Mantuani* (1554)

Codex of pen and ink drawings with colour wash; 304 pp.; 41.9 x 28 cm
Victoria & Albert Museum, Department of Prints and Drawings (E 1725-2031-1929)

The book is divided into two parts, each preceded by title pages; the second title page to the first part includes at the bottom a view of Mantua showing the façade of Sant'Andrea. The first 101 pages are drawings of trappings, horse bards, horses, equestrian masque costumes, saddle steels and stirrups, armours and part armours, parade helmets and sword hilts; the remainder show horse bits. The drawings are accompanied by one or more captions describing the function of the object shown or recommending the merits of the design. It is one of three recorded versions. A second, closely similar, version (including the same view of Mantua) is in the library of the former Dukes of Brunswick-Wolfenbüttel in Wolfenbüttel, while the third, which comprised the second part and only depicted bits, was seen on the London art market some thirty years ago.

The drawings illustrate the latest fashion and were presumably intended for the guidance of clients wishing to emulate the style of the Gonzaga court. This codex was formerly in the possession of Marcus Sitticus, Count of Hohenembs and Archbishop of Salzburg (1574-1619); the second codex, which also went north (to Brunswick), contains the dates 1540, 1558 and 1559 on different drawings.

72 (see also above p. XVI)

A document recently found (ASM, Archivio Notarile, Estensioni Notarili *ad annum*, V) shows that the Italian form of the artist's name is Orsoni.
Similarities between Orsoni's designs and armours, believed to have been built by the Mantuan court armourer, Caremolo Modrone, suggest that Orsoni may have supplied Modrone with designs for decoration of armour. While his drawings include many helmets and other elements bearing the devices of the Emperor Charles V and of the French kings, François I and Henri II, those of Duke Federico Gonzaga are not represented. The pageant costumes and many of the variations of

the classical Roman helmet are executed in a vein of pure fantasy, but some of the armour drawings show complete mastery of contemporary fashion and construction. One page shows the various types of helmet appropriate for field and tournament, another a complete armour for man and horse of the construction then usual in Mantua, as is indicated by the caption of the Wolfenbüttel version of the drawing "similar armours with more relief ornament were made in Mantua and worn by a gentleman of Brescia in France". As a whole the drawings are of minor artistic merit; Orsoni was at his best in devising sword hilt constructions, but even in these he introduces crowded Mannerist detail which required the fourbisseur to work iron in a manner more appropriate for precious metal.

J.H.

BIBLIOGRAPHY: Mann, 1938, pp. 240-336; Ward-Jackson, 1979, no. 212, pp. 101-07.

ADDITIONAL BIBLIOGRAPHY: J.F. Hayward, *European Armour, Victoria & Albert Museum*, London, 1965, pls. 25, 27, 29; L.G. Boccia and E. Coelho, *Armi Bianche Italiane*, Milan, 1975, pls. 355-65; J. F. Hayward, *Virtuoso Goldsmiths*, London, 1976, p. 318, pls. 238-40; V. Posio, "Una inedita veduta della Mantova del 1554", *Quadrante padano*, II, March 1981, 1, pp. 42-45.

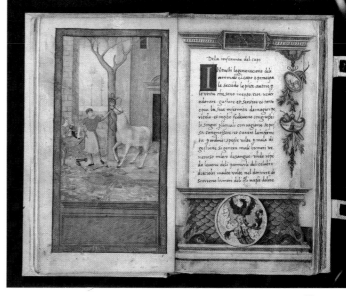

73

73

The treatise of a Mantuan horse-doctor on horses' illnesses; late 15th century

Zanino di Ottolengo, *Delle infirmità delli cavalli*
Manuscript in Italian on paper; scribe unknown; 20 x 11 cm; II + 158 + II fols; title page cc. 17v-18r illuminated.
Fondazione d'Arco, Mantua

In a letter to Marchese Federico Gonzaga dated 2 January 1480 (ASMAG 2424) the signatory Zanino di Ottolengo is described as the former farrier of Federico's father Marchese Ludovico (*Zaninus de Ottolengo iam merescalchus illustris quondam domini genitoris vestri*). In this letter Zanino offers his renewed services, understanding the present farrier to be unsatisfactory and makes clear that he was skilled not only in shoeing but also in the medical treatment of horses (*le ferrature et simelmente le medicine*). The inference seems reasonable that the present manuscript of his treatise was made for Marchese Federico (d. 1484) whether or not Zanino was reappointed. On the other hand the book may, as a work of authority, have been copied slightly later for Federico's son Marchese Francesco whose enthusiasm for horses was unbounded. The illuminated margin of the first page of text shows two Gonzaga devices (see Cat. 62, 127), the deer with the motto BIDER KRAFT and the crucible, though this has the motto HINC FALSA ("From here falsehoods") rather than DOMINE ME PROBASTI ET COGNOVISTI, adopted by Francesco after 1495, which suggests a terminal date. Zanino clearly derives much from Albertus Magnus (*c.* 1200-80) "De infirmitatibus Equorum" (Lib. XXII of his *De animalibus*) and probably from L. Rusius, *Liber Mareschalchie equorum* written *c.* 1282 by a Roman farrier, known also in an Italian version, and printed *c.* 1486 (at Spires ?) and in Rome (1490). Zanino's treatise starts with illnesses in the head and discusses morbid symptoms and suggested remedies for sickness in almost any part of the horse's body; there is a long section on the maladies of horses' legs and hooves, and the one illustration in the present manuscript suggests less that the tethered horse is going to be shod (there is no sign of anvil or forge) than that it is to undergo some more serious operation. Another copy, in the Biblioteca Comunale, Mantua (MS. A III 17 81) contains a note dated 1571, in what appears

to be the hand of Duke Guglielmo Gonzaga's brother Ludovico Duke of Nevers, deploring as diabolical a number of remedies suggested in the final section of the work; for instance Zanino suggests a wicked horse (*cavallo iniquo*) can be tamed by the application of a noose by which a man has been hanged, and he prescribes incantatory spells to be used before the castration of a horse and to cure worms.

D.S.C.; R.S.

BIBLIOGRAPHY: Cavriani, 1909, pp. 3-12; Meroni, 1966, p. 83; Mantua, 1979, *La Scienza a Corte*, pp. 65, 67, n. 13; G. Amadei and others, 1980, p. 234.

ADDITIONAL BIBLIOGRAPHY: J. Agrimi, *Tecnica e scienza nella cultura medievale*, Florence, 1976, p. 61; L. Rusio, ed. P. Delprato and L. Barbieri, *La mascalcià di Lorenzo Rusio volgarizzamento del secolo XIV... aggiunta il testo latino*, Bologna, 1867.

74

A book on falcons and other birds of prey written for Marchese Francesco Gonzaga

Author unknown (? Giulio Prudenzio), *Libro de piaceri et doctrina de ocelli*; *c.* 1500
Manuscript in Italian on paper, IX + 193 fols; 30 x 21.5 cm; spaces for illuminated initials left blank
Bodleian Library, Oxford (MS. Canonici Italiani 120)

Hawking and fowling in the marshy country round Mantua was enjoyed by the Gonzaga as much as hunting, and they bred falcons as they bred horses and dogs. The sport had for long been popular in courtly art and literature, and the science of falconry had an exalted past, depending since the thirteenth century upon the treatise of a supposed Armenian King called Dancus, the book of Emperor Frederick II and the scholastic works of Albertus Magnus and Pietro Crescenzi (Cat. 76). The treatise, shown here like Zanino's book on horses (Cat. 73), is very derivative, and a reminder that many areas of learning changed little in the Renaissance period. There is no title page but in the dedicatory *Epistola* the author quotes the title (as above) by which he wishes his work to be known; he had, he declares, laboured for many years collecting the material, both from old books and his own experience, so he does make some claim to be original if also reviving knowledge which he says had declined from ancient standards (... *questa dottrina essendo transmutata et spinta de la sua antiqua et natural forma*). The work ends (fol. CLXXXX r) with the signature *Julius Prudentius Volanti Calamo S(cripsit)* – "Giulio Prudenzio wrote it with his rapid pen" – but the name more probably refers to the scribe than the author. Nothing is known about Prudenzio.

A postscript dated 1561 in the hand of Ludovico Gonzaga Duke of Nevers mentions the dedication to his grandfather and that he had taken this together with another book on the subject dedicated to his father Federico; he was critical of some of the remedies proposed but valued the book and inscribed it with his name for fear of loss (*Io tolsi con un altro libro di Questa materia dedicato al suddetto Duca mio padre. Questo è piú copioso ma specialmente delle nature de ucelli dove dice piú il vero che negli rimedii... benche tenendolo come facio molto caro non dubito si perdi*). Ludovico also had from Duke Guglielmo's library the copy of Zanino's *Libro de Cavalli* now in the Biblioteca Comunale, Mantua (see Cat. 73).

D.S.C.

BIBLIOGRAPHY: Meroni, 1966, p. 37.
ADDITIONAL BIBLIOGRAPHY: A. Mortara, *Catalogo dei Manoscritti Italiani... nella Biblioteca Bodleiana*, Oxford, 1864, cols. 135-36; J.E. Hartin, *Bibliotheca Accipitraria, A. Catalogue of Books relating to Falconry* (London 1891, repr. 1964); Federick II, *De arte venandi cum avibus* trans. and ed. C.A. Wood and F.M. Fyfe, London etc., 1943, with bibliography; R.S. Oggins, "Albertus Magnus on Falcons and Hawks" in J.A. Weisheipl, *Albertus Magnus and the Sciences*, Toronto 1980, pp. 441-62.

75

Gonzaga racehorses, *c.* 1499-1518
Silvestro da Lucca, *Codice dei palii gonzagheschi*
Manuscript in Italian on vellum; 24 x 16 cm; unknown illuminators
Biblioteca Giustiniani-Recanati, Venice.

Silvestro da Lucca, a debt collector of the Gonzaga Court (*exactor Curie*), wrote to Marquis Francesco on 10 September 1512 (ASMAG b. 2485) that he remembered the Marquis had mentioned several times that he would like to have an illustrated record of his race horses and list of the prizes they had taken (*far un libro di carta di capretto et in quello ritrar li Barbari dal naturale et poi subsequentemente scriver li palii per loro habuti*). Having twenty-four ducats in hand Silvestro reckoned this would be enough to cover the cost of materials and hire of an illuminator (*anchora da pagar el miniatore che fara et dipingera epsi cavalli dal naturale che sera opera bella et memorabile*). The outcome was clearly this book dedicated to the Marquis by Silvestro and containing miniatures of thirty-five different horses, giving their names and prizes. The title page showing against an architectural background "Il Dainosauro", who won the palio of gold brocade at Ferrara, Florence and Mantua (the years are not filled in), is of much finer quality than the other illustrations, which suggests that Silvestro took the work from the original illuminator and gave it to another who charged less. Other pages contain much more information about races, however, going back in time as far as 1499 and forward to 1518; one horse "El Mozone barbaro" won as many as eight prizes in three years (1500-02) in places as far away as Siena and Florence as well as nearby Verona and Ferrara, though "El Serpentino" won the same number over a longer period, 1500-08, winning twice in Rome (1503-

75

04): it is clear that Gonzaga racehorses were sent long distances to compete. Most of the horses are portrayed against vague landscape backgrounds; only one, "Isdormia Secondo", who won twice in Mantua in 1514 and three times in Florence in 1515-16, is shown with the jockey.

D.S.C.

BIBLIOGRAPHY: Cavriani, 1909, pp. 3-17; Meroni, 1966, pp. 31, 83.

76

A treatise on agriculture and rural science copied for Marchese Francesco, *c.* 1500
Petrus de Crescentiis Bononiensis (Pietro de'Crescenzi of Bologna, 1233-1321), *Rei Rusticae libri duodecim*
Manuscript in Latin on vellum; I + 224 fols; 22 x 32 cm; unknown scribe (follower of Bartolomeo Sanvito) and illuminators; title page with Gonzaga arms and initials I(ohannes) F(ranciscus)
Oesterreichische Nationalbibliothek, Vienna (Handschriften und Inkunabelsammlung, Cod. 2313)

The treatise of Crescenzi, written *c.* 1303-04, was for long regarded as a standard authority on all branches of agriculture and estate management and is believed to have influenced the rise of the villa farm, owned and operated by a literate *signore*. Crescenzi, a professional judge, owned an estate near Bologna and his work combines precept from classical sources

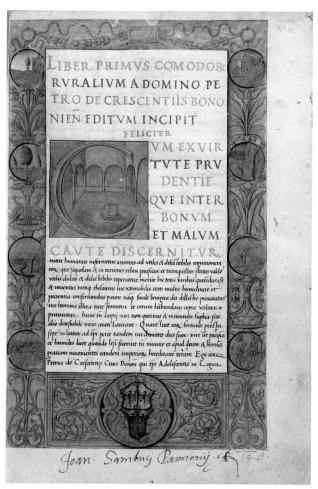

76

early translations into Italian, French and German. The first of twenty-eight printed editions of the Latin text appeared in 1471, and an Italian edition, *Il Libro della Agricoltura* was printed at Florence (1478) and Vicenza (1490).

D.S.C.

BIBLIOGRAPHY: Meroni , 1966, p. 34, pl. 126-29.
ADDITIONAL BIBLIOGRAPHY: L. Frati, *Pier de' Crescenzi e l'opera sua*, Bologna, 1920; H.J. Hermann, *Die Handschriften and Inkunabeln der italienischen Renaissance* in J. Schlosser and H.J. Hermann, *Beschreibendes Verzeichnis der Illuminierten Handschriften in Oesterreich*, n.f. vol. VI, 1, Leipzig 1930, pp. 100-07, ed. T. Alfonsi O.P., Società Agraria di Bologna, *Pier de' Crescenzi, Studi e documenti*, Bologna, 1933.

77

Photograph: **Letter from Cardinal Christopher Bainbridge, Archbishop of York, to Marquis Francesco Gonzaga**, Rome, 1 March 1514
Manuscript in Italian on paper; autograph signature
Archivio di Stato, Mantua (Archivio Gonzaga, b. 862)

Cardinal Bainbridge, who acted from 1509 to 1514 on Henry VIII's behalf in Rome, also promoted good relations between the Tudor and Gonzaga courts. He hinted in the autumn of 1513 that the King would appreciate a gift of horses and in this letter announces that Sir Thomas Cheyney, who was on his way home to England, would pass through Mantua "to see that celebrated and famous city" and pay his respects. The Cardinal also sent greetings to the Marquis' son Federico, whom he knew, since the boy had been Pope Julius II's pledge for the Marquis' military loyalty and had to live in Rome from 1510 to 1513. Later correspondence reveals that Bainbridge, who hoped soon to return to England, proposed to escort for a visit there the Marquis' younger son Luigi (later renamed Ercole, the future Cardinal). That the letter is written in Italian is remarkable. There were Italian members of Bainbridge's household, but it may have been composed by his versatile humanist secretary, Richard Pace.

D.S.C.

ADDITIONAL BIBLIOGRAPHY: D.S. Chambers, *Cardinal Bainbridge in the Court of Rome*, Oxford, 1965, pp. 67-70, 160-61.

78

Photograph: **Letter of Henry VIII to Marchese Francesco Gonzaga**, Eltham, 16 July 1514
Manuscript in Latin on parchment; autograph signature
Archivio di Stato, Mantua (Archivio Gonzaga, b. 578, c. 11)

Henry VIII thanks Marchese Francesco for his reception of Sir Thomas Cheyney (see Cat. 77) and for showing him the stables, and declares that after receiving four most beautiful, noble and excellent horses he now counts Francesco and his sons among his dearest friends. In fact (as letters of the Marchese to Cardinal Bainbridge and to the King, dated 17 and 28 March make clear) Cheyney himself had declined to choose any horses, he was already taking some others to England, but Francesco himself made a selection which he sent by his emissary Giovanni Ratto. (In letters from London dated 20 and 27 June Ratto reported Henry as saying that he could not have been more pleased had he been presented with another kingdom; he had never ridden better horses. He was looking out for some of English breed and also some dogs to send in return). The letter is countersigned by Andreas Ammonius

with practical experience. It has sections on the nature of plants, vines, trees, orchards, crops etc., on ploughing, sowing, harvesting, pruning; also a chapter on the raising of cattle, sheep, horses, donkeys, goats etc. Book Ten is on falconry and the trapping of wild animals. The appeal and usefulness of such a work to the Gonzaga is obvious; their business and leisure interests and correspondence were so much taken up with such things and with the running of their estates in the Mantuan dominion.

This very fine manuscript was formerly judged to be in the hand of Bartolomeo Sanvito, but Dr. A. de la Mare has expressed doubt, while conceding that the capital letters resemble his. It includes a full page illustration, possibly of a manorial court in session, facing the first of the twelve title pages which are richly decorated with illustrative detail; these represent the work of two different artists. The title page of Book Ten depicts, among other scenes of sporting life, a man fishing in the Lake, with a view of Mantua and the Ponte di San Giorgio.

Numerous copies of Crescenzi's treatise survive, including

(1477-1517), Henry's Italian-born Latin secretary, who was a friend of Erasmus, Colet and Sir Thomas More.

D.S.C.

BIBLIOGRAPHY: Cavriani, 1909, pp. 19-21; Luzio, 1917-18, p. 180; Luzio, 1922, p. 125.
ADDITIONAL BIBLIOGRAPHY: *Letters and papers of the reign of Henry VIII*, I. ed. R.H. Brode, London 1920, no. 3078.

79

Letter of Marchese Francesco Gonzaga to Henry VIII, Mantua, 21 November 1514
Manuscript in Latin on paper; autograph signature in Italian
Public Record Office, London (SP I/9 fol. 129)

Henry VIII's return gift (cf. Cat. 78) of horses with precious caparisons and trappings so delighted Marchese Francesco that he declared in this letter nothing conferred on him by nature, fortune or military skill had so raised his esteem in Italy as this. He intends to send twelve more of his own horses (*equos armentales ex omnibus pecuariis meis*) with Henry's emissary, Sir Griffith Don, and invites future emissaries to take their pick of his stables every year. In a letter of 15 October (ASMAG, b. 2922, Lib. 235, fol. 15r) the Marchese told Isabella d'Este that she would be delighted by the fine trappings (*guarnimenti*), more sumptuous than any she would have seen before, gifts truly worthy of such a King (*iudicando veramente esser degni di uno tanto Re donatore*).

D.S.C.

BIBLIOGRAPHY: Cavriani, 1909, p. 21; *Letters and Papers* (as in Additional Bibliography above) I, no. 3459.

80

Photograph: **Letter of Edward VI to Duke Francesco Gonzaga,** Greenwich, 10 June 1549
Manuscript in Latin on paper; autograph signature
Archivio di Stato, Mantua (Archivio Gonzaga, b. 578, c. 46)

This unpublished letter of the eleven-year old King to the sixteen-year old Duke refers to a Mantuan called Matteo Barba who had for many years been riding master at the English court. A letter also exists from Matteo himself in London written on 29 January 1533 to Duke Federico Gonzaga (ASMAG, b. 578; cf. letter of Henry VIII of 8 January 1533 in *Calendar of State Papers, Venice*, IV, 1867, no. 841). This mentions that his son Giovanni Matteo was returning to Mantua with a present of a horse; he himself very much wanted to return, but the King had refused to let him go (*disse non volere per conto alcuno ch'io partissi...*). However the present letter shows that Barba was now returning to Mantua with warm recommendations. The signature of Protector Somerset appears (Duke Francesco, likewise a minor, was meanwhile being supervised by his uncle Cardinal Ercole Gonzaga) and also that of Peter Vannes (d. 1563) who had in earlier years been to Italy on various diplomatic missions and had succeeded his relative Ammonius as the King's secretary (Cat. 78).

D.S.C.

81

Painted chest (*cassone*) **of Elisabetta Gonzaga** (1471-1526) **and Guidobaldo di Montefeltro, Duke of Urbino;** late fifteenth century

Wood, the front and lid curved, with tempera painting and gilding; h. 55 cm; length 147.5 cm; depth 44.5 cm
Victoria & Albert Museum, Department of Furniture and Woodwork (Inv. no. 47-1882)

Elisabetta Gonzaga, sister of Marchese Francesco, was betrothed to Guidobaldo di Montefeltro (1472-1508) in 1486 with a settlement of 26,000 ducats; she left Mantua for Urbino in February 1488, taking with her an additional dowry of jewels, gold and silverware, bedding, tablecoverings etc. (Luzio and Renier, 1893, pp. 8, 12, 293-95).
If, as has been assumed, the *cassone* was a marriage chest, it was presumably made to carry some of these items. It bears on the lid and front the arms of Gonzaga impaled with Montefeltro together with six repeated panels of four compartments each containing devices. The flames were one of the oldest devices of the Montefeltro (Dennistoun, I, p. 422) and appear, for instance, in the marquetry of Federico di Montefeltro's *studiolo* (Rotondi, 1951, II, fig. 346); the letter A appears in the marquetry of another door in his apartments (Ibid., fig. 425); the censer is less easily recognized.

81

A number of chests similar in form to this one have been noted; one (in Philadelphia Museum) has been identified as a "nunnery chest" i.e. brought to a convent by a *beatella* retiring there (Schubring, 1915, p. 225; van Falke, 1930, fig. 641); another is in the Decorative Arts Museum, Copenhagen.
The marriage chests of another Gonzaga lady of the late fifteenth century, Elisabetta's aunt Paola, wife of Leonhard Count of Gorizia (Cat. 46) were very different. She had a *cassone* painted with legends of the Emperor Trajan (Landesmuseum, Klagenfurt) and two coffers with ivory panels in relief including the Gonzaga device *Bider Kraft* (Graz Cathedral).

D.S.C.

ADDITIONAL BIBLIOGRAPHY: J. Dennistoun, *Memoirs of the Dukes of Urbino*, London 1851, I, pp. 420-22; P. Schubring, *Cassoni, Truhen und Truhenbilder der italienischen Frührenaissance*, Berlin, 1915; C. van Falke, *Die Sammlung Figdor, Wien*, Berlin, 1930; P. Rotondi, *Il Palazzo Ducale di Urbino*, II, Urbino, 1951; R. Milesi, *Mantegna und die Reliefs der Brauttruhen Paola Gonzagas*, Klagenfurt, 1975.

82

The Book of the Courtier by Baldassare Castiglione (1478-1529)
Baldesar Castiglione, *Il Libro del Cortegiano*, Venice (*nelle case d'Aldo Romano d'Andrea d'Asola*), 1528; an engraving after the portrait by Raphael (Louvre) is pasted in to face the title page.
British Library (31. g. 9)

The setting of this famous dialogue on courtly morals, which incorporates much of the humanist debate about education, the uses of language and the nature of love, is the court of

149

Urbino in 1506, but its links with Mantua are very close. Castiglione was born at Casatico in Mantuan territory and his mother was a Gonzaga though not of the ruling lineage. He was in Marchese Francesco Gonzaga's service 1499-1504, seeing military action with him, but in June 1504 obtained permission against Francesco's wishes to transfer to Guidobaldo di Montefeltro, Duke of Urbino; until 1513 he became *persona non grata* at the Mantuan court. But to Elisabetta Gonzaga, Duchess of Urbino, Castiglione professed reverential devotion, and she presides in the dialogue; others connected with the Mantuan court, such as Cesare Gonzaga, Vincenzo Calmeta and Giancristoforo Romano also appear in it, though Castiglione excludes himself as a participant by the device of dating the fictitious discussion to the time of his own absence in England where he went as Duke Guidobaldo's proxy to receive the Order of the Garter. Probably he first drafted the book after his return to Mantuan territory, where he married (1516) and settled until being sent as ambassador for Marchese Federico in Rome (1519-22). Between 1524 and 1527 Castiglione was preparing the final manuscript for this first printed edition. By 1600 there had been sixty Italian editions and many translations, so great was the work's success and influence. Sir Thomas Hoby's *The Courtyer Done into Englyshe* was first published in 1561 and a translation into Latin was also published in London in six successive editions, 1587-1612.

D.S.C.

BIBLIOGRAPHY: DBI (extensive bibliography); STC 4778-4787.
ADDITIONAL BIBLIOGRAPHY: *Il libro del Cortegiano*, ed. B. Maier, Turin, 1955.

83

Elisabetta Gonzaga, Duchess of Urbino (1471-1526)
Medal, bronze; diam 83 mm; *c.* 1495
Attributed to Adriano de' Maestri, called Adriano Fiorentino (d. 1499)
Victoria & Albert Museum, Department of Sculpture (Inv. A. 204-1910; Hill, *Corpus*, no. 344c)

In May 1495 a letter from Elisabetta Gonzaga to her brother Marchese Francesco recommended Adriano as a good sculptor who during a three months stay at Urbino had made some beautiful medals and also distinguished himself as a sonnet writer and lyre player. This provides a date for the present medal, inscribed on the obverse ELISABET[TA] GONZAGA FELTRIA DVCISS[A] VRBINI, and also for one of her sister-in-law and companion Emilia Pia, though an explanation has yet to be found for the enigmatic reverse which alludes to the need for steadfastness in the face of ill-fortune and has been connected, not very convincingly, with Cesare Borgia's capture of Urbino in 1502, three years after Adriano's death.

D.S.C.

BIBLIOGRAPHY: Hill and Pollard, 1967, no. 107, p. 25; Hill rev. Pollard, 1978, pp. 81-82.
ADDITIONAL BIBLIOGRAPHY: C. von Fabriczy, "Adriano Fiorentino", *Jahrbuch der Preussischen Kunstsammlungen*, XXIV, 1903, pp. 82-83, 96-97.

84

Francesco Gonzaga, fourth Marchese of Mantua (1466-1519)
Bartolommeo Melioli (1448-1514)
Medal, bronze; diam. 72 mm. Signed on reverse ADOLESCEN-

150

TIAE AVGVSTAE MELIOLVS DICAVIT (Meliolus dedicated to the noble youth)
Victoria & Albert Museum, Department of Sculpture (501-1864; Hill, *Corpus*, no. 196f)

The adolescent Francesco is shown beardless with elaborately curled hair, dressed in a cap and ornate cuirass. The inscription reads D. FRANCISCVS GON D FRED III M MANTVAE F SPES PVB[LICA] SALVSQ[UE] REDIVI[VA]; (the divine Francesco Gonzaga son of the divine Federico Marchese of Mantua; public hope and welfare renewed). This might suggest that the medal dated from before Federico's death (14 July 1484; misdated to 1481 by Hill, *Corpus*), yet comparison with the portrait medal by Ruberti (Cat. 85) on which Francesco is clearly designated Marchese show little change in his appearance. The occasion of the making of the medal is further obscured by the reverse: a female figure stands between fire and water holding in her left hand a staff and two ears of corn, in her right, a woven muzzle decorated with a scroll inscribed CAVTIVS (more carefully). This Gonzaga device of the *museruola* (which appears on a floor tile of the 1490's (Cat. 128) may signify that restraint and control are conducive to good government. Other devices were the muzzled dog and the *mangilia*, or manicle (Gerola, 1918). Hill misinterpreted the object as Pandora's box, and the Panofskys took the figure to be a personification of Health holding a box of medicines with which to cure Francesco; but there seems to be no foundation for d'Arco's assertion that he was dangerously ill in 1484 (d'Arco, 1857), although he was sick from March to May 1481 (Luzio, 1908). The wording of the inscription suggests that it was the public safety rather than the boy's health which had been endangered (famine hit Mantua and Ferrara in 1482, which might explain the corn). Nicolai Rubinstein remarks on the similarity between this inscription on the obverse and that beneath Lorenzo de'Medici (SALVS PVBLICA) on the medal struck after the Pazzi conspiracy of 1478 and widely disseminated, which refers to the survival of public order. Luzio's suggestion that Francesco's medal was begun before and finished after Federico's death should not be dismissed out of hand: the inscription may express a desire for continued wise government after the premature death of the former Marchese and the suppression of a conspiracy against Francesco by his uncles in 1487. Isabella d'Este received a medallion of her future husband in August 1484, which may have been this one or that by Ruberti; she confesses she would have preferred to see Francesco himself.

J.T.M.

BIBLIOGRAPHY: d'Arco, 1857, p. 75; Luzio, 1908, p. 25; Gerola, 1918; Mazzoldi, 1961, II, pp. 84-90; Hill and Pollard, 1967, no. 69.
ADDITIONAL BIBLIOGRAPHY: D. and E. Panofsky, *Pandora's Box*, New York, 1956, p. 23, n. 20.

85

Francesco Gonzaga, fourth Marchese of Mantua (1466-1519)
Medal, bronze; diam. 50 mm, pearled border, signed under ground line on reverse IO[ANNIS] FR[ANCISCI] RVBERTO OPVS
Gianfrancesco Ruberti della Grana (active 1483-1526)
British Museum, Department of Coins and Medals (Hill, *Corpus*, 203e)

The obverse shows Francesco presumably soon after his succession in 1484 aged eighteen: his appearance is very close to that on the Melioli Medal (Cat. 84). He is described as FRANSCISCVS. MARCHIO. MANTVAE. IIII. Over scale armour he wears

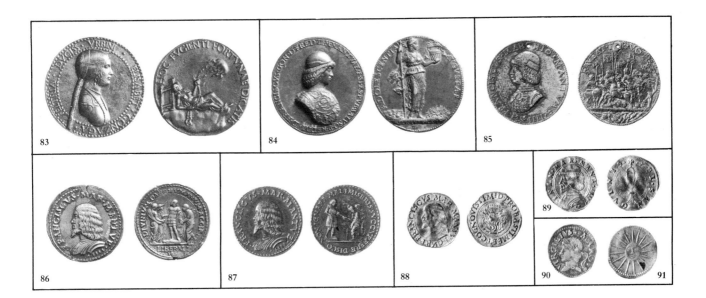

a breast plate decorated with a bird standing on a branch (perhaps the dove on a tree stock already used as a Gonzaga device on coins by 1462; see essay by Gobio Casali, above). The reverse, inscribed FAVEAT. FOR[TVNA]. VOTIS (let fortune favour your wishes), shows a cavalry skirmish, probably generically *all'antica* rather than an illustration of a specific event (the horsemen ride bareback and wear improbably elaborate helmets). A standard is decorated with a chalice (possibly the relic of the Holy Blood); against a withered tree trunk leans a shield with the stripes of the old Gonzaga arms, and from a branch is suspended an ansate tablet inscribed CAV(?), perhaps an abbreviation of the motto CAVTIVS (see Cat. 84). Beneath in the exergue various martial attributes are displayed including a shield inscribed EPO, another Mantuan device alluding to Virgil as E(picorum) P(oetarum) O(ptimus) (see Cat. 43).

This is the only known signed medal by Ruberti, plausibly identified as the *Gio Francesco*, goldsmith, first mentioned in Mantua in 1483 (Bertolotti, 1885, p. 89) More recently it has been suggested that he is also the master whose signature (also inscribed on the ground line as in this medal) IO[ANNES] F[RANCISCVS] F[ECIT] appears on a group of plaquettes in the Kress collection (Pope-Hennessy, 1965, nos. 97-110). The similarity between the battle scene here and Kress no. 100 is noteworthy. Ruberti worked at the Mantuan mint from 1491, introduced an improved method for striking coins in 1492, and was confirmed as *saggiatore* of the mint in 1520. For the Marchese Federico he was commissioned to execute Mantegna's designs for *all'antica* vases in 1483 (Bertolotti, 1888, p. 274); he designed decoration for weapons and for horses' trappings for Francesco in 1514 (Bertolotti, 1885, p. 89). Isabella d'Este received a golden parrot from him in 1494, and although he shocked her profoundly by a savage attack on a courtier in her presence, she continued to entrust him with the delicate task of pawning her jewels in times of financial stringency (Luzio, 1896, p. 302).

J.T.M.

PROVENANCE: George III.
BIBLIOGRAPHY: Bertolotti, 1885, p. 89; Bertolotti, 1888, p. 274; Luzio and Renier, 1896, p. 302; Hill and Pollard, 1967, no. 71.
ADDITIONAL BIBLIOGRAPHY: J. Pope-Hennessy, *Renaissance bronzes from the Samuel H. Kress collection, Reliefs, plaquettes, statuettes, utensils and mortars*, London, 1965.

86

Francesco Gonzaga, fourth Marchese of Mantua (1466-1516)

Attributed to Gian Marco Cavalli, (before 1454-after 1508)
Medal, bronze (struck); diam 34 mm
Victoria & Albert Museum, Department of Sculpture, (Inv. 7911-1863; *Corpus*, 241 c)

The obverse shows Francesco bareheaded, with a pointed beard, dressed in a cuirass, and is inscribed FRANCISCVS. MAR. MANTVE. IIII. On the reverse the Marchese is clad in *all'antica* armour, standing on a garlanded base, giving three ears of corn to a toga'd figure, while a bald-headed supplicant approaches on the left. Behind stands a helmeted female figure carrying a palm. The inscription reads "liberality; it is divine to give and human to receive" (LIBERALITAS DIVINVM DARE HVMANVM ACCIP[ERE]). A similar medal (or pattern for a coin) illustrating Francesco's charity, also attributed to Cavalli, has a different obverse and an inscription from the *Æneid* (Cat. 87). They may date from after 1500 (on Sperandio's 1495 medal the Marchese appears far younger); a silver *testone* (Hill and Pollard, 1967, no. 644) is closer in appearance. Cavalli lived at Viadana and worked for the Mantuan mint between 1481 and 1505; in 1497 he designed *testoni*, but an attempt by the Marchese in 1501 to get him to Mantua with his tools to make coins was abortive; Cavalli accused the supervisors at the Mint of gross stupidity. In 1506 he made a *testone* for the Emperor Maximilian in the Tyrol. Battista Spagnoli describes a portrait of Francesco by Cavalli made of gold (*Corpus*, p. 61). In 1483 he failed to execute a ewer designed by Mantegna (whose will he witnessed) which had been ordered by Federico, but he made a miniature copy of the antique *Spinario* for Bishop Ludovico Gonzaga.

J.T.M.

BIBLIOGRAPHY: Hill and Pollard, 1967, no. 84.
ADDITIONAL BIBLIOGRAPHY: U. Rossi, "Gian Marco Cavalli", *Rivista Italiana Numismatica*, I, 1888, fasc. 4, pp. 439-54.

87

Francesco Gonzaga, fourth Marchese of Mantua (1466-1516)

Attributed to Gian Marco Cavalli, (before 1454-after 1508)

Medal, bronze (struck); diam. 32 mm
British Museum, Department of Coins and Medals (1933-11-12-6; Hill, *Corpus*, 243)

The obverse portrait is taken from the same die as Cat. 86, the reverse shows the Marchese in armour holding a sceptre, distributing alms to three men. The inscription NON. IGNARA. MALI. MISERIS. SVCCVRRERE. DISCO is taken from Virgil, *Æneid*, i, 630, and are the words spoken by Dido when welcoming Æneas to Carthage: "not unschooled in woe do I learn to succour unhappiness". Another impression of this medal in lead (*Corpus*, 243a) is also in the British Museum. For further comment see Cat. 86 above.

J.T.M.

BIBLIOGRAPHY: Hill and Pollard, 1967, no. 85.
ADDITIONAL BIBLIOGRAPHY: Virgil, *Aeneid*, trans. J. Jackson, Oxford, 1908.

88

Ducat of Marquis Francesco
Gold coin; diam. 22 mm; wt 3.42 g
British Museum, Department of Coins and Medals (55.6.12. 205)

Mantuan coinage reached a high level under Marquis Francesco, particularly during the years 1497-1510 (Magnaguti I, 1913, pp. 32-33). The Marquis' head appears on the obverse of this gold ducat (which corresponds roughly to the standard weight of the Venetian ducat) and his device of the crucible (*crogiolo*) on the reverse with an abbreviation of its accompanying motto D[OMINE] PROBASTI ME ET COGNOVISTI M[E] adopted after his dismissal from Venetian service in 1497.

D.S.C.

BIBLIOGRAPHY: CNI, IV, p. 236, 11; Magnaguti, I, 1913, pp. 30-33.

89

Scudo of Marquis Francesco
Gold coin; diam. 22 mm; wt 3.46 g
British Museum, Department of Coins and Medals (55. 6. 12. 204)

The profile of the Marquis on the obverse of this coin, with long hair and wearing a beret, and the reliquary of the Precious Blood on the reverse, corresponding closely to the coinage of his grandfather Ludovico and his father Federico, suggests that it was struck early in his reign, 1484-c. 1495 (Magnaguti).

D.S.C.

BIBLIOGRAPHY: CNI, IV, p. 236, 6; Magnaguti, I, 1913, p. 31.

90-91

Virgil's head on a "soldino" of Marquis Francesco
Silver coin; diam. 14 mm; wt 0.67 g
British Museum, Department of Coins and Medals (1908-10.11.455; 55.6.12.208)

A head inscribed VIRGILIVS MARO appears on the obverse of this low denomination coin, but the poet had been used as a

civic emblem, almost a patron saint, of Mantua long before the advent of the Gonzaga. Indeed the earliest known Mantuan coin, a double *denaro* of the late eleventh century, is inscribed VIRGILIVS, and the use of this image on coins continued throught the communal period to the Bonacolsi and Gonzaga Captains, usually with the inscription VIRGILIVS DE MANTUA, and the head probably modelled on the image which still adorns Palazzo Broletto. Marquis Ludovico had a coin struck with a type showing Virgil crowned with laurel and inscribed VIRGILIVS MANTVANVS POETA. The usage in Francesco's time therefore was traditional rather than intending a particular allusion to current projects for a Virgil monument. The reverse shows the Gonzaga device of the sun.

D.S.C.

BIBLIOGRAPHY; CNI, IV, pp. 260, 1, 3; Magnaguti, I, 1913, pp. 31-32; Magnaguti, 1923, pp. 277-83; Comune di Mantova, *A Virgilio La Patria*, 1927, p. 59; Trapp, 1980, p. 6.

92

Design for a Monument to Virgil *c.* 1499
School of Andrea Mantegna (*c.* 1431-1506)
Pen and bistre ink and wash on paper, traces of black chalk beneath; the lower part of the pedestal, the inscription, swag, and putti pricked for transfer
Inscribed P. VERGILII / MARONIS A / AETERNAE / SVI MEMORI / AE IMAGO
33.9 x 21.4 cm (cut to gable shape at top)
Musée du Louvre, Cabinet des Dessins (R.F. 439)

The idea of raising a monument to Virgil, a native of Mantua, had been suggested by Platina to Marchese Ludovico in the 1450's. Humanists, including Vergerio, and later Pontano and Equicola, were incensed by the (possibly apocryphal) story of Carlo Malatesta, Lord of Rimini, throwing an antique statue of Virgil into the river in 1397 because he thought the Mantuans worshipped their poet as if he were a saint.
By 1499 the project was being discussed again, as a letter from Jacopo d'Atri, Francesco's ambassador in Naples, to Isabella d'Este dated 17 March indicates. On a visit to the humanist Giovanni Pontano (1426-1503) he had talked of Isabella's idea of a statue; Pontano had particularly praised the Marchesa's initiative given that she was "a young woman, unable to read Latin" (*una dona tenera d'eta, senza lettere*). They discussed the form the statue should take, whether it should

92

94

be made of bronze or marble (bronze was considered *più nobile*, but given the dangerous times, marble was the more durable material). Battista Fiera (Cat. 96) claimed to have discovered an authentic likeness of Virgil; the head of the statue could be based on this bust. The poet was to be dressed in either a toga or senatorial robes, crowned with a wreath of bay, and shod in sandals (*scarpe a lantiqua*). He was to hold nothing in his hands.

Mantegna had already been chosen to design the work, although a suitable sculptor (*degno sculptore*) had still to be found. It was suggested that the base be inscribed *Isabella Marchionissa Mantuae restituit*, although Pontano offered to compose a more eloquent epigram or verse if Isabella so wished, an offer the Marchesa received gratefully when replying to d'Atri in May 1499.

Neither the inscription nor the details of this drawing correspond exactly with Pontano's original suggestions (although these may have been modified later) and Portioli suggested that the local humanist, Fiera, may have composed the final inscription. He wrote a poem, dedicated to Francesco Gonzaga, on the subject of raising a statue to Virgil (Faccioli, 1959 p. 60-61, Cat. 97) Howard Burns has suggested that the pedestal is derived from the base of the Column of Trajan (Nash, I, pl. 337). This drawing has been so heavily overdrawn in ink that its original character has been destroyed (traces of black chalk are visible under the right putto), but given that Mantegna was involved in the project, and that he was known to provide designs for sculptors, it is likely that it records an idea of Mantegna's rather than that of one of his competitors (Kristeller, 1901, p. 403). The project was in fact never realized.

J.T.M.

PROVENANCE: His de la Salle.
BIBLIOGRAPHY: Baschet, 1866², p. 488; Portioli, 1877-78, pp. 3-30; Luzio and Renier, 1889, p. 43; Kristeller, 1901, pp. 402-03; Faccioli, 1959, pp. 60-61; Mantua, *Mostra Mantegna*, 1961, no. 126; Béguin, 1975¹, no. 50 (incorrectly labelled as inv. No. 239). Trapp, 1980, pp. 5-6.
ADDITIONAL BIBLIOGRAPHY: E. Nash, *Pictorial Dictionary of Ancient Rome*, 1968.

93

Mantua's new Virgil: Bucolic Poems by Battista Spagnoli

Baptista Mantuanus (Battista Spagnoli), *Adolescentia seu Bucolica*, Mantua 1498
British Library (IA. 30683)

Battista Spagnoli (1447-1516), who had been educated in Mantua, entered the Carmelite Order in 1463. By this date he had already composed all but two of the eight *Eclogues*, treating of love in a pastoral genre, first printed in Mantua in this edition so many years later. His fame as a scholar in theology, Greek, natural science and other branches of learning was well established, and as a writer of Latin verse he was compared to Virgil by Sabbadino degli Arienti in his *Porretane* (composed before 1478) and, in a letter of 1496, by Erasmus who called him "the Christian Maro not much less in glory and celebrity than his co-citizen". Battista taught for many years in Bologna, and also had lived in Rome, but in 1489 he returned permanently to Mantua where his brother Pietro was in Gonzaga service. His literary output was prodigious, much of it on moral and spiritual themes, and by the end of the sixteenth century his various writings had been printed in over 600 editions; but it was the *Bucolica* which did most to assure his fame throughout Europe (see Cat. 94).

D.S.C.

BIBLIOGRAPHY: Mustard, 1911; Coccia, 1960; Faccioli, 1962, pp. 151-202.

94

Mantua's new Virgil in English translation

The Eglogs of the Poet B. Mantuan Carmelitan Turned into English Verse, and set forth with the Argument to every Egloge by Geo. Turbervile, Gent. London, H. Bynneman, 1567.
British Library (238. 1. 17)

Battista Spagnoli's Latin *Adolescentia seu Bucolica*, composed in his youth and printed when he was about fifty, probably did most to spread his fame as the new Virgil of Mantua. Editions rapidly appeared, including at least thirteen in England (1523-98). In 1512 or 1514 the *Bucolica* had been prescribed for use at St. Paul's School by Dean Colet and their wide use in Latin teaching is reflected in Shakespeare (e.g. Holofernes' speech, *Love's Labour's Lost*, IV, 2). George Turberville's translation of the first nine *Eclogues* had been printed three times before the end of the sixteenth century.

D.S.C.; J.B.T.

BIBLIOGRAPHY: STC (2nd edn.) 22990; Mustard, 1911; Coccia, 1960.
ADDITIONAL BIBLIOGRAPHY: T.W. Baldwin, *William Shakspere's small Latine and lesse Greeke*, vol. I, Urbana, 1944, pp. 642-52 and passim.

95

Battista Spagnoli's poetic consolations for the captive Marquis

F. Baptistae Mantuani Carmelitae Theologi, *Ad Franciscum Gonzagam Marchionem Mantuae Venetorum Captivum Consolabile Carmen*, [Venice ?], 1510
British Library (Voyn. 2)

The greatest humiliation in Marquis Francesco Gonzaga's military career was to have been captured during the night of 7-8 August 1509 at Isola della Scala, just over the Venetian frontier with Mantuan territory, and taken as a prisoner to Venice; he was allied to the League of great powers (Pope, Emperor and France) which had recently invaded and occupied much of the Venetian mainland. The Carmelite Battista Spagnoli (see Cat. nos. 93-94) was not exactly a court poet of the Gonzaga, but he had commemorated the Marquis' success in the Battle of Fornovo against the French (1495) in his *Trophaeum Gonzagae pro Gallis expulsis* (c. 1498) and now offered comfort in this temporary adversity. Having referred to notorious victims of fortune in ancient times, Spagnoli points out that the Marquis had not been deprived of his power nor of his family; he had not been imprisoned by barbarians but by the civilized Venetians; moreover he had many intercessors including most of the cardinals in Rome and his wife, "faithful as Penelope". Pope Julius II had made his peace with Venice in February 1510, but it was not until July that the terms were agreed for Francesco's release. In September 1510 he was appointed military commander (*Gonfaloniere*) of the Church.

D.S.C.

BIBLIOGRAPHY: Mustard, 1911, p. 22; Cessi, 1913; Mazzoldi, 1961, pp. 210-18.

96

Battista Fiera *c.* 1507-08

Lorenzo Costa (1459/60-1535)
Oil on panel 51.4 x 38.7 cm. Inscribed on the parapet BATTA. FIERA. MEDIC. MANTVA; an identical inscription painted on the

153

back of the panel; another inscription in cursive hand has been gouged out, but the name "fiera" is discernible
National Gallery, London (no. 2083)

Battista Fiera (c. 1465-1538) was born in Mantua, studied medicine and logic at Pavia, and was in Rome in the 1480's and 1490's in the circle of Pomponio Leto. Although he attempted to ingratiate himself with the powerful in Rome, by dedications of his writings to Cardinal Raffaele Riario, nephew of Sixtus IV, and to Popes Leo X and Adrian VI, it was at Mantua that Fiera was able to reign as resident court humanist, poet, and physician. Here he could advise Marchesa Isabella on the appearance of Virgil (see Cat. 92-97) and write laudatory poems for the Gonzaga. Later he was physician to Baldassare Castiglione, and acted as tutor to his children.
Fiera was acquainted with the court artists and passed judgement on their works: Mantegna he encountered in Rome in 1488-90 when both were far from Mantua: *De iusticia pingenda* (*On the Painting of Justice*) is probably based on Mantegna's observations on the trials of working under the direction of humanists (Wardrop, 1957); Fiera witnessed Mantegna's will in 1506. His comments on Francesco Bonsignori and on Costa are incorporated in his *Hymni divini* (Cat. no. 97); he appears to have favoured the former for painting "serious matters, and the burgeoning seeds of history" (*seria... et subnascentia rerum semina*), the latter for "cosmetic softness and blandishments... a delicious Venus..." (*molles fucos et blandimenta... deliciosa Venus*).
The identification of the sitter is old. An engraving of the painting was used as the frontispiece of the 1649 edition of Fiera's *Coena*, and Carlo Avanzi says in the introduction that Fiera's great-grandson has given him information about the

poet. The clumsy inscription on the parapet in the painting, which accords ill with Fiera's own elegant humanist hand, appears to have been added at a slightly later date: splashes of mordaunt, the glue used to attach the gold leaf, are discernible on the tunic. The portrait is in Costa's Bolognese style. Lorenzo Costa arrived in Mantua as court artist in 1507; by August 1508 he was suffering appallingly from symptoms of venereal disease, which he describes in vivid detail in a letter to Marchese Francesco (who suffered from syphilis and eventually died of it) (Brown, 1970, p. 106; Luzio and Renier, 1885, pp. 408-32). It would seem likely that the court artist would be sent to the court physician and this portrait may have been painted partly in recompense for that treatment. Costa lived until 1535, though in a letter of 1516 to Federico Gonzaga (Brown, 1970, p. 108) he lamented that his libido was severely hampered by his complaint.

J.T.M.

PROVENANCE: Exported from Milan between 1814 and 1848; John Samuel; bequeathed by the Misses Cohen as the John Samuel Bequest 1906.
BIBLIOGRAPHY: Luzio and Renier, 1885, pp. 408-32; Wardrop, 1957; Brown, 1970.
ADDITIONAL BIBLIOGRAPHY: C. Gould, *National Gallery, London: The Sixteenth Century Italian Schools*, London, 1975, p. 73, no. 2083.

97

Battista Fiera's Latin Verse
B. Fiera, *Hymni Divini, Sylvae, Melanysius, Coena* (Mantuae, per Franciscum Bruschum, 1515)
Bodleian Library, Oxford (4° B 140(1) Jur.)

Battista Fiera hoped for fame as a writer of Latin verse and prose as well as a physician, a philosopher, a theologian and a moralist, but posterity, like his contemporaries, has treated him unkindly. The poet Niccolò d'Arco (1492/3-1546/7) said that his poetry ought either to be burned or thrown into the Mincio. Modern critics, though giving him credit for his knowledge of the ancient poets, have thought his verse feeble and obscure.
In his early twenties, Fiera was one of the circle of Pomponio Leto, in Rome, where his first extant published work was printed, probably in 1490. This was a suite of Latin verse epigrams on the medicinal and other properties of various foods, entitled *Coena* (*The Supper*). By 1530 it had been reprinted on its own in Italy, France and Germany, as well as included in the miscellany volume of Fiera's works here exhibited; in 1537 it formed part of a second collection of Fiera's writings, printed at Venice, and it was again reprinted singly in 1649, with a portrait frontispiece (see Cat. 96). Perhaps at about the same time as he wrote the *Coena*, Fiera wrote a prose dialogue between Mantegna and Momus, the carping critic, entitled *De iusticia pingenda* (*On the Painting of Justice*; see Cat. 96), which is also included in the volume on show. The *Coena* had been dedicated to Cardinal Raffaele Riario, the foremost Roman literary patron of his time and nephew of Pope Sixtus IV; the opening poems in this volume, the *Hymni divini* are dedicated to Pope Leo X. In 1522, Fiera dedicated his *De deo homine* (*On God made man*) – Christian subject matter in Virgilian hexameters – to Pope Adrian VI. This was a poem of the kind made fashionable by Battista Spagnoli (Cat. 93-95) and further developed by Jacopo Sannazzaro (1456-1530) and Marco Girolamo Vida (c. 1485-1566). Fiera's transformation from a Pomponian humanist to a Christian Virgilian must have owed much to the friendship and example of Spagnoli. He continued to write humanist verse, as

96

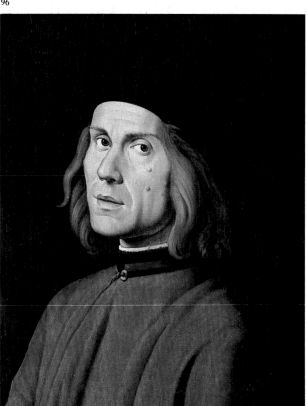

Quid lanias miseræ pessima Mater Itym?
Paruus Itys te Mater eo, tibi basia porgo
Credibile est illu Qualia ferre suæ.
Ne quæso ne Dura mane, cape basia nostra?
Ne quæso amplexus effuge Dura meos.
Nõ ego sum Tereus, tu certe tu impia Progne es,
Sim Philomela quidé, sim, ego paruus Itys.
Sim potius Clamosus Epops, ubi pessime Tereu?
Heu ubi sis Progne? dic ubi Sæua mea es?

De Virgilio per Statuam restituto.

O mea iam fœcunda parens, o Terra beata,
O iam blanda altrix Roma secunda mea,
Tu iam Marte potés, tu Pallade docta resurgis,
Nec n.si grande Sophos Compita plena sonant.
Dii tibi nunc læti arrident, tumefacta superbi:
Cæsaris ut sentis numina magna tui.
De Cœlo Vates tam gratos sentit honores,
Si Nasci est magnum, Restitui haud minimum est.
At tu qui Patrieq; suum Romæq; Maronem
Priscaq; iam nobis tempora uisa facis:
Pro meritis Conzaga tuis, pro munere tanto,
Aeternum in Terris cum Ioue habe Imperiũ.

Iantha ad Melanysium.

Ardoris monimenta mei Signumq; Fidele
P z

well as works on medicine, and natural and moral philosophy, until his death.

Fiera's poetry is valuable to students of the art of his time, and especially of Mantegna (see essay by Elam, above), not only through his *De iusticia pingenda*, but also because poems in the *Melanysius* and the *Sylvae* (*Miscellanies*) possibly refer to lost works by the painter, illustrate his reputation, and bear wit-

pieces, addressed to members of the Gonzaga family – epithalamia, panegyrics, laments for the death of a favourite puppy or falcon. The *Andina*, a verse celebration by Fiera of the Mantuan countryside and its associations with Virgil and with Marchese Francesco, prince, patron and breeder of horses, remains in autograph manuscript.

R.J.; J.B.T.

BIBLIOGRAPHY: Wardrop, 1957; Dionisotti, 1958; Faccioli, 1959-62, I, pp. 79-84; II, pp. 366-73; Rhodes, 1956, p. 165; Battisti, 1965; Jones, 1981.

98-99-100

Marchese Francesco Gonzaga, Virgil and Battista Spagnoli ["Battista Mantovano"] 1514

Anon. North Italian sculptor, early XVI century
Terracotta, h 95, 74, 76 cm respectively
Museo del Palazzo Ducale, Mantua (Inv. nos. 11905-7)

Busts of these three men were commissioned by Battista Fiera (Cat. 96, 97) as a public tribute to his prince and protector and to the poets of his native city, ancient and modern, whom he most admired. They were set up inside the arch of Porta Nuova, refurbished by Fiera in 1514, adjacent to the cloister of San Francesco and his own house, at the top of Via Stabili. He and his brother had renovated the house in 1504 and Fiera placed over the portal the punning inscription BONIS MERC-VRIALIBVS, implying that the work had been done with the proceeds of his physician's practice. Fiera wished to be buried, dressed in a toga and holding a book, at the foot of his arch.

From the centre of the internal face of an arch, Marchese

ness to an embarrassing *faux pas* on Fiera's part about the *Parnassus* for Isabella d'Este's *studiolo*. The poem here shown – *De Virgilio per statuam restituto* – datable late 1498 or early 1499, is related to another project of Mantegna's for Isabella, the monument to Virgil (Cat. 92). Other poems in this volume range from the sacred to the erotic. Many are occasional

Francesco presided over the smaller but still more than lifesize images of Virgil to his right and Spagnoli to his left, lower down, on the inner sides of the arch proper. All three were in uniform, Marchese Francesco in armour as the warrior patron of the arts, Virgil and Spagnoli both wearing the poetic laurel and Spagnoli his friar's habit as well. Below Marchese Francesco was an inscription composed by Fiera: ARGVMENTVM VTRIQVE INGENS SI SECLA COISSENT ("How splendid for each of these had they lived at the same time"). Under the arch was another: BAPTISTAM FIERAM SIC DEBVISSE PVTATVM EST ("Battista Fiera accepted this obligation"). Arch and busts were protected by an edict dated 25 June 1514 (ASMAG, b. 2038-9, fasc. 11, fol. 25). The busts were taken down in 1852, when house and arch were demolished.

All three busts are probably copies after others of which only that of Marchese Francesco, attributed to Gian Cristoforo Romano (Cat. 62), is now known certainly to survive. The portrait of Spagnoli, Vicar-General of the Carmelite order from 1513 and beatified in 1885, famous in the Renaissance as "Mantuan", the Christian Virgil, was probably originally taken from a life-mask. Virgil's bust is presumably modelled on the antique representation supposedly in Fiera's possession (Cat. 97). This can hardly have been either of the two medieval Mantuan statues known as Virgil which are now extant, one in Piazza Broletto and the other in Palazzo Ducale (Inv. no. 11605). Nor, in all probability – Fiera's Virgil being toga'd as well as garlanded and not long-haired – was it the antique Roman marble head now in Palazzo Ducale. Erroneously identified as a portrait of Virgil on its rediscovery at Sabbioneta in 1775, this head appears to have been known in Mantua at the end of the fifteenth century. Mantegna used it for the head of St Michael in his *Madonna della Vittoria* (Pl. 29), but it was not used for the drawing of Isabella d'Este's Virgil monument, of his school (Cat. 92). There are similarities between the head and shoulders in the drawing and in Fiera's bust, to which a sixteenth-century marble bust, again in Palazzo Ducale (Inv. no. 12126), also shows some resemblances. A marble replica of Fiera's Virgil is, or was, in Ferrara.

J.B.T.

BIBLIOGRAPHY: Venturi, VI, 1908, pp. 1135-137; Ozzòla, 1951, nos. 23, 60, 61, 65, 563; pp. 24, 27, 33, 34, 35, 103; Wardrop, 1957; Dionisotti, 1958, pp. 401-18; Faccioli, 1959, I pp. 60-61; 79-83; Paccagnini, 1960, I, p. 521; Paccagnini, 1961, pp. 94-96; Mantua, *Mostra Mantegna*, 1961, nos. 109-111.

101

The Aldine Virgil

Virgil, *Opere*, Venice, (Aldus Manutius) 1501; printed on vellum; manuscript decorations
British Library (C. 19. f. 7)

Famous as the first book printed in the so-called "italic" typeface designed for Aldo Manuzio by Francesco Griffo da Bologna, this was an edition avidly sought by Isabella d'Este. Her agent in Venice Lorenzo da Pavia wrote to tell her on 26 July 1501 that it was ready and would cost five ducats – its small format and typeface resembling chancery script made it, he said, the most beautiful book he had ever seen. Isabella certainly acquired a copy; on 16 May 1505 she wrote to ask Aldo for unbound copies on good paper of all his recent editions of Latin works except for the Virgil which she already possessed, though no Aldine Virgil is listed in the 1542 inventory of her books (Luzio and Renier, XLII, 1903). This de luxe edition on vellum bears the coat of arms of a rampant lion which has nothing to do with the Gonzaga or d'Este; on the other hand, it is certainly a book from the Gonzaga library, because the name of Isabella's son Cardinal Ercole is signed in it several times (perhaps Ercole had acquired it for himself from the original owner). There is also an autograph note (fol. 1v) written by Duke Vincenzo, dated 26 October 1594, invoking Virgil as his fellow-citizen of Mantua (*O Concivus mi Carissi-*

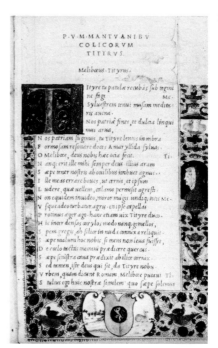

me Virgili, quantum tibi debeo!) and expressing deep sorrow, shortly after the death of his mother Eleonora of Austria. Aldo, who later proposed to bring out a more scholarly text, protested that as Virgil's printer he deserved better treatment when arrested by mistake on Mantuan territory in July 1506.

D.S.C.

BIBLIOGRAPHY: Baschet, 1867, pp. 9-11, 21-22, 29-30; Luzio and Renier, 1899, pp. 16-21; Rhodes, 1954.
ADDITIONAL BIBLIOGRAPHY: A.A. Renouard, *Annales de l'imprimerie des Alde*, I, Paris, 1803, pp. 39-40.

102

Isabella's Aldine Petrarch

Francesco Petrarca, *Le cose volgari*, Venice 1501; printed on vellum; manuscript decorations.
British Library (C. 20. b. 29)

Isabella d'Este was anxious to obtain, as well as his Virgil (see Cat. 101) Aldo Manuzio's printing of Petrarch's *Canzoniere*. Lorenzo da Pavia, her agent in Venice, assured her in his letter of 26 July 1501 that the edition would be ready within ten days and although only fifteen copies were being printed on good quality paper, she had been promised *el più belo*. The text had been prepared by Pietro Bembo from a manuscript then believed to be Petrarch's autograph, which Bembo had been lent by an unknown admirer of Isabella's in Padua. That she received it is implied by her letter to Aldo of 27 May 1505 asking for copies of his editions in small format on *carta membrana* but not the Petrarch. The entry in the inventory of her books made in 1542 of a *Petrarca in ottavo in carta pergamena stampa d'Aldo* confirms that her copy was this de luxe example printed on vellum and decorated by hand, bearing the Gonzaga-d'Este arms.

D.S.C.

BIBLIOGRAPHY: Cian, 1885, pp. 95-98; Baschet, 1867, pp. 9-11, 23; Luzio and Renier, XXXIII, 1899, pp. 16-21; XLII, 1903, p. 81; information from Dr. G. Frasso.

A History of Gonzaga Mantua
Mario Equicola, *Chronica di Mantua,* [Mantua] 1521
Warburg Institute, University of London (HNH 775)

The humanist writer Mario Equicola (1470-1525) had followed Isabella d'Este to Mantua from Ferrara by 1500; his treatise on women, *De Mulieribus,* first published in 1501, has a
section designed to flatter the Marchesa. He became her tutor
in 1508 and her secretary in 1519, the year when Marchese
Francesco Gonzaga died. Equicola had by then already written much of the *Chronica,* dedicating it to Francesco, but
Federico, the new Marchese, persuaded him to extend it into
his own reign; Equicola transferred his attentions from mother to son and became Federico's secretary probably in 1523.
The publication of the *Chronica* in 1521 intentionally coin-
cided with Federico's appointment as Captain General of the
Church. Typographically the work failed to rise to the occasion and is remarkably old fashioned for its date; the defects –
and there are in this copy manuscript corrections presumably
carried out in the printer's workshop – probably convinced
Equicola not to entrust his most important work, the *Libro de
natura de amore* to that "ignorant" Mantuan printer he mentions in an unpublished letter (the printer's identity is unknown). Although such a work could not avoid being encom-
iastic (Mantua and the Gonzaga dynasty were inseparable)
Equicola places particular emphasis on the autonomy of historical enquiry and takes a critical attitude towards previous
works of Mantuan historiography. Hence the enduring value
of the *Chronica* (a linguistically revised version appeared in
1607). The last two of the five "commentaries" which make
up the *Chronica* represent a break with the rest in that Equicola writes as an eye-witness of events; moreover Francesco and
Federico are portrayed not simply, like their predecessors, as
just but also as magnificent rulers.

S.K.

BIBLIOGRAPHY: Luzio, 1899, pp. 13-14; Rhodes, 1956, p. 166;
ADDITIONAL BIBLIOGRAPHY: D. Santoro, *Della vita e delle opere di Mario
Equicola 1470-1525,* Chieti, 1906, pp. 155-64; D.E. Rhodes, "Notes on the
'Chronica di Mantua' of Mario Equicola", *Gutenberg Jahrbuch,* 1957, pp.
137-41; G. Pillini, "La 'Chronica de Mantua' di Mario Equicola e la sua
posizione nella storiografia rinascimentale", Mantua, *Convegno* 1978, pp.
145-50.

102

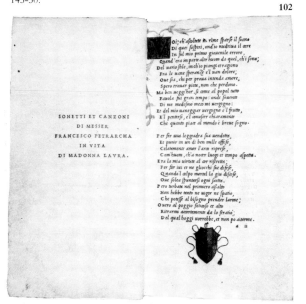

A literary and political miscellany from the court of Francesco Gonzaga and Isabella d'Este *c.* 1517
Manuscript in Italian and Latin on paper in various hands;
32.5 x 24 cm; 245 fols
British Library (Harley MS 3462)

The name of Gian Giacomo Calandra (1488-1543), courtier
and castellan of Marchese Francesco, appears on fol. 1r of this
manuscript but it does not seem likely that this can have been
his exclusive commonplace book (*zibaldone*) much less a letter
register strayed from the Gonzaga archives. The contents are
mostly copies of miscellaneous letters, both official and private, from the years 1506-17; included are some exchanged
between Henry VIII and the Marchese and a description of
the consummation by proxy of Mary Tudor's marriage with
King Louis XII of France in 1514 (fol. 142r). Part of the text
of a letter of Giovanni Aurelio Augurello (*c.* 1456-1524)
about how Italian should be used as a literary language is
shown here followed by verses by Augurello about Isabella
d'Este's marble Cupid which was believed to be the work of
Praxiteles (fol. 10v -11r). The letter is addressed to Girolamo
Avogadro when the latter was podestà (chief magistrate) in
Mantua in 1511; he was writing a commentary on Petrarch
for Isabella d'Este but in spite of assurances about near completion it does not seem that the commentary was ever delivered.

D.S.C.

BIBLIOGRAPHY: DBI.
ADDITIONAL BIBLIOGRAPHY: R. Weiss, "Giovanni Aurelio Augurello, Girolamo Avogadro and Isabella d'Este", *Italian Studies,* XVII, 1962, pp.
1-11; J. Shearman, "The Florentine Entrata of Leo X, 1515", *Journal of the
Warburg and Courtauld Institutes,* XXVIII, 1975, pp. 138-39.

105

A song book of Isabella d'Este
Canzoniere of chansons and textless pieces by various com-
posers, written *c.* 1480-90
Manuscript on vellum; 27 x 20 cm; 162 fols; unknown
scribes and illuminator
Biblioteca Casanatense, Rome (MS 2856)

103

The Casanatense manuscript is one of the earliest of an important group of North Italian songbooks which transmit the international chanson repertory, and in common with others of the group it also contains a number of pieces by local composers, some to Italian texts. The illuminations facing (f. 2r) the first page of music include an escutcheon displaying the Este and Gonzaga arms impaled, while the contents reflect to a considerable degree repertory current at the Ferrarese court during the 1480's. For these and other reasons, including the division of scribal labour in the book, it seems likely that the manuscript was begun about 1480, perhaps in celebration of the betrothal of Isabella d'Este to Francesco Gonzaga in that year, but that additions continued to be made after their marriage ten years later. Although the copying was nev-

105

er completed, the manuscript was taken to Mantua by Isabella and is recorded in the inventory of her effects made in 1542. While Isabella's musical interests are clear from a variety of evidence, the Casanatense manuscript is the only music manuscript that can be definitely associated with her. The quality of its decoration places it among the finest chansonniers of the period.

I.F.

PROVENANCE: Giuseppe Ottavio Pittoni; Collegio germanico, Rome; Giuseppe Baini.
BIBLIOGRAPHY: Fenlon, 1980 , p. 21.
ADDITIONAL BIBLIOGRAPHY: J.M. Llorens, "El Codice Casanatense 2.856 identificado como el cancionero de Isabella d'Este (Ferrara) esposa de Francesco Gonzaga (Mantua)", Annuario musicale, XX, 1967, p. 161; A. Atlas, "Some 18th-century transcriptions of 15th- century chansons", Journal of the American Musicological Society, XXIV, 1971, p. 100; L. Perkins and H. Garey, The Mellon Chansonnier, 2 vols. New Haven, 1979.

106

Partbook containing sacred music (by various composers) for Marchese Francesco's chapel
Published by Ottaviano Petrucci in 1505-09
Paper, contemporary binding, 16 x 23 cm
Conservatorio di musica "Giuseppe Verdi", Milan, (S.B. 178)

Although there is a great deal of evidence testifying to Isabella d'Este's interest in secular music, it seems that the arrangements for the first Gonzaga cappella were made by her husband Marchese Francesco. A private chapel with permanent musicians became an important aspect of court ceremonial in princely households from the 1470's onwards, beginning with the examples of the Sforza in Milan and the Este at Ferrara. The Gonzaga chapel was founded in 1510, prompted perhaps by the availability of musical talent released by Alfonso I d'Este's temporary disbanding of the Este cappella. From 1511 the musical arrangements for the Gonzaga chapel, established by Francesco in the chapel of Santa Maria dei Voti in the cathedral of San Pietro, were directed by the distinguished composer and performer Marchetto Cara.
Among the books and manuscripts which survive from the Santa Barbara library, a small body of printed material seems to represent the repertory of Francesco's chapel: a group of ten books of masses and motets published by Ottaviano Petrucci between 1502 and 1509 and bound in an early sixteenth-century style. As might be expected in volumes intended for practical use, the superior parts from the set are bound together, as are those for tenor and bassus. The altus parts are lost. Repertorially the collection is ambitious; settings of the ordinary of the mass are numerous and the work of Josquin and Obrecht predominates.

I.F.

PROVENANCE: Library of the Palatine Basilica of Santa Barbara; Mantua; Collection of Don Giuseppe Greggiati, Ostiglia.
BIBLIOGRAPHY: Barblan, 1962, pp. 22-23 (first book of the series only); Fenlon, 1980, Appendix II.
ADDITIONAL BIBLIOGRAPHY: W.F. Prizer II, "La cappella di Francesco II Gonzaga e la musica sacra a Mantova nel primo ventennio del cinquecento" in Mantua, Gonzaga Convegno, 1978, pp. 267-76.

107

Photograph: **Hunting scene in Isabella d'Este's apartments,** 1522
Lorenzo Leombruno (1489-?after 1537)
Palazzo Ducale, Mantua (Sala della Scalcheria)

Leombruno was a favoured court painter of the Gonzaga between the death of Mantegna (1506) and the arrival of Giulio Romano (1524). He worked, for instance, for Marchese Francesco at his Palace of San Sebastiano and for Isabella d'Este in her new apartments in the Corte Vecchia of the Ducal Palace. This lunette is one of thirteen hunting scenes he painted on the upper part of the walls of the so-called Sala della Scalcheria, a large room which leads to Isabella's studiolo and grotta.

BIBLIOGRAPHY: Marani and Perina, 1961, pp. 392-96.

III Isabella d'Este, the Insatiable Collector

108

Isabella d'Este, 1499
Copy after Leonardo da Vinci (1452-1519)
Black chalk with wash and some white highlights on the
sleeves, on two pieces of coarse-grained paper joined hori-
zontally: roughly incized around the head and right sleeve.
Very crudely overworked, and lines reinforced in black chalk;
considerable damage on bottom edge of paper; cut all round.
63.0 x 48.3 cm (Upper sheet 29.5 cm high)
Ashmolean Museum, Oxford (Cat. no. 19)

"I am afraid I shall weary not only Your Highness, but all
Italy with the sight of my portraits" (*Dubito venire in fastidio
non solum a la S. V. ma ad tuta Italia cum mandare questi miei
rectracti in volta*, Luzio, 1913, p. 198) Isabella wrote to her
brother-in-law Ludovico il Moro, Duke of Milan, on 13
March 1499, when asking permission to send a portrait of
herself to Isabella of Aragon. By the end of the year the
French king, Charles VIII, had invaded Milan, the Duke had
fled, and the court artist Leonardo da Vinci, with the mathematician Luca Pacioli, had made his way to Mantua. There he
made two drawings of Isabella d'Este, one of which he showed to his friend the musical instrument maker Lorenzo da
Pavia in Venice early in 1500; the other remained at Mantua.
On 13 March 1500 Lorenzo wrote to Isabella of the portrait
"It is a very good likeness of Your Ladyship. It is so well done
that it would not be possible to improve on it" (*... de la S. V.
che è molto naturale a quela. Sta tanto bene fato, non è possibile
melio*. Luzio, 1913, p. 200). The second version of the portrait
was given away by Isabella's husband as she tells Fra Pietro da
Novellara, her former confessor, in a letter of March 1501.
Both he and Leonardo were in Florence, and she asks Novellara to persuade the artist to send her "another drawing of our
portrait" (*un altro schizo del retracto nostro*). But Novellara had
no success in soliciting a copy from Leonardo whose life was
"diverse and inconsequential, so that it appears he lives from
day to day" (*varia et indeterminata forte, si che pare vivere a
giornata*, Luzio, 1887, p. 32 n. 1).
As late as May 1504 Isabella was still trying to persuade Leonardo to make a painting from the cartoon drawn in Mantua
(*quando fusti in questa terra et che ne retrasti de carbono, ne promet-
testi fami ogni mo' una volta di colore*, Luzio 1887, p. 34). But it
appears that her wish was never satisfied. In the same letter
she even suggested that her portrait might be converted into a
figure of the young Christ.
It is somewhat ironical that, although a considerable number
of portraits of Isabella (drawings, paintings, and sculptures)
existed during her lifetime, today the most certain likeness of
her is a medallion (Cat. 109); and it was only in the nineteenth
century that a concerted effort was made to rediscover her
appearance. In 1888, Charles Yriarte suggested that a life-
sized coloured drawing in the Louvre (Pl. 46) of a woman
with her head in profile was one of the lost drawings of
Isabella by Leonardo. This cartoon is carefully pricked for

transfer, and no doubt was used as a basis for several replicas,
including the Ashmolean drawing, which corresponds in the
measurements of the head to that of the Louvre. The Oxford
drawing has in turn been used as the basis of another copy, as
the crudely incised line around the contours indicates, and the
clumsy overdrawing makes it very difficult to date with any
accuracy. It shows that the Louvre cartoon has been cut on all
sides and has lost significant elements including the hands and
a book and part of the right shoulder, as well as a strip at the
top.
The quality of the Louvre cartoon makes it very likely that it
is by Leonardo, and comparison to the Romano medallion
(Cat. 109) makes the identification of the sitter as Isabella convincing. G.G. Trissino gives a description of the Marchesa in
I Ritratti delle Bellissime Donne d'Italia (written 1514) in which
he recalls her descending from her carriage to go to Mass at
Milan Duomo holding an open book in her hand as if she had
just been reading — as in the Oxford drawing; her hair was
long, parted in the centre, and held back by a silk ribbon.
Equicola also describes her flowing hair (*de Mulieribus*, 1501).
The exchange of portraits was commonplace between Isabella
and her friends; portraits were also given away as tokens of
political accord (as was probably the case with the first Leonardo drawing), so copies were frequently made of portraits
of an earlier date. Isabella's vanity, and her boredom at having to sit to painters were not the only factors in the production of replicas.

108

The pose with the head shown in profile, in the Leonardo
drawing is unusual, even archaic at this date, and might suggest that he was copying her features from a medal; alternatively it may gave some connotation of rank and status. But the
vitality of expression in the Louvre drawing makes it likely

that it was made from life, and that it is the best record we have of Isabella's appearance at the age of twenty-five.

J.T.M.

PROVENANCE: Udny; Douce.
BIBLIOGRAPHY: Luzio, 1887, p. 31 ff; Cartwright, 1903, I, pp. 150-51; Luzio, 1913, p. 198.
ADDITIONAL BIBLIOGRAPHY: M. Equicola, *De Mulieribus*, Mantua, 1501; G. G. Trissino, *Tutte le Opere...*, ed. Maffei, Verona, 1728, II, pp. 272-73; A. Popp, *Leonardo da Vinci Zeichnungen*, Munich, 1928, p. 44; K.T. Parker, *Catalogue of the Collection of Drawings in the Ashmolean Museum*, II *Italian Schools*, 1972, p. 13, no. 19.

109

Isabella d'Este (1474-1539)
Giancristoforo Romano (*c.* 1465-1512)
Medal; bronze; diam. 89 mm
Victoria & Albert Museum, Department of Sculpture (A. 232-1910, Hill, *Corpus* 221e)

The obverse, inscribed ISABELLA ESTEN MARCH MANTVAE, shows the Marchesa facing to the right, her long hair caught up in a heavy knot, wearing a necklace. Her appearance is close to that in Leonardo's cartoon of 1499 (Pl. 46). The casting of the medal may have been proposed in 1495, when Isabella wrote to Giancristoforo Romano, then sculptor and musician to her sister Beatrice, Duchess of Milan, asking if he was prepared to make 'that engraved sculpture' (*quello intaglio sculptura*; Brown, 1973, p. 158). On Beatrice's death in 1497 Giancristoforo moved to Mantua but still in May 1498 Isabella's kinsman Niccolò da Correggio was being pressed to invent an original motto to be inscribed on the medal, previously he had suggested *Benemerentium causa*, but Isabella had seen this used elsewhere, and not wishing to adopt anything used by anyone before, asked for alternatives.

Niccolò produced *Benemerentium ergo* (for those who deserve well) which was accepted (letter of 19 May 1498, Luzio and Renier, 1893, p. 254), and by September the medal was in circulation.

To be sent a medal was a mark of signal favour; some were moved to write sonnets to it (Venturi, 1888, p. 193), the ladies at the court of Naples kissed it (Cartwright, II, p. 12), and the Duchess of Urbino together with Giancristoforo himself tormented Unico Aretino by showing him a medal (intended for him by Isabella) but refusing to allow him to keep it (August 1506, Venturi, 1888, p. 150). Many medals were in circulation (Hill lists fifteen specimens) and since it was cast (not, as Luzio thought, struck) it was easily reproduced; on some specimens the last four letters of the obverse inscription were omitted and the motto on the reverse was corrected (the specimen has the erroneous spelling BENEMOE-RENTIVM ERGO). Isabella herself kept a gold version set in a frame of diamonds and enamel which was in the same cupboard as an antique cameo of Caesar and Livia (1542 inventory, Luzio, 1908, p. 414). This is probably the medal now in

Vienna (see essay by Fletcher above, Pl. 49).

The reverse has never been satisfactorily explained, the winged female figure has been described variously as a victory, a personification of astrology, and as Hygenia; she holds a wand with which she appears to strike a serpent, the object in her left hand has been called a quill pen. Above her is the sign of Saggitarius, the astrological sign for 22 November - 21 December; no significant event in Isabella's life falls within this month, the archer is also the astrological sign of the night house of the planet Jupiter (de Tervarent, 1958, col. 332). Isabella was well versed in astrology, and had her horoscope cast in 1494, after which she gave up riding for a time (Cartwright, 1903, II, p. 33).

Giancristoforo Romano was one of the most highly praised medallists of his day, he worked as a sculptor, architect and medallist in Milan, Mantua, Rome and Urbino. He was also one of Isabella's correspondents and advised her on collecting antiquities.

J.T.M.

PROVENANCE: Salting bequest.
BIBLIOGRAPHY: Venturi, 1888, p. 193; Luzio and Renier, 1893, p. 254; Cartwright, 1903, II, pp. 12, 33; Luzio, 1908, p. 44; de Terverant, 1958, col. 332; Brown, 1961, p. 538; Hill and Pollard, 1967, no. 76.

110

Portrait of a Lady, traditionally called Isabella d'Este
Giulio Romano (*c.* 1499-1546)
Oil on panel 115.5 x 90.5 cm
Her Majesty the Queen

It is generally accepted this court portrait is the work of Giulio Romano, and there can be no doubt that it represents a lady of the highest rank; it was catalogued as "an Italian Dutchesse" painted by Raphael in the James II inventory of the Royal Collection. Mariette (1857-58, p. 167) first suggested Giulio's authorship, connected the Louvre drawing to it (Cat. 108) and suggested Isabella d'Este as the sitter, a thesis to which most writers subscribe, although it has no documented Mantuan provenance.

The identification of the sitter as Isabella raises serious problems. Those who accept it take this to be a portrait from life painted immediately after Giulio's arrival in October 1524. Her features are difficult to establish. Mario Equicola writing in Mantua in 1501 describes her eyes as dark (*Niger oculus*). It seems she grew fat at an early age: already complaining of her corpulence in 1509, she was unable to negociate stairs in 1531 and moved to a ground floor apartment (see essay by Fletcher). Her notorious vanity led her to request painters to revise her appearance and her favourite image of herself is recorded in Titian's copy (Pl. 47) of a lost portrait by Francia, itself painted from another artist's cartoon in 1511 when she was aged thirty-seven. She asked Francia to lighten the eyes (*commutar gli occhij de nigri in bianchi*; Luzio, 1913, p. 213) which he refused to do, but Titian in his copy of 1534 seems to have been more compliant: she appears with blue eyes. A less flattering but perhaps more accurate image, a copy by Rubens (also in Vienna) of a lost Titian, probably of *c.* 1530, shows her with dark eyes and an expanding waistline. By 1534 Aretino describes the Marchesa as "arch-dishonestly beautified... with ebony teeth and ivory brows" (*arcidisonestamente imbellettata... i denti di hebano et le ciglia di avorio*, Luzio, 1900, p. 68). Making the most generous allowance for flattery or for the possibility that this is a retrospective portrait, copied from the Francia portrait in November 1524 (see Luzio

109

1913, p. 222 note), it is difficult to reconcile the present sitter with what we know of Isabella's appearance. While Giulio may have been persuaded to "revise" the colour of her eyes to green, more significantly the face lacks the roundness of both Vienna portraits and the Gian Cristoforo Romano medal (Cat. 109); in both the Titian and Rubens paintings, the neck is much shorter and the chin less prominent than in this picture. The exceptional costliness of the dress also militates against the Marchesa being the sitter; there is abundant evidence of her continual financial straits throughout the 1520's and 1530's. The presumption that this is a Mantuan portrait is strong, given the fact that Giulio rarely worked outside his adopted town. Were it not of Isabella, there are various alternative candidates. Isabella's third son, Ferrante, married the heiress Isabella of Capua around 1530, but her appearance (Cat. 147) would seem to exclude her. Given that Giulio was, above all, Federico's artist, two other women should be considered: his mistress Isabella Boschetti (although the visitors in the background would be difficult to explain) or his wife, Margherita Paleologo (1510-66).

A description of a dress Margherita wore just prior to her marriage to Federico at Casale in October 1531 has much in common with the elaborate and expensive dress seen here: "Today the Duchess wore a dress of white satin embroidered all over with gold thread, and slashed at the front, but in some places the under-dress of blue satin, also embroidered with gold thread, could be seen through the large slashes. She wore a cross of beautiful diamonds around her neck, and on her head one of the turbans which Your Excellency sent, and at her side Your Excellency's lapis rosary. She always wears the stockings which Your Excellency sent" (*hoggi la S^ra Duchessa haveva una veste da raso bianco recamata tutta da cordoni d'oro, e perché è schiapata dinanti, ma chiapata in qualche loco, per li talii che erano grandi si vedea la sottana di raso turchino rechamata pur di cordoni d'oro. Una croce haveve di bellissimi diamanti al collo, in testa una de le schuffie che li mandato V. Ex^ia, e dal lato la corona de lapis de V. Ex^ia. Continuamente porta le calze che V. Ex^ia li ha mandato*). (Cappino to Duke Federico, 28 September 1531, ASMAG b. 747, Davari, 1891, p. 65, mistranscribed). Obviously the dress is not identical, but the lapis rosary, a present from the Duke, and the *schuffa* (turban or bonnet) also sent from Mantua and modelled on those made fashionable by Isabella d'Este, match those in the painting. Her necklace may have been designed by Giulio (London, 1980, pp. 114-15, Cat. G3) as may the fan holder of the lady coming through the door (ibid., Cat. G4). Rosaries were frequently worn ornamentally, (cf. Titian's portrait of Federico (Pl. 81) wearing one as a necklace, and the Rubens portrait (after Titian) of Isabella (Vienna) where the large paternoster beads are of a different design and the smaller beads divided by gold elements.

No likeness of Margherita of this date survives; the Schloss Ambras collection of Gonzaga portraits includes a feeble copy of a portrait of her in late middle age; she has light grey-brown eyes (communication of Dr Klaus Demus), a high forehead, straight nose and strong chin (Kenner, 1891, p. 193; Amadei and Marani, 1980, p. 51); a medal of 1561 (Cat. 145) shares many of these features. If Giulio had painted her portrait soon after her arrival in Mantua in November 1531 she would have been twenty-one. Age is a notoriously difficult factor to judge in Renaissance portraits, and although this sitter may appear matronly, one might reflect on the medal of Ippolita Gonzaga (Cat. 148), who appears to be considerably older than her sixteen years.

Isabella d'Este worked with Giulio Romano to furnish rooms fit for Margherita, an heiress, the descendant of the eastern emperors and the first Duchess of Mantua (Federico was crea-

110

ted duke by Charles V in 1530). In the *Camera delle Arme* they arranged the most highly prized paintings of the collection, including two portraits of Federico, one by Raphael, the other by Titian, and left space for "the large painting that Messer Giulio is to make" (*quello quadro che farà messer Julio*; Pungileoni, 1829, p. 182). It may be that a portrait of the new Duchess was already planned to hang beside those of her husband.

The background detail, clearly an important feature for the painter, seems to underline the paramount status of the sitter. Three visitors emerge through a green curtain held back by a lady-in-waiting. An elderly nun and a young woman accompany a middle-aged woman, who wears a cloth-of-gold widow's veil over her raised head-dress, and carries an ostrich feather fan. Were the sitter not Isabella d'Este, it would be possible that she is shown in this figure (as Hartt suggested, 1958, p. 83). She was greatly attached to her daughter-in-law, and wrote to Anna of Monferrato, Margherita's mother "I discover that I have acquired a daughter who in her beauties, excellence and comportment, is after my wishes and desire" (*mi trovo have fatto acquisto d'una figliuola, che di bellezze, di virtu et de' costumi e secondo il proprio mio volere et desiderio*; Davari, 1891, p. 67). Isabella may have been indulging in flattery, for an anonymous Venetian ambassador at Mantua in 1540 described Margherita as "Of less than average beauty" (*di men che mediocre bellezza*; Kenner, 1896, p. 193). The attendant visitors could be Isabella's other daughter-in-law, Isabella of Capua, and the nun, her old Ferrarese friend Margherita Can-

161

telma, Duchess of Sora (d. 1532), who settled in a Mantua convent after the death of her husband and sons, and made Isabella her heir.

Vasari, a great admirer of Giulio's, who spent some time in Mantua looking at his works, makes a confusing statement in the 1568 edition of his *Lives*. A painting of the *Virgin and Child and St John* (Dresden) is accurately described, but with a background scene of "small figures", certain gentlewomen who come to visit her (Vasari, ed. Milanesi, V, pp. 545-46). These do not appear in the Dresden painting, but are reminiscent of the background group in this portrait. Vasari compounds the confusion by adding that the painting was given by Federico to his mistress Isabella Boschetti: John Shearman has suggested that Vasari saw both paintings, but part of the text was omitted so that the two were combined. In all events it is unlikely that the Duke would have given a portrait of either his mother or his wife to his mistress given both those ladies' intense dislike for La Boschetta: possibly the Dresden painting was the gift.

The prototype for this kind of portrait set in an interior is that of *Jeanne d'Aragon* (Louvre), designed by Raphael, and probably executed by his assistant, Giulio Romano.

J.T.M.

PROVENANCE: Gerard Reynst, Amsterdam; presented by the States of Holland to Charles II between 1660-66 (but not part of the "Dutch Gift"); Inventory of Charles II (at Whitehall); Inventory of James II (at Windsor); and by descent.
BIBLIOGRAPHY: Vasari ed. Milanesi, 1878, V, pp. 545-46; Kenner, 1896, p. 193; Luzio, 1913, p. 213; Lauts, 1952, p. 420 (dates *c.* 1535, uncertain of identity of sitter and artist); Hartt, 1958, pp. 82-84, 257; London, 1980, *Princely Magnificence*, pp. 114-15; Amadei and Marani, 1980, p. 51; Shearman, forthcoming Catalogue.
ADDITIONAL BIBLIOGRAPHY: M. Equicola, *De Mulieribus*, Mantua, 1501; P. Pungileoni, *Elogio Storico di Raffaello Santi da Urbino*, Urbino, 1829; P. Mariette, *Abecedario* (*Archives de l'Art francais*), VIII, 1857-58, p. 167; S. Davari, "Federico Gonzaga e la Famiglia Paleologa del Monferrato", *Giornale Ligustico di Archeologia, Storia e Letteratura*, XVIII, 1891; A. Luzio, *Un Pronostico satirico di Pietro Aretino (1534)*, Bergamo, 1900.

111

A Young Woman holding back a Curtain *c.* 1531-33
Giulio Romano (*c.* 1499-1546)
Pen and bistre wash 23.3 x 15.8 cm
Musée du Louvre, Cabinet des Dessins (No. 3568)

Mariette (1857-58, p. 167) suggested that this was a study by Giulio for the figure holding back the green curtain in the

111

background of Cat. 110. It seems very unlikely that it is a studio copy after the painting (Nicolson, 1947) given the dis-

crepancy in the patterns on the head-dress between the sketch and the painting. It was probably made at a fairly advanced stage in conception of the painting since the light source has already been determined (lit from the left). The girl, perhaps one of Isabella's *donzelle* (ladies-in-waiting) wears a high head-dress, very fashionable in North Italy by this date, and clogs.

J.T.M.

PROVENANCE: Crozat.
BIBLIOGRAPHY: Hartt, 1958, p. 289, n. 45; Shearman, forthcoming Catalogue.
ADDITIONAL BIBLIOGRAPHY: Mariette, 1857-58, p. 167 (see Cat. 110); B. Nicolson, "Di alcuni dipinti Veneziani nelle Collezioni Reali d'Inghilterra", *Arte Veneta*, I, 1947, p. 225.

112

Young Woman with a Lap Dog *c.* 1500
Lorenzo Costa (*c.* 1460-1535)
Oil on panel (poplar) 45.5 x 55.1 cm
Her Majesty the Queen (Inv. No. 355)

Berenson first suggested that this might be a portrait of Isabella d'Este (1894, no. 17), and Luzio went so far as to identify the lap dog as Aura, Isabella's *vergine cuccia* (virgin puppy) who died fleeing from the advances of *un indiscreto adoratore* (Luzio, 1913, p. 208). Costa painted two portraits of Isabella (one perhaps a copy of the other) and one of her sixteen year old daughter Eleonora in 1508; Marchese Francesco had the portraits of his wife and daughter with him while held captive in Venice in 1509 (these were still in Venice in 1525, the other Costa portrait of Isabella was given to the ambassador of Henry VIII of England in 1514; Luzio, 1913, p. 208-9). Objections were raised to identifying the present sitter as Isabella on the grounds of her youthfulness, and it was suggested that this was the portrait of Eleonora (Gronau, 1928). Recently it has been proposed that this painting dates from an earlier period of Costa's career.

On stylistic and sartorial grounds John Shearman has assigned the portrait to the years *c.* 1497-1500, when Costa was still working for the Bentivoglio family in Bologna; he has also suggested that it originally formed the right-hand panel of a diptych because the left-hand edge of the panel is carefully planed and bevelled, as if to allow for hinges (Shearman, forthcoming Catalogue). If this were so it could have been for a marriage or betrothal (the dog is a traditional symbol of fidelity). The dress (dated by Stella Newton just before 1500), originally ornamented with gold, has detachable sleeves comparable to those worn by Isabella herself in Leonardo's cartoon of 1499 (see Cat. 108).

The sitter cannot be identified with any certainty, although it is possible that she is a member of the Bentivoglio family. The Gonzaga and the Bentivoglio families were closely related by marriage: Annibale Bentivoglio married Isabella's half-sister Lucrezia d'Este in 1487, Giovanni Gonzaga, brother of Francesco, married Laura Bentivoglio in 1494 (she was painted at this time, possibly by Costa, but the Schloss Ambras copy bears no relationship to this portrait; Kenner, 1896, pp. 191-92).

Violante Bentivoglio, niece of Annibale, was a favourite of Isabella's and stayed in Mantua in 1504. It was Annibale's brother, Antongaleazzo Bentivoglio, who first suggested that Lorenzo Costa should contribute a picture to Isabella's *studiolo* in 1504, he also supervised the painting of the allegory and paid for it (Cat. 114). It is not known when this work was completed, and it has been suggested that the *quadro* mentioned in Antongaleazzo's letters to Isabella of August 1505 and

January 1506 refer to a portrait painted for Isabella, and not to the allegory (Verheyen, 1971, p. 17 ff.). Somewhat poignantly it was Costa who wrote to Marchese Francesco Gonzaga in 1513 soliciting an interview, and presumably financial assistance for his old patron Antongaleazzo, after the Bentivoglio family had been driven from Bologna by Julius II (Brown, 1970, p. 107).

The attribution to Costa, first made by Morelli, has never been doubted. Lorne Campbell has observed that the technique, with minuscule attention paid to such details as individual strands of hair, is based on a rather poor interpretation of Netherlandish painting; this would be fitting for Costa, by birth and training Ferrarese, who would have had the opportunity to see Flemish portraits at the d'Este court. However the close viewpoint is characteristically Italian. This kind of portrait, whether a diptych or a single panel, is typical of those sent from court to court by Isabella and her circle of friends and relations. Given that several near-contemporary copies and adaptations of the portrait exist (Sterbini Coll., Rome; Bache Sale, New York, 23 April 1945), it is likely that the sitter belonged to a ruling house.

J.T.M.

PROVENANCE: Charles II inventory, Whitehall (516); thereafter by descent.
BIBLIOGRAPHY: Kenner, 1896, pp. 191-92, Luzio, 1913, pp. 208-09;

Brown, 1970, p. 107; Verheyen, 1971, p. 17; Shearman, forthcoming Catalogue.

ADDITIONAL BIBLIOGRAPHY: London, Burlington Fine Art Club, 1894, n. 17 (Berenson); G. Gronau, "Frauenbildnisse des Mantuaner Hof von Lorenzo Costa", *Pantheon*, I, 1928, pp. 235-41.

113

A Woman, formerly believed to be Isabella d'Este, holding a Portrait of a Man *c.* 1525-35
Attributed to Bernardino Licinio (*c.* 1485/9–*c.* 1550)
Oil on Canvas, 77.5 x 91.5 cm (cut down to 58.5 x 73 cm earlier this century, relined and the cut pieces reattached in 1955)
Pinacoteca del Castello Sforzesco, Milan (no. 28)

The romantic hypothesis that this represented Isabella d'Este holding the portrait of her son Federico painted in the early 1520's originated with Luzio (1913, p. 225). It was partly based on the confusion of two painters, Licinio and Pordenone made by Vasari. Pordenone is known to have worked in Mantua, but Licinio hardly ever moved from his native Venice where, by the 1530's he had established a flourishing studio producing many portraits and religious works, not all of a high quality. He was an uncomplicated eclectic, influenced in turn by Palma Vecchio, Titian, and Giulio Romano. Morphologically this woman has nothing in common with Isabella in her mid-forty's, and it is likely that this represents a young woman holding the portrait of her husband (possibly posthumous given the plain black frame). The woman's bodice is embroidered with two dogs and a pair of griffons, she wears a headdress and elaborate belt similar to those in a signed and dated portrait of a woman of 1532 by Licinio (Coll. Mrs E.D. Brandegee, Boston, Mass).

J.T.M.

PROVENANCE: Presented to the Castello Sforzesco by Malachia de Cristoforis 1876.
BIBLIOGRAPHY: Luzio, 1913, p. 225.
ADDITIONAL BIBLIOGRAPHY: *I pittori bergamaschi: il Cinquecento*, ed. P. Zampetti, Bergamo, 1975, p. 425, no. 70 (inaccurate measurements) with full bibliography.

113

Isabella d'Este's *studioli* and *grotte*: Introduction

Italian Renaissance rulers with aspirations to learning liked to make a place in their castles or palaces for *studioli* – small rooms to house books, precious objects and paintings. Fifteenth century *studioli* often had paintings set above illusionistic marquetry wainscoting which formed cupboard doors. Isabella d'Este's uncles, Leonello and Borso d'Este, had decorated their *studioli* in Ferrara with paintings of the Muses following a programme by the humanist Guarino. Thus Isabella was following these earlier examples when she gathered around her in her *studioli* moralising classical allegories by the "excellent painters today in Italy" (Canuti, II, p. 208) and made her *grotta* into a treasure chest of antiquities and curiosities (see essay above by Fletcher).

Isabella's first apartments were on the first floor of the Castello S. Giorgio near the *Camera Picta* (Cat. 29; see plan, Pl. 3). Soon after her marriage in 1490 she prepared herself a *studiolo* in a turret room overlooking the Ponte S. Giorgio; the *grotta*, of which we hear first in 1498 (Gerola, p. 7), was immediately below. Initially the painting of the *studiolo* was confined to a frieze of horsy Gonzaga *imprese* (Brown, 1978, p. 170) and to decoration inside the cupboards, but by 1492 there were hopes that "Mantegna will not fail on his side" (Gerola, p. 6 n. 2); suggesting that Isabella already had in mind a more ambitious pictorial scheme. Both paintings and furnishings proceeded slowly, perhaps in several campaigns (Verheyen). Majolica floor tiles with Francesco Gonzaga's devices came from Pesaro in 1496 (Cat. 127, 128) and a doorway with inlaid coloured marbles and sculptured tondi of Muses and animals was made, probably by Giancristoforo Romano (Pl. 59-61). Other items such as silk hangings (Verheyen p. 14) and marquetry cupboards, may have decorated the *studiolo*.

The *grotta* was probably so named by Isabella because of its lower position and its cavernous vault. This beautiful wooden barrel vault (Pl. 57) with stucco reliefs of two of Isabella's devices – the lottery tickets and the music with no notes (see essay by Praz, above) – was made by the Mola brothers, who annoyed Isabella by their slowness in finishing the inlaid marquetry cupboard fronts (see Cat. 120). The vault, alone of the original decoration, remains *in situ* in the first *grotta*. Both rooms were later incorporated as passages into the Palazzina Paleologa (see essay by Gombrich, above).

After her husband's death in 1519 Isabella changed her apartments to the ground floor of the Corte Vecchia (see plan, Pl. 3a). Here she reconstructed the *studiolo* and *grotta* as interconnecting rooms on one level, entered from a corridor leading from a new room, the *Scalcheria* (decorated by Leombruno Cat. 107) to a secret garden (Pl. 56). As much as possible of the old decor was redeployed in the new complex (two doorways, some inlaid panels, perhaps a part of the ceiling, and the pictures), but the different shape and size of the new rooms required some new panelling and a new ceiling (by a certain Sebastiano, 1522), and at least one new door (by Tullio Lombardo, 1521). The 1542 inventory (Cat. 118) gives a remarkably detailed picture of the objects and their arrangement in the two rooms.

The second *studiolo* and *grotta* as they appear today are a modern reconstruction (1933) of the apartment: its original furnishings had been incorporated by Charles de Nevers into the *Appartamento del Paradiso* on the upper floor of the Nova Domus in the 1630's (see Pl. 3).

The Paintings (Photographs)

Initially Isabella may have hoped to hang her *studiolo* entirely with allegories by Mantegna. But the painter's notorious slowness was already a cause for concern in 1492; his *Parnassus* and *Expulsion of the Vices* (Pl. 89, Pl. 30) were not completed until 1497 and 1502 respectively (Brown, 1978, p. 171). By 1496 Isabella had opened negotiations with Bellini, but her hopes were to be disappointed (see essay by Fletcher). Leonardo da Vinci proved even more elusive, but Perugino, first approached in 1497, produced his disappointing *Battle of Love and Chastity* (Pl. 54) finally in 1505. The previous year Isabella had started to campaign for works by allegedly speedier and more tractable artists in Bologna. Costa, though his first painting (Cat. 114) was not produced till 1506, proved acceptable enough to Isabella's taste to succeed Mantegna as court painter and to complete the *Comus*; Francia was also willing, but had his *historia* removed in 1505 because Isabella wanted to "change the sentiment" (Luzio, 1907, p. 863); she never sent him fresh instructions, despite his renewed offers in 1511. Thus, after many vicissitudes, Isabella ended up with two paintings by Mantegna, two by Costa, and one by Perugino, together with the two Correggios (Pl. 52-53) commissioned later to complete the second *studiolo*. Two small grisailles by Mantegna also hung there in 1542. Given the number of artists and subjects with which Isabella was juggling at any one time, it is unlikely that a fixed overall iconographic programme was ever possible, although the paintings are clearly linked by common themes, such as the opposition of virtue and vice, the dual nature of love, and the flourishing of the arts. These themes are also suggested in the marble roundels of Giancristoforo Romano's door. The uneven results she obtained from the painters reflect the incompatibility of her novel desire to collect the best masters, and her old fashioned expectation of wielding the control earlier court patrons had exercised over their resident artists.

C.E.

BIBLIOGRAPHY: Luzio, 1886, 1887, 1888, 1890; Luzio and Renier, 1890, 1893, 1896, 1899-1903; Luzio, 1900, 1901, 1906, 1909, 1913, 1916; Foerster, 1908; Gerola, 1928; Cottafavi, 1930, 1934; Canuti, 1931; Wind, 1948; Marani and Perina, 1961, II pp. 378-89; Brown, 1967-68; 1969[2]; 1969[3] 1976, 1977, 1978; Paccagnini, 1969; Verheyen, 1971; Béguin, 1975[1], 1975[2]; Liebenwein, 1977.

114

An allegory painted for Isabella d'Este's studiolo

The Garden of the Peaceful Arts, sometimes known as *Allegory of the Court of Isabella d'Este*, or *The Coronation of a Lady*; 1504-06 [Pl. 62]
Lorenzo Costa (*c*. 1460-1535)
Tempera and oil on canvas (transferred: see Béguin, 1975[1], p. 61)
Musée du Louvre, Paris (Inv. 255)

Costa, a Ferrarese artist who was invited to become court painter at Mantua after the death of Mantegna, completed this picture for Isabella d'Este's *studiolo* while still in Bologna working for the Bentivoglio family. An amusing exchange of letters (listed in Brown, 1967-68) documents the progress of the commission from November 1504, although Costa's name is not actually mentioned until August 1505. Isabella turned to artists in Bologna at the advice of the Protonotary Antonio Galeazzo Bentivoglio, who had promised to find her a well-disposed and fast-working painter there. In the event, Costa's canvas took at least a year, perhaps even two (Brown, 1967-68, p. 319), interrupted by bouts of illness and work on other commissions. (Verheyen's argument (1971, p. 17) that the painting was completed by March 1505 is unacceptable). Even so, Costa's progress was less "exhausting" to Isabella than that of Mantegna, Bellini or Perugino.

The programme was as usual supplied by Paride da Ceresara, well-trained by now "to make new *invenzioni* every day" for Isabella (Luzio, 1909, p. 863). Isabella was not optimistic of being as well served by the painter, for "one has to accept from them what they are willing or know how to do" (Luzio and Renier, 1903, p. 89). A Mantuan painter was sent to Paride in Ferrara to make a drawing of the programme "so the Bolognese can't make a mistake" (ibid.). As well as the *poesia*, the sketch, and instruction about the size of the canvas, Isabella sent on further request, as she had to Perugino, details of Mantegna's medium – here described as *guazo* with an oil varnish – and lengths of string giving the height of the principal figures in his pictures for the *studiolo* (Luzio, 1909, p. 864) but there is no record of a reply to Bentivoglio's anxious enquiries about the direction of light indicated in the sketch, which he believed to be the contrary of that intended (Luzio, 1913, pp. 206-07; Brown 1967-68, pp. 321-22). (It is notable that of the five paintings made for the original *studiolo*, only one, Mantegna's *Expulsion of the Vices*, is lit from the right.) Despite Isabella's precautions, Costa cannot be said to have translated Paride's lost programme into a readily comprehensible allegory. Although the general sense of the iconography is clear – we see the peaceful pursuit of the arts contrasted with the violence of war – not a single figure can be certainly identified. This must partly be blamed on Costa's curiously elusive and indeterminate style (Venturi (1914) notes that the figures "bend like weeping willows"), and on his failure to discriminate between different genres of painting. This is not the only one of his works where it is hard to tell if the figures are intended to be contemporary portraits, allegorical personifications, or mythological figures.

Two protecting figures at foreground right and left (Apollo the dragon-slayer and Diana the huntress?) guard the fenced-off grove, accompanied by vigilant storks. On either side of the entrance two seated maidens crown a cow and a sheep with flowery garlands. Although portrait-like in feature and dress, these figures have been most plausibly explained (by Wind, refining Foerster) as representatives of Georgic and Pastoral poetry. Inside the enclosure four musicians playing stringed instruments, a writer and perhaps an artist drawing (extreme right) surround a seated female figure.

She holds on her knee a standing Cupid who crowns a fashionably dressed young woman with a myrtle wreath. A cavalry skirmish takes place on the shore in the left middle distance, and scantily clad figures in amorous dalliance are seen in the right background. Thus the arts flourish under the protection of the gods, free from violent or lascivious disturbance.

The most urgent question concerns the central group. Is the lady being crowned Isabella herself? Few have doubted the identification. Since Isabella was not likely by this stage to commission a truthful portrait (see essay by Fletcher, above), and since the lady carries no identifying attributes (unless those are Isabella's knots around her hem), it is hard to be sure. However, her costume is essentially realistic, whereas the other figures wear a variety of clinging drapery. If it is a portrait, it must represent Isabella. The woman on her right is probably an unworldly Venus, and the cupid may be, as Verheyen suggested, *Anteros* or *amor virtutis*, who has exchanged his darts for virtuous wreaths.

Costa's bland painting style, much in evidence here, was comfortingly familiar to Isabella from her father's court at Ferrara. Only this, and the artist's pliability, can explain her readiness to fill Mantegna's place with "soft little Costa" (Fiera, 1515).

C.E.

PROVENANCE: In Cardinal Richelieu's collection by 1636. To the Musée Central des Arts, later the Louvre, in 1801 (Béguin, 1975[1], p. 61).
BIBLIOGRAPHY: Yriarte, 1896, pp. 330-46; Foerster, 1901, pp. 171-72; Luzio and Reiner, 1903, p. 89; Luzio, 1909, pp. 863-65; Luzio, 1913, pp. 206-07; Venturi, 1914, VII, pp. 794-96; Wind, 1948, pp. 49-50; Brown, 1966, pp. 226-44, 360; Brown, 1969[2]; Verheyen, 1971, pp. 44-46; Béguin, 1975[1], no. 136; Schloder, 1975, pp. 230-33.

115

Allegory of Vice, *c.* 1531
Correggio (1489-1534)
Red chalk: 27.4 x 19.4 cm
British Museum, Department of Prints and Drawings (1895-9-15-736; Cat. 17)

Correggio painted two *Allegories* (Pl. 52-53) in tempera, to fit in with the works of Perugino, Mantegna, and Costa in Isabella d'Este's *studiolo*. This drawing is a *modello* (Popham, 1957) for the *Allegory of Vice*, and the differences between it and the painting show the artist putting the finishing touches to an already highly evolved design. The painting is less wide, and the draperies of the side figures are cut at the edges. All the figures become smoother and fleshier, the trees and distant landscape are more polished, and a tree stump is moved just far enough to ensure the decency of the piping girl. The only significant alteration is the inclusion in the foreground of a puckish boy holding a bunch of grapes. A vine winds round the tree in both drawing and painting, and the greater prominence of the grapes in the canvas is presumably meant as an iconographic clue. The vine in Mantegna's *Samson and Delilah* (National Gallery, London) also underlines the notion of man as a prisoner of his desires, in Samson's case obviously amorous. Correggio's pair of paintings should be read as morality not myth (Wind, 1948): attempts to identify the bearded figure as Marsyas/Silenus (Soth, 1964) or Vulcan (Verheyen, 1971) have proved unconvincing. The precise meaning was lost as early as 1542, when an inventory (d'Arco, 1845) usefully records the *Allegories* on either side of the door of the *studiolo*, but calls *Vice Apollo and Marsyas*, in spite of the palpably female breast of the figure blowing the pipe. With regard to dating, *Vice* follows *Virtue*, and is typical of

115

Correggio's late manner, as seen in such works as the Parma Cathedral pendentives (Gould, 1976), and the Dresden *Madonna of Saint George*.

D.E.

PROVENANCE: J. Richardson the Elder; E. Bouverie; Sir J.C. Robinson; J. Malcolm.
BIBLIOGRAPHY: d'Arco, 1845, appendix II; Wind, 1948, pp. 52-54; Béguin, 1975[2], pp. 221-26; Verheyen, 1971, pp. 57-61; Gould, 1976, pp. 127-30.
ADDITIONAL BIBLIOGRAPHY: A.E. Popham, *Correggio's Drawings*, London, 1957, pp. 100-01, 167, no. 91; L. Soth, "A Note on Correggio's Allegories of Virtue and Vice", *Gazette des Beaux-Arts*, LXIV, 1964, pp. 297-300; A. E. Popham, *Italian Drawings in the Department of Prints and Drawings in the British Museum: Artists working in Parma in the XVI Century*, London, 1967, no. 17, pp. 10-11.

116

Relief with two Dancing Satyrs
Greek marble; 36 x 45 cm
Museo del Palazzo Ducale, Mantua (Inv. 6700)

A considerable portion of the relief has been broken off at the top, particularly on the right side, so that the upper part of the body of the satyr on the right is missing. The face and right arm of the satyr on the left have also been broken off.
This antique relief shows two satyrs dancing before an altar; the one on the left is playing the lyre. This seems to be one of the first antiquities acquired by Isabella d'Este, as it was sent to her from Rome in 1501, already in a damaged state. It was

displayed in the Palace above a fireplace in the *Scalcheria*, the large room through which Isabella's *Studiolo* was approached.

In the background of the relief between the satyrs there is a building with two arched windows, and behind the satyr on the right part of a column set on a pedestal can be seen; the upper part of this column is missing, but it may have supported a statuette of the deity worshipped at the altar. The decorated altar stands on lion's paw feet, and on each of its two visible sides there is a round-headed niche in which a small figure of a nude youth is represented. There is a garland round the top of the altar, and above it there is a small cover in the form of a baldacchino supported on the figures of three small sphinxes which would have protected the fire lit on the altar after a sacrifice. An altar with a similar cover in the form of a baldacchino is shown on a relief from the Tomb of the Haterii, Rome (Vatican Museum). The satyr on the left is playing an elaborately decorated lyre, and both figures are wearing short cloaks of animal skins.

The figures of the satyrs are executed in high relief, while the details of the background are shown in low relief. Carved reliefs of this type were used in Hellenistic and Roman times to decorate the interiors of houses and public buildings. This example is probably late Hellenistic in date, although it may be Roman.

M.L.

BIBLIOGRAPHY: Levi, 1931, pp. 52-53 (with bibliography); Brown, 1976, p. 326, appendix 18 letter I, p. 345, n. 7.
ADDITIONAL BIBLIOGRAPHY: T. Schreiber, *Die hellenistische Reliefbilder*, Leipzig, 1894, pl. LVI a; M. Bieber, *Sculpture of the Hellenistic Age*, New York, 1961, pp. 152-55; R. Bianchi-Bandinelli, *Rome, the Centre of Power*, London 1970, pl. 242: Tomb of the Haterii.

116

117

117

Part of a Sarcophagus: **Persephone (Proserpina) in Hades**
Italian marble; 76 x 87 cm; probably mid 2nd century A.D.
Museo del Palazzo Ducale, Mantua (Inv. 6750).

The relief formed one of the short ends of an antique Roman sarcophagus. It represents the scene in the underworld when Hermes, the messenger of the gods, confronts Hades, ruler of the underworld, and Persephone whom he has abducted, bringing the orders of Zeus that Persephone should return to earth. It was acquired from Rome in 1524, by Isabella d'Este as a present from her son, who had obtained it from Pope Adrian; it had originally been acquired by Leo X, who was said to have paid 500 ducats for it at the time of its discovery in Rome. In Mantua Isabella incorporated this sculpture in the decoration of the *Studiolo*, where it was embedded in the wall beneath the window, as we know from an inventory of 1542. Drawings of the relief were made by Giulio Romano and by Amico Aspertini (the latter's is in the British Museum, Sketchbook 1, fol. 36 v. illustrated here). The myth of the abduction of Persephone by Hades was quite commonly represented on antique Roman sarcophagi; an almost identical scene with Persephone in the underworld is shown on the short side of a sarcophagus which was walled into the façade of the Casino of Palazzo Rospigliosi in Rome in the early seventeenth century.

Hades and Persephone are shown seated side by side on a

167

throne facing Hermes. The figure of Persephone is entirely covered by drapery, while in her hand she has a scroll, which may be her marriage contract with Hades. The three-headed dog Cerberus, traditional guardian of the underworld, sits beside Hades. The partially draped figure of a woman on the right side of the relief standing behind Cerberus may, it has been suggested, personify one of the rivers of the underworld.

M.L.

BIBLIOGRAPHY: Dollmayr, 1901, p. 183; Levi, 1926, pp. 214, 215, 217; Levi, 1931, p. 89 with full bibliography; Robert, III, 3, 1969, pl. 120, pp. 462-63, no. 365; Brown, 1976, pp. 326, 335.
ADDITIONAL BIBLIOGRAPHY: P.P. Bober, *Drawings after the Antique by Amico Aspertini*, London 1957, pp. 67-68, Figs. 78, 80; P.P. Bober and Ruth Rubinstein, *Antique Sculpture and Renaissance Artists*, forthcoming, Cat. no. 9.

118

Photograph: **The inventory of Isabella d'Este's Grotta**
Manuscript in Italian on vellum, with decorated initials and scroll patterns in blue, red and gold leaf
Archivio di Stato, Mantua (Archivio Gonzaga, b. 400)

Several copies survive of the inventory of Isabella's *Grotta* and some other rooms, drawn up by the notary Odoardo Stivini in 1542, three years after her death. This *de luxe* version was possibly made for the Duchess Margherita Paleologo, since a similarly decorated list of Margherita's jewels accompanies it. The inventory includes no less than 1,620 objects in 235 en-

118

tries; by far the greater number of these were coins and medallions, but there were 72 vases, flasks and cups and 46 engraved gems, 29 of them cameos (Brown, 1976, p. 328) – a far smaller collection of antique cameos, in fact, than that of Cardinal Francesco Gonzaga, which had had to be sold to pay off debt after his death (1483). The first item in the inventory is the famous large cameo with two heads in relief named as Caesar and Livia, mounted in a gold setting with laurel leaves of green enamel. How Isabella acquired this object is unknown (she was still buying cameos in the year of her death) but it continued to be a prized item of the Gonzaga collection

until the Sack of Mantua in 1630 and Rubens had admired it. Thereafter its history is obscure, and two twin-headed socalled Gonzaga cameos, one in the Hermitage Museum, Leningrad (Inv. 291), the other (Pl. 50) in the Kunsthistoriches Museum, Vienna (Inv. IX A81) are each claimed as the original owned by Isabella.

D.S.C.

BIBLIOGRAPHY: Luzio, 1908, pp. 413-25; Martindale, 1964, p. 106; de Grummond, 1974; Brown, 1976; Neverov, 1977; Brown, 1977[1], p. 162; 1977[2], p. 80; Brown, 1980.

119

Antique onyx vase from the Grotta of Isabella d'Este
Roman, *c.* 198 A.D.
h. 15.3 cm, max diam. 6.5 cm
Herzog Anton Ulrich-Museum, Brunswick

This originally had the form of a *lekythos*, an oil-pouring jug, but the handle is missing. In the 15th century the vessel was given gold mounts so that it could again be used for pouring, and, to take the gold fixing bands, two channels were carved in the decoration above and below the main figurative area. These mounts were stolen in 1831. Their appearance is recorded in a drawing by Oeding. The onyx is five-layered, the colours being, from the inside out, chocolate brown, white, yellowish-brown, white and yellow. The main figurative band is carved with the young god, Triptolemos, in a chariot pulled by winged snakes, accompanied by Demeter and the goddess of Fortune. Tellus reclines half-naked, her elbow on a basket, in front of the chariot. Women bringing sacrificial offerings approach from the right, while two priestesses, a child and Priapus are emerging from the building on the left. The lower area is carved with utensils appropriate to a mystery cult: a basket from which a snake emerges, a set of pipes with a mask above them, a *Krater*, a barely draped phallus, two *thyrsoi*, and torches. The scene depicted was thought to represent the initiation of a young imperial prince into the mysteries of Eleusis, and to date from the 1st century A.D. (Fürchtwangler III, p. 338). However, G. Bruns has shown that the vessel must have been carved for the imperial family around 198 A.D., when Caracalla was elevated by his father, Septimius Severus, to co-regent. The young man in the chariot is, therefore, Caracalla, together with his mother, Empress Julia Domna, led by the goddess of Fortune and venerated by members of the imperial family.

Although no reference to the acquisition of this vase by Isabella d'Este has been found in her surviving correspondence (Brown, 1976, p. 325) it appears in the inventory of her possessions drawn up in 1542 (Luzio, 1908, p. 414; see Cat. 118) as "a cameo vessel with coloured figures in relief; handle, foot and spout of gold" (*un vaso di cameo con figure di relievo de varii colori, fornito d'oro con manico e piede e bocchino*) and was kept in the middle of three cabinets in the wall opposite the window in the second *Grotta*, along with 71 other objects including many more of her precious cups and vases, cameos and other *objets d'art* (Brown, 1977, p. 161). It remained in the Gonzaga collection until 1630, and was thought to be from Solomon's Temple in Jerusalem. Shortly before this date the gold mounts were repaired.

The vase narrowly escaped destruction in the sack of the Ducal Palace in 1630. A mercenary officer in the imperial army, Claude Latouf, Baron de Sirot, bought it for 17 ducats from a soldier who was about to destroy it for the sake of its gold mounts.

A.S.C.

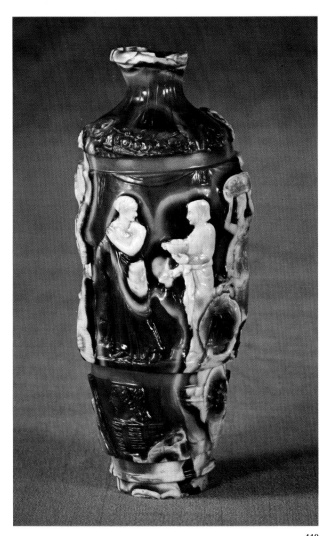

119

PROVENANCE: Palazzo Ducale, Mantua; Baron de Sirot; given by him to Franz Albrecht, Duke of Lauenburg; 1666 inherited by his wife Sophie Elizabeth of Brunswick; presented by the family to the cabinet of art and natural sciences, later the Anton Ulrich-Museum.

BIBLIOGRAPHY: Luzio, 1908; Brown, 1976, pp. 325-27; Brown and Lorenzoni, 1977, p. 161.

ADDITIONAL BIBLIOGRAPHY: A. Fürchtwangler, *Antike Gemmen*, 1900, III, p. 338; G. Bruns, "Das Mantuanische Onyxgefäss" and A. Fink "Die Schicksale des Onyxgefässes" in *Kunsthefte des Herzog Anton Ulrich-Museums* (Braunschweig), V, 1950, pp. 1-20.

120

Reproductions of marquetry from Isabella d'Este's apartments

Made for the Lombardy pavilion of the International Exhibition of Art, Rome 1911
Two panels showing musical instruments, h. 71.5, w. 44 cm; architectural design 71.5 x 71 cm
Museo del Palazzo Ducale, Mantua

The original panels of which these are facsimiles now form part of the wainscoting of Isabella d'Este's second *studiolo* in the Corte Vecchia. Inlaid (marquetry) panels were made for the first *studiolo* or *grotta* by the brothers Antonio and Pietro

Mola, Mantuan woodwokers who also made the *grotta's* wooden barrel vault in 1507. In 1506 Isabella threatened the brothers with the dungeons for their delays in completing the eight panels they had promised, only two of which were apparently finished that year (Luzio, 1909, pp. 868-69). It is generally assumed that the six surviving marquetry panels, four with architectural scenes one of them with the musical notation of Ockeghem's canon (see essay by Fenlon above and Pl. 90) and two depicting musical instruments (Pls. 91-92), are those made by the Mola brothers. The two types vary, however, in style and execution. The architectural scenes, with their skilful deployment of variegated pieces of wood to produce urban perspectives, of a strongly Venetian character, may well be by the Molas, who had in 1496 made sacristy cupboards for San Marco in Venice, including a view of the church (Marani and Perina II, p. 178). The *trompe l'oeil* musical instruments are markedly inferior in execution. They could possibly be by the "Maestro Sebastiano", known from other documents as an *intarsiatore* (d'Arco, I, p. 87), who is mentioned in 1522 as having finished the cornices and *alcuni quadri* (some panels) for the *grotta* (Gerola, p. 18). In other words, new *tarsie* could have been commissioned to fill gaps when the second *grotta* was assembled. In the 1630's the wooden fittings of the *studiolo* and *grotta* were moved to the *Appartamento del Paradiso* in the Nova Domus.

D.S.C.; C.E.

BIBLIOGRAPHY: Luzio, 1909, pp. 868-70; Gerola, 1929, pp. 257-59; Cottafavi, 1934, pp. 236-38; Marani and Perina, 1961, p. 580; Paccagnini, 1969, p. 102, figs. 71-75; Brown, 1976, p. 330.

121

Photograph: **Letter to Isabella d'Este from Andrea Mantegna**, 13 July 1506
Archivio di Stato, Mantua (Autografi 7, c. 146)

Written exactly two months before Mantegna's death, the letter records his reluctant decision to sell his "dear antique

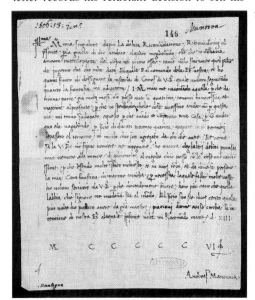

121

marble Faustina" to Isabella d'Este (see Cat. 122). Although subsequent correspondence shows that the Marchesa hoped to profit from plague in Mantua and the artist's debts to obtain

169

the bust for a quarter of the asking price, even attempting to elicit a low valuation from the sculptor Antico (see essay by Radcliffe, above), Mantegna stood out for the 100 ducats he finally received. Mantegna also mentions here his progress in applying "that little gift God has given me" to his third painting for Isabella's *studiolo*, the *Comus*, left at his death as little more than a drawing, and completed by Costa (Pl. 55). This last letter to his Gonzaga patrons is typical of almost all his surviving correspondence in its preoccupation with money. Mantegna's beautiful handwriting varies considerably according to his state of mind and health: here it is slightly crabbed by illness. He uses the Latinate form of his name which had become his normal signature by the late 1470's. In earlier letters he often signed himself "Mantenga".

The date of the letter is wrongly given by an archivist at top left as 13 January. It can be dated to July by subsequent exchanges (Brown, 1978).

C.E.

BIBLIOGRAPHY: Kristeller, 1901, Doc. 76, p. 496; 1902, Doc. 174, pp. 577-78; reprod. in Martindale and Garavaglia, 1967, p. 84; Brown, 1969, p. 38; Brown, 1978, p. 82.

122

Bust of Faustina the Elder
Greek marble; h. of bust 68 cm, h. of head 25 cm. The left part of the neck and the tip of the nose have been restored. The bust has been broken in several places and repaired.
Museo del Palazzo Ducale, Mantua (Inv. 6749)

This antique Roman bust portrays Faustina the Elder; she married Antoninus Pius, who became emperor in 138 AD. She was the daughter of a Roman senator, M. Annius Verus, and the mother of Faustina the Younger (see Cat. 248). She died in 140/4 AD. This bust reputed to be the one of Faustina the Elder which was owned by Mantegna, and sold by him to Isabella d'Este in 1506, shortly before his death, on account of his serious financial difficulties (see Cat. 121). The agent who collected the bust for Isabella reported to her that Mantegna

122

parted with it with such regret that he thought he would die of the loss. The bust was most probably of such value to Mantegna because it was a genuine Roman antiquity.

Isabella had a bust of Faustina the Elder displayed in her *grotta*, where she kept most of her collection of antiquities and copies of antiquities. The position of the bust of Faustina on

123

the moulding above the wainscot of the north-west wall of the room is recorded in the inventory compiled in 1542.

It is possible to identify the bust as a portrait of Faustina the Elder by comparing the features and hair style with those of the Empress shown on coins. The distinctive hair style with the hair set in waves around the face and with plaits coiled up top of the head seems to have been a fashion popularized by Faustina the Elder.

M.L.

BIBLIOGRAPHY: Crowe and Cavalcaselle, II, London, 1912, p. 115; Levi, 1931, pp. 63-64, pl. LXXI (with full bibliography); Brown, 1969, p. 32; Brown, 1976, p. 325, 326, 329, 332.
ADDITIONAL BIBLIOGRAPHY: J.J. Bernouilli, *Römische Ikonographie*, II, 2, Stuttgart, 1891, 155, no. 18; A.L. Smith, *British Museum, Catalogue of Sculpture in the Department of Greek and Roman Antiquities*, III, 1904, no. 1904, pp. 160-161, pl. XVII.

123

Antoninus Pius
Pier Jacopo Alari-Bonacolsi, called Antico (*c.* 1460-1528)
Bronze head, inlaid with silver, on coloured plaster bust
h. (overall) 66.5 cm; h. (bronze head and neck) 32 cm
Seminario Vescovile, Mantua

The eyes are inlaid with silver. The plaster bust, which appears to date from some time in the sixteenth century, was originally coloured red and re-painted in cream probably in the eighteenth century.

This is one of four bronze heads of Roman emperors evidently by Antico, all set in identical plaster busts, which, together with four antique marble busts, form a set of eight busts first recorded in the old Episcopal Palace at Mantua (now the Seminario Vescovile) in 1762. At this time all of them appear to have been covered in a coating of plaster.

The set of busts was identified and fully published in 1976 by Ann Allison, who suggested that the bronzes may have been made for Bishop Ludovico Gonzaga (d. 1511). This is probably correct, but it is worth noting that Isabella d'Este had a number of bronze heads and busts displayed high up *sopra il cornisotto piú alto* in her second *Grotta*, according to the 1542 inventory (*Di piú numero dicisette fra figure e mezze figure e teste antiche et moderne di brongio*) (Luzio, 1908, p. 422; Hermann, 1910, p. 216).

A variant portrait of Antoninus Pius by Antico is in the Metropolitan Museum, New York (Inv. no. 65.202). This is a full bronze bust, with draped shoulders, and is parcel-gilt.

A.F.R.

PROVENANCE: Recorded in 1762 in the Palazzo Vescovile, Mantua.
ADDITIONAL BIBLIOGRAPHY: A. Allison, "Four new busts by Antico", *Mitteilungen des Kunsthistorischen Institutes in Florenz*, XX, 1976, pp. 213-24.

124

Diana, Mars and (?) Venus; *c.* 1495-1505
Andrea Mantegna (1431-1506)
Pen and ink with brown wash, white highlights, and extensive shading in red (Mars) and blue (Venus), 36.4 x 31.7 cm
British Museum, Department of Prints and Drawings (1861-8-10-2; Cat. 156)

The drawing is one of several highly finished late studies by Mantegna with added wash and/or colour (cf. Cat. 126) which, as Michael Hirst has observed, have the appearance of "presentation drawings" rather than preliminary designs for paintings or engravings (cf. the 1491 *Judith* in the Uffizi, whose finished character is confirmed by the signature and date). The allegorical subject and the figure style of this sheet

124

are close to Mantegna's two paintings for Isabella d'Este's *studiolo*, finished in 1497 and 1502 (Pls. 30, 89).

The identification of the mythological figures, and hence of the overall meaning of the composition, is uncertain. "Mars" appears to have the attributes both of a civil ruler (sceptre) and of a soldier (spear and armour). He turns towards "Diana" (characterized by bow and quiver) who extinguishes a torch (frequently a symbol of vice in Mantegna) and away from the goddess on the right whose coiffure and provocative pose (similar to that of the Venus in the *Expulsion of the Vices*) suggest a carnal Venus. Thus a moral choice, like that of Hercules at the crossroads, may be represented. The group has also been associated with the seated Comus flanked by a naked and a clothed Venus which Mantegna designed for the *Story of Comus* (Verheyen), but the attributes do not fit this interpretation.

Mantegna may have drawn the central figure first and added the two goddesses. "Diana's" bow and right arm are on a separate strip of paper carefully added by the artist. It is possible that "Diana" has lost some of her white heightening and that a white red and blue colour scheme was intended, like that of the couch in the *Parnassus*, which Lehmann interprets heraldically (cf. hose in "Meeting Scene" of *Camera Picta*, Cat. 29).

C.E.

PROVENANCE AND EARLY BIBLIOGRAPHY: Popham and Pouncey, 1950, no. 156, pp. 94-95.
BIBLIOGRAPHY: Tietze-Conrat, 1955, p. 206; Verheyen, 1971, n. 98, p. 48; Lehmann, 1973, p. 165; Béguin, 1975¹, p. 46.

125

The Fall and Rescue of Ignorant Humanity: after a lost work by Mantegna
Anonymous engraver, after Andrea Mantegna; second half of sixteenth century or later
Engraving, 27.1 x 20.0 cm
British Museum, Department of Prints and Drawings

The allegory reproduced in this engraving (from two plates) can be identified with a lost work by Andrea Mantegna possibly for the Palazzo of San Sebastiano in Mantua. Michelangelo Biondo, in his treatise *Della nobilissima pittura*, Venice 1549, records (fol. 18ʳ) a composition showing Mercury pulling Lady Ignorance out from below, where she is shown with a great number of others ignorant of learning and of the arts (*... Mercurio con madonna Ignorantia sopra una tella, il quale parea che strassinasse la detta Ignorantia di sotto con gran copia di altri ignoranti di varie scientie e arti...*). Biondo was mistaken in identifying Ignorance herself with the blind person rescued by Mercury but his description is clearly linked to this composition. The identification, first proposed by Förster, is confirmed by the existence of Mantegna's drawing for half of the composition (see Cat. 126), two engravings after Mantegna (possibly by Zoan Andrea) inscribed *virtus combusta* and *virtus deserta*, as well as by the later engraving exhibited here reproducing the whole composition.

In this very rare print based on the two engravings after Mantegna, the letters (A to X) probably refer to a commentary that is now lost on the personifications and their attributes. The upper part of the engraving shows the rule of Ignorance, who, with the help of other vices, leads a blind woman to her fall. Unaware of the danger in front of her, she is about to tumble into a pit full of blind companions. In the lower part, Mercury, the god of logic and learning, rescues one of these unfortunates. *Virtus* is shown in the shape of a tree, aband-

125

oned by all; a fate she preferred to being a despised goddess, according to Alberti in his dialogue entitled *Virtus dea*. In the earlier engraving by Zoan Andrea, one of the stone blocks was inscribed VIRTVTI S.A.I., which has been expanded to read *Virtuti semper adversatur Ignorantia* (Ignorance is always the opponent of Virtue), a maxim found twice in Mantegna's letters to Francesco Gonzaga (1489 and 1491).

Tietze-Conrat has convincingly related Mantegna's allegory to the introduction of Lucian's treatise *Slander*, a text that the painter knew as he illustrated another passage from it, the *ekphrasis* (rhetorical description) of the Calumny. Lucian describes the influence of Ignorance on humanity: "Truly, we all resemble people lost in the dark - nay, we are even like blind men. Now we stumble inexcusably, now we lift our feet when there is no need of it... In short, in everything we do we are always making plenty of missteps". Lucian, in fact, refers back to this idea in conclusion to his essay: "... But the cause of this (slander) and all the rest of it, as I said in the beginning, is Ignorance, and the fact that the real character of each of us is shrouded in darkness. Hence, if some one of the gods would only unveil our lives..." (Lucian, Loeb edn., I, 1913, pp. 361, 363). This saviour, for Mantegna and his patron, could only be Mercury, the god of eloquence and wisdom.

J.M.M.

BIBLIOGRAPHY: Hind, 1910, p. 354, no. 12 (see also pp. 352-53); Hind, V, 1948, p. 29 (also pp. 27-29); Popham and Pouncey, 1950, p. 96 (also pp. 95-97); Tietze-Conrat, 1955 p. 206; Levenson and others, 1973, p. 222, note 2 (also pp. 222-27 no. 84).
ADDITIONAL BIBLIOGRAPHY: R. Förster, "Studien zu Mantegna und den Bildern in Studierzimmer der Isabella Gonzaga", *Jahrbuch der königlich preussischen Kunstsammlungen*, XXII, 1901, pp. 78-87, ill. p. 80; D. and E. Panofsky, *Pandora's Box, The Changing Aspects of a Mythical Symbol*, Princeton, 1956, pp. 42-48, fig. 23; Battisti, 1965, pp. 33-36; forthcoming article by J.M. Massing.

126

The Realm of Ignorance: upper part of *The Fall and Rescue of Ignorant Humanity*, *c.* 1490-1500
Andrea Mantegna (1431-1506)
Drawing heightened by colour wash; 28.7 x 44.3 cm
British Museum, Department of Prints and Drawings (Cat. no. 157)

This unfinished study showing the upper part of Mantegna's allegorical *Fall and Rescue...* (Cat. 125) is reproduced in the

engraving, possibly by Zoan Andrea, inscribed *Virtus combusta* (virtue consumed in flames) (Hind no. 22). The subject is the realm of Ignorance, a fat blind woman who governs the world. As in Mantegna's painting *Minerva expelling the vices* (Pl. 30) for the *studiolo* of Isabella d'Este, Ignorance appears with two of her companions, Ingratitude and Avarice. On their right, three Vices encourage a blind woman who is about to fall into a pit. One, with long ears, is probably Error, while another, who simulates blindness, could symbolize Fraud; the third, an ithyphallic satyr playing a bagpipe, clearly personifies Lewdness. The burning laurel tree symbolizes the destruction of Virtue under the rule of Ignorantia, her arch-enemy. Some of the personifications were copied by Lorenzo Leombruno and identified with inscriptions in his *Allegoria della Fortuna* (Brera, Milan), a painting based on Alberti's pseudo-Lucianesque dialogue *Virtus dea* and on Lucian's description of the *Calumny* of Apelles.

J.M.M.

126

BIBLIOGRAPHY: Popham and Pouncey, 1950, pp. 95-97, no. 157; Tietze-Conrat, 1955, pp. 205-06, pl. 120 (cf. fig. 49-50). See bibliography for Cat. 125.

Floor tiles with Gonzaga devices, as laid in Isabella's first studiolo, 1494

127

Six floor-tiles; *c.* 1492-94
Pesaro; workshop of Antonio dei Fedeli (?)
Tin-glazed earthenware decorated in blue, green, orange-brown and purple. Each tile square, the back with an arrangement of three concentric rings separated by areas from which the clay has been scooped. Each approximately 24.00 cm square (but some slightly trimmed at the edges); h. 4.80 cm
Victoria & Albert Museum, Department of Ceramics (334-1903; Rackham, 1940, no. 193).

Each tile is painted with a Gonzaga emblem: The arms of Gonzaga; a white doe beneath a scroll inscribed in German "BIDER GRAFT" (Righteous power); a dove perched on a coiled and smoking tree-stock inscribed in French "VRAI AMOVR NESE CHANGE" (true love does not change); a craggy island, with three successive plateaux, surmounted by a diamond and surrounded by brands discharging smoke, at the base of the island is a tablet inscribed in Greek "AMVMOC" (blameless); a sejant hound, muzzled and leashed; a steel gauntlet with attached scroll inscribed in Spanish "BVENA FE NONES MVDABLE" (Good faith is not changeable).
From the documents cited by Gobio Casali (see essay above) it seems likely that these tiles and Cat. 128 are of the type described in 1494 as decorated with the devices of the Marquis Francesco. That set was apparently first ordered for the Gonzaga villa at Marmirolo but in the event some of the tiles were laid in Isabella's *studiolo* in the Castello di San Giorgio at Mantua itself. It is not known from which location most of the surviving tiles came, through according to Signora Gobio Casali fragments of this tile pavement have been discovered recently in the vicinity of Marmirolo. Many complete examples appeared on the market from an unknown source or sources in the late 19th century: in 1878 Attilio Portioli owned at Mantua about 40 tiles with Gonzaga *imprese* (Corona, 1879, p. 214, note 1); also in 1878 Willelmo Braghirolli said that he had bought in Mantua tiles clearly described as of this set (Ibid, p. 207). Presumably many of the tiles now widely scattered came from these two collections. The examples at the Museo del Castello Sforzesco (see Cat. 128) were acquired on the Milanese art market in 1884; those in the Musée Jacquemart-André at Paris were acquired in 1893 at Bologna from a Signor Angiolin; those in the Louvre, at Florence in 1909. Other examples are at Amsterdam (Rijksmuseum); Cambridge (Fitzwilliam Museum); Florence (Museo Bardini); the Hague (Gemeente Museum); Hamburg (Museum für Kunst und Gewerbe); New York (Metropolitan Museum). The Victoria and Albert's set was presumably once in the same ownership as a set of 12 illustrated by Yriarte in 1896 as in the collection of Mme E. André, and a set formerly in the Berlin Schlossmuseum (Lauts, 1952, Fig. 21) since all three sets were once similarly mounted.
The unglazed backs of the tiles constituting this set are unusual, if not unique, in having concentric rings and depressions. Sacchi (1934, p. 294) suggests that they were made this way in order to assist adhesion to the mortar of the floor, but this was not thought necessary in other instances. More probably these unusually thick tiles were shaped in this manner in an attempt to dry them out more quickly in a damp winter season, so that they could be given their first or biscuit firing. In his letter of 5 January 1493, Giovanni Sforza wrote to

Francesco II that delay was to be expected in the making of the tiles "because the weather is rather unsuitable for drying them".
The potter responsible for the tiles delivered in 1494 is not mentioned in the correspondence. However, he may well have been the same Pesaro potter, Antonio dei Fedeli of the family documented by Bonini (*Corriere dei Ceramisti*, April 1941, pp. 107-19), from whom the Gonzaga were ordering tiles in 1496 (see essay by Gobio-Casali).

J.V.G.M.

PROVENANCE: Castello di San Giorgio or Marmirolo? Collection of J.H. Fitzhenry, by whom these six tiles were given to the Victoria and Albert Museum in 1903.
BIBLIOGRAPHY: Braghirolli, 1878; G. Corona, *La ceramica, Biografie e Note Storiche*, Milan, 1879, pp. 206-7 and p. 214, note 1; Yriarte, 1895, p. 391; H. Wallis, *The Maiolica Pavement Tiles of the 15th century*, London, 1905, pp. XXV-XXVI and figs. 89 and 90; J.J. Marquet de Vasselot, "Quelques

127

Carreaux du Château de Mantoue au Musée du Louvre, *Bulletin des Musées de France*, 1910, p. 2, fig. 2; T. Borenius, Italian Maiolica in the Collection of the Rt. Hon. F. Leverton Harris, *Apollo*, 1925, I, pp. 269-71, for the piece now in the Fitzwilliam Museum, Cambridge; Gerola, 1929, pp. 255, 261; Gerola, 1930, pp. 381-402; F. Sacchi, "Le Mattonelle dei Camerini di Isabella d'Este Gonzaga della Raccolta dei Civici Musei del Castello Sforzesco, *Città di Milano, Rivista Mensile del Comune*, June, 1934, pp. 291 et seq.; A. Minghetti, *Ceramisti*, Milano, 1939, p. 144; Rackham, 1940, No. 193 and Pl. 30; Mann, 1943 pp. 23-24, Pl. XXXIII-XXXIV; Chompret, 1949, fig. 817, where the Victoria and Albert examples are illustrated but confused with those at Milan; the Hague, Gemeentemuseum, *L'Italia Splendida*, exhibition catalogue, August-October, 1956, no. 121; Detroit Institute of Arts, *Decorative Arts of the Italian Renaissance, 1400-1600*, exhibition catalogue, Detroit, 1958, No. 89; Lane, 1960, p. 50 and pl. 27A; F. Sacchi, "La Raccolta delle Maioliche del Castello Sforzesco a Milano", *Faenza*, 1965, p. 62, Pl. XXVIII; R. Rückert, *Bilderhefte des Museums für Kunst und Gewerbe Hamburg, II Majolika*, Hamburg, 1960, no. 11; A. Berendsen and others, *Fliesen, ein Geschichte der Wand-und Bodenfliesen*, Munich, 1964, p. 80, (line block of three of the Victoria and Albert tiles) p. 81 and colour plate (of the Hague tile) following p. 94; Giacomotti, 1974, nos. 158-163.

128

Two floor-tiles; *c.* 1492-94
(As above, Cat. 127)
Museo del Castello Sforzesco, Milan

Both tiles are painted with Gonzaga emblems: a sunburst entwined by two ribbons inscribed in French "PER VND / IXIR"

128

(for a desire); a muzzle beneath a ribbon inscribed in Latin "CAVTIVS" (more cautiously).

This set of tiles in discussed above, Cat. 127.

J.V.G.M.

PROVENANCE: Castello di San Giorgio or Marmirolo?; Milanese Art Market, 1884.

BIBLIOGRAPHY: For Bibliography see Cat. 127. Amongst the items there listed those under Wallis, Sacchi, Minghetti and the Hague particularly concern the examples in Milan. Seven of the eight at Milan were shown at The Hague in 1956, but apparently not the Sun emblem. Chompret 1949, vol. I, p. 152-53 says, wrongly, that the Milan tiles bear dates,; in vol. II, fig. 817 he illustrates the Victoria & Albert set in error for the Milan set.

129

Seven floor-tiles; *c.* 1510-25

Le Marche (?)

Tin-glazed earthenware painted in blue, green and orange-brown, comprising three octagonal tiles, one square tile and three triangular tiles.

Museo Internazionale delle Ceramiche, Faenza (Nos. 18869, 18872, 18880).

The three octagonal tiles are decorated on an orange-brown ground with a ring of chain-like pattern, the links of which are alternately decorated with a leaf and an anthemion flower on a blue ground; inside the ring, within blue circles, are inscriptions: ISAB / ESTE. MR / MAN (Isabella Estensis, Marchesana Mantuae) and NEC / SPE. NEC / METV. The square tile is centred by a stylized flowerhead; the triangular tiles are similar but with the design sliced in half.

Two other groups of tiles from this set have been published: at Rotterdam (see Cat. 130) and five octagonal tiles in the Museo di Palazzo Ducale at Mantua itself (Ozzòla, 1953, p. 5 and pl. I). The illustrations published by Ozzòla, show that,

in addition to the devices represented in the present exhibition, the set once included Isabella's candelabrum *impresa* (see essay above by Praz).

Though the set of tiles to which these and the tiles in Cat. 130 belong is beyond dispute shown by the inscriptions and devices it bears to have been made for Isabella d'Este (also discussed by Gobio-Casali, above) little else can be confidently affirmed about it. No written evidence has been convincingly shown to refer to this set; nor do we know in which room it was found in modern times. We therefore have to date the tiles upon the evidence they themselves provide. One clue is the vexed question of the date when each of the *imprese* that appear on them was introduced (see pp. 65-66, 175).

The earliest record of the candelabrum *impresa*, for instance, seems to be in 1512 (Gerola, 1930, pp. 381-402). Then there is the question of style. Lane (1960, p. 50), followed by some others, believed he recognised in the tiles the peculiar colour-scheme associated with Giovanni Maria of Castel Durante. The style and colour-combination, however, seem impossible to parallel at all closely on other ceramics, and may indicate the intervention of a designer who was not a potter. The tiles in any case are so different in construction, thickness, design and colour from the set that seems to have given satisfaction in 1494 (Cat. 127 and 128), that it seems improbable that they are the set that was being made a mere two years later by Antonio dei Fedeli. The very classical appearence of the present set suggests a date after 1510.

J.V.G.M.

PROVENANCE: Dr. Ing. Antonino Rusconi, Trieste, by whom the tiles were given in 1977.

BIBLIOGRAPHY: Rotterdam, Boymans Museum, *Tentoonstelling van Oud-Aardewerk mit de Verzameling Bastert- Van Schaardenburg*, Rotterdam, 1940, No. 43 and pl. VI; L. Ozzòla, Mattonelle Isabelliane, *Faenza*, 1953, p. 5 and pl. I; H.E. Van Gelder, *Glas en Ceramiek*, Utrecht, 1955, p. 73 and pl. XXI; Lane, 1960, p. 50; Anne Berendsen and others, *Fliesen,* Munich, 1964, pp. 80-81 and illustration facing, p. 87; Mantua, *Tesori*, 1974, p. 75, No. 34.

130

Four tiles; *c.* 1510-25

Le Marche (?)

Museum Boymans-van Beuningen, Rotterdam

From the same set as Cat. 129. These examples bear the following inscriptions: ISAB / ESTE MR / MAN (Isabella d'Este, Marchesana Mantuae); YS in monogram as a contraction of her christian name; NEC / SPE. NE [C] / METV (neither with hope nor fear) and XXVII (Vinti Sette) - see the introductory essay by Praz, above.

When exhibited in 1940 by Bastert van Schaardenburg at the Boymans Museum, these four tiles were still associated with one of the smaller, square tiles intended to fill the spaces between the octagons.

PROVENANCE: Bastert van Schaardenburg Collection.

BIBLIOGRAPHY: As above, Cat. 129; especially the items there listed under Rotterdam, Van Gelder and Berendsen.

129

130

The Este-Gonzaga Service, made for Isabella d'Este c. 1525 by Nicolò da Urbino (active c. 1520-40)

Twenty-one plates and bowls from this set (see introductory essay, above, by Mallet) are recorded, two with biblical subjects, the rest with subjects from ancient history or mythology. Each piece bears the arms of Gonzaga impaling Este, either isolated at the centre or incorporated in the *istoriato* scenes.

The large dishes and the larger plates bear in their well a delicate palmette motif enamelled on the white ground in a paler tone of white. The service incorporates, in various combinations, the following of Isabella d'Este's personal devices and *imprese*: the *lotto*, or bundle of lottery tickets; the musical device or *pause; Nec spe nec metu;* the crucible; *XXVII (vinti sette);* the monogram YS for Isabella, *A ω* crossed with a paraph (alpha and omega, the beginning an the end); the candelabrum (see introductory essay by Praz, above). There have been attempts (notably by von Falke, 1923) to use these devices as a means of establishing when the service was made; but most of the *imprese* were in use long before the earliest possible date arguable on grounds of style. For instance the beginning of Isabella's widowhood, in 1519, can no longer be accepted on Giovio's word as the time when she first used the candelabrum device (see above, Cat. 129), and we have no reason to believe she ever abandoned its use. Nor need much importance be given to the sighting at Bologna in the mid-19th century of a vase supposedly from the Service and reputedly bearing the date 1519 (see essay by Mallet, above). If we discount the evidence of that mysterious vase (which has never been seen again) nothing prevents the acceptance of any date suggested by the style of the pieces, so long as it is after about 1519, when Raphael's *Logge* were completed (see Cat. 138), and before Isabella's death in 1539.

The attribution of the set to Nicolò da Urbino, apparently first suggested by A. W. Franks (Fortnum, 1873, p. 324), has not been seriously challenged. It should, however, be mentioned that Nicolò can no longer confidently be accepted as identical with a man known to us from documents as Nicola Pellipario, as used at one time to be thought (Wallen, 1968, p. 101). A consequence of this is that we no longer need to believe that Nicolò da Urbino ever worked at Castel Durante. Equally, Rasmussen is surely right to reject as Nicolò's own work the piece that has been used to document a supposed stay by Nicolò at Fabriano in 1527 (Rasmussen, 1972, p. 53). The conventional attribution of the Este-Gonzaga Service to Castel Durante has here been abandoned in favour of the neighbouring town of Urbino, for lack of evidence that Nicolò ever worked anywhere else. Only two pieces dated by Nicolò himself are recorded: a dish of 1521 at the Hermitage, Leningrad (Kube, 1976, 58) and a dish of 1528 in the Bargello, Florence (Conti, 1973, Pls. CVIII and 207) which documents his presence in Urbino that year. The

only other datable piece that seems securely attributable to Nicolò's hand is a plate formerly in the Sir Stephen Courtauld collection (London, Sotheby's 18 March, 1975, Lot 25) that has had the date 1531 added with other lustred embellishments in the workshop of Maestro Giorgio at Gubbio. The Este-Gonzaga Service seems to fit into this series mid-way between the Leningrad and the Bargello piece, about 1524-25. As suggested (in the essay by Mallet, above) Isabella might possibly have ordered or been given the Service when she passed through the Duchy of Urbino in 1525.

Attempts to discern a "programme" in the choice of subjects painted on the Service have not so far been convincing. Indeed the present writer inclines to the belief that whereas Nicolò was clearly given models of Isabella's arms and *imprese* to copy, no such control was exercised in the choice of sacred and profane subjects. These last look as though they were picked somewhat at random and perhaps in haste from Nicolò's stock-in-trade of engraved sources. In particular he used compositions and figures from the Venetian edition of Ovid's *Metamorphoses* published in 1497, or from later re-issues of its woodcuts.

In the interval between painting the Correr and the Este-Gonzaga Services, Nicolò added several Raphaelesque sources to his stock of figures and compositions: Cat. 138 may derive directly from a drawing after a scene in Raphael's Vatican *Logge*; Agostino Veneziano prints were used for pieces at Hamburg and in the Robert Lehman collection at New York; a dish from the Baron Robert de Rothschild Collection (Liverani, 1938, p. 334) reproduces a scene from the *Quos Ego* print that has sometimes been assigned to Marcantonio Raimondi; a large dish at Leningrad (Kube, 1976, 56) also echoes a print sometimes ascribed to Marcantonio.

J.V.G.M.

BIBLIOGRAPHY: Wallis, 1905, especially p. 65, Appendix A; von Falke, 1923, Introduction; Liverani, 1937, pp. 89-93 (with list of the Service); Liverani, *Faenza*, 1938, pp. 90-92; Liverani, 1938 and 1939; Rackham, 1940, pp. 180-84; Kube, 1976, no. 56, Hausmann, 1972, pp. 233-35 gives further bibliography and a list to which no additions need be made, though two subsequent sales should be noted: the plate with Aeneas and Anchises was in the Dr Giuseppe Caruso sale (London, Sotheby's, 20 March, 1973, lot 25); the much-damaged plate with the Fall of Phaeton was sold from the Lehman collection (London, Christies, 4 April, 1977, lot 40). See also below under entries for individual plates.

131

Plate with Apollo and Python and Apollo and Daphne; *c.* 1525

Urbino; Nicolò da Urbino (active *c.* 1520-40)
Tin-glazed earthenware with polychrome decoration. Sunken centre and broad, straight border. Diam. 27.00 cm
British Museum, Department of Medieval and Later Antiquities (Bernal 2049)

Painted in the centre with the arms of Gonzaga impaling Este, supported by two putti. Below this is the motto "NEC SPE NEC METU". The remainder of the obverse painted with the stories of Apollo and Python, and Apollo and Daphne (Ovid, *Metamorphoses* I): Left, Apollo stands triumphing over the dead monster, Python; above Cupid prepares to make Apollo fall

175

in love with Daphne; bottom, Daphne's father, the River-God Peneus, looks on while (right) Apollo pursues Daphne, who is shown on the point of turning into a laurel. From a tree to the left hangs a shield bearing the crucible device. Yellow rim. The reverse with four grooves towards the rim, which is painted with a band of yellow. A further yellow line outlines the foot.

The figures, with the exception of Peneus, are modelled on those in the woodcut on fol. VII of the Venice *Metamorphoses* of 1494, though the figures of Cupid and Apollo in the clouds are reversed. The landscape is an independent creation of Nicolò's. Nicolò treated the subject of Apollo, Daphne and Peneus alone (omitting Python) on a plate now in the Museo del Castello Sforzesco, Milan, which in turn seems closely related in design to a plate in the same Museum by the contemporary of his whom I have named "The Painter of the Milan Marsyas" in the forthcoming transactions of the 1980 Seminar held at Rovigo on Francesco Xanto Avelli. On these two last mentioned plates the figures of Daphne being transformed and of the river god Peneus clearly derive from the same sources as those on Nicolò's Este-Gonzaga plate with this subject.

J.V.G.M.

PROVENANCE: Bernal Collection, London, Christies, 24 March, 1855, lot 2049.
BIBLIOGRAPHY: Fortnum, 1873, pp. 324-25; Fortnum, 1896, pp. 190-01; Wallis, 1905, p. 65; M. L. Solon, *A History and Description of Italian Maiolica*, 1907, colour plate XXI; Bernard Rackham, "A New Work by Nicola Pellipario at South Kensington", *Burlington Magazine*, XLI, 1922, p. 128 and pl. IId; Bernard Rackham, "Italian Maiolica", *Faenza* (1930) pl. XXXVa; Mann, 1943, pl. XXXV; Liverani, 1938, p. 337 and 1939, p. 8; Chompret, 1949, vol. II, fig. 118.

132

Plate with Latona and the Lycian Peasants; *c.* 1525

Urbino; Nicolò da Urbino (active *c.* 1520-40)
Tin-glazed earthenware with polychrome decoration. Sunken centre and broad, straight border. Diam. 27.00 cm
Fondazione Museo Miniscalchi-Erizzo, Verona

Painted (top left) with the arms of Gonzaga impaling Este, shown suspended from the branches of a bush growing from a crag. The *istoriato* scene represents the story of Latona and the Lycian peasants (Ovid, *Metamorphoses* VI). To the left, by the bank of a lake, Latona kneels and implores the peasants to let her and her children drink; as described by Ovid, the children, too, stretch out their arms; however the Lycian peasants, right, deliberately muddy the water with their feet and hands. In the foreground lies a scroll inscribed NEC SPE NEC METV and from a bush to the right hangs a shield painted with the *lotto impresa*.

No engraved source has yet been traced for this piece. The identification of the rather rare subject is confirmed by comparison with a plate of about 1525-30 in the Castello Sforzesco at Milan painted by Nicolò's close follower, the Milan Marsyas Painter, with a closely related composition in which some of the peasants are shown already metamorphosed into frogs. On the back of that piece is an explanatory inscription *De i vilane/mutate. in/rane* (concerning the peasants changed into frogs). A somewhat later-looking plate also by the Milan Marsyas Painter (formerly in the Passavant-Gontard Collection; sold at Sotheby's 31 July 1973, lot 356 and again 14 April, 1981, lot 3) diverges further in composition from Nicolò's Este-Gonzaga version. Also probably related in some way to Nicolò's composition is a plate in the

Musei Civici at Pesaro assigned by Polidori (1953), pp. 49-50 and pl. XXVII, fig. 31 to Nicolò himself, though evidently by the anonymous painter who decorated in the Urbino workshop of Guido Durantino most of the Montmorency Service.

J.V.G.M.

PROVENANCE: Conte Mario Miniscalchi-Erizzo Collection, Verona. According to Liverani (1937, p. 89) the plate came by inheritance with other items from Contessa Teresa Moscardo, who married into the family in 1785.
BIBLIOGRAPHY: Mantua, *Mostra Iconog.*, 1937, p. 117, n. 3; Liverani, 1937, pp. 89-93 and pl. XIII; Liverani, 1938 and 1939, reproduced on pp. 332 and 8 respectively; Polidori, 1953, pp. 49-50 and pl. XXVII.

133

Plate with Apollo and Marsyas; *c.* 1525

Urbino; Nicolò da Urbino (active *c.* 1520-40)
Tin-glazed earthenware with polychrome decoration. Sunken centre and broad, straight border. Diam. 27.00 cm
The Wernher Collection, Luton Hoo (211-205)

Painted in the centre with the arms of Gonzaga impaling Este, supported by two putti. Below this, on a plaque, is the *impresa* "XXVII". The border is painted with the contest between Apollo and Marsyas. To the left, Athena is seated playing the bagpipes; to the left, bottom, the nude Apollo stands holding a stringed instrument; bottom centre, Marsyas, nude, has picked up the bagpipes thrown down by Athena and is drawn into competition with Apollo; bottom right, Marsyas is punished for this by Apollo, who flays him alive. In the landscape to the left is a castle, and from a tree hangs a scroll inscribed NEC SPE NEC METV; in the background, right, is a circular temple of Bramantesque appearance. Yellow rim. The reverse with concentric grooves at the rim.

The figures are adapted from those on the woodcut of fol. 49v., of the 1497 Venetian *Metamorphoses* (reproduced in Wallis, 1905, p. 14, fig. 14), though in the woodcut only the flayed Marsyas is shown nude, the central piping figure is reversed and much altered, while the two figures to the right are so different that they may be wholly independent of this source. On the other hand, Nicolò has taken some hint from the woodcut in placing a castle in the left background and a circular temple to the right. Nicolò's representation corresponds very little with the perfunctory account in Ovid, *Metamorphoses* VI, but is based on the version illustrated and described in the Italian language version published by Lucantonio Giunta in 1497. The same woodcut was adapted by Nicolò, though in a very different manner, for a plate in the earlier service now in the Museo Correr at Venice (Wallis, 1905, p. 39, fig. 16; Conti, 1973, 140). Giuseppe Liverani ("Ancora Nuovi Piatti del Ser-

133   135   136   138

vizio d'Isabella D'Este-Gonzaga", *Faenza*, 1938, pp. 91-92) points out how the scene on the present plate differs from that on the plate from the same service formerly in the Spitzer Collection, now in the Lehman Collection at the Metropolitan Museum in New York (George Szabò, *The Robert Lehman Collection, a Guide*, New York, 1975, p. 37 and fig. 151). The Lehman plate, as Szabò points out, represents the rather similar myth of Apollo's contest with Pan, judged by Midas (Ovid, *Metamorphoses* XI). The Lehman plate is also based on a woodcut from the Venetian *Metamorphoses* of 1497, and has its counterpart in Nicolò's earlier Correr Service.

J.V.G.M.

PROVENANCE: Possibly, like Cat. 134 formerly in the Gatterburg-Morosini Collection, Sale, Venice, 15-22 May 1894, lots 173-175 or 177 (?); Lady Ludlow Collection, Luton Hoo; Sir Harold Wernher Collection, Luton Hoo; The Wernher Trust.
BIBLIOGRAPHY: Liverani, 1938, pp. 90-92 and pl. XXIIb; Rackham, 1945, p. 148 and pl. IIA.

134

Plate with Meleager and Atalanta; *c.* 1525 [Pl. 42]
Urbino; Nicolò da Urbino (active *c.* 1520-40)
Tin-glazed earthenware with polychrome decoration. Sunken centre and broad, straight border. Diam. 27.00 cm
The Wernher Collection, Luton Hoo (212-204)

Painted in the centre with the arms of Gonzaga impaling Este, supported by two putti. Below this, somewhat aslant, lies a tablet inscribed NEC SPE NEC METV. On the border is what appears to be the story of Meleager and Atalanta: (Ovid, *Metamorphoses*, VII) the nude figure, right of centre, plunging his spear into the boar's shoulder is presumably meant for Meleager, the female figure, at the extreme left, for Atalanta; the two retreating youths, left of centre, and the horseman at the extreme right presumably represent some of Meleager's companions in the chase; in the background is a landscape with two fortified towns; from a tree to the left hangs a shield with the candelabrum *impresa*; from a tree to the right hangs a scroll with the musical *impresa delle pause*. The border, between 10 and 2 o'clock has been broken but is virtually all present. Dark blue rim. The reverse has concentric grooves towards the rim.

J.V.G.M.

PROVENANCE: Probably Gatterburg-Morosini Collection, Sale, Venice 15-22 May, 1894, Lots 173-175 or 177 (?); Lady Ludlow Collection, Luton Hoo; Sir Harold Wernher Collection, Luton Hoo; the Wernher Trust.
BIBLIOGRAPHY: Probably the piece mentioned as the boar-hunt with Adonis by Federigo Argani, *Il Rinascimento delle Ceramiche Maiolicate in Faenza*, Faenza, 1898 p. 53; Liverani, 1937, p. 93 (listed, but whereabouts unknown); Liverani, 1938, pp. 90-91 and pl. XXIIb; Hausmann, 1972, p. 235.

135

Plate with Hippolytus and Phaedra; *c.* 1525
Urbino; Nicolò da Urbino (active *c.* 1520-40)
Tin-glazed earthenware with polychrome decoration. Sunken centre and broad, straight border. Diam. 27.00 cm
Victoria & Albert Museum, Department of Ceramics (C. 2229-1910, Rackham, 1940, no. 547)

Painted in the centre with the arms of Gonzaga impaling Este, supported by two putti. Below this is Isabella d'Este's musical device, the *Impresa della Pause*. The remainder of the obverse painted with the story of Hippolytus and Phaedra (Ovid, *Metamorphoses* XV): right Hippolytus (or Theseus?) emerges from a building drawing his sword and followed by Phaedra; left, Theseus, with drawn sword, banishes his son, Hippolytus, whose stepmother Phaedra had falsely accused him of attempted seduction; top left Hippolytus drives a chariot towards the seashore; in the foreground a balustrade divides the two episodes and bears the motto XXVII twice and NEC SPE NEC METV. Yellow rim. The reverse with concentric ridges towards the rim. The rim and edge of the foot are each emphasized by a yellow line.
The composition bears a tenuous relationship to the woodcut on fol. 15 v. of *Ovidio Methamorphoseos Vulgare* published at Venice by Lucantonio Giunta in 1497.

J.V.G.M.

PROVENANCE: Bernal Collection, London, Christies, March 24 1855, Lot 2050; Roussel Collection, Paris; Fountaine Collection, Christies, 16 June 1884, Lot 36; Bequeathed to the Victoria & Albert Museum by George Salting.
BIBLIOGRAPHY: Fortnum, 1873, pp. 325-27; Burlington Fine Arts Club, *Catalogue of Specimens of Hispano-Moresque and Maiolica Pottery Exhibited in 1887*, London, 1887, no. 221; Fortnum, 1896, pp. 191, 193; Wallis, 1905, p. 65; M. L. Solon, *A History and Description of Italian Maiolica*, London, 1907, colour plate XXII; von Falke, 1923, Introductory Essay; Rackham, "Italian Maiolica", *Faenza*, 1930, pp. 147-150 and pl. XXXVI; Rackham, 1933, pp. 55-56; Liverani, 1938 and 1939; W. B. Honey, *European Ceramic Art, Illustrated Historical Survey*, London, 1949, pl. 51c; G. Polidori, "Pelliparesca", *Faenza*, 1953, pp. 112-13 and pl. XXXI; G. Polidori, 1962, p. 350 and fig. 6; Scott Taggart, *Italian Maiolica*, London, 1972 p. 42.

136

Plate with Peleus and Thetis; *c.* 1525
Urbino, Nicolò da Urbino, (active *c.* 1520-40)
Tin-glazed earthenware with polychrome decoration. Sunken centre and broad, straight border. Diam. 30.20 cm
Fitzwilliam Museum, Cambridge (C. 30-1938)

Painted in the centre with the arms of Gonzaga impaling Este, supported by two putti. Below this on a scroll is the emblem XXVII. In the well is a palmette pattern painted in pale white on the white ground. The border of the plate bears *istoriato* decoration of the story of Peleus and Thetis (Ovid, *Metamorphoses*, XI) in which Thetis assumes various forms in her attempt to escape the embrace of Peleus: left, Peleus catches sight of the naked nymph, Thetis, asleep in a grove; as he grasps her (below) she turns successively into a bird and a dragon, the last form frightening Peleus into letting her go; to the right, Thetis is seen praying at an altar to the gods of the sea, and being answered by Proteus, who tells him how to gain the object of his desire. From a tree to the left hangs a shield bearing the crucible *impresa*.

As Guy de Tervarent (1950, p. 24) has pointed out, in Ovid's version there is a tigress, not a dragon; the latter was substituted in the Italian version of the *Metamorphoses* published in Venice in 1497. The same substitution of a dragon for the tigress is found on a plate in Nicolò's earlier service in the Correr Museum, Venice, as pointed out by Wallis (1905, pp. 15-16) where the woodcut from the Venice Ovid is reproduced. It may be noticed that on the Este-Gonzaga service Nicolò has followed the engraved source with considerable fidelity whereas on the earlier Correr Museum plate he appears to have taken the merest hint from the woodcut for the figures of Peleus and the dragon, while otherwise illustrating quite different incidents from the myth.

J.V.G.M.

PROVENANCE: A Rothschild Collection (which branch is not known); C. Damiron Collection, Lyons, sold London, Sotheby's, 16 June, 1938, lot. 63.
BIBLIOGRAPHY: B. Rackham, "The Damiron Collection of Italian Maiolica" II, *Apollo*, XXVI, November 1937, pp. 251-57 and fig. VIII: Chompret, 1949, vol. I, p. 30 and vol. II, p. 16, fig. 120; G. de Tervarent, "Enquête sur le Sujet des Majoliques", *Kunstmuseets Årsskrift*, XXXVII, 1950, pp. 1-48, especially p. 24; R. Haggar, *The Concise Encyclopedia of Continental Pottery and Porcelain*, London, 1960, pl. 90a.

137

Dish on low foot with a legend of Trajan; *c.* 1525 [Pl. 43]
Urbino; Nicolò da Urbino (active *c.* 1520-40)
Tin-glazed earthenware with polychrome decoration. The dish with slightly convex centre, the sides curving uninterruptedly to the rim (approximately Rackham, 1940, shape 14); diam 27.00 cm
British Museum, Department of Medieval and Later Antiquities (Bernal 2015)

The coat of arms without supporting putti, is, unlike all other pieces from the Service, enclosed within a wreath set against the background of a tower, top centre. In the foreground Trajan, distinguished by his crown, rides a grey horse and with his right hand signals his cavalry to halt; a woman in a blue dress, right, stands with hands raised in distress over the corpse of her child. Behind the Emperor, one of his lieutenants transmits the command to other horsemen, led by one holding a flag, who occupy the left and middle distance. In the background is a walled city with towers, palaces and a building with a flat dome. In the foreground a tabet inscribed NEC SPE / NEC METV is attached to a tree-stump. Yellow rim. The reverse with yellow outlines to the rim and foot.
According to a legend told by John the Deacon in his 9th century *Life of St. Gregory,* Trajan, on his way to war, halted his army in order to see justice done to a poor widow for the death of her son. The story was repeated by Dante, *Purgatorio*, X.

J.V.G.M.

PROVENANCE: Bernal Collection, London, Christies, 24 March, 1855, Lot 2015.
BIBLIOGRAPHY: Fortnum, 1873, p. 324; id., 1896 pp. 190-91.

138

Plate with Isaac and Rebecca watched by Abimelech; *c.* 1525
Urbino; painted by Nicolò da Urbino (active *c.* 1520-40)
Tin-glazed earthenware with polychrome decoration. The border, everted towards the rim, forms a continuous curve with the sunken centre. Diam 27.00 cm
Musée du Louvre, Département des Objets d'Art (OA 7578, Giacomotti, 1974, n. 819)

The coat of arms of Gonzaga impaling Este is suspended from a wall to the right; to the left of centre, Isaac and Rebecca, seated, are shown embracing while Abimelech, King of the Philistines, catches sight of them from a window above and guesses they are man and wife (*Genesis*, 26); the scene takes place by the light of a blue moon, in a palace with a fountain and a loggia which opens into the countryside. In the foreground lies a scroll inscribed NEC SPE NEC METV.
The subject is rather faithfully copied, architecture and all, from a scene frescoed in Raphael's *Logge* in the Vatican. Nicolò may have worked from a drawing, since no engraving early enough seems to be recorded.

J.V.G.M.

PROVENANCE: Solomon de Rothschild Collection (bequeathed in 1922).
BIBLIOGRAPHY: J.J. Marquet de Vasselot, "Une Assiette du Service d'Isabelle d'Este au Musée du Louvre", *Arethuse*, I, 1924, pl. XIII; Verlet, "La Majolique italienne. Essai de Chronologie", *Gazette des Beaux-Arts*, 6th series, vol. XVI, 1936, p. 128 and fig. 4.ii, Liverani, 1938 and 1939, reproduced on p. 335 and p. 6 respectively; Rackham, 1945, p. 147 and pl. IIF; Chompret, 1949 vol. II, fig. 115; Liverani, 1958, colour plate 56A; id., "Raffaello, l'Opera, le Fonti, la fortuna", in *Raffaello*, Novara, 1967, vol. II, pp. 698-99 and fig. 14; Béguin, 1975¹, no. 20.

139

The Veneration of the Beata Osanna Andreasi; 1519
Francesco Bonsignori (*c.* 1460 (?)-1519)
Oil on canvas 206 x 154 cm
Museo del Palazzo Ducale, Mantua (no. 11498)

Osanna Andreasi (1449-1505), member of a noble Mantuan family, was in life and death the centre of a local devotional cult. From earliest childhood she experienced visions and, since parental opposition forbade her to take full vows, she became a tertiary Dominican which, happily, enabled her to appear at court. During a military campaign in 1478, Marchese Federico entrusted Osanna with the care of his family, and thereafter the Gonzagas held her in high and affectionate veneration.
She was believed to possess the gift of prophecy, and stories of the efficacy of her prayers reached even the French court. Federico II was called the son of prayer (*figlio d'orazione*) after Osanna had prayed for a Gonzaga heir, and later Isabella was cured of violent toothache by prayers to Osanna.
Both Francesco and Isabella were present at her death; Francesco immediately commissioned a life of Osanna from Fra Silvestro Ferrarese, and Isabella planned and financed the building of a tomb/shrine in S. Domenico, completed in 1508. In 1505 it seems that a painted altarpiece was planned to be incorporated in it, as Fra Silvestro wrote from Milan "Gian Cristoforo (Romano) has made a beautiful design for the shrine in such a way that I believe you could place the altarpiece that Your Ladyship is having made between the columns" (*Quanto all'arca Joanne Cristoforo ha fatto un bello disegno et in tal modo che credo che se gli poterà tra le colonne ponere la*

anchona che V. S. fa fare, Bagolini, Ferretti, 1905, p. cviii). But, given the usual Gonzaga insolvency, the shrine was modified (Gian Cristoforo wrote optimistically that it could be amplified when funds were available).

The altarpiece exhibited here was probably always intended for S. Vincenzo, a cloister Osanna frequented; a nun there was able to see her mystic wedding ring invisible to many (Ferrarese). It must date from after her beatification in December 1514; Isabella had campaigned strenuously for Osanna's canonization, but had to be content with the lesser honour awarded by Leo X, sanctioned only for the diocese of Mantua. The observation that the foremost lay figure kneeling before the Beata bears a strong resemblance to Isabella (Berenson, 1894, p. 90) and that she wears widow's dress (Schmitt, 1961, p. 106-07) would date the painting to after 29 March 1519 (the day of Francesco's death), and make it one of Bonsignori's last works. It is just possible that one of the young dominican nuns is Isabella's daughter, Ippolita.

139

The life and writings of St Catherine of Siena (*c*. 1347-1380) inspired Osanna's devotion to Christ (whom she addressed as *Mammolino, dolce fantino*, Bagolini, Ferretti, p. 42), and many of her mystic experiences followed those of the earlier Dominican nun, and explain the iconography of the picture. When she was aged five "a most beautiful angel" (seen on the left) took her by the hand and showed her Paradise. Soon afterward the Child Jesus, wearing a crown of thorns and carrying a cross appeared to her (on the right). Aged seven she consecrated her virginity to Christ (the lily), and later Jesus appeared to her holding her pierced heart. Aged eighteen she experienced a mystic marriage to Christ, and between 1476-78 she received the wounds of the stigmata and the Crown of

thorns. For some it was possible to see rays of sanctity around her head, and she was frequently plagued by visions of evil spirits: in the painting she is seen standing triumphant on one of these terrible apparitions. (Bagolini, Ferretti, pp. 42, 82, 104, 87, 82, 73). Bonsignori was, according to Vasari, a profoundly devout man, refusing to provide the profane paintings requested of him by the Marchese Francesco. The devotional character of this altarpiece anticipates many of the characteristics of Counter-Reformation art.

J.T.M.

PROVENANCE: S. Vincenzo, Mantua, (suppressed); Carlo d'Arco; Palazzo Ducale, Mantua.
BIBLIOGRAPHY: Mantua, *Mostra Mantegna*, 1961, p. 114, no. 79 (with bibliography); Schmitt, 1961, pp. 106-107, 117 no. 9 (with bibliography).
ADDITIONAL BIBLIOGRAPHY: B. Berenson, *The Venetian Painters of the Renaissance*, New York and London, 1894, p. 90; G. Bagolini and L. Ferretti, *La Beata Osanna Andreasi*, Florence, 1905.

140

Study for Isabella d'Este in the Altarpiece of the Beata Osanna Andreasi; 1519

Francesco Bonsignori (*c*. 1460 (?) - 1519)
Black chalk on discoloured white paper 28.5 x 18.7 cm
British Museum, Department of Prints and Drawings (no. 1895-9-15-541)

The connection between this drawing and the Beata Osanna *Pala* (Cat. 139) was made by Pouncey (1951-52); he argued convincingly that this was a preparatory study of Isabella made from life. In the drawing she is shown with a double chin, a detail which has been suppressed in the painting, but the set of both mouth and chin is still close to that in G.C. Romano's medallion (Cat. 109). Pouncey also drew attention

140

to the pentimento on the face and neck, and the forward bend of the head (upright in the painting), all of which favour the view that this is a preparatory drawing and not a later copy. The widow's dress has been very carefully observed, and again slightly changed in the altarpiece. This sheet represents an otherwise unknown aspect of Bonsignori's art.

J.T.M.

PROVENANCE: Richardson (?); Bouverie Sale, 1859; Robinson; Malcolm Collection.
BIBLIOGRAPHY: Mantua, *Mostra Mantegna*, 1961, p. 114; Schmitt, 1961, p. 123, no. 23
ADDITIONAL BIBLIOGRAPHY: P.M.R. Pouncey, "A Drawing by Francesco Bonsignori", *British Museum Quarterly*, XVI, 1951-52, pp. 99-101.

IV   Federico Gonzaga, the terrestrial Jupiter

Erasmus called Pope Julius II the "Terrestrial Jupiter", though the name might equally have been applied to Federico Gonzaga, who ruled Mantua from 1519 to 1540 and in 1530 became its first Duke. It is questionable whether he was in reality a Jove either in war of love, though he was certainly one of the most handsome of the Gonzaga rulers and was interested in the outward forms of political power, strengthening Gonzaga dependence upon the Empire.

Images of Jupiter, erotic and imperial, are abundant in the works of art he commissioned; in general his patronage (see essays by Hope and Gombrich) was unequalled in scope and significance. His brothers Ercole and Ferrante, respectively a Prince of the Church and commander serving the Emperor, likewise raised the fame of the Gonzaga, and the pretensions of the main branch of the family were imitated in the second half of the sixteenth century by their relative Vespasiano who ruled Sabbioneta; he, too, combined military distinction with magnificence and Jupiter's thunderbolt was one of his family emblems.

141

Federico Gonzaga, first Duke and fifth Marchese of Mantua (1500-40)
Anon. Mantuan
Bronze medal; diam. 57 mm; Struck
Victoria & Albert Museum (A. 306-1910; *Corpus*, 270b)

The obverse, inscribed FEDERICVS. II. MAR. V. MANTVAE, dates the medal, possibly the pattern for a coin, between Federico's accession in 1519 and 1530, when he was created Duke. He wears plate armour and has a short beard; his appearance being close to that of another rather crude medal of the Marchese, the reverse of which shows St Catherine (*Corpus*, 269). The reverse shows the Mount Olympus *impresa*; a mountain around which ascends a spiral road with an altar inscribed FIDES at the summit and a female figure holding a sword and cornucopia. Beneath, is inscribed in Greek AMΩMOΣ. This device had already been used on the reverse of a medal on which the Marchese would appear to be even younger than this example (*Corpus*, 595e); there is no basis for dating all medals depicting Mount Olympus before 1522, when Charles V is said to have conferred the device on Federico for his defence of Pavia, or when he was created Duke (Cat. 142). An earlier *impresa* of a mountain surmounted by a diamond had long been used by the Gonzaga. The Olympus device was later included in the *Sala delle Imprese* in Palazzo Te (Hartt, 1958, pp. 109-10).

J.T.M.

PROVENANCE: Salting Bequest.
BIBLIOGRAPHY: Hartt, 1958.

142

Double ducat of Marchese (later Duke) Federico
Gold coin; diam. 26 mm; weight 6.95 g
British Museum, Department of Coins and Medals, (55. 6. 12. 209)

During Federico's reign Cardinal Wolsey expressed his admiration of Mantuan coins so warmly (April 1527) that he wanted a master capable of such work for the Royal Mint (ASMAG b 1461; Luzio, 1917, p. 182). The head on the obverse of this example appears to be based on that of a Roman Emperor, which may reflect not only Federico's concern for outward expressions of power and status, but also a deliberate imitation of ancient coins, of which his mother was an avid collector. The reverse shows the device of Mount Olympus surmounted by Faith (FIDES) which already appears on coins from *c.* 1520, so that it cannot have been invented (as is sometimes suggested) when the Emperor Charles V made him a Duke. The imperial diploma of 1530 does however recommend its use so that it came to be associated with Gonzaga allegiance to the Emperor.

D.S.C.

BIBLIOGRAPHY: CNI, IV, p. 266, 6; Magnaguti, II, 1915, pp. 42-45.

143

Proof of double ducat of Marchese (later Duke) Federico
Copper pattern for gold coin; diam. 26 mm; weight 8.16 g
British Museum, Department of Coins and Medals (70. 5. 7. 8667);

Corresponding to the gold coin described above (Cat. no. 142) this proof enables the reverse to be seen.

D.S.C.

BIBLIOGRAPHY: CNI, IV, p. 266, 2.

144

Half "testone" of Duke Federico
Silver coin, diam. 26 m; weight 3.17 g
British Museum, Department of Coins and Medals (55.M6. 12. 210)

A *testone* was in origin a Venetian coin representing one *lira* or pound (twenty *soldi*) of account, struck with the head of Doge Nicolò Tron (1471-73). As with the Mantuan gold ducat, the Mantuan silver *testone* imitated a Venetian example. The half *testone* (c. 1530-36) did not follow the same types as the *testone*, while the head of the Duke resembling a Roman Emperor appears on the obverse, the reliquary of the Holy Blood sup-

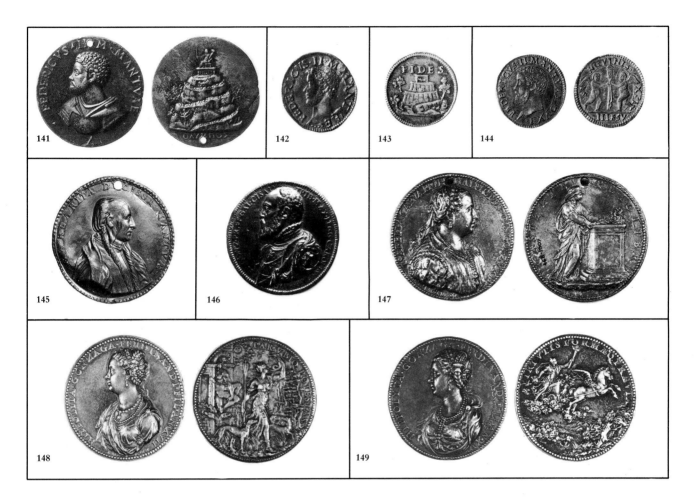

141   142   143   144

145   146   147

148   149

ported by two cherubs is on the reverse; other types show for instance St Catherine or the Madonna with angels.

D.S.C.

BIBLIOGRAPHY: CNI, IV, pp. 283, 164; Magnaguti, II, 1915, pp. 43-44.

145

Margherita Paleologo Gonzaga, first Duchess of Mantua (1510-66)
Pastorino Pastorini (1508-92)
Lead medal; diam. 65 mm; inscribed MARGARITA DVCISSA MANTVAE, signed on truncation: 1561 I(?)P, Uniface, hole bored in border
British Museum, Department of Coins and Medals (1930-7-7-30)

This is the only certain portrait of Margherita, wife of Federico, first Duke of Mantua, portrayed twenty-one years after his death, dressed in a widow's veil (her portrait in the Schloss Ambras collection of Gonzaga likenesses appears to show her at about the same age). Titian was commissioned to paint portraits of Federico and Margherita for the Duke of Bavaria (information from Charles Hope, Rott, 1912) but was prevented from doing so by the former's death in 1540. The Paleologo marriage was of great territorial and financial advantage to the Gonzaga: Margherita brought a dowry of one hundred thousand gold ducats (Luzio, 1913, p. 7) and the Duchy of Monferrato (acquired on her uncle's death in 1533). Pastorino, a fashionable and prolific medallist, was born near

Siena and trained as a glass painter by Guillaume de Marcillat. His portraits, modelled in wax and usually cast in lead, are mostly uniface (without a reverse). He popularized the raised pearl border, and was renowned for his faithful delineation of textures and costume. Master of the Mint successively at Parma, Reggio, and Ferrara (1554-59) he settled in Florence in 1576. In the same year that he portrayed Margherita, he also made medals of her son, the ruling duke, Guglielmo Gonzaga, and of his wife Eleonora (Cat. 220)

J.T.M.

PROVENANCE: Wagner collection.
BIBLIOGRAPHY: Forrer, 1909, IV, pp. 408-21; Luzio, 1913 p. 7; Thieme Becker; Hill and Pollard, 1967, pp. 60-61.
ADDITIONAL BIBLIOGRAPHY: H. Rott, "Zu den Kunstbestrebungen des Pfaltzgrafen Otto Heinrichs", *Mitteilungen zur Geschichte des Heidelberger Schloss*, VI, 1912, pp. 192-240.

146

Ferrante Gonzaga, Lord of Guastalla (1507-57)
Leone Leoni (1509-90)
Lead medal, uniface; diam. 71 mm
British Museum, Department of Coins and Medals (M 0169)

Ferrante, who became one of the most powerful and feared men in Italy, had been educated from 1524-27 at the Spanish court where he was sent with the papal envoy Baldassare Castiglione; no other Italian except Alfonso d'Avalos obtained such complete trust from the Emperor Charles V. When the imperial troops were sacking Rome (1527) he was

181

able to help his mother Isabella d'Este to escape, and in 1529-30 at the age of twenty-two he succeeded to the Prince of Orange as commander of the Imperial army besieging Florence. This was much resented by other military leaders in Italy. Thereafter he saw active service in Tunisia and the Low Countries. He had an important part in arranging the secret treaty of Crépy in 1543, and at the age of fifty he died in Brussels of injuries received at the Battle of St Quentin. In Italy he had served as the Emperor's viceroy in Sicily (1535-46) and as Governor of Milan (1546-55); meanwhile he acted, with his brother Cardinal Ercole, as (absentee) regent of Mantua during the minority of their nephews. Scandal eventually tarnished him, for his implication in the assassination of Pope Paul III's son Pier Luigi Farnese, and his mishandling of the government of Milan for which he was denounced (1554). After a form of trial in Brussels before Philip II he was vindicated (1555) and it was then that the double sided medal was cast by Leone, the obverse with his portrait wearing the order of the Golden Fleece reads FER. GONZ. PRAEF. GAL. CISAL. TRIB. MAX. LEGG. CAROLI. V. CAES. AVG. ("Gallia Cisalpina" referring to his governorship in Lombardy). The reverse (not on this example) with Hercules destroying the Hydra, signified his triumph over calumny. Ferrante was a notable patron; he prompted many military building projects including the defences of Guastalla, patronized Giulio Romano (Cat. 189) and Leoni, sharing his delight in the complex and bizarre. Leoni executed a life-size statue of Ferrante overcoming the Hydra, which still stands at Guastalla.

J.T.M.

BIBLIOGRAPHY: Armand, 1883-87, I. 164, 12; Plon, 1887, pp. 267-68, 379, pl. XXXII; Milan, *Tiziano*, 1977, no. 104, p. 142.

147

Isabella of Capua, Princess of Molfetta, wife of Ferrante Gonzaga
Jacopo Nizolla da Trezzo (1515/19-89)
Bronze medal; diam. 71 mm; signed on obverse IAC[OBVS] TREZ[ZO]
Victoria & Albert Museum, Department of Sculpture (486. 1907)

Isabella faces right, wears an elaborate headdress, earrings and a necklace; she is identified as the Princess of Molfetta and wife of Ferrante Gonzaga (1507-57) by the inscription ISABELLA CAPVA PRINC MALFICT FERDIN GONZ VXOR. Their marriage was sometime in 1529/30, but owing to Ferrante's ceaseless military campaigning it was not consummated until much later. Isabella's dowry included Molfetta, Giovinazzo and other Neapolitan territory, and her fortune enabled Ferrante to buy the principality of Guastalla. Amongst their children were the legendary beauty Ippolita (Cat. 148, 149), and two cardinals: Gianvincenzo and Francesco, Bishop of Mantua (Cat. 221). She lived in Palermo when her husband was viceroy of Naples, and later in Milan, where he was governor (1546-55). The reverse of the medal shows a veiled woman (either identified as a vestal virgin or as Isabella herself) tending a flame at an altar inscribed CASTE ET SV[P] PLICETER (chastely and humbly): other casts show the altar decorated with a sun and the word NVBIFVGO (to the cloud chaser, i.e. the sun). This has been taken to indicate that the medal was cast after her husband's death, although she seems to have returned to Naples to supervise her estates from then until her death in 1559, and it is more probable that this medal was made in Milan. Trezzo was born in Milan, and served Cosimo II de' Medici as gem cutter, his earliest medal is dated 1550. He worked for Philip II of Spain in the Netherlands (1555) and in Madrid (1559-89). He copied medals of Leone Leoni on several occasions (Cat. 148-49); a medal of uncertain standing (British Museum 530.313.23) has Ferrante taken from Leoni's medal of 1556 on the obverse and Isabella as portrayed on this medal on the reverse. It may be a later, composite medal, but it raises the possibility that Leone had made a portrait of Isabella later copied by Trezzo.

J.T.M.

BIBLIOGRAPHY: Hill and Pollard, 1967, no. 439; Amadei and Marani, 1980, pp. 81-82; Milan, *Tiziano*, 1977, no. 109, pp. 144-45.

148

Ippolita Gonzaga (1535-63)
Leone Leoni (1509-90)
Bronze medal; diam. 67 mm; signed in Greek on obverse Leone Aretinos
Victoria & Albert Museum, Department of Sculpture (A. 249-1910)

The daughter of Ferrante Gonzaga and Isabella of Capua, Ippolita was renowned as one of the most beautiful and accomplished women of her day. Poets, including Tasso, sang her praises, and she was endlessly portrayed. Unlike "some women who regard marriage as the end of their education" she continued her studies, wrote poetry, and was portrayed on a medal with the instruments of music, astronomy and poetry (Affò, p. 101; Hill and Pollard, 1967, no. 433 attr. to Leoni). An Englishman visiting Mantua in 1555 speaks of "Hippolita, one of the fairest ladies in the world" (Mann, 1939, p. 273). Aged thirteen she was married to Fabrizio Colonna (nephew of Vittoria) in 1548, but he died after campaigning with his father-in-law in August 1551, the year in which this medal was made. In 1554 she married Antonio Carafa, Duke of Mondragone; she died suddenly in Naples in 1563 aged twenty-eight. The medal, probably made in Milan, is inscribed HIPPOLYTA. GONZAGA. FERDINANDI. FIL[IA]. AN[NO] XVI, (i.e. aged sixteen). The reverse is a threefold representation of Diana; as the huntress blowing her horn accompanied by three hounds, as goddess of the moon, and, in the guise of Proserpina, goddess of the underworld (on the left Pluto abducts her to the underworld through the gates of hell which are guarded by Cerberus). The inscription: PAR. VBIQ. POTESTAS (her power is equal everywhere), implies that Ippolita reigns supreme in all spheres; dear to the heavens for her piety, to the earth for her learning, and formidable against death, which had already robbed her of her husband (Affò, p. 105). Pietro Aretino, writing to Tancredi thanking for this medal, also interpreted her triple kingdom as symbolizing the virginity, marriage and widowhood through which Ippolita had already passed (letter of January 1552, Affò, p. 127). The obverse was copied a year later by Trezzo (Cat. 149).

A violent and jealous character, Leoni was born near Como of Aretine parents "I was born an Aretine, who have a name for eccentricity" (*io mi sia nato Aretino, che hanno nome di bizzari*; Plon, p. 354), he worked for the papal mint (1537-40) was sent to the gallies for a brutal attack on a papal jeweller but released through the intervention of Andrea Doria, the great admiral. With Cardinal Granvelle, Ferrante Gonzaga was one of his chief protectors; Leoni worked for the Imperial mint at Milan throughout Ferrante's governorship and later in 1550-89. He was employed by both Charles V and Philip II as a bronze sculptor and medallist, but although he travelled to Augsburg, Flanders and Spain, he lived chiefly in Milan, dying there in the bizarre Palazzo Omeoni which he designed himself.

J.T.M.

BIBLIOGRAPHY: Hill and Pollard, 1967, no. 432 (obv. only); Milano, *Tiziano*, 1977 no. 11 p. 145; Hill rev. Pollard, 1978, p. 24; Jones, 1979, pp. 59-60.
ADDITIONAL BIBLIOGRAPHY: I. Affò, *Memorie di tre Celebri Principesse della Famiglia Gonzaga*, Parma, 1787; E. Plon, *Les Maitres Italiens au service de la Maison d'Autriche... Leone Leoni et Pompeo Leoni*, Paris, 1887.

149

Ippolita Gonzaga (1535-63)
Jacopo Nizolla da Trezzo (*c*. 1515/19-89)
Bronze medal, diam. 67 mm 1552, signed on obverse
Victoria & Albert Museum, Department of Sculpture (A. 270 1910)

The obverse is a rather crude copy of Leone Leoni's portrait of 1551 (Cat. 148), it is somewhat impudently signed by Trezzo. The inscription (HIPPOLYTA. GONZAGA. FERDINANDI. FIL. AN. XVII) describes her as seventeen years old. The reverse shows Aurora riding through the sky in a chariot drawn by Pegasus, she bears the torch of dawn, and scatters flowers in her wake over the wild landscape beneath. The inscription reads VIRTVTIS FORMAEQVE PRAEVIA (she who leads the way of virtue and beauty). This was interpreted to mean that just as Aurora is the precursor of the sun, so Ippolita in the freshness of her youth was a portent of her future splendour (Affò, p. 128n), a hope cut short by her premature death (see Cat. 148). Trezzo also made a medal of Ippolita's mother, Isabella of Capua (Cat. 147).

J.T.M.

PROVENANCE: Salting Bequest.
BIBLIOGRAPHY: Hill and Pollard, 1967, no. 438, Milan, *Tiziano*, 1977, no. 110, p. 145.
ADDITIONAL BIBLIOGRAPHY: I. Affò (see Cat. 148).

150

Laura Gonzaga Trivulzio
Anon. Italian (*c*. 1550)
Bronze medal; diam. 47 mm
Victoria & Albert Museum, Department of Sculpure (A. 317-1910)

Laura Gonzaga appears to have been the daughter of Sigismondo (1499-1530) of the Vescovato line of the Gonzaga

family. She married two members of the Milanese family the Trivulzio; firstly Giovanni, and after 1549 Giangiacomo. She may have been born *c*. 1525-30, and is recorded as being present at the carnival celebrations held at Milan in February 1559 to celebrate the Peace of Cateau-Cambrésis (*Storia di Milano*, IX, pp. 889-94). It has been suggested that she wears a widow's veil and that the medal dates from her first widowhood. Her ties with her own family seem to have remained strong: the reverse shows the River god Mincio (inscribed MINC) reclining under a tree holding a pitcher of water indicating that he is the source. The inscription reads SEMPER ILLAESA: (always undiminished/pure).

J.T.M.

PROVENANCE: Salting Bequest.
BIBLIOGRAPHY: Milan, *Storia*, 1961, IX, pp. 889-94; Hill and Pollard, 1967, no. 506.

151

Camillo Gonzaga, Count of Novellara (1521-95)
Anon. Italian (1554)
Bronze medal; diam. 47 mm
Victoria & Albert Museum, Department of Sculpture (A. 315-1910)

The son of Alessandro Gonzaga, Camillo succeeded his father as Count of Novellara in 1533. In 1555 he married Barbara Borromeo (d. 1572) and a portrait medallion of her aged seventeen describes her as Camillo's wife; it is slightly larger in diameter (49 mm) than that of Camillo and is attributed to Galeotti (Hill and Pollard, 1967, no. 347a). With his two brothers, Camillo served in the Imperial army, fighting in Flanders and Germany. He retired to Novellara and led a life of exemplary piety. The obverse shows the Count aged thirty-three, his cuirass decorated with lion's masks at the shoulder and throat. The inscription reads CAMILVS GONZ. COM. NOVELL. AN. XXXIII. On the reverse, against a landscape background, emblems of war and peace are contrasted: against a dead tree stump are placed a helmet, cuirass, halberd, bow and arrows and a mace; a young olive tree flourishes nearby. The inscription is from the *Aeneid* II, 61: .AD. VTRVMQVE. PARATVS. (Prepared for either (war or peace)).

J.T.M.

PROVENANCE: Salting Bequest.
BIBLIOGRAPHY: Armand, 1883-87, II, p. 202, no. 3; Mantua, *Mostra Iconog.*, 1937, pp. 95-96; Hill and Pollard, 1967, p. 65.

152

Photograph: **Sword-Hilt with the Pommel decorated with the Mount Olympus device**
Giulio Romano (*c*. 1499-1546)
British Museum, Department of Prints and Drawings, (Cat. no. 107)

The Mount Olympus device was frequently used by Federico Gonzaga; it appears on medals (Cat. 141) and coins, as well as in the decoration of Palazzo Te. Presumably this would have been for a ceremonial sword; a more practical weapon was the hand-and-a-half sword "which he used to keep in the space between his bed and the wall" (Mann, 1943, p. 29).

J.T.M.

BIBLIOGRAPHY: Mann, 1943, p. 29; Pouncey and Gere, 1962, pp. 73-74, no. 107.

152

153

Portrait of a Man in Armour (*c.* 1530)
Titian (*c.* 1485-1576)
Oil on Canvas, 85.3 x 68.2 cm; signed TICIANUS
Private Collection, London

The attribution of this painting to Titian has been accepted by all qualified scholars who have seen it. Recent cleaning has revealed, beneath the sitter's right hand, the inscription TICIA-NUS, and there is no reason to doubt the authenticity of this signature. The early provenance of the picture is unknown but its attribution to Titian is not recent; when Waagen saw the painting in the Lonsdale collection at Lowther Castle he referred to it as by Titian, described it as the portrait of a Spanish general in armour and admired its noble conception and glowing colour (Waagen, 1854 , III p. 265). Despite this praise, the portrait seems to have been neglected by scholars, and has remained unmentioned in the Titian literature.

The painting probably dates from about 1529-30 when Titian, after earlier intermittent contacts with the Mantuan court, established himself as one of Federico Gonzaga's most cherished artists. The refinement in the handling of paint, the restrained yet resonant colour, the concern with an elegant display of the hand, can be matched in portraits of the late 1520's, not least in Titian's surviving Prado portrait of Federico (Pl. 81). The spelling of the signature also agrees with Titian's practice of this period (compare Cat. 155). The fashion of portraying rulers and prominent military sitters in armour was longstanding in North Italian painting and sculpture (see Cat. 98). Nevertheless, it seems to have been in this period of *c.* 1530 that Titian took up the genre with unprecedented enthusiasm and produced a whole series of armoured portraits whose example would be an inspiration still for Rubens. A documented portrait of Federico Gonzaga in armour (now lost) was in Titian's studio in February 1530; this was followed by portraits of the Emperor Charles V and of Ippolito de' Medici in armour, neither of which survives. An example from the first half of the 1530's which has survived is that of Alfonso d'Avalos, Marchese del Vasto (Wethey, 1971, pl. 56).

The identity of the sitter is unknown. That he is both youthful and of high military rank is obvious. He holds what is

either a baton with a turned moulding, or a war-hammer. The armour, with rolled gold edges, datable around 1530, is almost certainly of Italian manufacture and very expensive. A suggestion that the subject could be Alfonso d'Avalos cannot be excluded, but the resemblance to Titian's other portraits of him is not very compelling. Another candidate is the younger brother of Federico, Ferrante Gonzaga, born in 1507. No likeness of Ferrante as a young man seems to survive. His features in middle-age show him as heavily balding, something his earliest biographer attributed to his scarcely ever putting aside his helmet. They are recorded in a medal of 1555-56 by Leone Leoni (Cat. 146), in an undistinguished painting now in Mantua (Mantua, *Mostra Iconog.*, p. 82), itself the model for the feeble record in the Schloss Ambras collection (Amadei and Marani, 1980, p. 79) and in Leoni's full-length statue at Guastalla. Our sitter's features are strikingly close to those of Federico in Titian's Prado portrait; the two heads share the very dark eyes, high brows which turn down at the side, and the full lips (compare Pl. 81); indeed, it is difficult to resist the speculation that this might be Titian's lost Federico in armour referred to above. However, our sitter seems somewhat younger. The features of the subject are not irreconcilable

with those of the old Ferrante in the painting now at Mantua, and the characterization seems appropriate for the Ferrante of *c.* 1529-30, already one of the greatest soldiers active in Charles V's service in Italy. The armour painted here by Titian is very similar to Ferrante's suit of half-armour preserved at

Vienna (Mann, 1938, pl. XIXa). However, it seems unlikley that Titian had the armour he has depicted in front of him as he painted, for there are anomalies in the rendering of the left shoulder (communication of Claude Blair). No meeting of Titian and Ferrante is recorded, but it cannot be excluded that they met in the second half of November 1529 at Bologna, when both Federico and Ferrante were there. Nor can it be excluded, given our knowledge of Titian as a portraitist, that he could have made his portrait from another likeness, without Ferrante sitting for him at all. Were the sitter Ferrante, the picture must date before 1532, for he was awarded the Golden Fleece by Charles V at Tournai in early December 1531 (Sanuto, LV, col. 399), absent in this painting.

M.H.

PROVENANCE: The Earls of Lonsdale, Lowther Castle; Sotheby's sale.
BIBLIOGRAPHY: Mantua., *Mostra Iconog.*, 1937, p. 82; Mann, 1938, pl. XIXa; Wethey, II, 1971, pl. 56. Amadei and Marani, 1980, p. 79.
ADDITIONAL BIBLIOGRAPHY: M. Sanuto, *I diarii di Marino Sanuto*, Venice, 1879-1903; G.F. Waagen, *Treasures of Art in Great Britain*, 1854, III, p. 265.

154

Portrait of Giulio Romano (*c*. 1576)
Titian (*c*. 1485-1576)
Oil on Canvas; 108 x 87 cm
Private Collection

This portrait of the court artist and architect Giulio Romano (on his career see essay by Gombrich, above) is listed in the 1627 inventory of the Gonzaga collection (d'Arco, II, 1857, p. 155). It has been dated *c*. 1536 on the grounds of its stylistic similarity to the portrait of Francesco Maria della Rovere dated to 1536-38 and the portrait of Alfonso d'Avalos probably of 1536 (Shearman, 1965, p. 173). The fluted column in the background and the dome of St Peter's on the right are later additions. The addition of St Peter's may have been a reference to the story, reported by Vasari, that Giulio had been invited to assume the direction of the rebuilding of St Peter's after the death of Antonio da Sangallo the Younger. Giulio was a friend of Titian, and the two artists collaborated in the *Gabinetto dei Cesari* at the Ducal Palace between 1536-38 (see Cat. 168-180). Giulio is shown holding a plan. This recalls Vasari's account, that on his visit to Mantua in 1541, Giulio had shown him his vast collection of drawings of ancient buildings. Giulio then opened a large cupboard and showed him plans of all the buildings which had been built after his designs. Vasari commented that one could not see any more novel more beautiful or more commodious *fantasie di fabbriche* (Vasari, ed. Milanesi, V, pp. 552 ff).
The plan Giulio holds is certainly one of these designs. It shows a circular building articulated by niches, which on the interior becomes cruciform in plan, with four apsidal chapels articulated by niches in the antique thermal manner; their entrances are screened by eight slender columns. Shearman has suggested that the plan may relate to the church of Santa Croce in Corte Vecchia (1965, pp. 174-75). However another Mantuan building may correspond with the plan.
Before and after Giulio's restoration of the Duomo, a free standing circular building stood at the end of the left transept. This building is clearly visible in Bertazzolo's view of Mantua, VRBIS MANTVAE DESCRIPTIO 1628 (Cat. 1). This building was founded by Bishop Ludovico Gonzaga in 1511 and left incomplete on his death. It was notable for the beauty of its stone ornament (Donesmondi, 1616, VII, p. 172ff). A memorandum written in the sixteenth century records that in 1536, the stone ornament for the *rotunda* was handed over by

154

the Marchese of Rovigo, heir to Ludovico's estate, to the chapter of the Duomo, for the completion of the building. The building was completed and still stands at the end of the transept now called the chapel of the Sacrament. Its present form is however greatly modified. The *rotunda* was badly damaged at the end of the sixteenth century, when the transepts and choir were demolished, on the orders of Bishop fra Francesco Gonzaga for the enlargement of the choir. In a note of 1640, it is described as a late antique building, a temple dedicated to Mars. The building was restored using the stone architectural members which were still there. It gained its present octagonal form in the restoration of Paolo Pozzo at the end of the eighteenth century, but the eight beautiful columns and imposts ornamented with naturalistic decoration are the original sixteenth century *pietra d'istria* columns. The octagonal plan is certainly the result of Pozzo's work. His provision of an elaborate system of corridors linking the Chapel of the Immacolata, the Sacristy and the Duomo severely restrict the site of the Chapel of the Sacrament. Archaeological evidence confirms that the building reconstructed in the seventeenth century was larger, and that it had apses, not however articulated by niches like the plan held by Giulio. The eight columns of Istrian stone may very well be attributable to Pietro and Tullio Lombardo (communication of Howard Burns).
The probable date of the portrait and the certain date of Giulio's project, as well as the scale of the building, make it very plausible that the plan which Giulio shows to Titian is the

185

rotunda. It would be a particularly suitable choice, in the light of Giulio's architectural practice where he so often took over the work of other architects and gave them a new, and dignified form.

L.F.

BIBLIOGRAPHY: Donesmondi, II, 1616, d'Arco, II, 1867, p. 155, Vasari ed. Milanesi, V, p. 552ff.
ADDITIONAL BIBLIOGRAPHY: J. Shearman, "Titian's Portrait of Giulio Romano", *Burlington Magazine*, CVII, 1965, no. 745, p. 171ff.

155

Madonna and Child with St Catherine and a rabbit
(*c.* 1528–1530)
Titian (*c.* 1485–1576)
Oil on canvas; 70 x 84 cm; inscribed: Ticianus F.
Musée du Louvre (Cat. 1578)

It has long been recognized that this is the composition of "Our Lady with St Catherine" which Titian was reported to have been painting for Federico Gonzaga on 5 February 1530. He then expected to complete it in about a month, and he probably did so, since he received a substantial payment from the Marquis early in March (ASMAG, b. 1464, fol. 387v). The picture is one of the latest and finest examples by Titian of a type of subject relatively common in his early career. It is often compared to the *Madonna and Child with St Catherine and the Infant Baptist* in the National Gallery, London, which was in the d'Este collection by 1598; but this is slightly looser in handling and so presumably even later.

X-Ray photographs of the Louvre picture reveal that Titian modified his original design in various ways, notably the figure of Mary, who was initially looking towards the shepherd. Mme. Béguin has suggested that the earlier composition dates from about 1520, but while the analogies with Titian's work of that period are very clear, lack of comparative evidence from the later 1520's makes the argument inconclusive. Moreover, there is good reason to believe that Federico himself commissioned the picture, and this implies that it can hardly have been begun before March 1528, when the artist wrote to him offering his services (Luzio). As has several times been noticed, the shepherd bears a strong resemblance to the Marquis, which can hardly be fortuitous, since Titian was also painting a potrait of him in February 1530. But if this figure is Federico he must have been intended as such from the first. The direction of the Virgin's glance in the original composi-

tion singled out the shepherd as a donor, rather than just a picturesque accessory, and the facial features were not significantly changed when Titian revised the picture.

Mme. Béguin has also argued that the prominent rabbit has a symbolic character, alluding to the virginity of Mary, since rabbits, according to Pliny, were capable of parthenogenesis. There is little evidence, however, that this particular association of ideas was in common currency, nor does it seem especially apposite, since there would then have been a certain incongruity in the child's playful interest in the animal. Again, the proposal that the rabbit is a hieroglyphic image of "something obvious or self-evident" must surely be rejected, because in that case Titian, on the authority of Horapollo, ought to have shown a hare. But there are other details which seem more amenable to a rather simple symbolic reading, for example the apple and grapes in the basket, which could allude to the Fall and Redemption, or the sheep under the solicitous care of the shepherd, perhaps a reference to Federico's role as ruler of a state. Even this may be going too far. As so often with religious paintings of this period, although we cannot exclude the possibility that contemporaries looked for symbolism in apparently naturalistic features, it is by no means certain that the artist intended them to do so.

C.H.

PROVENANCE: Mantua, collection of Federico Gonzaga; probably given to Cardinal Richelieu by Vincenzo Gonzaga, c. 1624-25; collection of Duc de Richelieu, acquired by Louis XIV in 1665.
BIBLIOGRAPHY: Wethey, I, 1969, pp. 105f, Cat. 60 (with earlier bibliography).
ADDITIONAL BIBLIOGRAPHY: A. Luzio, Pietro Aretino nei primi suoi anni a Venezia e la corte dei Gonzaga, Turin, 1888, p. 25, n. 2; S. Béguin, "A propos de la Sainte Conversation et de la Vierge au lapin de Titien du Louvre", Tiziano e Venezia, Vicenza, 1980, pp. 479-84.

156

Palazzo del Te, Mantua
Model made by the Istituto Statale d'Arte, Mantua (scale: 1:100) for the Museo del Palazzo Te

The project for the Te, originally a piece of land surrounded by water to the west of Mantua, began when Federico Gonzaga asked Giulio Romano to improve older structures on the site (including stables), and build a retreat where he could enjoy the company of his mistress Isabella Boschetta. Vasari gives detailed information about its building history (reappraised by Shearman, 1967, pp. 434ff.). Giulio designed a single block villa with rooms on each side of a double central loggia, (one facing north for summer, and one facing south for winter) and work began in late 1524 or early 1525. Shearman noted that the early villa must have corresponded to the north wing (on the right of the garden façade), and which contains the Sala dei Cavalli (Cat. 164-165), the Loggia delle Muse, and Isabella's appartments to the west of the loggia. Archaeological evidence has come to light confirming this (Forster and Tuttle, 1971, p. 268 ff).

Vasari continues his account by writing that the building with its façade articulated by a classical order and rooms ornamented with elegant coffering and vaults, so impressed the Marquis that he decided to extend the building and turn it into a palace. This was done by planning the building around a courtyard, with centrally placed logge or vestibules in each wing. Vasari records that Giulio then made a modello in opera rustica of the exterior and interior façades. The Strada drawings may well be copies of this modello. (Cat. 157-163).

Giulio's project reflects sixteenth century research into late

156

antique palace architecture. These researches and their conclusions that antique palaces were planned with centralized blocks around a central courtyard can be seen in the drawings of Francesco di Giorgio, and in the plates of Serlio. Giulio himself had been involved in the evocation of an antique villa, when he was working in Rome at the Villa Madama. Elements in the plan, the peschiera (fishpond), below the east garden façade, the central courtyard, the columnar west entrance vestibule, the tripartite logge, as well as the multimedia decorative system of painted, sculptural and architectural ornament, reflect his experience there. The interior of the Te was elaborately decorated with mural paintings, mainly of classical mythology (see introductory essays by Burns, Hope and Gombrich, above) and was used for the entertainment of the Emperor Charles V in 1530 and 1532.

The model shows the building as it now stands. Paolo Pozzo restored the building in the eighteenth century and drastically altered its appearance (Forster and Tuttle, 1971, p. 280 ff). He did not restore the continuous attic which is shown on the Strada drawings (157-163) linking all of the façades. He built a pediment over the Loggia di Davide on the east garden façade, instead of restoring the gallery with an attic supported on thin colonnettes shown in the Strada drawing (159).

The garden was originally enclosed on the east by the grotte and a straight wall broken by a gateway as shown in the Bertazzolo view (Cat. 1). The present currency screen (exedra) was built by Niccolò Sebregondi c. 1651 in imitation of the garden at La Favorita (Cat. 271).

L.F.

BIBLIOGRAPHY: Vasari ed Milanesi, V, p. 536 ff; Verheyen, 1977, Forster and Tuttle, 1971; Belluzzi and Capezzali, 1976.
ADDITIONAL BIBLIOGRAPHY: C. Hülsen, Die romischen Skizzenbücher des Marten van Heemskerck, Berlin, 1913-15; J. Shearman, "Osservazioni sulla cronologia e l'evoluzione del Palazzo del Te", in the Bollettino del Centro Internazionale di Studi d'Architettura A. Palladio, vol. IX, 1967 p. 434 ff.

157, 158, 159

Elevations of the external façades of the Palazzo del Te
Ippolito Andreasi (c. 1548-1608)
Pen and brown ink with grey wash over incised construction lines.
North façade, 18.2 x 8.4 cm; West façade, 17.2 x 8.4 cm; East garden façade, 21.3 x 8.42 cm
Kunstmuseum, Düsseldorf, Graphische Sammlung (Inv. FP 10920-22)

These drawings provide the only documentation for the original appearance of the Palazzo del Te, which was modified in

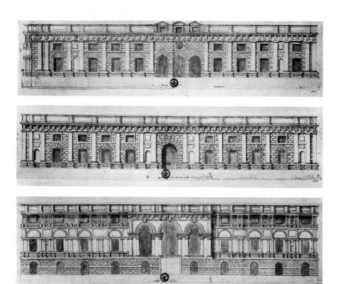

157 158 159

the eighteenth century restoration by Paolo Pozzo (Forster and Tuttle, 1971). They are thought to have been commissioned by Jacopo Strada (1507-88) from Ippolito Andreasi. Strada is known to have been in Mantua in 1567-68, working on a set of drawings of the Te and its decorations, presumably for Albrecht V, Duke of Bavaria. He also planned to publish a series of drawings of the façades of the Te in a *Descrizione di tutta Italia* (Verheyen, 1977, note 7, p. 57).

The imperial *antiquarius*, Jacopo Strada had been trained as a goldsmith in Mantua. He worked there during the 1530's and may have executed some of Giulio's designs for gold and silverware. From 1556 he was resident in Vienna. Before 1562, Strada had acquired Giulio's collection of drawings from his son Raffaello, who had inherited them on Giulio's death in 1546. The present drawings regularize features which

160 161 162

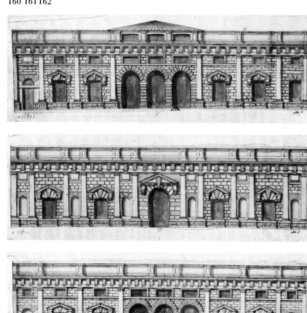

are irregular in the actual building. This could suggest that they are copies of Giulio's originals.

The northern façade shows a continuous attic and a loggia above the *Loggia delle Muse*, which are not present in the actual building. The windows at the eastern end of the façade (on the left) are shown in the centre of each bay, while they are off-centred in the building. On the left a thin strip of paper has been added to the sheet, it shows, in a different ink, the profile of the east garden façade and how it joins the completed northern block.

The drawing of the west façade also shows the continuous attic, but is otherwise like the building.

The elevation of the east garden façade shows elegant panelling in the spandrels of the arches. On each side of the central loggia there is a gallery supported on thin colonnettes with the continuous attic above. There are still traces of the colonnettes in the upper storey of the Palazzo del Te, but neither of these features were restored by Paolo Pozzo, who built the pediment (Forster and Tuttle, *op. cit.*).

L.F.

160, 161, 162, 163

Elevations of the courtyard at the Palazzo del Te
Ippolito Andreasi (*c.* 1548-1608)
Pen and brown ink with grey wash over incised construction lines
Northern courtyard façade, 15.6 x 5.35 cm; Eastern courtyard façade, 14.1 x 5.38 cm; Southern courtyard façade, 14.2 x 5.34 cm; Western Courtyard façade, 13.6 x 5.36 cm
Kunstmuseum, Düsseldorf, Graphische Sammlung (Inv. no. FP 10943-46)

Here too a continuous attic is shown running the full length of all the façades. On the north façade there is a loggia in the attic which looks into the courtyard. On the northern façade the window frame which is cut by the corner of the buildings is shown, but the position of the pilasters is regularized. In all of the elevations the delicate handling of the stucco *bugnate*, which contrasts so strongly with Pozzo's work, is visible.

L.F.

BIBLIOGRAPHY: Verheyen, 1967; Forster and Tuttle, 1971; Verheyen, 1977.

164-165

Elevation of the west wall of the "Sala dei Cavalli" at the Palazzo del Te
Ippolito Andreasi (*c.* 1548-1608)
Pen and brown ink with grey wash
30.5 x 45.1 cm

Elevation of the east wall of the "Sala dei Cavalli"
Pen and brown ink with grey wash
40.2 x 44.5 cm
Kunstmuseum, Düsseldorf, Graphische Sammlung (Inv. no. FP 10926 and 10927)

Jacopo Strada (Cat. 157-163) had a series of drawings done of interior decorations in the Palazzo del Te. These two show the architectural and trompe l'oeil painting of the *Sala dei Cavalli*, the largest and most imposing room at the Te. Its sober architecture, consisting of the Corinthian order, framing arched and trabeated openings, and supporting a coffered ceiling, is one of Giulio's favorite schemes. He used it on the façade of San Benedetto Po, and for the elevation of the chapel entrances at the Duomo. On the west wall niches con-

164

165

taining the painted statues of Mars and Venus flank the portrait of one of Federico's favorite horses, GLORIOSO, standing in front of a window opening to a painted landscape; on the east wall an unnamed horse is flanked by the statues of Jupiter and Juno.

The source for the decorative scheme of horses set in an architectural setting may well have been the *Sala dei Cavalli* at the Gonzaga villa at Marmirolo. The scheme here is certainly a reference to the fact that Federico kept his stables of thoroughbreds there (cf. Cat. 75). Other horses named in this series of drawings (not exhibited here), are BATTAGLIA and DARIO (Verheyen, 1977, p. 115). Federico inherited his father's passion for horses; there were 514 in the stables in 1540, the year of his death (Cavriani, 1909, pp. 22-27).

L.F.

BIBLIOGRAPHY: Cavriani, 1909; Verheyen, 1977.

166

An Allegory of Gonzaga Rule (*c.* 1531-34)
Giulio Romano (*c.* 1499-1546)
Pen and brown ink over red and black chalk 22 x 29.4 cm.
Inscribed in a later hand Giulio Romano, and on the back "Painted in the Palace of T at Mantua"
British Museum, Department of Prints and Drawings (Cat. 79)

The *Loggia della Grotta* in the north east corner of the garden of the Palazzo Te was probably constructed by 1530, and decorated between 1531-34. It consisted of a suite of rooms surrounding a secret garden, with a *loggia* from which Duke Federico could observe the rest of the garden unseen, a *grotta* with a pool decorated with shells, and other rooms, the most important being that of the *Sala of Attilio Regulus*. Its ceiling, divided into compartments, showed scenes of Roman stoicism, personifications of the virtues of Justice, Charity, Fortitude and Prudence, and the central octagon was frescoed with "a woman holding imprese of the Duke". (Jacopo Strada; Verheyen, 1977, p. 129-30). This drawing is an early design for the octagon, first sketched in red and black chalk, the satisfactory figures then outlined in ink. A second drawing (Chatsworth, no. 93) concentrates on figures only indicated

166

in chalk on the British Museum sheet and adds new ones. Hartt accepts a Louvre drawing (no. 3501) as the final *modello*, Verheyen suggests that it is a studio copy (1977, p. 130). There is a marked change in subject matter between the earlier and later decorations in the Palazzo Te, from the erotic to the majestic, inspired no doubt by the Emperor Charles V's visit to Mantua in 1530 when Federico was created duke; the *Grotta* frescoes belong to the latter. Federico believed that his, and Mantua's fortunes were inextricably bound to those of the Emperor; this octagon has been interpreted as the presentation of princely attributes to an allegorical representation of Mantua (Hartt, 1958, p. 143). The central figure reaches for a book while a putto offers her an inkstand; this may be a allegory of history: Federico's military deeds and patronage of the arts demand that a new chapter be written (Verheyen). The genii presenting the palms of victory and musical instruments are already in this drawing; later Mercury, and genii bearing a wreath (fame), a cuirass (martial valour), and a set square (architecture) appear, together with the Gonzaga symbols of Mount Olympus and an eagle. The fresco, executed by Giulio's assistants, was later heavily restored, as the scroll inscribed Vincent (Vincenzo I) indicates. This is one of the drawings Lanier (Cat. 274) took for himself when negociating to buy the Mantuan collection on Charles I's behalf.

J.T.M.

PROVENANCE: N. Lanier (marked with a star); J. Richardson Jun.; Sir J. Reynolds; Malcolm.
BIBLIOGRAPHY: Hartt, 1958, p. 142, 147, no. 177; Pouncey and Gere, 1962, p. 62, no. 79; Verheyen, 1977, pp. 33-35, 129-30 and full bibliography.

167

A giant crushed under a rocky mountain [Pl. 88a]
Giulio Romano (*c.* 1499-1546)
Pen and brown ink with brown wash lightened with white, squared in black chalk; 27.2 x 17.7 cm
Her Majesty the Queen (Inv. no. 0503)

This is a drawing of one of the giants in the *Sala dei Giganti* at the Palazzo del Te. The room is situated in the south east corner of the palace (to the left of the garden façade). It is the most spectacular room at the Te, designed as a piece of theatrical illusionism rather than for habitation. The ceiling, walls and floor, all combine in a single illusion, which represents Jupiter hurling a thunderbolt and crushing the giants, (a theme based on Ovid's Metamorphoses I). Vasari gives a detailed description on the room (ed. Milanesi, V, p. 541 ff). He records a fireplace (now lost) built in *opera rustica*, the light from which flickered across the frescoes and increased the illusion of a collapsing world. The room has been extensively restored. The floor, originally a river bed, has been replaced by a design by Paolo Pozzo. (Forster and Tuttle, 1971, p. 285 ff).

L.F.

BIBLIOGRAPHY: Popham and Wilde, 1949, no. 363; Hartt, 1958; Forster and Tuttle, 1971; Verheyen, 1977.

The Cabinet of the Caesars

Between 1536 and 1538 a new suite of rooms, called the *Appartamento di Troia*, was fashioned out of a part of the Palazzo Ducale which dated from the fourteenth century. Duke Federico supervised their construction and decoration closely, and frequently corresponded with Giulio Romano and the chamberlain Maffei when away from Mantua. The apartment was set high above the lake and commanded views of garden all around; the rooms were mostly small and irregular in shape, and each had a decorative theme: horses, falcons, and famous generals. Most of the decoration was undertaken by a team of painters and stuccoists working to Giulio Romano's designs. However the *Cabinet of the Caesars* was designed to house eleven canvases by Titian of Roman Emperors, Giulio's task was to provide an appropriate setting for the series. The ceiling was stuccoed and probably incorporated an allegorical painting; more stucco work and niches containing statuettes alternated with Titian's emperors, and beneath them, forming a basamento, was a series of scenes from the lives of the Emperors (the subjects taken from Suetonius' *The Twelve Caesars*) interspersed with smaller panels of mounted Roman soldiers and one Victory with a horse. The choice of subject matter reflects Federico's obsession with Imperial themes, stimulated by the Emperor Charles V's visits to Mantua in 1530 and 1532. Evidently the work was completed in a hurry: Giulio made drawings for the scenes and figures for the *basamento*, and the paintings were executed by his assistants, often several specialists (in landscape, or figures) collaborating on one panel. Even the wood used is of poor quality and barely primed (Shearman, forthcoming Catalogue); Federico was impatient to receive the paintings from Titian, works which he hoped would rival the allegories painted for Ferrara, and was unconcerned about the standard of the secondary decoration. Most, if not all the paintings were still *in situ* at the time of the 1627 inventory. The Emperors by Titian perished in a fire in Spain in the eighteenth century, and the other panels were dispersed: some are still in the Royal Collection, one in the Louvre, others in private collections. The original appearance of the room cannot be reconstructed exactly, although Jacopo Strada's drawings made in 1568 of three of the walls goes some way towards clarifying the decoration (Verheyen, 1967).

J.T.M.

168-178

Roman Emperors, after Titian (*c.* 1568)
Ippolito Andreasi (*c.* 1548-1608)
Pen and ink with grey wash; each *c.* 20.5 x 16 cm
Kunstmuseum, Düsseldorf, Graphische Sammlung (FP 10910-15; FP 10931-5)

Titian's series of eleven portraits of Roman Emperors, his most important undertaking for Federico Gonzaga, was commissioned for the *Gabinetto dei Cesari* in the summer of 1536 and completed in 1540, possibly even after the Duke's death

168 Galba

in June of that year (Wethey, p. 235; Braghirolli, pp. 90f, 122-24). Ideally there should have been twelve Emperors, following the canonical list given by Suetonius, but the last, Domitian, had to be omitted for lack of space. The rest of the decorative scheme, including elaborate stucco frames and historical scenes, was by Giulio Romano and his assistants (Cat. 180-182).

The portraits themselves were all destroyed by fire in Spain in 1734, but their compositions are recorded in these drawings made for the antiquarian and art dealer Jacopo Strada. To judge from the many extant copies of the paintings, most of which are rather later, Andreasi was more accurate than Aegidius Sadeler, who engraved the whole series probably in 1593 or 1594 (Cat. 179). But the differences between the drawings and the prints, which are mostly confined to the backgrounds, are not very significant.

The fame of Titian's paintings is demonstrated by the fact that they were copied in his own lifetime probably more often than any of his other works, no less than seven complete sets being recorded before 1576. But none of the surviving reproductions of the *Emperors* in any medium is particularly impressive, and certainly none captures anything of the striking quality that the originals undoubtedly possessed. Of Titian's surviving works the celebrated portrait of Francesco Maria della Rovere in the Uffizi, painted between 1536 and 1538, probably gives the best idea of what they must have looked like. The effortless way in which the artist was able to create new variations on a single, somewhat restricted theme, from the comparative stiffness of *Augustus*, the earliest of the series, to the more marked contrapposto of *Vitellius, Vespasian* and *Otho*, demonstrates his extraordinary inventiveness as a portraitist. For the features of the individual Emperors Titian made use of coins and statues, and his pictures are remarkably faithful to the spirit of Roman portraiture, even though he was not unduly concerned about archaeological accuracy in the costumes. The cuirass of *Claudius*, for example, is copied from one belonging to Guidobaldo della Rovere, whose portrait Titian completed in 1538 (Gronau). This picture no longer exists, but the cuirass itself is preserved in Florence.

C.H.

PROVENANCE: Collection of Jacopo Strada; probably Munich, collection of the Dukes of Bavaria; in Düsseldorf by 1790.
BIBLIOGRAPHY: Braghirolli, 1881, pp. 59-124; Verheyen, 1966, especially pp. 170-74; Verheyen, 1967, pp. 62-70; Wethey, III, 1975, pp. 43-47 and 235-40, cat. L-10 with bibliography.
ADDITIONAL BIBLIOGRAPHY: R. von Busch, *Studien zu deutschen Antikensammlungen des 16. Jahrhunderts*, Tübingen, 1973, pp. 204 f. and 342, n. 90; G. Gronau, *Documenti artistici urbinati*, Florence, 1936, p. 93, no. XXXI.

Vespasian   173 Caligula   176 Augustus   178 Vitellius

179

The Emperor Claudius, after Titian; probably *c.* 1593
Aegidius Sadeler (*c.* 1570-1629)
Engraving; 34.7 x 24.1 cm
Victoria & Albert Museum, Department of Prints and Drawings (E1630-41-1935)

180

Omen of the Future Greatness of the Emperor Augustus
(*c.* 1536-39)
Giulio Romano (*c.* 1499-1546)
Pen and light brown ink and wash over black chalk, squared in black chalk 37.1 x 24.0 cm
Her Majesty the Queen (Cat. no. 350)

This is the right hand half of a *modello* for the painting to go beneath Titian's picture of the Emperor Augustus on the north wall of the *Gabinetto dei Cesari*. The left hand half of the drawing is in the Albertina, Vienna (Popham and Wilde, 1949). The subject is taken from Suetonius, *The Twelve Caesars*, II, 94: "When Augustus was still an infant,… he was placed by his nurse at evening in his cradle on the ground floor and the next morning had disappeared. After a long search he was at last discovered on a lofty tower, lying with his face towards the rising sun" (trans. J. Rolf, Loeb edition, 1914). This fable was inserted to illustrate the Emperor's descent from Apollo, the Sun God, and the other half of the composition showed Apol-

lo in his quadriga flying over the city of Rome. The painting may, together with Cat. 181 and 182, have been removed from the *Gabinetto dei Cesari* before the 1627 inventory and used as a *sopraporta* in the *Camerino dell'Ancoria* (described as *il Carro di Fetonte con alcune Ninfe*; Luzio, 1913, p. 151), but this would imply that it had been replaced by a copy in the *Gabinetto*, since there were still twelve *Favole* there by Giulio at that date. (Shearman, forthcoming Catalogue). The painting is now lost, but the whole composition was engraved by Giulio Bonasone (Bartsch XV, p. 155, 174).

J.T.M.

BIBLIOGRAPHY: Popham and Wilde, 1949, p. 236, no. 350 (with bibliography); Hartt, 1958, pp. 171-72, 300, no. 225; J. Shearman, forthcoming Catalogue (see entry for *A Roman Soldier on Horseback*, Workshop of Giulio Romano).

181

The Omen of Claudius's Imperial Power (*c.* 1537)
School of Giulio Romano
Panel 122.4 x 94 cm, considerable damage on right-hand side
Her Majesty the Queen (Inv. no. 1334)

Painted to go beneath Titian's *Claudius* on the east wall of the Cabinet of Caesars, the subject is taken from Suetonius, *The Twelve Caesars*, V, 7. Claudius, created a consul by his nephew the Emperor Gaius, received an omen of his future greatness: "as he entered the Forum for the first time with the fasces, an eagle that was flying by lit upon his shoulder". The choice of this incident was presumably determined by the eagle, symbol both of the Empire and the Gonzaga's, being an augur of great fortune, and it is painted with its wings outstretched in a suitably heraldic fashion. As in the Nero panel (Cat. 182), Claudius's profile would appear to derive from an antique medal. Giulio's original drawing is lost; the panel seems to have been painted by at least two artists, the architectural specialist being considerably more competent than the figure painter. The combination of Claudius and his military escorts being dressed *all'antica*, and the contemporary costume of the fruit vendors on the palace steps and of the women leaning over the balcony has its charm. The architecture of the palace with a giant order of pilasters, heavy rustication, and statues set in niches is reminiscent of the Palazzo del Te. This panel appears to have been moved to the *Camerino dell'Ancoria* by 1627.

J.T.M.

PROVENANCE: *Gabinetto dei Cesari*, Palazzo Ducale, Mantua; 1627 in the

179   **180**

181

18[

Camerino dell'Ancoria; bought by Charles I, sold in a Commonwealth Sale, recovered at the Restoration, thereafter by descent.
BIBLIOGRAPHY: Luzio, 1913, p. 151; Hartt, 1958, pp. 172-73; Shearman, forthcoming Catalogue.

182

Nero Playing while Rome Burns (*c.* 1537)
School of Giulio Romano (*c.* 1499-1546)
Panel (softwood) 121.3 x 103.7 cm
Her Majesty the Queen (Inv. no. 918)

Originally beneath Titian's painting of *Nero* (see Cat. 168-78) in the centre of the south wall of the *Gabinetto dei Cesari*, this panel illustrates a passage from Suetonius' *The Twelve Caesars*, VI, 38, which describes Nero setting fire to the city of Rome for his own entertainment and singing the entire *Iliad* while watching the blaze. "Pretending to be disgusted by the drab old buildings... he brazenly set fire to the city,... This terror lasted for six days and seven nights, causing many people to take shelter in monuments and tombs... Nero watched the conflagration from the Tower of Maecenas, enraptured by what he called "the beauty of the flames"; then put on his tragedian's costume and sang *The Sack of Illium* from beginning to end" (trans. Graves, 1957). The drawing for the composition is lost, but the painter obviously followed Giulio's design closely. Giulio, born in the area of the Roman Forum, had studied the ruins with care (Vasari, ed. Milanesi, V. p. 530), and archaeological interest, if not ac-

curacy, is evident here; several Roman buildings, arranged in an arbitary fashion are visible in the painting. Nero is seated in the Septizonium, a building on the Palatine identified with the Tower of Maecenas in the sixteenth century (now destroyed); and the Colosseum, the Arch of Constantine, and the Pantheon are all recognizable. Suetonius makes no mention of Nero playing a musical instrument, but here it is interpreted as some form of lute. Nero's profile is derived from an antique coin (Hartt p. 173); Federico was interested in the accurate portrayal of historical figures: Titian's emperors were also based on antique prototypes. The foreground figures are reminiscent of Michelangelo's *Deluge* on the Sistine Ceiling. Shearman suggests that the artist may have been an assistant of Correggio's who stayed in Mantua after his master's death in 1534. By the time of the 1627 inventory this panel, together with Cat. 181 seems to have been moved to the *Camerino dell'Ancoria* (Luzio, 1913, p. 151), and replaced by a copy in the Cabinet of the Caesars.

J.T.M.

PROVENANCE: Gabinetto dei Cesari, Palazzo Ducale, Mantua, 1627 in the *Camerino dell'Ancoria*. Bought by Charles I, sold in the Commonwealth Sale, recovered at the Restoration, thereafter by descent.
BIBLIOGRAPHY: Vasari, ed. Milanesi, V; Luzio, 1913, p. 151; Hartt, 1958, p. 173-74; Shearman, forthcoming Catalogue.

183

Antique Relief with the Throne of Jupiter
Italian marble, h. 57 cm, length 94 cm, max. thickness 13 cm.

192

The relief has been repaired, but the reattached parts – the eagle's beak and left wing, part of the thunderbolt, and the lower left angle of the relief – are certainly ancient
Museo del Palazzo Ducale, Mantua (inv. 6721)

This antique Roman relief represents the throne of Jupiter Capitolinus together with the god's attributes, the triumphal robe draped over the throne, the eagle, the thunderbolt and the sceptre. Judging from the style it should probably be dated to the mid first century A.D. Although it is a subject not commonly illustrated, there are other examples of the representation of the empty throne of a deity in Roman relief sculpture. There are several reliefs on which empty thrones flanked by putti are shown, such as that of the throne of Saturn (Louvre) which is also covered with drapery, and the fragment of a relief in the Uffizi, in which a putto supports a thunderbolt very similar to the one represented in the Mantua throne relief.

M.L.

Although it is not known when or how Federico Gonzaga acquired this relief (or if it were acquired by an earlier member of the family) its likely appeal to him is obvious enough with the imperial attributes of Jupiter. In 1538-39 Giulio Romano mounted the relief for Duke Federico in a wall niche in the *Loggia dei Marmi* (leading to the *Appartamento di Troia*) where ancient statues, busts and reliefs were arranged – together with copies after the antique – according to a formal thematic scheme. Five detailed drawings among those commissioned from Ippolito Andreasi by Jacopo Strada in 1568 reveal the original arrangement (compare those of the Palazzo Te, Cat. 164-65). The Jupiter's throne relief was on the right hand side of the west wall of the room (seen in Andreasi's drawing, Kupferstich Kabinett, Düsseldorf, FP 10879). Above Giulio added a stucco relief of Ganymede (now lost) which provided a thematic link with the three Bacchic reliefs (two of them antique) placed in the matching niche. In 1572 the *Loggia* was doubled in size; some of the sculptures were removed and subsequently sold, stolen, or destroyed. Of the six statues only one can now be found, and all the busts are lost. But nearly all the reliefs – both the antiques and those designed by Giulio – are still in Mantua, though mostly not in their original positions. Three large spandrel reliefs were removed in 1774 under Paolo Pozzo's direction to Palazzo Te, where they were enlarged and placed in rectangular settings. The Jupiter's throne relief cannot have retained its position on the west wall after the *Loggia's* enlargement since the size of the niche on the enlarged west wall is 10 cm narrower than the relief itself. Later it was transferred to the Villa La Favorita (built by Duke Ferdinando in the early seventeenth century); it was listed there in 1789 above the door of a *loggia* leading

into the garden, various other pieces from the *Sala dei Marmi* being placed nearby (d'Arco, 1857, p. 219).

J.B.

BIBLIOGRAPHY: Levi, 1931, pp. 74-75;
ADDITIONAL BIBLIOGRAPHY: A. Levi, "I simboli dell'impero in un rilievo del Palazzo Ducale di Mantova", *Historia*, III, 1929, pp. 270-76. Burckhardt 1978 (unpublished).

184

Jupiter Suckled by the Goat Amalthea
Giulio Romano (*c.* 1499-1546)
Pen and brown ink and wash, central group originally sketched in black chalk, traces of squaring in black chalk. 39.7 x 55.1 cm. Damaged, top right and lower left corners made up
British Museum, Department of Prints and Drawings (Cat. no. 86)

This is the *modello* for one of a series of paintings of scenes from the infancy, youth, and family of Jupiter. The original location and the exact number of these panels is uncertain, but they were all based on drawings by Giulio and painted by his workshop. Several of the drawings and paintings survive, other lost scenes are known from engravings, and using these Hartt assembled a series of twelve scenes and suggested that they originally decorated some rooms in the Castello at Mantua. (Shearman has emended the list and amplified the number of scenes to sixteen or eighteen). The emphasis on the birth and regency of the gods favours Hartt's thesis that the series was connected to the birth of the Gonzaga heir Francesco in 1533. In 1534 two small rooms were being decorated for his mother, the Duchess Margherita Paleologo; it is also possibile that they decorated a Gonzaga villa elsewhere.
The subjects are drawn from a number of classical texts including Ovid's *Fasti*, Lactantius, and Callimactus's *Hymn to Zeus*. The Mantuan tradition exemplified by Isabella d'Este's *Studiolo* might suggest that a local classicist was asked to draw up a programme based on the idea of his Gonzaga patron, and using several classical sources, rather than a single text being the basis of all the scenes as Shearman has suggested.
The *modello* is the first of the series (the child is new born and bald, in the next scene (Cat. 185) he has grown in scale and acquired abundant curly locks). Jupiter was the only child to escape when Saturn devoured his children. He was taken to the island of Crete where, according to some sources he was suckled by the goat Amalthea and fed on honey (the nymph on the right is taking honey from a beehive behind her). The shepherds and the other nymph gently assist the goat with her delicate task.
The freedom of the pen and wash technique over a brief chalk sketch all testify to Vasari's observation that "Giulio always expressed his ideas better in drawings than in works or pictures... because he would make a very spirited drawing in an hour... while he spent months or years carrying out the painting" (Vasari ed. Milanesi. V, p. 528). In fact, as Vasari continues, he quickly tired of the execution of the actual paintings and, following his master Raphael's practice, he employed a large number of assistants, none of outstanding ability, to paint his designs. This is true of the painting made from this *modello* (Royal Collection Hampton Court, no. 110) which is of low quality, perhaps painted by two artists; the landscape, which is not particularly Cretan in character, is rather better than the figures. Vasari knew this subject from an engraving after the drawing by Giovanni Battista Mantovano (*la capra Alfea che, tenuta da Melissa, nutrisce Giove*; Vasari ed. Milanesi, V, p. 550), but he never saw the original set of paintings,

184

Saturn, prone to devouring his own children, should be unable to discover his hiding place. The pose of the child may have been based on one of the sleeping Cupids (one by Michelangelo, one attributed to Praxiteles) in the Mantuan Collection (Wilde, 1932). Another autograph drawing of similar scale has recently appeared in a sale (Christies, 9 December 1980). It is the modello for *Jupiter and Juno take possession of the Throne of Heaven* (Hampton Court, no. 302) and is squared up in black chalk, which would imply that Giulio's assistants worked up the paintings directly from these small drawings with no further assistance from their master. The painting of *Jupiter Guarded by the Corybantes on Crete* (National Gallery, London, Cat. 624) is the work of one or more hands. It is listed in the 1627 inventory of the Mantuan Collection (Luzio, 1913, p. 114, no. 30).

J.T.M.

PROVENANCE: Flink; 2nd Duke of Devonshire (probably).
BIBLIOGRAPHY: Luzio, 1913, p. 114; Hartt, 1958, p. 305, no. 303; Gould, 1975 p. 118-19.
ADDITIONAL BIBLIOGRAPHY: J. Wilde, "Eine studie nach der Antike", *Mitteilungen des Kunsthistorischen Institutes in Florenz*, IV, 1932, p. 53.

186

The Hunting of the Calydonian Boar
Giulio Romano (*c.* 1499-1546)
Pen and brown ink and wash over black chalk, 30.3 x 54.5 cm
British Museum, Department of Prints and Drawings (Cat. no. 85).

This is one of a series of preparatory drawings of hunting scenes illustrating classical texts in which mortals meet their death after falling foul of the gods. Hartt connected it with a *modello* of the *Death of Procris* (Städelsches Institut Frankfurt), and an engraving by Santi Bartoli after Giulio of *Hylas and the Nymphs*, to which a drawing of the *Death of Adonis* (formerly Ellesmere Coll.) was added by Pouncey and Gere. Hartt suggested that the hunting themes made them suitable decoration for the villa at Marmirolo, which served Duke Federico as a hunting lodge, and dated the drawings around 1530. No paintings made from the drawings have come to light.
The subject for this scene is taken from Ovid, *Metamorphoses*, VIII, 329ff. Diana, believing that she had not received the honour accorded to other deities from the king of Calydon, set loose a wild boar which ravaged the kingdom, destroying herds and trampling crops and vines. A group of warriors, together with the virago Atalanta, managed to kill the beast after a fearsome battle. Some of the hunters spread out nets,

suggesting that they were in an inaccessible area of the palace, or a villa he failed to visit (had they been in Giulio's house, as Shearman suggests, he is more likely to have seen them). The painting, not in the 1627 inventory, is included in Nys's purchase list of 1627 (Luzio, 1913, p. 152), which might suggest that they had been moved in from another palace for the sale (Shearman).

J.T.M.

PROVENANCE: Desneux de la Noue; E. Jabach, Marquis de la Mure; Payne Knight.
BIBLIOGRAPHY: Vasari ed. Milanesi, V, pp. 528, 550; Luzio, 1913, p. 152; Hartt, 1958, no. 304, Pouncey and Gere, 1962, p. 65, no. 86; Shearman, forthcoming Catalogue.

185

The Infant Jupiter guarded by the Corybantes on Crete
Giulio Romano (*c.* 1499-1546)
Pen and bistre wash, damaged and patched, corners cut. 33.2 x 54.9 cm
Chatsworth House (Inv. no. 99)

In the second scene of the mythological series (see Cat. 184) Jupiter, rocked in a rustic cradle by three nymphs, has grown; in the background the Corybantes or Curetes, semi-divine inhabitants of Crete, are clattering their weapons and musical instruments to drown the infant's cries so that his father,

185

186

some unleashed dogs, but several of their number were kil- led, and Nestor of Pylos only escaped by using his spear as a vaulting pole to leap into a tree (seen in the background). The twins, Castor and Pollux mounted on white horses ride up behind the beast, but the first wound was inflicted by Atalan- ta, whose arrow grazed the boar's back. Meleager, the king's son, who had fallen in love with the girl at first sight (Cupid is aiming his bow at the hero) then threw two spears and killed the animal. But the jealousy of the other hunters at the honour awarded by Meleager to Atalanta led eventually to his death.

J.T.M.

PROVENANCE: Earl of Pembroke, C. Schwerdt, bought by Colnaghi for the British Museum.
BIBLIOGRAPHY: Hartt, 1958, pp. 225, 305, no. 293; Pouncey and Gere, 1962, pp. 64-65. no. 85.

187

Design for a Gonzaga organ-case
Baldassare Peruzzi (1481-1536)
Pen ink and wash, heightened with white, 56.5 x 38 cm
Her Majesty the Queen (Inv. 5495; Cat. 683)

This is one of the largest and most impressive of Peruzzi's architectural projects, and can be securely attributed to him, not only on the basis of the draughtsmanship, but also be- cause the explanatory note is written in his self-consciously elegant hand: "It is to be noted that on this side go the small pipes of the organ and on the other, where the large pipes go, the round moulding marked 'B' is to be left out. Furthermore if one wishes one can remove the pediment or quarter- round under the satyrs and have a straight cornice, using the upper pediment. One can also remove both pediments and make it after the fashion of a triumphal arch". The note clear- ly indicates the function of the structure, which is also alluded to in the statue of Apollo at the top, and the two seated Muses in the attic. The two figures in the niches on the left carry wind instruments. The note is typical of Peruzzi's almost obsessional devising of alternatives, and suggests that the drawing was to be sent to the patron, and needed full expla- nations of the sort that could normally be made personally. This likelihood is strengthened by the presence of the Gon- zaga arms, and Federico's *impresa* of Mount Olympus sur- mounted by an altar with the inscription FIDES (Belluzzi and Capezzali, 1976, p. 33). There is no reason to suppose that this organ is the alabaster organ bought by Castiglione for Isabella d'Este in Rome in 1522 (Popham and Wilde, 1949, p. 293) and much more likely that this was a design sent from Rome to Federico, probably for execution in wood in Mantua, in the period between Federico's accession in 1519 and the arrival of Giulio in Mantua late in 1524. Apart from Raphael and Giulio, Peruzzi would be the obvious choice for a design of this sort. The style of the drawing fits a date in these years, and the architectural scheme, with superimposed niches between the columns and a pulvinated frieze, closely resembles Peruzzi's monument to Pope Adrian VI in S. Ma- ria dell'Anima, of 1523/4 (Frommel, 1968, p. 115; cf. *ibid.*, pl. LXXIXb). The project displays Peruzzi's great love and knowledge of the antique (for instance in the wriggly marine monsters over the pediment, and the panels with candelabra and swags quoted from the Pantheon portico) and his bril- liance as a draughtsman. It is not known whether the organ- case was ever constructed.

H.B.

BIBLIOGRAPHY: Popham and Wilde, 1949; Belluzzi and Capezzali, 1976.
ADDITIONAL BIBLIOGRAPHY: C.H. Frommel, *Peruzzi als Maler und Zeich- ner*, 1968, Vienna, 1967-68.

Giulio Romano's designs for silversmiths

On his tour of the Palazzo del Te, Vasari was particu- larly impressed by the painting of silver and gold dishes in the *Feast of Cupid and Psyche*: there were "bizarre vases, basins, jugs, cups... fashioned in various forms and fantastic styles". It was in this form of invention that Giulio was "diverse, rich and copious in his inven- tion and artifice". Like stucco, silver was a peculiarly suitable malleable medium for Giulio's designs, in which he combined classical motifs with vegetation, fantastic monsters with studies from nature. His master Raphael designed exotic gold and silver vessels, includ- ing two particularly famous dishes of embossed gilt bronze in the antique style made for the Duke of Urbi- no. When driven into exile by Leo X, the two duchess- es, Elisabetta and Eleonora (both Gonzaga by birth) took refuge at Mantua and presented these dishes to Isabella; however financial necessity meant that they, with other family plate, had to be melted down the same year (July 1516, Golzio, 1936, p. 50). Giulio ap- pears to have been designing both jewellery and plate from the time of his arrival at Mantua, replacing that which had been destroyed.

In 1525-26, Giulio's design for a salt cellar for Federico was sent to Rome to be made up by an unknown silver- smith (Cellini says that the best silversmiths in the city before the Sack were Lombards). Possibly at this date there were no craftsmen in Mantua competent to exe- cute Giulio's designs. Hartt (1958, p. 865) suggested that the vast number of silver designs of Giulio's which have survived (in part due to Lanier's assiduous collect- ing habits, Cat. 274) all date from the years 1524-26, but a series of five letters of Giulio's written to Ferrante Gonzaga, published by Pungileone in 1818 and over- looked in recent literature, show he was making silver designs up to the last months of this life, a fact also implied in the heartbroken letter written by Cardinal Ercole to Ferrante on Giulio's death (see essay by Gom- brich).

The first letter, dated 24 February 1542, is addressed to Ferrante in Sicily where he was serving as Viceroy. Giulio sends him the designs for a pitcher and ewer (*boccale e bacino*), the latter decorated with a whirlpool, and the pitcher with drops of water radiating in waves. He is somewhat dubious about entrusting the design to Sicilian craftsmen, saying it is necessary to be on the spot to see the piece well made, and recommending a Mantuan craftsman who has just finished a pair of *baci- ne* for Cardinal Ercole which have been well received. Giulio hopes that Ferrante will agree to his designs being made up in Mantua because "in truth the design needs careful working because there is nourishment for the eye in that variety of fish, which are hard to distin- guish from real ones" (*in vero lo disegno li vuol fattura perché li è da pascer l'occhio in quella varietà de' pesci quale bisogneria vederli dalli veri*). This design may have re- sembled a Chatsworth drawing (no. 104, Hartt, no. 111).

In the second letter sent to Palermo (21 October 1546) Giulio explains that by some error he still has the *Caldarino* (boiler/skillet) ordered by Ferrante, but since it is a piece of importance he awaits further instructions. Yet on 6 February 1546, the *Caldarino col manico* (boiler/skillet with a handle) and all the other silver work (*altri lavori d'argento*) are still at Mantua. We learn the name of Giulio's favoured silversmith: Ettore Donati; he is making a sword the merchants are presenting to "our illustrious Lord" and a warming pan (*scaldaletto*) ordered by the Cardinal.

In 1546 Ferrante was created Governor of Milan and Giulio writes (23 June 1546) enclosing the design for an unspecified object. Ettore Donati is prepared to abandon all other work to make it and once they have the money it should be ready in eight or ten days. It will be extremely richly worked and larger than the drawing which Giulio asks to have returned since he has no copy. But if he kept no copies of this designs, he was punctilious about recording for whom he had made each drawing: many of the silver designs were inscribed in Giulio's hand (possibly at a later date) with the name of the patron.

The final letter of September 1546 addressed to Ferrante in Milan, was written within two months of Giulio's death when he already had premonitions that he was mortally ill. He made his will on 23 October; one of the witnesses was the silversmith Ettore Donati (*Magistro Hectore filio quondam Hieronymi de Donatis de Corigia aurefice*) (d'Arco, 1842, p. XXXI).

"One of Your Excellency's servants has brought me a vase, which does not correspond in any way to my design and even when it did agree with it, it does not surprise me that it did not turn out well since I was not present, because when one wants to make unusual form, it is always necessary to make a model of wood or some other material, and test it first so that any defect emerges, and many times results can be achieved with an effort. Nevertheless I shall see if it is possible to remedy the fault, and I send you what is to hand at the moment, a candlestick and a vessel/pot for the altar, of which I should like of hear from Your Excellency if they are suitable before I make the others, and concerning the candlesticks already made by Master Ettore I hear that Your Excellency was not satisfied with them which saddens me: they were not liked by most people in Mantua and the above mentioned servant said they were considered to be too churchy, and if Your Excellency wanted to use them for this purpose, very good: but if Your Excellency disliked them and it would please you, I shall get Master Ettore to take them back and return the silver. In such bad health as I am, if Your Excellency wishes for my service every time I can be of use to you, I shall not stop because of illness, unless it gets worse, which I fear, and I kiss Your Excellency's hand and humbly recommend myself. From Mantua 15 September 1546. Your Illustrious and Excellent Lordship's Humble Servant Julio Romano".
(*Per un servitore de V.S. mi è stato portato un vaso, quale in conto alcuno non si somiglia a mio disegno e quando pur*

somigliasse non mi maraviglio che non sia riuscito non essendoci stato presente, perché volendo fare foggie insolite, bisogna sempre fare un modello di legno o d'altra cosa, e farne prima la sperienza nella quale si chiarisce del difetto, e molte volte con fatica si conduce. Tuttavia vederò se'l serrà possibile remediare, e mando quello mi è sovvenuto per hora un Candeliere e un Caldarino da Altare, delli quali desiderarria intendere da V. Ex.ia se sono al proposito prima che faccia li altri, e circa li candelieri già fatti da Maestro Ettore intendo non son satisfatti a V. Ex., del che mi duole: in Mantova non son piaccuiti alla più parte e il soprascritto Servitore mi disse che erano judicati da chiesia, e quando V. Ex. li volesse operare a tal effetto, bene: pure quando V. Ex. li fussino in odio, quando li sia in piacere farò che Maestro Ettore [Donati] li torrà indreto e restituirà l'argento. E così mal sano se V. Ex. si vorrà servire di me, tutte le volte che li serrò grato non restarò per il male, caso che non me venga peggio, come ho sospetto, a V. Ex. baso la mano e humilmente mi recomando.
Di Mantova alli XV. di settembre MDXLVI

Di V. Ill.ma et Ex.ma. S. Humil Servidore Julio Romano.)
J.T.M.

I should like to express my gratitude to Dr Laura and Professor Giulio Lepschy for their great kindness and patience in helping me with the translation of these letters. The text is as published by Pungileone, with minor changes according to modern editorial principles.
BIBLIOGRAPHY: Golzio, 1936, p. 50; d'Arco, 1842; Hartt, 1958.
ADDITIONAL BIBLIOGRAPHY: P.L. Pungileone, *Lettere sopra Marcello Donati... medico del Duca Guglielmo Gonzaga etc.*, Parma, 1818, pp. 53-58.

188

Design for a Flask for Federico Duke of Mantua

(1530-40)
Giulio Romano (*c.* 1499-1546)
Pen and greyish-brown wash 36.5 x 19.1 cm. Cut at top and laid down. Autograph inscription in lighter ink *fati alo Illmo duca di Ma[n]toa*
The Picture Gallery, Christ Church Oxford (Cat. no. 427)

There seems no reason to doubt the artist's inscription that this design was made for the Duke of Mantua. Hartt (1958 p. 86) dated all these drawings for silver 1524-26, that is before Federico was made Duke in 1530, but it is evident that Giulio made silver designs throughout his time in Mantua. It is difficult to envisage what metal or material the linked strapwork handle would have been made of, and to determine if the goats heads formed spouts (Hartt, p. 291), or merely served as handles.

J.T.M.

PROVENANCE: General J. Guise.
BIBLIOGRAPHY: Hartt, 1958, pp. 86, 291 no. 74; Byam Shaw, 1976, I, p. 132, no. 427.

189

Design for a covered dish for Ferrante Gonzaga

Giulio Romano (*c.* 1499-1546)
Pen and bistre wash 17.6 x 30.8 cm. Inscribed in Giulio's

hand *Questo feci alo S^r do[n] ferante gonzaga*
Chatsworth House (Inv. no. 117)

The inscription records that the box was made for Ferrante
Gonzaga (1507-57), brother of Duke Federico. In 1531, when
Ferrante was made a Knight of the Golden Fleece, Giulio
designed his collar (*Princely Magnificence*, 1980-81 p. 114-15
no. G3h). This box, called a sweetmeat box by Hartt, was
probably part of a set of tableware, to which the candlestick
(Cat. 190) may have also belonged. Hartt dated it between
1524-26, at which time Ferrante, in his teens, was with Castiglione at the Spanish court, and hardly likely to have been
ordering elaborate silver designs. Throughout the 1520's he
was in active service in Charles V's army; the first possible
time that he might have ordered such silver was after his
marriage to the heiress Isabella of Capua (1530). Soon after he
bought the Principality of Guastalla with the dowry. The
descriptions of silver designs that Ferrante ordered from Giulio in the 1540's do not coincide with this box. (Pungileone,
1818, p. 53-58). The putto emerging from acanthus leaves
and holding a water pitcher must be a reference to Ferrante's
astrological sign; born on 28 January (Marani and Perina, p.
173), he was an Aquarian.

J.T.M.

BIBLIOGRAPHY: F. Hartt, 1958, p. 86, 291, no. 65; Marani and Perina,
1965, p. 173; London, 1980, *Princely Magnificence*, p. 115.
ADDITIONAL BIBLIOGRAPHY: P. Pungileone, 1818 (see pp. 53-58) as above.

190

191

mised to donate them to the Gonzaga collection; Bertolotti,
1885, p. 69). But this Francesco is unlikely to have been styled
Illmo by Giulio. An alternative reading might be *feran* (Ferrante); for a comparable inscription see that on another silver
design made for Ferrante (Victoria & Albert Museum, Cat.
no. 160). The motif of lions emerging from acanthus leaves
and putti might suggest that this candlestick was part of the
same set of silver as Cat. 189. The second inscription is probably some guide of the silversmith; from the drawing it is
difficult to ascertain if the base was to have four or five feet.

J.T.M.

PROVENANCE: Guise.
BIBLIOGRAPHY: Bertolotti, 1885, p. 69; Hartt, 1958, p. 294, no. 121; Byam
Shaw, 1976, I, no. 424.

188   **189**

190

**Design for a Candlestick, with putti supporting the hol-
der and lion heads emerging from acanthus leaves
around the base**
Giulio Romano (*c.* 1499-1546)
Pen and brown wash, roughly cut to shape and laid down.
Inscribed (in Giulio's hand) *Illmo s^r feran[te] [Gonz]aga*, and
under the base: *[t]anto piu il piede solo*. 20.4 x 16.6 čm
The Picture Gallery, Christ Church, Oxford (Cat. no. 424)

The inscription was cut when the design was roughly silhouetted: Hartt (1958, p. 294) read the right hand fragment as
fnaci, which is meaningless; Byam Shaw (1976, no. 424) correctly taking it to be part of the overall inscription deciphered
it as Ill° Sr fran(cesco Gonz)aga, but failed to offer a candidate
for the patron. An early dating might suggest Francesco, the
cousin of Federico Gonzaga, who served as his ambassador in
Rome, and arranged for Giulio's collection of antiques to be
transported to Mantua in 1524. (Giulio appears to have pro-

191

Design for a Salt Cellar for Cardinal Ercole Gonzaga
Giulio Romano (*c.* 1499-1546)
Pen and bistre wash, roughly silhouetted 87.2 x 15.6 cm
(max); Autograph inscription *feci a mo[n]signor d[i] ma[n]toa
cardinale*
The Picture Gallery, Christ Church, Oxford (Cat. no. 446)

Made for Cardinal Ercole Gonzaga (1505-65), this is a sober
design for a rectangular salt cellar with stygil ornament and
acanthus and lion feet. Giulio has indicated the depth of the
cellar for the silversmith.

J.T.M.

PROVENANCE: General J. Guise (donated to the gallery in 1765).
BIBLIOGRAPHY: Hartt, 1958, p. 293, no. 103; Byam Shaw, 1976, I, p. 134,
no. 446.

192

Design for a Ewer for Cardinal Ercole Gonzaga
Giulio Romano (school?) (*c.* 1499-1546)
Bistre ink and wash over black chalk on paper, roughly sil-
houetted and laid down 28.2 x 15.3 cm
Autograph inscription (top line erased) *Sr Cardinale di Ma[n]-
toa co[n] tuti questi ormiti* (= ornamento)
Victoria & Albert Museum, Department of Prints and Draw-
ings (E. 5129-1910)

Although rather weak in execution and somewhat tentatively
attributed to Giulio by Ward-Jackson (1979, p. 78) this draw-

197

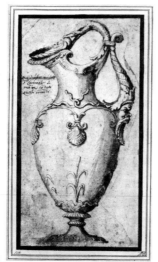

192

ing bears all the marks of the artist's imagination and the *pentimento* of an alternative swan's neck handle suggests that it is not a pupil's copy. The decoration combining bullrushes, shells, snakes with a swan's head and the grotesque mask which forms the base of the handle is typical of his invention. Presumably the shell held in the swan's beak was hinged to allow the ewer to pour. Giulio wrote to Ferrante Gonzaga in 1542 that he had just designed a basin and ewer for the Cardinal which were made up by a Mantuan silversmith (probably Ettore Donati) and are very beautiful (Pungileone, 1818, p. 54), and this design is likely to date from the time of Cardinal Ercole's regency (1540-50).

J.T.M.

PROVENANCE: J. Richardson Sr.; J. Thane; W. Esdaile; 5th Duke of Argyll (?); Sir J. Robinson; bought by the Museum in 1910.
BIBLIOGRAPHY: Ward-Jackson, 1979, no. 159.
ADDITIONAL BIBLIOGRAPHY: Pungileone, 1818, as above.

193

Photographs: **Details of plates, dishes, jugs etc. from the banqueting table in the "Feast of Cupid and Psyche",** Palazzo Te
Giulio Romano (*c.* 1499-1546)

See above, introductory passage before Cat. 188.

194

Plate with the arms of Federico II and his wife, Margherita Paleologo, and with the Chariot of Mars (*c.* 1531-40)
Urbino; Nicolò da Urbino (active *c.* 1520-40)
Tin-glazed earthenware with polychrome decoration. Sunken centre with a central slightly sunk area roughly corresponding to the foot on the underside of the piece; broad, straight border. Diam 27.50 cm
Museo Internazionale delle Ceramiche, Faenza (Inv. no. 7030)

Above, on a central axis but at the intersection of the well and border, are the arms of Gonzaga impaling Paleologo beneath a ducal coronet held from above by an *amoretto*; Mars is depicted at the centre of the plate, being drawn through the clouds by two young women, while a third stands behind him in his chariot and is about to crown him with a wreath; on the far side of the chariot (centre, right) Cupid shoots an arrow. Yellow line border. On the back is the inscription *del caro del dio Marte*, (concerning the chariot of the god Mars).

Two other plates by Nicolò da Urbino bearing the arms of Gonzaga impaling Paleologo beneath a ducal coronet are recorded, the piece not here exhibited being that in the Wallace Collection (Norman, 1976, no. C. 92), the other being Cat. 195. All must have been made for or after the marriage in 1531 of Federico II to Margherita Paleologo, and belong to Nicolò's late style, which is characterized by relatively loose handling and extensive use of rust-coloured shadow on the flesh. If Rackham (1940, p. 192) is right in thinking the design of the Gonzaga-Paleologo pieces dependent on Gabriele Giolito's set of engravings of the Planets, then the Este-Paleologo set cannot be earlier than 1533; however this dependence is denied by Norman (1976, no. C 92). (For the improbable suggestion that the design of the present piece has something to do with Giulio Romano see essay by Mallet). Pieces by Nicolò bearing Federico's Olympus *impresa* (Cat. 197) have sometimes been thought to be part of the same set; in any case they belong to much the same period of Nicolò's activity. It is less likely that a plate with the simple Paleologo arms, in the Museo Correr at Venice (Liverani, 1938 and 1939 pp. 348 and 12 respectively) belongs to the Service. On the other hand, Cat. 196 (which is dated 1533) may belong to the set, although it is by a different Urbino painter, Francesco Xanto Avelli; instances can be cited of armorial services executed by more than one painter.

J.V.G.M.

PROVENANCE: Dr Federico Tessmann Collection, Bolzano; Dr. Ing. Antonino Rusconi, Trieste, by whom the plate was presented in 1955.
BIBLIOGRAPHY: Mantua, *Mostra Iconog*, 1937, no. 7; Liverani, 1938 and 1939; Liverani, "Un Piatto di Nicola Pellipario al Museo di Faenza", *Faenza*, 1955, p. 12, pl. VII; Polidori, 1962, p. 350, fig. 4; Giuseppe Liverani, "Selezione delle Opere", *Faenza*, 1963 p. 36, no. 59; Claude Frégnac, *La Faience Européenne*, Fribourg, 1976, p. 88, fig. 106.

195

Plate with the arms of Federico II and his wife, Margherita Paleologo, and with Apollo and Minerva in Council (*c.*1531-40)
Urbino; Nicolò da Urbino (active about 1520-40)
Tin-glazed earthenware with polychrome decoration. The plate has a central shallow depression which reflects the shape of the foot, which has no foot-ring. Diam. 27.50 cm
British Museum, Department of Medieval and Later Antiquities (Bernal, 1809)

At the top right, suspended from a tree is a shield with the arms of Gonzaga impaling Paleologo beneath a ducal coronet. Right of centre in the foreground stands the nude Apollo conferring with Minerva, who holds her shield and spear; behind these appear Mercury with his winged helmet and Diana with her half-moon emblem; at the extreme right is a further female half-length nude, possibly here intended for Venus; in the foreground, left, are two reclining river-gods. In the background is a landscape with classical ruins. The rim outlined in yellow. The reverse with concentric turned lines and yellow rings. Under the flat foot is inscribed in grey *del Chonseglio de/apollo . e . minerva* (of the Council of Apollo and Minerva).
All the figures are extracted from the print of the Muses and Pierides after G.B. dei Rossi (Bartsch XV, p. 89, no. 53 or p. 295, no. 28). The figure of a woman ot the right, evidently a minor deity in the print, has been pushed into the group of senior gods by Nicolò, who perhaps intended her to represent Venus. The river god nearest to Apollo on the maiolica plate has been reversed by Nicolò. It is not clear whether Nicolò

194

195

196

intended this plate to represent an incident in the story of the Contest between the Muses and the Pierides (Ovid, *Metamorphoses* V) or simply an unspecified consultation taking place among the gods.

J.V.G.M.

PROVENANCE: Bernal Collection, London, Christies, March 22, 1855, lot 1809.
BIBLIOGRAPHY: Mentioned but not illustrated by Liverani, 1938, p. 345; id, 1939, p. 16, where he wavers between an attribution to Nicolò and to Xanto; Liverani, 1958, p. 36, gives it without comment to Nicolò; Norman, 1976, no. C. 92, where the Wallace Collection plate, and by inference this also, is given as "Urbino, possibly by Nicolò da Urbino, or by a follower, about 1535-40".

196

Dish with the arms of Federico II and his wife, Margherita Paleologo, and with the Marriage of Alexander and Roxana (dated 1533)

Urbino; Francesco Xanto Avelli (Signed)
Tin-glazed earthenware with polychrome decoration. Broad, flattish centre, clearly defined well and comparatively narrow border. No foot-ring. Diam 46.50 cm
Victoria & Albert Museum, Department of Ceramics (1748-1855; Rackham, 1940, no. 632)

Painted, left of centre towards the top, with the arms of Gonzaga impaling Paleologo beneath a ducal coronet, all shown as if suspended from a drawn-up curtain. Beneath this is the Marriage of Alexander and Roxana: Alexander (centre) is conducted towards a bridal couch on which, with a gesture of modesty, sits Roxana, accompanied by two amoretti and two orientals; further amoretti are shown to the left of centre and in the foreground dancing in a ring and sporting with Alexander's armour. Further soldiers are shown to the left. In the background a landscape is glimpsed through a colonnade. Yellow rim. On the reverse is the inscription in black: *.M.D. XXXIII. / Hor vedi la magnanima Reina / chuna treccia rivolta, e, laltra sparsa / corse alla, Babilonica ruina. / Nel.I.libro di Trogo Pompeio.* and below: ÷ *Frā : Xāto .A. / da Rovigo, ī / Urbino.* (1533. Now see the noble queen who ran with one tress bound up, the other loose, at the fall of Babylon. In the first book of Trogus Pompeius. Francesco Xanto Avelli da Rovigo in Urbino). Concentric ridges, grooves and yellow lines towards the rim. Possibly intended as part of the same set as Cat. 194 and 195, although those are by Nicolò da Urbino.
The central group, from the dancing amoretti (left of centre) to the amoretto standing behind Roxana, derive from Caraglio's print after Raphael of the same subject (Bartsch XV,

62). Raphael's composition was an attempt to reconstruct a lost classical painting by Aëtion as described by Lucian. The print was used by Francesco Xanto Avelli on many other occasions; perhaps closest to the present piece is a large dish in the Metropolitan Museum at New York dated 1534 and with lustred additions. This last piece bears a closely similar inscription at the back, though without the reference to Trogus Pompeius (Ballardini, 1938, Nos 129 and 307R). In order to fill out the composition on the Victoria & Albert's plate, Xanto has made use of figures from other prints including: *La Bataille au Coutelas* (Bartsch XIV, 212, under Marcantonio Raimondi) for the two running soldiers at the extreme left; Agostino Veneziano's print of *the Death of Cleopatra* (Bartsch, XIV, 161, 198) has been used in reverse for the weeping amoretto in the foreground; *Christ in the House of Simon the Pharisee* by Marcantonio Raimondi (Bartsch, XIV, 23) or more probably one of the reversed copies, for the head and shoulders of the turbanned oriental on the far side of the bridal couch; *The Sacrifice of Noah* (Bartsch, XIV, 4) for the other figure of an oriental in a turban, to the right of the couch; *Aeneas and Anchises* by Caraglio after Raphael (Bartsch, XV, 60) for the figure of a half-nude boy to the extreme right.
Xanto's inscription follows, with inaccuracies, three lines from Petrarch's *Trionpho di Fama* referring not to Roxana but to Semiramis. As Förster (1894, pp. 199-200) pointed out, the incident was not derived by Petrarch from Gnaeus Trogus Pompeius but from Valerius Maximus; the error was started in Vellutello's edition of Petrarch published in 1525 in Venice. Francesco Xanto Avelli was born at Rovigo, perhaps around 1485, and was active as a maiolica painter at Urbino, certainly from 1530 and probably some years earlier. His latest works are dated 1541. He had pretensions to be a poet (Vitaletti, 1918) and his work often bears elaborate inscriptions and literary allusions.

J.V.G.M.

PROVENANCE: Bernal Collection, London, Christies, March 23, 1855, lot 1938.
BIBLIOGRAPHY: Fortnum, 1873, p. 396 and woodcut facing; R. Förster, "Die Hochzeit des Alexander and der Roxana in der Renaissance", *Jahrbuch der Königlich Preussischen Kunstsammlungen*, XV, 1894, pp. 199-200; Fortnum, 1896, p. 215; G. Vitaletti, "Le Rime di Francesco Xanto Avelli", *Faenza*, 1918, pp. 11-15 and 4; Rackham, 1933, p. 62 and pl. 328; Ballardini, 1938, figs. 82 and 278R; Liverani, 1938 and 1939 pp. 344-45 and 15-16 respectively; W.B. Honey, *European Ceramic Art, An Illustrated Historical Survey*, London, 1949, pl. 56A; Reginald Haggar, *The Concise Encyclopedia of Continental Pottery and Porcelain*, London, 1960, pl. 91C; Liverani, 1968, pp. 697-8 and fig. 12; Conti, 1973, fig. 212; Claude Frégnac, *La Faience Européenne,*, Fribourg, 1976 p. 89, fig. 108; Forthcoming Transactions of the Seminar on the work of Francesco Xanto Avelli, held at Rovigo, 1980.

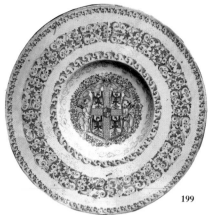
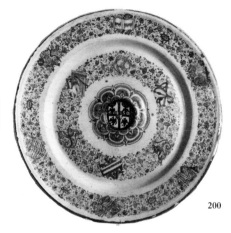

197   199   200

197

Dish with the Olympus device of Federico II and with the Rape of Helen (c. 1535-40)

Urbino; Nicolò da Urbino (active c. 1520-40)

Tin-glazed earthenware with polychrome decoration. The sunken centre with a shallow depression nearly corresponding in extent to the flat foot (without a footring) on the underside of the piece; slightly sloping straight rim. Diam. 45.50 cm

Victoria & Albert Museum, Department of Ceramics (C. 2246-1910; Rackham, 1940 no. 575)

Painted at the rim, top, slightly left of centre, with a ducal coronet above a shield bearing Duke Federico's Olympus device (a mountain with spiral ascent) above the word ΑΜΩΜΟΣ   and below the word FIDES (faith). The remainder of the obverse decorated with the Rape of Helen: she is being seized (left of centre) by a bearded nude man and a satyr, whilst others, with two horses, wait to receive her. To the right, beneath a canopy twined round a tree, naked figures are shown as though interrupted at a banquet table, from which two men spring up with drawn swords in an attempt to prevent the abduction. Yellow rim. The reverse inscribed on the flat foot: *Chome paris Rapi . Elena . al / iltenpio* . The foot, the join between the well and the border and the rim are emphasized by concentric yellow lines. In addition there are concentric grooves towards the rim. An area towards the rim at 9 o'clock and a smaller area at 5 o'clock are replaced in plaster. The figure composition and many other details, including the circular temple in the background, are copied from a print of which a version by Enea Vico (Bartsch, XV, 30) is dated 1542. The design is said by Vasari to be from a drawing by Rosso Fiorentino, a statement not now generally accepted. The engraving has no inscription explaining its subject, and the one supplied by Nicolò for his dish corresponds with Vasari's identification of the scene as Theseus, King of Attica, carrying off the young Helen from the temple in order to marry her. An Urbino dish copied by another hand from the same composition is in the Kunstgewerbemuseum, Berlin, and is reproduced along with the engravings by Hausmann (1972, no. 206).

The device of Mount Olympus with the motto FIDES was granted by the Emperor Charles V to Federico Gonzaga, supposedly soon after Federico's defence of Pavia in 1522. A second piece apparently from the same set, a plate 27.50 cm in diameter bearing the inscription *chome Apollo fecie parlamento con minerva* (how Apollo held a consultation with Minerva), survives in the Museo Correr (Lazzari, 1859, p. 81, no. 285; reproduced in Liverani, 1938 and 1939, pp. 342 and 13 respectively). Both pieces are typical of the late style of Nicolò da Urbino.

A difficulty arises concerning the date of this Service because the date of the Vico print, 1542, is two years after Duke Federico's death. Although the Olympus device was occasionally used by Federico's successors, as on a seal bearing Duke Guglielmo's name (Amadei and Marani, *I Gonzaga a Mantova*, Milano 1975, p. 78, fig. 87), it seems unlikely that Federico's eldest son and immediate successor, Duke Francesco, would have required maiolica of this character for several years after succeeding, since he was only seven at the time of this father's death. Nicolò's influence on other Urbino maiolica painters seems virtually to vanish by about 1540, suggesting that he was no longer active. It seems likely that, for the painting of the Olympus service, Nicolò had access to this composition in some form that preceded the 1542 state of Vico's print.

J.V.G.M.

PROVENANCE: Salting Collection.
BIBLIOGRAPHY: V. Lazzari, *Notizia delle Opere d'Arte e d'Antichità della Raccolta Correr*, Venice, 1859; Rackham, 1933, p. 61 and pl. 36a; Liverani, 1938 and 1939, pp. 345 and 16 respectively; Hausmann, 1972, pp. 282-4.

198

Dish on low foot with the arms of Gonzaga, probably for Federico II, with a music book and grotesques

(c. 1530) [Illustration on back cover]

Castel Durante or Urbino

Tin-glazed earthenware decorated in blue, yellow, orange-brown, yellowish-grey, black and white. The dish with slightly convex centre, the sides curving uninterruptedly to the rim (Approximately Rackham, 1940, Shape 14). diam. 24.50 cm

London, Victoria & Albert Museum, Department of Ceramics (C.2224-1910; Rackham, 1940 no. 567)

Painted with the arms of Gonzaga above an open book of music inscribed at the top left DUO and bottom right VERTE FOLIVM (turn the page). The remaining ornament is set against a dark blue ground and consists of a cherub (from whose neck the shield of arms appears to be suspended), a human-headed, winged monster to either side of the arms; below the book, a bearded grotesque head and dolphin-and-cornucopia grotesques from which are suspended what appear to be two pairs of horns and two ducal coronets. Yellow rim. The reverse plain.

If the two ring-shaped objects which appear below the book are intended for ducal coronets, then this dish was presumably made after 1530, when Marchese Federico became first Duke of Mantua. Rackham (1940, no. 567), who does not mention these emblems and seems to have considered them, rightly or wrongly, to be of no significance, dated the piece "about 1525" and attributed it to "Nicola Pellipario", or as we should now say, Nicolò da Urbino. Comparison with dated *coppe* decorated with grotesques suggests on grounds of style a possible date-range of from about 1522 (Rackham, 1940, no. 559 and Ballardini, 1933, 118 and 119) to 1533 (eg. Ballardini, 1938, nos. 26-32 and 80-81). Mr. Iain Fenlon has commented that the music in the open part-book is a two-part textless piece, and is therefore probably intended for instrumental performance. No other pieces of this class seem to be recorded with a music book crossing the entire centre of the dish, though an undated *coppa* at Pesaro, probably by the same hand, shows two open music books painted on a smaller scale (Polidori, 1953, pl. XXXVIII). As for the attribution to Nicolò da Urbino, although that painter does seem to have been responsible for some ornament in this style, the drawing of the human-headed grotesques, in particular, suggests a lesser hand, probably that of a close associate. The automatic attribution of this class of dish to Castel Durante rather than Urbino no longer seems to have any secure basis now that Nicolò da Urbino's biography has to be separated from that of Nicola Pellipario (see introduction preceding Cat. 131). In our present state of knowledge it seems impossible to say which pieces came from which of these two neighbouring towns.

J.V.G.M.

PROVENANCE: Alexander Barker Collection; Castellani Collection; Salting Collection.
BIBLIOGRAPHY: J.C. Robinson, *Catalogue of the Special Exhibition of Works of Art … on Loan at the South Kensington Museum, June, 1862.* London, 1863, no. 5198 (lent by Alexander Barker); Castellani Sale Catalogues, Paris, 27 May, 1878, lot 190 and Rome, 1 April 1884, lot 122; *Burlington Fine Arts Club, Catalogue of Specimens of Hispano-Moresque and Majolica Pottery*, London, 1887; Fortnum, 1896, p. 290 (attribution to Ferrara suggested, owing to the arms being confused with those of d'Este); Rackham, 1933, p. 57; Liverani, 1938 and 1939, pp. 339, 345 and 10, 16; Rackham, 1940, no. 567; Polidori, 1953, p. 69 and pl. XL, I, fig. 50.

199

Dish with the arms of Gonzaga, probably for Federico II (*c.* 1525)
Castel Durante or Urbino
Tin-glazed earthenware decorated in blue, green, yellow, orange-brown, pale brownish-pink and opaque white. The centre with a slightly sunken flat area roughly corresponding to the area of the foot on the underside; the well curves upward to form a sharp angle with the straight border. The underside with flat foot without foot-ring. Diam. 34.00 cm.
Victoria & Albert Museum, Department of Ceramics (C.2144-1910; Rackham, 1940, no. 566).

In the centre, within a blue, green and yellow floral wreath, are the arms of Gonzaga supported by two cupids and suspended from a cherub-head; on the well is a band of plant-scroll in pale brownish-pink; the same colour is used, in conjunction with blue, for the three concentric zones of plant-scroll on the border, and also to provide a thin line at the rim. The back, plain but somewhat speckled in firing, has concentric grooves near the rim. Broken through and repaired, the main line of breakage passing down the line of the left-hand cupid, but virtually all present.
A larger dish with an emplacement for a ewer at its centre, of similar character and bearing the same arms, exists (Schmidt, 1929, no. 67, pl. XVII). A further dish with emplacement at Leningrad (Kube, 1976, 54) has the arms of Gonzaga and the putto supporters painted in such a closely similar manner that it must clearly be from the same workshop as the other two, though the blue monochrome decoration in that instance comprises not only plant-scroll, but also four profile heads of Roman emperors and interlacing strapwork (*tirata*).
An attribution of these pieces to the immediate circle of Nicolò da Urbino seems justified by comparison of their ornamental borders to such pieces as a plate in Berlin (Hausmann, 1972, no. 172) which has at its centre a representation of Europa and the Bull that is very close indeed to the character of his *istoriato* painting, though probably, like the present piece, not from his own hand. Also pointing towards an attribution to the Duchy of Urbino is the existence of pieces with similar borders belonging to a set with the arms of Peroli of Urbino (Rackham, 1940, no. 565; Giacomotti, 1974, no. 776). The pink pigment, which in parts has turned yellow or green, may represent an unsuccessful attempt at producing lustre.

J.V.G.M.

PROVENANCE: Seillière Collection; George Salting Collection (bequeathed in 1910).
BIBLIOGRAPHY: Paris, Georges Petit, Collection Seillière, 5 May, 1890, lot 36; R. Schmidt, *Sammlung Murray, Florenz*, Berlin, 1929; Rackham, 1933 pp. 57-8.

200

Dish with the arms of Gonzaga probably for Federico II (*c.* 1525)
Cafaggiolo (Marked)
Tin-glazed earthenware painted in blue, yellow, black, opaque white and red. In the centre is a raised boss with sunken emplacement probably intended for an ewer; sharply angled but comparatively shallow well; straight border with a groove before the rim; the underside with unemphatic footring.
Diam. 37.50 cm.
Victoria & Albert Museum, Department of Ceramics (c. 2145-1910; Rackham, 1940, no. 339)

Apart from the heraldry the dish is painted in blue monochrome. The boss surrounding the central emplacement is painted as a heraldic rose; encircling this is a delicately painted band of floral scrolls interrupted by three groups of musical instruments and three books and three trophies of arms. The reverse more loosely painted in blue with plant-scrolls and inscribed in the centre: *I chafaggulo* (Cafaggiolo, near Florence). A number of other plates and dishes with related border patterns are known, some of them with the incription *I chafagguolo* written at the back. See Chompret, 1949, II Figs. 54, 55 and 58. Rackham (1940, p. 118, n. 339) compares the border of the present piece to that of a dish with the Sacrifice of Abel, in the British Museum. However, none of these is dated and it is therefore only possible to hazard a guess that they may be roughly contemporary with pieces which, like Cat. 199, have similar bands of delicate leaf-scroll ornament and appear to have been made on the other side of the Appenines at Castel Durante or Urbino around 1525.

J.V.G.M.

PROVENANCE: Fau Collection; Salting Collection (bequeathed in 1910).
BIBLIOGRAPHY: Fau Sale Catalogue, Paris, 5 March, 1884, lot 32; Rackham, 1933, p. 39; Chompret, 1949, II, fig. 56.

Dish on high foot with the arms of Gonzaga encircled by the Order of the Golden Fleece, for Ferrante Gonzaga, Duke of Ariano and Prince of Guastalla (*c.* 1531-35)
Cafaggiolo (?)
Tin-glazed earthenware painted in blue, yellow, red and yellow lustre. The dish with slightly convex centre, the sides curving uninterruptedly to the rim; the unusually tall hollow stem with turned ridges at the junction with the bowl and at the foot itself. Ht. 11.50 cm, Diam. 26.00 cm.
Victoria & Albert Museum, Department of Ceramics (652-1884; Rackham, 1940, no. 348)

Painted in the centre with the Gonzaga arms beneath a yellow coronet and encircled by the yellow and red collar of the Order of the Golden Fleece, part of which is painted over areas from which the white ground had been previously scratched off. Beyond this is a white symmetrical ornament comprising open books and formalised flowers amongst acanthus and other leaf-scroll, all painted in blue on a yellow lustre ground. Yellow lustre rim. The underside and the stem decorated with crane's-bill flowers and foliage on continuous undulating stems in blue and yellow lustre within blue lines; the foot with a band of radiating acanthus leaf stopping short of the yellow-lustred edge of the foot. The bowl has been cracked through and the foot is re-stuck, though scarcely any of the piece is missing.

201

202

The only member of the Gonzaga family who held the order of the Golden Fleece at a period compatible with the style of this dish is Ferrante (1507-57), Duke of Ariano and Prince of Guastalla, youngest brother of Federico, first Duke of Mantua. Ferrante spent the greater part of his life fighting in the service of the Emperor Charles V, who awarded him the Golden Fleece in 1531; on grounds of style this dish cannot be much later than that year.
Two unusual technical features should help identification of this dish's place of production: the use on the coat of arms of a red pigment formed from the earth known as Armenian bole; and the employment of a yellowish lustre pigment. The red pigment seems to have been virtually confined to Tuscany (especially Cafaggiolo, Montelupo and Siena) but it was also occasionally used at Faenza. The use of lustre was even more restricted, demanding the use of a specially constructed kiln and specialised experience: Deruta and Gubbio were the main centres associated with the technique, but short-lived experiments seem also to have been made at Faenza, around 1500,

and Cafaggiolo, around the first quarter of the 16th century. A case could be made, on grounds of the style of the ornamental border, for an attribution to Castel Durante, in which case the piece could have been sent, like many others from the district, to have lustre added at a final firing at Gubbio; but it has never been demonstrated that the potters of Castel Durante and elsewhere in the Duchy of Urbino used the red pigment. Siena, which on grounds of style seems more likely than Faenza, is not known to have had access to the facilities needed for the application of lustre. On balance the present writer agrees with Rackham's attribution to Cafaggiolo (Rackham, 1940, p. 120, no. 348), while accepting that writer's warning that 1531 seems somewhat late for the use of lustre there.

J.V.G.M.

PROVENANCE: Alessandro Castellani Collection.
BIBLIOGRAPHY: Castellani Sale Catalogue, Paris, 31 March, 1884, lot 47.

Duke Vespasiano Gonzaga of Sabbioneta on horseback
Unknown (?Venetian) Woodcarver.
Horse and rider in two pieces; carved of willow and poplar;
polychrome repainting in 18th century; 2.52 m x 2.18 m. x
1.10 m
Palazzo Ducale, Sabbioneta

Of the equestrian statues surviving from the original twelve
carved in wood *c.* 1587 (see Cat. 48) for Duke Vespasiano
Gonzaga of Sabbioneta (1531-91), the one of Vespasiano himself alone has some claim to be near to a portrait from life. It
shows the Duke in black armour with gold ribands and the
insignia of the Golden Fleece granted to him in 1585 by Philip
II of Spain. Vespasiano had been in his service, away from
Sabbioneta, from 1568 to 1577 and in 1577 the Emperor Ru-
dolf II had conferred on him the Dukedom. Vespasiano's
long military career in Imperial and Spanish service, and his
applied knowledge of military architecture and urban planning at Sabbioneta (about twelve miles south west of Mantua)
make him second only to Ferrante Gonzaga lord of Guastalla
as the most distinguished Gonzaga prince of a cadet branch of
the family during the sixteenth century. His rebuilding of
Sabbioneta as fortress, town and seat of princely government
had begun in the 1550's, but it was after his return from Spain
in 1577 that works on the gateways, walls and Palace were
completed and a further building campaign included the Villa
or Casino and the Corridor Grande, the churches of the As-
sunta and Incoronata and the Theatre. Vespasiano's reputation as a patron who saw himself as a quasi-Emperor in miniature has endured better than his reputation as a psychopath-
ic personality who murdered his first wife, which has long
been relegated to legend (Luzio, 1922, II, pp. 254-58).

D.S.C.

BIBLIOGRAPHY: Affò, 1780, pp.91-92, 103; Mantua, *Mostra Iconog.*, 1937,
no. 283, pp. 63-64; Mann, 1938, pp. 263-64; Marani and Perina, 1965, pp.
402, 416 n. 8; Paccagnini, 1972, p. 127.
ADDITIONAL BIBLIOGRAPHY: K. Forster, "From "Rocca" to "Civitas": Urban Planning at Sabbioneta", *L'Arte*, II, 1969, no. 1, pp. 16-40.

203

V   The Beauty of Holiness

203

Photographs: The Cathedral of Mantua
Giulio Romano (*c.* 1499-1546)

On the 15th of April 1545, Cardinal Ercole and Ferrante Gonzaga petitioned the Mantuan people to contribute to the rebuilding of the Duomo, by levying a salt tax (d'Arco, 1857,
II, doc. 169) The petition describes the building as so small,
ugly and poorly made that the congregation could barely see
or hear. Giulio's task was to enlarge the church and to make
the presbytery more visible to the congregation. His project
was restricted by the necessity of retaining the gothic external
walls of the church, and the elegant Venetian gothic facade,
which had been designed and executed by Jacobello and Pietro Paolo dalle Masegne between 1396 and 1403 (Torelli,
1913, p. 67) and was illustrated in Morone's painting (Cat. 2).
The present façade was built at the end of the eighteenth
century.
The appearance of the old church is known from a description
by Jacopo Daino, archivist to the Mantuan court (Paccagnini,
1960, p. 115 n. 19) The church was divided into three aisles
with deep side chapels. The nave was covererd by a wooden
ceiling. At the end of the nave there was a choir raised above a
crypt. Giulio retained the outer walls but demolished the internal arrangement, and he obtained a wide area which could
be exploited to the maximum by inserting a five aisle basilical
plan comparable to that of Old St Peter's.
Work on the Duomo began in May 1545 and continued rapidly after Giulio's death in 1546 until 1547, when the structural
work was substantially complete. With a minimum of scaffolding, Corinthian columns of Veronese marble were inserted below the walls of the clerestory, one by one, as the old
piers were demolished. The wooden ceiling in the central
nave was replaced by a magnificent, gilded coffered ceiling in
the basilical manner. Giulio achieved splendid spatial effects
by the alternation of light wooden coffering in the central
nave and outer aisles with richly ornamented barrel vaults over
the inner aisles. The alternation of trabeation and arch, which
forms the elevation of the chapel entrances, reflects the cross
section through the nave. The sober architectural forms refer
to the elegant painted architecture in the *Sala dei Cavalli* at
Palazzo Te.
The interior of the nave is all that remains of Giulio's church.
His transept and apse which had been contained within the
perimetral walls of the gothic church, were demolished at the
end of the sixteenth century, and replaced by the present
domed crossing and elongated apse. The account books indicate that very little structural work was done in the crossing
and apse. After the demolition of the choir and crypt, the
walls were simply repaired and stuccoed. The east end of
Giulio's church may well have looked very similar to the
crossing and apse of Old St Peter's, which Giulio himself
reconstructed in his fresco of the *Donation of Constantine* in the
Sala di Costantino in Rome.

The modernisation of the Duomo came as the conclusion to a thorough reform of the diocese, and a programme of improvements to its churches undertaken by Cardinal Ercole. It may well have been Cardinal Ercole who promoted the idea of using an ideal reconstruction of St Peter's, Rome for the Duomo (also dedicated to St Peter).

The decision to retain the outer walls of the church, demonstrates not only the wish to economise, always uppermost in the Cardinal's mind, but also a desire to conserve the aspect of the piazza. To conserve while giving a new and beautiful face to old structures is central to Giulio's architectural practice in Mantua.

L.F.

BIBLIOGRAPHY: d'Arco, 1857; Paccagnini, 1960; Marani and Perina, 1961. ADDITIONAL BIBLIOGRAPHY: P. Torelli, "Jacobello e Pietro Paolo dalle Masegne a Mantova", *Rassegna d'Arte*, 1913.

204

Design, possibly for a Tapestry, with the arms of Cardinal Ercole Gonzaga

Giulio Romano (*c.* 1499-1546)
Pen and bistre wash, traces of chalk beneath, 42.7 x 28.8 cm
Chatsworth House (Inv. no. 117)

On the premature death of his brother Federico in 1540, Cardinal Ercole Gonzaga took up permanent residence in Mantua acting as regent for his nephew Duke Francesco (1533-50). Giulio Romano would have left the town on the death of Federico had the Cardinal not entreated him to stay. The Cardinal esteemed Giulio's work as highly as his brother had before him, and told Vasari, who visited Mantua, that the artist was more the master of that state than he was (Vasari, ed. Milanesi, v. p. 553).

This design would seem to be an initial *modello* for a tapestry glorifying the Cardinal's regency. Ercole's cardinal's hat and his arms are borne by winged genii, while a third winged genius (possibly Cupid) drives the chariot of state, reining in the four Gonzaga eagles, and preparing to hurl his dart (its barb only indicated in chalk). Possibly the Cardinal objected to the cupid, for in a second version of the design (Teylermuseum, Haarlem) he has been replaced by a draped female figure with a rudder (Hartt suggested she represented Wisdom, but the rudder is Fortune's attribute) and a scroll inscribed RENOVABITVR VT AQUILAE IUVENTVS, from Psalm 103,

204

V-VI: "Who satisfieth thy mouth with good things, so that thy youth is renewed like the eagle's. The Lord executeth righteousness and judgment for all that are oppressed".

J.T.M.

PROVENANCE: Sir Peter Lely; William, 2nd Duke of Devonshire.
BIBLIOGRAPHY: Hartt, 1958, pp. 252-53, 308, n. 362.
ADDITIONAL BIBLIOGRAPHY: Exhibited: Royal Academy, London, 1953, n. 59, Royal Academy, London, 1960, n. 571; *Drawings from Chatsworth*, London, Royal Academy, 1969, no. 27.

205

Letter of Cardinal Ercole Gonzaga to Queen Mary of England, Mantua, 8 July 1554

Manuscript in Italian on paper; autograph signature.
Public Record Office, London (SP 69/4 fol. 162)

Cardinal Ercole Gonzaga's congratulations upon the marriage in June 1554 of Queen Mary to Philip II, who had visited Mantua in 1549, were fulsome: he declared "the great contentment that all of us feel upon the marriage of Your Majesty with our most serene King", (*la gran contentezza che tutti noi qui sentiamo per lo felice matrimonio di Vostra Maesta col Serenissimo Re nostro*). The Bishop of Nola would be coming to present formal messages, meanwhile Ercole declared that the event came by the hand of God and promised great hopes for the future welfare of all Christendom, (in this he was deeply interested; he nearly became Pope in 1555 and presided over the Council of Trent a few years later).

Anglo-Mantuan relations became particularly close during Mary's reign and there was a resident Gonzaga ambassador in London, Annibale Litolfi, who in the summer of 1557 wrote not only political news but a general dscription of the country. Coming from a city with recent buildings designed by Alberti, Giulio Romano and Bertani it is not suprizing that he commented (after a brief remark about the King's Palace of Whitehall) that most buildings in England were without much architecture (*senza molto architettura*).

D.S.C.

BIBLIOGRAPHY: Luzio, 1917-18, pp. 212-222 for original text of Litolfi; *Cal. State Papers. For. (1553-8)*, 1861, no. 234 p. 103.

206

An architectural treatise dedicated to Cardinal Ercole Gonzaga

Giovanni Battista Bertani, *Gli oscuri et dificili passi dell'opera ionica di Vitruvio, di latino in volgare et alla chiara inteligentia tradotti et con le sue figure a luochi suoi*, Mantova, 1558
Collection of the Marquess of Northampton, Castle Ashby

Bertani's translation and commentary on Vitruvius on the Ionic order was written in 1556 and dedicated to Cardinal Ercole. The preface flatteringly refers to the Cardinal's Vitruvian erudition (he was in fact a discerning architectural patron). Bertani's text, which is critical of the theoretical and technical ignorance of other Vitruvian commentators (Alberti, Fra Giocondo, Serlio, and Barbaro) boasts of his own knowledge of the antiquities of Rome. The frontispiece, showing Hercules having slain the Hydra, was designed by Bertani himself and engraved by Giorgio Ghisi (1520-82). It seems more probably a reference to the Cardinal and his labours (cf. Cat. 205) than a "witty self-portrait" of Bertani having confuted misinterpreters of Vitruvius (Stedman Sheard, 1978).

206

Bertani (c. 1516-76) was born and educated in Mantua, His commentary refers to two visits to Rome during the Papacy of Paul III. In May 1549 he became *prefetto delle fabbriche ducale* in Mantua. The Patent refers to his architectural practice in Rome and elsewhere (d'Arco, 1857, II, doc. 172), as well as his excellence in painting and sculpture. He was employed as an architect by Duke Guglielmo, building for him vast extensions to the Ducal Palace, as well as the palatine church of Santa Barbara, a scheme which was strenuously opposed by Cardinal Ercole, who employed Bertani at the Duomo in the administrative post of *Presidente della fabbrica*. Documents of 1549-52 relating to work on the Duomo refer to stucco decoration.

He inserted a serliana into the facade of the Duomo, most probably following Girolamo Genga's model. Genga had been in Mantua in 1548-49 supervising the construction of a large-scale wooden model for the facade. Bertani's most important work for Cardinal Ercole, now lost, seems to have been a decorative scheme in stucco, for the transepts, crossing, and apse of the Duomo. This was commissioned in 1557 following the death of Ferrante, and was intended as a memorial to Gonzaga bishops and to the Regency of Ferrante and Ercole.

Bertani's position at the Gonzaga court, gave him prestige outside Mantua. In 1550 he was invited to take part in the competition for the Rialto Bridge in Venice. And his treatise, which was written probably as a piece of self-advertisement placed him in the mainstream of architectural debate in Italy. He was invited by Martino Bassi, along with Vasari, Vignola, and Palladio, to contribute to the debate about Pellegrino Tibaldi's project for Milan cathedral. His reply was published in 1572 in Bassi's *Dispareri in materia d'architettura*. Bertani's house in Mantua is ornamented with a stone Ionic portal, on the right of the portal a fluted ionic semi-column is shown, and the geometric construction of the ionic volute, as illustrated in his treatise, is carved on the left.

L.F.

BIBLIOGRAPHY: d'Arco, 1857; DBI
ADDITIONAL BIBLIOGRAPHY: F. Pellati, "G.B. Bertani architetto, pittore e commentatore di Vitruvio", in *Scritti di storia dell'arte in onore di Mario Salmi*, Rome, 1963, vol. III, pp. 31-38; W. Stedman Sheard, *Antiquity in the Renaissance*, Smith College Museum of Art Exhibition 1978, Northampton Mass., 1979, no. 98.

207

Literary appreciations of Cardinal Ercole Gonzaga after his death (1563)

Giulio Castellani, *Componimenti volgari et latini di diversi et eccellenti autori, in morte di Monsignore Hercole Gonzaga, Cardinal di Mantova, con la vita del medesimo descritta dall'Asciutto, Academico Invaghito,* in Mantova appresso Giacomo Rufinelli, 1564

British Library (11431 c23)

Castellani (1528-86) the erudite compiler, and in part author, of this elegiac volume, had been secretary to Cesare Gonzaga Prince of Guastalla and in 1562 was a founding member of the Accademia degli Invaghiti at Mantua, which among other functions held twice-weekly lectures on Aristotle's *Ethics*. The Academicians bestowed nicknames upon each other, his being "Asciutto" (the dry); twelve others also contributed verses in Italian praising their deceased patron, including Bernardo Tasso who proclaimed him a new Hercules and champion of Christ (*Hercole nuovo, gran campion di Christo*, p. 42v). In his short biography Castellani insisted that Ercole could have become Pope but lacked this ambition (in fact he nearly had been elected in 1555) and emphasized among his Herculean labours, church reform in his diocese of Mantua. There is also emphasis on his eloquence (*hebbe... una lingua faconda e purissima si latina come volgare nell'isprimerse i suoi pensieri*), and the pleasure he took in intellectual debates and in comedies with a moral significance.

The printer, Giacomo Ruffinelli, was printing books in Mantua from 1547 to 1589.

D.S.C.

BIBLIOGRAPHY: Rhodes, 1957, pp. 24-26; DBI

208

Photograph: **The Abbey church of San Benedetto Po**
Giulio Romano (c. 1499-1546)

The Benedictine monastery of San Benedetto Po, on the south bank of the River Po about twelve miles south east of Mantua, had longstanding links with the Gonzaga family, who had obtained some of its estates as early as the twelfth century. As rulers of the Mantuan territories, the Gonzagas co-existed with the monks as manorial lords as well as powerful ecclesiastical patrons. Since the middle of the fifteenth

208

century Gonzaga prelates succesively held the office of the *prepositus* of S.Benedetto, drawing a pension from the revenues of the monks' estates.

However the rebuilding of the church in the middle of the sixteenth-century was on the initiative of the monks. They had been procrastinating over this since 1503, when Lucrezia Pico della Mirandola had bequeathed a large estate for this purpose. In 1539 the chapter finally commissioned a design from Giulio Romano.

Giulio responded with a magnificent and economical scheme, by retaining the structural elements of the gothic church. The nave piers were enclosed in brick and stucco and converted into the tall Corinthian order, which rises to the springing of the steeply pitched vault (disguised by lozenge painting). The pointed arches of the nave bays and their irregular dimensions were masked by using the serliana motif. The dimension of the arch of the serliana remains regular in each bay, while the trabeation expands and contracts to mask the different dimensions of the nave arcades. The serliana is supported on squat columns with eccentric capitals which had been prepared in 1498 for use in the building of the library at San Benedetto. The ambulatory, to provide space for five new altars is the only addition made by Giulio; this is a rare feature in northern Italy. Its architectural articulation with niches and pilasters with continuous mouldings rather than capitals, derives from the Villa Madama in Rome.

A large choir was required at San Benedetto, both to accomodate its own large congregation, and for regular meetings of the General Chapter of the Cassinense Congregation, to which it belonged. It had to be located in the nave, on the site of the gothic choir, because the arrangement of the cloister prevented the building of a retro-choir, usually built at other Cassinense churches. The rich ornamental effects, which contrast with the severity of the other churches, was in great part conditioned by the use of brick and stucco which Giulio was forced to use because of limited availability of stone.

The façade and side elevation had to be homogeneous, because both can be seen on entering the piazza. Giulio's solution is an adaptation of Bramante's Belvedere motif, but he departed from the prototype by bracketing the entablature foreward over the arches, thereby emphasising the tripartite opening of the portico. The irregularity of the flank is concealed by stressing the arches, all of the same dimension. Many details on the facade belong to the eighteenth century restoration. The facade's original appearance is uncertain.

L.F.

ADDITIONAL BIBLIOGRAPHY: B. Luchino, *Cronica della vera origine et attioni della Illustriss. et famoss. contessa Mathilda,* Mantua, 1592; R. Bellodi, *Il monastero di San Benedetto in Polirone nella storia e nell'arte,* Mantua, 1905 (reprinted Accademia Polironiana, San Benedetto Po, 1974); P. Piva and G. Pavesi, "Giulio Romano e la chiesa abbaziale di Polirone: Documenti e Proposte filologiche", in *Studi su Giulio Romano,* Accademia Polironiana, San Benedetto Po, 1975.

209

Photograph: **The Palatine Basilica of Santa Barbara**
Giovanni Battista Bertani (*c.* 1516? - 1576) [Pl. 40, 94]

The basilica of Santa Barbara, consecrated in 1564 although not complete until 1572, was designed with the requirements of a distinctive liturgy and with the performance of polyphonic music in mind (see essay by Fenlon). The façade and its portico and continuous attic recalls San Benedetto Po by Giulio Romano (Cat. 208), while the interior with its two tribunes is reminiscent of San Salvatore in Venice (see essay by Burns, n. 64). The cross patterned stucco work in the apse

may be a reference to the many relics contained in the church which relate to the Crucifixion.

L.F.

210

Jewel pendant with monogram of the Name of Jesus
Maker unknown (S. Germany)
Gold, partly enamelled, set with diamonds, rubies, opals, pearls; 7.5 x 6.8 cm
Basilica di Santa Barbara, Mantua

Presented by Duke Guglielmo Gonzaga to his new palatine church of Santa Barbara soon after its foundation, this jewel had possibly been sent when his son and heir Vincenzo was born or baptized as a present from Albrecht V of Bavaria and Ann of Austria, sister of Guglielmo's wife Eleonora. Its workmanship is definitely south German and it can be compared with objects illustrated in Albrecht V's jewel inventory of *c.* 1555. The monogram I.H.S. (*Iesus Hominum Salvator*) in gothic lettering appears beneath the figure of God the Father delivering a benediction; above is a crown and on one side a male figure and on the other a female, with an apple. One interpretation (Bosio, 1974) sees the meaning as Christ in the centre of creation and redemption, with diamonds representing the waters; rubies representing fire, turquoise the blue of the heavens etc. The two small figures (*putti*) at the bottom of the jewel are less easily explained as occult powers preserving the mysteries of nature.

The reverse of the medal depicts the Adoration of the Golden Calf, Moses receiving and breaking the Tables of the Law, a warrior, a woman gathering fruit, putti etc.; it bears the date 1562 and has two clips (attached at a later date). The style of the strapwork with tight scrolls combined with figures, the range of enamel colours and composition of the *basse taille* seen on the back relate this piece to another pendant dated *c.* 1560-70 (*Princely Magnificence,* no. 29, pp. 5, 27)

Another IHS pendant, also (presumably) made in south Germany is believed, curiously, to have been a gift in the other direction, from the young Duke Francesco Gonzaga (d. 1550) to his wife Catherina of Austria who married (1553) Sigismund King of Poland and bequeathed the jewel to Duchess Ann of Bavaria in 1572 (Thoma and Brunner no. 50, p. 68, Falk, 1575, p. 111).

D.S.C., A.S.C.

BIBLIOGRAPHY: I. Toesca in Mantua, *Tesori,* 1974, no. 2, p. 60; London, 1980, *Princely Magnificence* pp. 5, 27

ADDITIONAL BIBLIOGRAPHY: Y. Hackenbroch, "Un gioiello della corte di Monaco ora in Santa Barbara a Mantova", *Antichità viva,* VI, 1967, n. 3, pp. 51-58; L. Bosio, "Il gioiello di S. Barbara, sintesi cosmologica", *La Cittadella* 1 Dec. 1974, p. 11; H. Thoma and H. Brunner, *Schatzkammer der Residenz München,* Munich, 1971; F. Falk, *Edelsteinschliff und Fassungsformen,* Ulm 1975.

210

211

211

Reliquary in the form of a monstrance to contain the Precious Blood of Christ presented (1573) to St Barbara
Probably Italian; on stylistic grounds (*c.* 1530–50)
Gold; h. 37 cm
Basilica di Santa Barbara, Mantua

This elaborate reliquary, which enabled the palatine church of St Barbara to share with Sant'Andrea the privilege of possessing some drops of the Precious Blood, was evidently among Duke Guglielmo Gonzaga's many gifts of his new foundation; drops were contained in two small crystal reliquary pendants within the central chamber (originally surrounded by glass). Documentary evidence shows that it had been delivered by 3 November 1573 when the Blood was inserted (act of the notary Cinzio Petrozzani) and it is described in an inventory of 31 October 1611 together with a gold reliquary (no longer surviving) made to contain a relic from the Crown of Thorns. It was at first kept within the great gilded and glass chest (Cat. 213). The church of St Barbara was a treasure house of holy relics, and many still remain there.

D.S.C., A.S.C.

BIBLIOGRAPHY: L. Bosio in Mantua, *Tesori*, 1974, no. 6, p. 62

212

Reliquary casket for a bone of St Barbara
Unknown Venetian goldsmith, *c.* 1582
Silver gilt with panel of glass; figure of the saint in plaster upon the lid; 30 x 40 x 23 cm
Basilica di Santa Barbara, Mantua

This reliquary and its contents were a gift to Duke Guglielmo

Gonzaga for his new basilica from the Republic of Venice, as expressed by an illuminated sealed diploma in the name of Doge Nicolò Da Ponte which bears the date 21 September 1582; the relic of a rib (*de costis*) of St Barbara had, according to this, been placed in a gilded silver tabernacle prepared for it (*in tabernaculo argenteo aurato ad id praeparato*).
A notarial act (notary Francesco Petrozzani) records the reception of the relic in Mantua, where it had been brought by state barge (*bucintoro*), on 29 September 1582; St Carlo Borromeo was among those present.
The relic is not be confused with a relic of the jawbone of St Barbara which was presented to the Basilica in January 1601. The casket later came to be kept within the imposing chest (Cat. no. 213) intended for the reliquary containing the precious Blood.

D.S.C.

BIBLIOGRAPHY: L. Bosio in *Mantua: Tesori*, 1974, no. 8, p. 63.

213

Reliquary in the form of a chest, intended to contain the relic of the precious Blood and later used to contain the relic of St Barbara
Unknown Venetian workshop. *c.* 1600
Ebony with silver gilt set with polished, faceted and turned pieces of rock crystal; 28 twisted columns of crystal with bases and capital in silver gilt; base inside of gilded and engraved brass; 12 feet (original) with gilded bronze decoration upon original base of walnut; 70 x 94 x 60 cm
Basilica di Santa Barbara, Mantua

This astonishing work, apparently donated to Santa Barbara by Duke Vincenzo I, is recorded in an inventory of precious objects in the church dated 31 October 1610 as "a great chest made with wonderful art from crystal, and decorated with many columns, with the vessel of pure gold (Cat. 211) in which is shown the ampule with the Most Precious Blood of Our Lord Jesus Christ" (*Capsa magna ex cristallo miro artificio*

212

fabricata, ac multis columnis ornata, cum vase Aureo purissimo in quo exstat ampulla cum Pretiosissimo Sanguine Domini Nostri Jesu Christi). Later it was used to contain the silver gilt casket with the relic of St Barbara (Cat. 212).

That the chest was made in Venice seems certain. It may have similarities to a large crystal chest (*una cassa di cristallo molto grande*) which Francesco Sansovino observed (before 1581) in the shop of Antonio Maria Fontana in the Ruga dei Orefici (Huth, 1971, pp. 7-9) and is certainly related to a group of eight lacquered caskets dating from *c.* 1600 which, it has been suggested, show oriental influence. Two of these are particularly close: a chest 96 cm long in the Museo Nacional de Arte Antigua, Lisbon, and another 76 cm long in the City Art Museum, St Louis (Huth, pp. 16-17, plates 24, 26).

The same workshop must also have produced a hexagonal tabernacle in the church of San Donato, Murano. This has six twisted columns of crystal surmounted by a cupola and stands on a base of beechwood (max ht. 1.38 m). The ebony is lacquered and the bases of the columns are bronze not silver; the floor of the interior (max. diam. 36 cm) is also lacquered. The Santa Barbara chest is therefore much more elaborate and costly.

D.S.C., A.S.C.

BIBLIOGRAPHY: L. Bosio in Mantua, *Tesori,* 1974, no. 9, p. 63.
ADDITIONAL BIBLIOGRAPHY: H. Huth, *Lacquer of the West. The History of a Craft and an Industry 1550-1950,* Chicago and London, 1971.

214

The Breviary of Santa Barbara
Breviarii S. Barbara, 2 vols, Venice 1583
British Library (c. 36 f. 23)

208

The Palatine Basilica of Santa Barbara was responsible directly to the Holy See rather than the local diocesan authorities. One indication of its exclusiveness was the development of a distinctive Santa Barbara rite with its own separate missal and breviary based on reformist ideas. This liturgy, which to a considerable extent was designed by Duke Guglielmo Gonzaga, did not come into immediate operation when the Basilica was completed, but was the subject of lengthy negotiations between Mantua and Rome which, from the Vatican's point of view, were merely one aspect of the general reform of rite which had begun in earnest during the pontificate of Pius V and which had continued under Gregory XIII. The Santa

214

Barbara breviary finally appeared in 1583 in two versions: a pocket-sized edition, presumably designed for practical use by the Santa Barbara clergy, and a larger format to be used by the celebrant. The Basilica's own missal was published in the same year, and two years later the ducal printing house brought out the Santa Barbara *Officium defunctorum.* Taken together with the large series of plainchant books from the Basilica, these printed liturgies allow re-construction of the complete and distinct Santa Barbara liturgy for the entire church year, a liturgy which was then further embellished on feast-days by the performance of polyphony, much of it specially composed for the church.

I.F.

BIBLIOGRAPHY: Bohatta, 1937; Fenlon, 1980, Chap. III.

215

Mass settings by Palestrina (c. 1525/6-94)
Manuscript written by Francesco Sforza, 1587
Biblioteca del Conservatorio di Musica G. Verdi, Milan (S. Barbara MS 164, Cat 226)

Santa Barbara was designed as a dynastic chapel on a grand scale. At the instigation of its founder, Duke Guglielmo Gonzaga, special Papal privileges were acquired for the institution, including a separate rite and the prestigious rank of Apostolic Protonotary for some of its clergy. Guglielmo, a composer himself, took a considerable interest in the arrangements for the performance of polyphony, some of which was specially commissioned, not only from composers in Gonzaga employment, but also from men working elsewhere. The most significant of these commissions was that of a cycle of masses written by Palestrina, Maestro of the Cappella Giulia in Rome, which, together with a number of other specially composed works, remained mostly unpublished. Fortunately most of the Santa Barbara library, both manuscripts and printed books, has survived. MS 164 is a good example of the distinctive style of manuscript decoration in coloured inks practised by the Santa Barbara scriptoria during the late sixteenth and early seventeenth centuries; it is signed and dated 1587 by the principal scribe Francesco Sforza.
This includes five of Palestrina's masses for the Basilica, two for doubles and three Marian masses, together with Passion settings by Giaches de Wert and Francesco Rovigo and a *Missa Defunctorum*.

I.F.

PROVENANCE: Library of the Palatine Basilica of Santa Barbara, Mantua; collection of Don Giuseppe Greggiati, Ostiglia.
BIBLIOGRAPHY: Strunk, 1947; Jeppesen, 1950, 1953; Barblan, 1972, pp. 276-78; Fenlon, 1980, pp. 90ff, Appendix III.
ADDITIONAL BIBLIOGRAPHY: S. Reiner, "La vag'Angioletta (and others)", Part I, *Analecta musicologica*, 14, 1974, p. 26

216

Psalm settings by Giacomo Gastoldi and others
Manuscript on paper written by Francesco Sforza, dated 1614 and 1625
Biblioteca del Conservatorio di Musica G. Verdi, Milan (S. Barbara MS 155, Cat. 162)

This collection of psalm settings, copied by Sforza towards the end of his career, includes as well as psalm settings by Gastoldi, pieces by Wert, Antonio Taroni, and Francesco Gonzaga. As with the contents of MS 164, these pieces remained unpublished as a private repertory reserved for the exclusive use of the Basilica.

I.F.

PROVENANCE: As above, Cat. 215.
BIBLIOGRAPHY: Barblan, 1972, pp. 178-82, and as for Cat. 215 above.

216

215

217

Magnum opus musicum (Munich, 1614)
Orlando de Lassus (1532-94)
Paper, contemporary binding, 30.8 x 19.5 cm
Biblioteca del Conservatorio di Musica G. Verdi, Milan

In addition to manuscripts containing specially commissioned polyphony for the Basilica, the Santa Barbara library also includes a substantial collection of printed music spanning the period from 1505, just four years after the first books of printed polyphony were produced in Italy, to the early seventeenth century. Viewed chronologically these publications not only mirror the changing styles of Italian sacred music, but also reflect the expansion of the Santa Barbara musical establishment, and the important position of the Basilica in court ceremonial, during the rule of Duke Vincenzo Gonzaga. The *Magnum opus musicum*, assembled by Ferdinand and Rudolph de Lassus as a memorial to their father Orlando, is a lavish though incomplete corpus of the latter's motets ranging from two-voice compositions to pieces in twelve parts. Although there is some attempt at liturgical ordering in the book, it is essentially a random collection of compositions from various periods. The Santa Barbara set of partbooks, which has survived complete, is elaborately bound and finished with silk ties in the Gonzaga colours.

I.F.

PROVENANCE: Library of the Palatine Basilica of Santa Barbara, Mantua; collection of Don Giuseppe Greggiati, Ostiglia.
BIBLIOGRAPHY: Barblan, 1972, pp. 239-49; Fenlon, 1980, Appendix III.

218

Photograph: **View of the high altar of Santa Barbara during the funeral of Duke Carlo II Gonzaga** (1666) [Pl. 93]
Engraving by Frans Geffels (c. 1635/6-99)
Biblioteca Comunale, Mantua

This is the earliest known interior view of Santa Barbara; Geffels, who was born in Antwerp, was in Mantua by 1659 and had been employed by Carlo II as a painter and *Prefetto* of Buildings.

Scudo of Duke Guglielmo
Gold coin; diam. 22 mm; 3.28 g
British Museum, Department of Coins and Medals (57.9.
10.107)

Characteristic of Duke Guglielmo's prudent government was
his concern for the pure metal content of his silver and gold
coinage. He wrote on 31 January 1579 that "the prince's honour and the mint's profit cannot exist together" (Magnaguti,
II p. 27). A variety of types were used upon the reverses of his
gold *scudi* or ducats, including Virgil and the reliquary of the
Precious Blood. This example shows a twisted fillet with the
device VG VG, which has not been explained; it might possibly stand as an abbreviation for V (ir) G (ilius) or signify the
name of the heir, Vincenzo Gonzaga. The obverse shows the
Gonzaga arms.

D.S.C.

BIBLIOGRAPHY: CNI, iv, p. 300, 12 var.; Magnaguti, II, 1915, pp. 22-23

219   220

220

Eleonora of Austria (1534-94), wife of Duke Guglielmo Gonzaga
Pastorino dei Pastorini (1508-92)
Medal; lead; diam. 72 mm; uniface; signed 1561
Victoria & Albert Museum, Department of Sculpture (Inv.
A. 260-1910)

Duke Guglielmo married his Habsburg wife, daughter of
Emperor Ferdinand I, in 1561 and the medal struck by Pastorino (Cat. 145) commemorates this prestigious bride. Eleonora and Guglielmo were both extravagantly devout, though he
did not share her devotion to the Jesuit Order, which she
persuaded him to admit to Mantua only in 1584, three years
before his death. She was a generous benefactor to the school
founded by the Jesuits and to the church of San Salvatore to
which they were attached until their own purpose-built
church, dedicated to the Trinity, was inaugurated in June
1591; Eleonora was buried there (see essay by Signorini) and
Antonio Possevino the elder expressed the Order's appreciation in his short account of her life. Commenting on the number of eagles painted upon the catafalque, he pointed out that
she was not only an Emperor's daughter, but the niece of
another (Charles V) who ended his days in religious seclu-
sion, the sister of Emperor Maximilian II and aunt of the
reigning Rudolph II (pp. 10-11). Much given to prayer, fast-
ing and visitation of the sick, she sold her jewels to pay for
pious works and was pained even to see breadcrumbs fall out
of reverence for the material substance of the Sacrament (pp.
59-61).

D.S.C.

BIBLIOGRAPHY: Donesmondi, II, 1616, pp. 268-69; 275; 313-18; U. Baz-
zotti in Mantua, *Rubens*, 1977, pp. 28-30, 50-51.
ADDITIONAL BIBLIOGRAPHY: A. Possevino, *Vita et morte della serenissima
Eleonora Archiduchessa di Austria et duchessa di Mantova*, Mantua 1594.

221

221

Study for the tomb of Cardinal Francesco Gonzaga, 1566
Anonymous Mantuan School
Pen and brown ink and wash over black chalk on paper. Top
right hand corner made up, inscribed M.DLXVI. in black
chalk.
British Museum, Department of Prints and Drawings, (No.
1948-4-10-329)

The drawing was correctly identified as a design for a wall
tomb of Cardinal Francesco Gonzaga (1538-66) (see essay
above by Signorini). Previously it had been thought to be
intended for the tomb of his cousin Cardinal Federico Gonzaga (1540-65), posthumous son of the first Duke of Mantua,
but the date inscribed on the drawing is that of Francesco's
death. Signorini suggests that another British Museum drawing (Pl. 18), a far more elaborate tomb design including
figures of Faith, Charity, Justice, Fortitude and Fame as well
as a portrait bust of a cardinal and the Gonzaga eagles, may be
the project for Cardinal Federico's tomb. The portraits in the
two designs would appear to be very similar, but Signorini
has noticed some differences in the arrangement of the hair
which accords with their respective portraits in the Schloss
Ambras collection. Neither of the tomb designs was ever
executed.
For a brief period in 1563 the Gonzaga had three cardinals in
the family, by far the most distinguished being Cardinal Ercole, President of the Council of Trent and Bishop of Mantua, who died in May 1563 and was succeded successively as
bishop by his nephews Cardinal Federico (d. 1565) and Cardinal Francesco who collapsed in the Conclave that elected
Pope Pius V, died on 6 January 1566, and was buried in
S. Lorenzo in Lucina where an inscribed tomb-slab records his
brief career. The son of Ferrante Gonzaga of Guastalla, Francesco was brought up in his uncle, Cardinal Ercole's, household in Rome, he was created cardinal by Pius IV in 1561, and
two years later was instrumental in obtaining the cardinal's
hat for Federico. Another son of Ferrante's, Giovanni Vincenzo (1540-91) was created cardinal in 1578.

J.T.M.

BIBLIOGRAPHY: Chacon, 1677, vol. 111, pp. 934-35

222

Photograph: **Plan for a Gonzaga mausoleum in the crypt
of Sant'Andrea** [Pl. 13]
Unknown draughtsman (Antonio Maria Viani?), 1595

Watercolour drawing on paper, 40 cm x 54.8 cm.; scale 1.44; 129 cm
Archivio di Stato, Mantua, Mag. Camerale Antico b. B b 1 fasc. 4,3

The drawing, attached to the second will (dated 29 July 1595) of Duke Vincenzo I Gonzaga, shows the crypt of Sant'Andrea in the form of a Greek cross; along the walls are twenty-four tombs meant to contain the remains — or at least to commemorate the fame — of the twelve Gonzaga rulers of Mantua and their wives from Luigi the first Captain (d. 1360) to Vincenzo I, who sponsored this grandiose project, and his wife Eleonora de' Medici. Above the tombs in niches were to be placed life-size marble statues of the rulers (see essay by Signorini, and Cat. 223) kneeling in adoration of the relic of the Precious Blood of Christ preserved in a central chapel in the same crypt, and busts of their wives who earned distinction as the mothers of the Gonzaga line. The tombs were meant to display appropriate epitaphs. The project, never completed, was probably designed for the Duke by his Prefect of Buildings, Antonio Maria Viani. Vincenzo's personal commitment to it, however, is evident from the text of his successive wills, and the drawing bears some notes in his own hand as well as his signature and seal. He gives specific instructions for the facing in black and white marble of the Chapel of the Holy Blood, and for the use of marble for the columns and tombs. A cross indicates the places for the princes' tombs, two crosses the places for their wives. The text is as follows:
La cappella del santissimo sangue di Nostro Signore sia ingrostata di fòri di marmo nero et bianco. Le collonne tutte siano di marmo, compagne di quelle che hora vi sono et le sepolture delli dodeci principi siano, conforme al disegno, nelli loghi segnati colle sante + et le dodeci delle mogli colle ++ doppie, conforme all'altro disegno cioè dal mezzo in sù.
Mogli. Prèncipi.
Io, Vincenzo Gonzaga, duca di Mantova et di Monferrato, dichiaro questo disegno essere secondo la mia deliberata volontà.

R.S.

BIBLIOGRAPHY: Previously unpublished. Luzio, 1913, p. 182 believed the drawing to be lost. See essay above by Signorini.

223

Statue of Duke Guglielmo Gonzaga (d. 1587) **at prayer,** (c. 1600) [Pl. 16]
Unknown sculptor
Carrara marble; h. 1.44 m. w. c. 50 cm
Basilica di Sant'Andrea, Mantua

This statue was almost certainly intended to form part of the mausoleum or cenotaph of Gonzaga princes in the crypt of Sant'Andrea, where the much venerated relic of the Precious Blood of Christ was preserved: a project of Duke Vincenzo I first recorded in his will of 1595 (see essay by Signorini, and Cat. 222). The figure of Vincenzo's hunch-backed and intensely devout father was probably the only one of his eleven predecessors to have been completed for the scheme; the posture, and the rough unfinished left-hand side where the floral pattern of the mantle is not continued, certainly suggest that it was meant to be placed within the niche according to the drawing. Further evidence is provided by a letter dated 16 July 1599 from Tullio Petrozzani, high priest (*primicerio*) of Sant'Andrea, to Duke Vincenzo. This informed him that the sculptor commissioned to execute works in the crypt had satisfied the Prefect of the Ducal Buildings (Antonio Maria Viani) and had promised to send by September the *saggio* —

presumably a sketch or model — of a statue of Duke Guglielmo; if approved, he could then be commissioned to do a second figure (... *il scultore per il santuario de S. Andrea è stato qui et s'è ancora partito con haver dato buona sodisfatione di lui al signor conte Giovan Battista, al signor prefetto et a me, et ha promesso di mandar il saggio, datoli per tutto settembre, d'una statua, quella ciò è del serenissimo signor padre di vostra altezza di felice memoria, et da quella si farà il secondo, se sarà atto a servire, come crediamo, e con assai bona condicione*).
The letter goes on to mention that Viani had set to work a painter who specialized in fake marble to decorate one of the niches in the crypt, probably the one intended for Duke Guglielmo's statue.
On the other hand Amadei, the eighteenth-century editor of Mantuan chronicles, wrote that the statue was ordered by Duke Guglielmo himslf in 1574 when the Emperor Maximilian II had formally conferred on him the Dukedom of Monferrato, although he had already inherited this title.

R.S.

BIBLIOGRAPHY; Amadei, II, 1955, p. 799 followed by Marani, 1965, pp. 295, 306, n. 28; Perina, 1965, p. 92; Unpublished letter in ASMAG b. 2677.

224

St Barbara (c. 1620)
Domenico Fetti (c. 1589-1623)
Oil on canvas; 100.7 x 75.6 cm
Her Majesty the Queen (Cat. 472)

Cardinal Ferdinando Gonzaga had already employed Fetti, a pupil of Cigoli's when resident in Rome in 1611 (Paccagnini, 1956, p. 578). On returning to Mantua as ruler in 1612, Ferdinando sent for Fetti, who in 1613 was earning a salary of fifteen *ducatoni* a month as court artist, in addition to being paid for specific works for the Duke. He stayed in Mantua until 1622, decorating its churches (Sant'Orsola, Sta Trinita) and the Villa Favorita, and also producing many fine portraits and small parable scenes.
Two sets of paintings of half length saints are listed in the 1627 inventory of the Palazzo Ducale: eight (male) saints were in the *Galaria piciola* (Luzio, 1913, p. 109, no. 269), and seven male and female saints (*Santi e Sante diverse*) were in the oratory above the library, part of the new apartments built by Ferdinando (Luzio, 1913, p. 133). The oratory had a painting of the *Marriage of St Catherine* (unattributed) over the altar, and it is possible that it, and Fetti's saints were painted for this setting.
Michael Levey (1964, p. 78) identified this saint as Barbara, indicating the tower in the background in which, according to the *Golden Legend* she was imprisoned by her father. Levey dated the painting around 1620, remarking on the freedom of the brushwork and compositon compared to earlier Mantuan religious works. Fetti was influenced by Rubens, whose work he could have seen both in Rome and Mantua, but also by Paolo Veronese after his move north. St Barbara was popular with the Gonzaga, possibly a reflection of familial piety to Barbara of Brandenburg, wife of Ludovico Gonzaga; the great palatine chapel built by Duke Guglielmo was dedicated to the same saint.

J.T.M.

PROVENANCE; Palazzo Ducale, Mantua (1627 inventory); Charles I, sold during the Commonwealth, recovered at the Restoration.
BIBLIOGRAPHY: Luzio, 1913, pp. 109, 133, 285 ff; Paccagnini, 1956, pp. 578-84; Levey, 1964, p. 15, 78, no. 472, with full bibliography.
ADDITIONAL BIBLIOGRAPHY: *Venetian Seventeenth Century Painting*, National Gallery, London, 1979, p. 61.

224

225

225

St Carlo Borromeo (*c.* 1620)
Domenico Fetti (*c.* 1589-1623)
Oil on Canvas 100.7 x 75.2 cm
Her Majesty the Queen (Cat. 473)

St Carlo Borromeo (1538-84), Archbishop of Milan, who strictly applied the principles of the Council of Trent in reforming his diocese was born of an aristocratic Milanese family, the nephew of Pope Pius IV. He held the interests of his family close to heart, and maried all his three sisters to princes: the eldest, Camilla (d. 1582), to Cesare Gonzaga, Lord of Guastalla (d. 1575), son of Ferrante the founder of the line. Later St Carlo provided the dowry for his niece Margherita Gonzaga by means of a loan of 25000 *scudi* from the Duke of Tuscany. He visited Mantua on various occasions: in 1580 for the Translation of the relic of St Barbara, and in 1583 for the physical examination of Margherita Farnese which led to the dissolution of her marriage with Vincenzo Gonzaga (Luzio, 1922, p. 217). Duke Ferdinando had a particular reverence for St Carlo (he was in Rome for his canonisation in 1610, and made a pilgrimage to Milan in 1621 to venerate the saint's remains) (Askew, 1978, p. 282), and this together with the family connection probably prompted him to include his portrait amongst those commissioned from Fetti. The measurements of the painting would suggest that it belongs to the same series as St Barbara (Cat. 224). For further commentary see above.

J.T.M.

PROVENANCE: as Cat. 224
BIBLIOGRAPHY: Luzio, 1922, p. 217; Mantua, *Mostra Iconog.*, 1937, p. 84; Levey, 1964, p. 78, no. 473; DBI; Askew, 1978, p. 282.

226

Eleonora de' Medici (1567-1611) **wife of Duke Vincenzo I Gonzaga at prayer with their children** (c. 1600)
Unknown Flemish painter
Oil on canvas, 168 x 220 cm
Museo del Palazzo Ducale, Mantua (Inv. sta. 6023)

This painting, attributed by Luzio (1913) to Frans Pourbus the Younger, who arrived in Mantua in 1600, and more recently assigned to his workshop (Perina, Mattioli) may in fact have been by a Flemish artist who had nothing to do with Pourbus; its limited qualities of expression and the preciseness of its style are altogether different and archaic by comparison with Pourbus. The summary definition of space and rigidity of the kneeling figures also suggest this. Here, portrayed with their mother, are all the children of Vincenzo Gonzaga and Eleonora de' Medici (from left to right Francesco, Ferdinando, Vincenzo, Margherita, and Eleonora) who appeared a few years later in Rubens's *Adoration of the Trinity* (Cat. 228). Judging from the apparent age of the youngest daughter, Eleonora (b. 1598) the painting can be dated to *c.* 1600. The picture effectively conveys the religiosity of Eleonora de' Medici; the setting relates to no particular room or oratory within the Ducal Palace but simply evokes in the abstract the family's faith in

226

the Church. This is symbolized by the statues of St Peter and St Paul in the niches in the background and the figure of St Lawrence beside the crucifix on the small and partly visible altarcloth.

G.M.

PROVENANCE: Gift from Marchesa d'Arco di Bagno, 1921.
BIBLIOGRAPHY: Luzio, 1913, pp. 48-49; Mantua, *Mostra Iconog.*, 1937, p. 38; Ozzòla, 1949, no. 197 p. 11; Perina in Marani and Perina, 1965, II, p. 452; D. Mattioli in Mantua, *Rubens,* 1977, p. 74.

227

The church of Sant'Orsola presented by the architect to Margherita Gonzaga

Domenico Fetti (*c.* 1589-1624);
Oil on canvas, blue monochrome, lunette 245 x 276 cm;
(*c.* 1614-26)
Museo del Palazzo Ducale, Mantua

Margherita Gonzaga (1564-1618), sister of Duke Vincenzo I and widow of Duke Alfonso II d'Este of Ferrara (d. 1597), after returning to Mantua set up her own establishment in a convent formerly of Ursuline nuns which she transferred to the Order of Clarisses; and without taking vows herself nor renouncing her interest in political and dynastic matters, she presided there over a minor court surrounded by genteel but unwealthy young women. The church retained its dedication to Sant'Orsola and a new, octagonal building was projected in 1608 by the architect Gianbattista Viani. It was consecrated on 18 February 1613, the year of Fetti's arrival at Mantua in the steps of his patron Cardinal Ferdinando Gonzaga, the new Duke. The painting shows Viani presenting his building to Margherita; iconographically unusual in its exclusive reference to the donor, and its omission of the patron saint.

The portraiture is not very distinguished; it has been pointed out that the head of Viani is remarkably like the head of Christ in Fetti's painting of *St Martin in Ecstasy* (St Giovanni e Protasio, Mantua) and one may feel sceptical about the suggested identification of the two venerable figures on the left as Francesco Gonzaga Bishop of Mantua (1593-1620), who had a strong influence upon Margherita, and Tiberio Guarini her chaplain and adviser who wrote a short account of her new foundation. The commission for the main altarpiece went to Ludovico Carracci, but Fetti's paintings of *The Holy Martyrs* and *The Multiplication of Bread and Fishes* (both now in the Palazzo Ducale) were also for Sant'Orsola, and in all he made four chiaroscuro paintings, to be placed high over arches, this being the only one known to have survived. Meanwhile Fetti's sister Lucrina, a nun at Sant'Orsola, collaborated on a painting of St Barbara for the church. Margherita exerted strong personal influence: it was she who insisted that her nephew Duke Ferdinando should break with his mistress Camilla Faà (who became a nun elsewhere) and embark on his sterile marriage to Caterina de' Medici (1617).

D.S.C.

PROVENANCE: Sant'Orsola till its suppression (1786); Accademia Teresia-

na; unknown location till identified (1963) in collection of Antonio Nievo at Colloredo (Udine); bought by the State in 1978 for Palazzo Ducale, Mantua.
BIBLIOGRAPHY: Intra, 1895; Luzio, 1922, p. 275; Paccagnini, 1956.
ADDITIONAL BIBLIOGRAPHY: A. Rizzi, "Un opera del Fetti", *Arte Veneta,* XVII, 1963; pp. 182-85; Perina in Marani and Perina, III, 1965, pp. 455-56; U. Bazzotti and A. Englen in M.T. Cuppini, *Acquisizioni e Restauri,* Palazzo Ducale, Mantua, 1979.

Rubens, the Gonzaga and the "Adoration of the Trinity"

Rubens was probably recruited for the Gonzaga as a portraitist when he was in Venice in 1600. Another Flemish painter, Pourbus, had already received a court appointment; but Vincenzo I planned to establish a collection of pictures of beautiful women, and this undertaking was beyond one artist's capacity. 'He is not bad at painting portraits' is the Duke's only recorded judgement on Rubens (Rooses-Ruelens, 1887, p. 81). The artist's diplomatic talents were certainly soon exploited as well, notably when he was charged with an official mission to Spain in 1603, but to his chagrin his task as a painter on this occasion was confined to producing likenesses of court beauties (Rooses-Ruelens, 1887, pp. 225-30). Other patrons, however, were readier to give him commissions for more 'elevated' religious and mythological subjects, and these increasingly attracted him away from Mantua. In 1608, as Rubens himself pointed out, there was still no work of his in the ducal picture gallery (Rooses-Ruelens, 1887, pp. 403-08).

Not that Rubens produced only portraits in Mantua. An account of the artist's life (Weyerman, 1729, pp. 258-59 f.) relates how Vincenzo once found him painting the *Battle of Aeneas and Turnus* while declaiming in Latin the appropriate verses of Virgil, including the description of an ancient Mantuan hero (*Aeneid,* x, 198-201). It was reputedly the Duke's astonished recognition of the Fleming's prodigious learning and linguistic skill which led him to send the painter as his envoy to Spain. Although this sounds like the kind of legend with which art history abounds the picture itself must have been real enough. For just before his Spanish trip Rubens had evidently executed a whole Aeneas cycle. One episode, the *Departure from Troy,* survives in the painting of about 1602 recently discovered at Fontainebleau (Cat. 244). Another is recorded in two drawings of this period, preserved in Paris and Brunswick (Held, 1959, pp. 96 f., nos. 8 and 9; figs. 9 and 10). These show a female suicide, and must represent the *Death of Dido,* rather than *Thisbe,* as is always supposed; for in one part of the Paris drawing the figure wears a crown, and in another she falls on a sword on top of a mound indicated by vertical lines — clearly the funeral pyre. The splendid ceiling painting of the *Assembly of the Gods,* now in Prague (Castle, Museum), undoubtedly belongs to the same decorative scheme. Though rightly dated to 1602, this is not an astrological allegory, as has hitherto been suggested (Neumann, 1968), but shows Juno and Venus, the opposing heavenly protagonists of the *Aeneid,* reluctantly reconciled before Jupiter at the instigation of Apollo. This deity lays his hand on a sphinx as he remonstrates with Juno, indicating the prophetic role he plays throughout Virgil's poem, directing gods and heroes alike to their inevitable destiny and, in particular, to the union between Latins and Trojans which brings the epic to its conclusion. Rubens's picture even footnotes its textual source: the swan with the river god alludes to Virgil, the swan of Mantua.

These impressive works, Rubens's tribute both to the ancient poet and his birthplace, were presumably made for a room in one of the Duke's residences. The artist's most important Gonzaga commission, however, was for a painted frieze (*fregio*) in the *cappella maggiore* of the Jesuit church in Mantua. The three pictures were completed by May 1605, Rubens having probably submitted the final sketches for approval in the previous June (Müller Hofstede, 1977, p. 322); but he had already been planning at least the central composition as early as about 1601 (Norris, 1975; see Cat. 232) The church was dedicated to the Trinity, to which the Gonzaga family are seen expressing their devotion in the principal scene. To either side were the *Baptism of Christ* and the *Transfiguration,* representing New Testament appearances of the Trinity on earth. The subjects were chosen from those recently devised for the Gesù in Rome (Mantua, Rubens 1977, pp. 33 f; Huemer, 1977[2], pp. 105 f.), but the treatment was clearly left to Rubens's invention. The *Transfiguration* includes the episode of the possessed boy, here theologically irrelevant, in deference to Raphael's famous altarpiece, whose foreground group is at the same time transformed by daring foreshortenings inspired by Tintoretto. This artist also provided the models for the compositional scheme as well as the eerie colour of the *Baptism* (Jaffé, 1977[1], p. 72f.), while the male nudes struggling to discard the last of their clothes reveal more about Rubens's admiration for Michelangelo than about the mystery of the Trinity.

The decoration of the chapel is long dispersed. The *Transfiguration* was taken to Paris shortly after the French occupation of Mantua in 1797 (it is now in the Musée des Beaux Arts, Nancy), but the other two pictures remained in the church, which had become a military store. By September 1801, however, the *Baptism*, now in the Royal Museum, Antwerp, had already been sold abroad, while the *Adoration of the Trinity* was in fragments, some of which were missing. The officer in charge tried to justify this vandalism as a desperate measure to save what remained of a ruined painting, but his real aim in cutting out the most "outstanding" figures was probably to produce a collection of saleable portraits. Fortunately, the French general Miollis managed to put a stop to his activities and presented the remnants to the local library (Schizzerotto, 1979, pp. 99-109).

E.McG

BIBLIOGRAPHY: (on Rubens and the Gonzaga in general): Baschet, 1866[1]; Baschet, 1867; Rooses-Ruelens, 1887; Luzio, 1913, pp. 275-84; Mantua, Rubens, 1977; Jaffé, 1977[1], esp. pp. 42-78; Müller Hofstede, 1977, esp. pp. 68-75, 95-105; Van de Velde, 1978.

228

The image of the Trinity displayed by angels. Fragment of the **Adoration of the Trinity** (1604-05)
P.P. Rubens (1577-1640)
Oil on canvas; 185 x 462 cm
Museo del Palazzo Ducale, Mantua (Inv. no. 6846)

The Dukes Guglielmo and Vincenzo I Gonzaga together with their wives, Eleonora d'Austria and Eleonora de' Medici, kneel in adoration. Fragment of the *Adoration of the Trinity* (with other fragments attached on either side) (1604-05)
P.P. Rubens (1577-1640)
Oil on canvas; 185 x 462 cm (with additions)
Museo del Palazzo Ducale, Mantua (Inv. no. 6847)

The two large pieces of the *Adoration of the Trinity* that still survive comprise almost the entire central section of the composition (see Reconstruction II). The upper part, with angels presenting the Trinity on a tapestry, very nearly connects to the one that appeared below with the worshipping figures of Vincenzo I, his wife and his deceased parents; the odd portions of architecture, drapery and limbs at either side were used to extend this lower fragment in 1806 and were subsequently covered with painted curtains which are now removed (Ozzóla, 1952). A few of the heads cut out by the French officer have also been traced: the Gonzaga children Ferdinando (Cat. 229), Vincenzo (Kunsthistorisches Museum, Vienna) and Margherita (Coll. W. Burchard, London), as well as one of the halberdiers (Cat. 230); part of the younger daughter, Eleonora, is also visible behind her dog (Cat. 231). But even if other details may yet resurface, including a self-portrait of Rubens, large areas are lost for ever, and any reconstruction must supplement the visual evidence with written records.

The exact dimensions are unknown, but the picture evidently appeared the same size as its companions (*c.* 420 x 680 cm), and was certainly no taller, even if it may have been broader by a few centimetres (see Reconstruction II). The setting was a monumental colonnade open to the sky, with six twisted columns to either side. The grandiose architectural perspective and the massive "Solomonic" columns were both derived from Veronese, but it was Rubens's innovation to combine the two. The result is both decorative and decorous, since the scene of religious devotion was thus suitably framed by Eucharistic vine columns modelled on the famous set of twelve in St. Peter's, Rome, which had supposedly come from the Temple of Solomon. Within Rubens's *tempio* the whole Gonzaga family were shown in the foreground, *in atto di adorationе*, before the image of the Trinity; they were arranged *per ordine*, with the males on the more important Gospel side. The emphasis on precedence is significant and helps resolve the disputed identification of the child in the Vienna fragment, who appeared towards the front at the extreme left (see Cat. 233).

Attending the family was a group of halberdiers. At least two stood at the left (Cat. 229, 230) and five at the right as is indicated by the three halberds in the bottom corner of the Trinity fragment, for these cannot be associated with the pair of soldiers whose juxtaposed legs obviously belong in the foreground on this side (Reconstruction II). A drawing in Brussels (Jaffé, 1957, pp. 379 ff.; Mantua, *Rubens*, 1977, p. 46) is probably for the inner of the latter figures. Among those behind the Duchess was a guard with the artist's features *in atto d'amirar tutto il quadro*. To be looking at his picture at the same time as out of it (as any self-portrait does) Rubens must have been modestly in the background. A recently-published

Reconstruction I

self-portrait (Jaffé, 1977[2]) records the artist at about this date in just the appropriate pose and may even be a related study. Heads of this type, in oils on paper, were produced by Rubens only in preparation for large-scale compositions. The medical evidence adduced by Jaffé to date the portrait to 1607 seems inconclusive, while his suggestion that it was painted to be taken home to Antwerp as a record of an illness is consistent neither with Rubens's artistic practice nor with his psychology. The oil-study is the proper size and on the appropriate support for what was possibly a last-minute addition to the *Adoration*.

The secular emphasis of the *Adoration of the Trinity* has caused some surprise (Mantua, *Rubens*, 1977, p. 48). It was, however, not an altarpiece, but the central scene of a frieze surrounding an altar. Donors were traditionally represented on the walls of their chapels, and the Gonzaga had, after all, financed this whole church. Rubens, who it seems had made a special trip to Venice in connection with the commission, evidently felt that here he could draw on a Venetian genre which falls between the sacred and the secular – the images of Doges with their patron saints and the Virgin or Christ, frequently in comparable architectural settings, which adorned the Ducal Palace. This tradition also suggests that Rubens's representation of the Trinity, startlingly lifelike as an image on a tapestry – if even countering the effect of drapery folds – was not simply a display of baroque theatricality, but a brilliant pictorial solution to a theological problem. By conven-

tion only saints and the blessed dead are afforded heavenly visions. Charles V and his family had, admittedly, been allowed a sight of the Trinity in Titian's *Gloria*, but only by appearing prematurely wrapped in their shrouds; and even so it was a hopeful, indeed daring expression of the Emperor's piety. In the official pictures of doges, Venetian dignitaries stolidly ignore the apparitions besides them, to which the accompanying saints by contrast react with reverence and wonder. (Titian's *Fede*, the apparent exception, has a dead doge contemplating a personification, not a divine being). If the deceased parents of Vincenzo I might have been permitted an upward glance, Rubens could have presented a true celestial vision only before an otherwise unresponsive family. The tapestry showing the Trinity is in itself a proper object of Gonzaga attention, and provides pictorial interest. Counter-Reformation propriety is thus maintained; indeed, the artist even contrives to make a good Jesuit point, illustrating the devotion to images which the order particularly advocated (Müller Hofstede, 1977, pp. 101 f.). But by his calculated illusionism Rubens in the end has it both ways: confined within the boundaries of the tapestry this Trinity is to all appearances a real vision.

E.McG

PROVENANCE: Church of Santissima Trinità, Mantua, until July 1801; Commissaire des guerres E.-M. Siauve until September 1801; General S.-A.-F. Miollis (now as fragments), presented to Biblioteca Pubblica (later Comunale), Mantua, by 1802 (the smaller fragments added to either side of that with the Dukes in the restoration of 1806) and displayed above either doorway in the first room; by 1933 transferred to Palazzo Ducale, Mantua.

BIBLIOGRAPHY: Baschet, 1867; Luzio, 1911; Jaffé, 1961; Huemer, 1966; Held, 1966; Norris, 1975; Huemer, 1977[1], pp. 26-33 and 1977[2]; Mantua, *Rubens*, 1977, pp. 28-53 (Bazzotti), 54-67 (Navarrini); Müller Hofstede, 1977, pp. 100-05; Jaffé, 1977[1]; Jaffé, 1977[2], pp. 72-76; Schizzerotto, 1979, pp. 81-124; Downes, 1980, pp. 64-68.

Reconstruction I
Rubens's first plan for the three Gonzaga boys on the left of the *Adoration of the Trinity*, based on the evidence of the x-ray photograph of the Vienna fragment, the two Stockholm drawings (Cat. 232, 233) and the Saltram portrait (Cat. 257): (1) Vincenzo (b. 1594); (2) Ferdinando (b. 1587); (3) Francesco (b. 1586).

Reconstruction II
The Adoration of the Trinity
Note: This reconstruction largely reproduces (by kind permission) that made by Ugo Bazzotti (Mantua, *Rubens*, 1977, p. 42) which plausibily assumed the dimensions of the picture to be *c.* 420 x 680 cm (see above). Like him I have not attempted to show the soldiers whose presence is indicated only by their halberds. I have, however, ventured a hypothetical "greyhound" (Cat. 230, 231) on the left and have otherwise modified Bazzotti's scheme on this side by setting the eldest boy suitably higher (see Cat. 233); to the right I have altered the position of the arms of Margherita, who was probably

217

genuflecting, and introduced the head of Rubens based (to scale) on the picture (private coll., Paris) at present on loan to the Fitzwilliam Museum, Cambridge.

E.McG.

229

Ferdinando Gonzaga, Prince of Mantua. Fragment of the **Adoration of the Trinity** (1604-05)
Rubens (1577-1640)
Oil on canvas; 48 x 38.2 cm
Private collection

Ferdinando Gonzaga (1587-1626) was evidently shown in Rubens's *Adoration of the Trinity* kneeling upright beside his older brother Francesco (Cat. 233) and behind the younger Vincenzo. Standing guard at Ferdinando's back must have been one of the halberdiers; the glint of his armour and the red of his cloak or sleeve is visible in the fragment. Part of Ferdinando's own distinctive costume survives as the background to the head of Vincenzo in Vienna. Ferdinando is wearing the Maltese cross of the Knights of Jerusalem, which establishes his identity. Neither Francesco nor Vincenzo belonged to this Order; the illegitimate Silvio, who was a member, would certainly not have been included in the official family group. In any case the boy in this fragment is clearly Ferdinando as depicted in Rubens's preparatory drawing made some years before, in 1601 (Cat. 232).

Rubens of course altered his appearance in the final painting to accord with his age – when the *Adoration* was finished in 1605 Ferdinando had just turned eighteen – and had him kneel rather than stand. The pose of the head, however, remained unchanged. Ferdinando, soon to be made a cardinal,

229

230

is appropriately devoting his attention to his prayer-book, the open leaves of which are visible in the lower right corner of this fragment.

E.McG.

PROVENANCE: Church of Santissima Trinità, Mantua, until July 1801; Commissaire des guerres Etienne-Marie Siauve, sold (by September 1801) as a fragment; Private Collection, England, 1961; Private Collection, Wassenaar, Netherlands (in 1977).
BIBLIOGRAPHY: Norris, 1975; Exh. Antwerp, 1977, p. 43, no. 10; Huemer, 1977[2], p. 126; Müller Hofstede, 1977, pp. 320-23, no. 90.

230

Halberdier. Fragment of the **Adoration of the Trinity** (1604-05)
Rubens (1577-1640)
Oil on canvas; 128 x 77.5 cm
Museo del Palazzo Ducale, Mantua (Inv. no. 695)

This fragment of the *Adoration of the Trinity* shows the soldier who stood on the extreme left, in front of the outermost Solomonic column (see Reconstruction II). Leaning slightly forwards as he grasps his halberd, he was evidently posed with the studied nonchalance of the military figures who characteristically appear as onlookers in sixteeth-century Venetian pictures; these provide decorative variety in a crowd, and are invaluable compositional props, particularly for framing a scene. They were, as Veronese once put it, one of the painter's customary ornaments, and it was from Veronese and Titian that Rubens derived his idea of flanking the ducal family with a combination of halberdiers and columns. If Rubens's soldiers also provided a suitably protective presence around the Gonzaga, it seems unlikely that they had any more pointed significance. That "Swiss guards" were painted to express the pro-Spanish policy of Vincenzo I (Huemer, 1977[1], p. 27 f.; 1977[2], p. 108) can certainly be ruled out. Even if they were sometimes associated with the Habsburgs, Swiss guards are not an obvious symbol of Spain. But, in any case, the descriptions of Rubens's *Adoration* which refer to *svizzeri* or *guardie svizzere* seem to use the terms only loosely, to describe colourful halberdiers, like the one in this fragment; there is no evidence that any figure in the picture actually wore the distinctive Swiss guard's costume. Besides, from 1603 Duke Vincenzo had in fact turned away from Spain (Müller Hofstede, 1977, p. 105, n. 37); and had he ever wished to record his current political allegiance it is improbable that he, or any patron of the period, would have considered a permanent religious picture, even if it glorified his family, an appropriate place to do this.

A competition drawing submitted to the Mantuan Academy in 1769 has on the extreme left a soldier with a halberd in front of a twisted column, evidently, if feebly, derived from Rubens's figure in this fragment (Schizzerotto, 1979, fig. 5 and p. 113 f.). The drawing shows a page boy in front of the halberdier's legs. Had any such prominent feature been depicted by Rubens it would surely have been mentioned in one of the descriptions. The bottom left corner of the *Adoration* was, however, probably occupied by some pictorial diversion; the obvious candidate is the "greyhound" (see Cat. 231). Rubens would certainly have remembered how hunting dogs emerge from behind one of the pilasters in Mantegna's "*Meeting*" scene in the *Camera Picta* and Veronese, who enjoyed painting dogs even more than halberdiers, could supply a nice precedent for framing a picture with the two in conjunction.

E.McG.

PROVENANCE: Church of Santissima Trinità, Mantua, until July 1801; Commissaire des guerres Etienne-Marie Siauve, presumably sold (by September 1801) as a fragment; discovered in Milan (? in 1931) by M. Pelliccioli and bought by Count A. Contini-Bonacossi (Florence); presented in 1934 to Palazzo Ducale.
BIBLIOGRAPHY: Norris. 1975; Exh. Antwerp, 1977, p. 47, no. 12 (with earlier literature); Mantua, *Rubens*, 1977, esp. p. 46; Huemer, 1977[1], pp. 26-28 and 1977[2], esp. p. 128; Schizzerotto, 1979, pp. 84, 89, 112-17.

231

Lap dog with Eleonora Gonzaga, Princess of Mantua.
Fragment of the **Adoration of the Trinity** (1604-05)
Rubens (1577-1640)
Oil on canvas; 67 x 34 cm
Museo del Palazzo Ducale, Mantua (Inv. Sta. n. 696)

This fragment undoubtedly shows the "little dog with long curly hair" (*cagnolino... di pelo lungo arricato*) described with the female contingent of Gonzagas in the *Adoration of the Trinity*. The hand discreetly fondling the animal can only be that of the youngest child, Eleonora, who was kneeling at the front of the family group; she was rather nearer the centre of the picture than her elder sister, Margherita, who, however, was evidently much higher, and was perhaps not kneeling, but genuflecting. Part of her mother's trailing fur-trimmed cloak appears in front of Eleonora's green and gold dress in the bottom left corner of this fragment and helps to establish

its exact position (see Reconstruction II).

Lap dogs of the type shown here are the familiar companions of court ladies in sixteenth- and seventeenth-century Italian paintings, and Rubens's animal might have been taken straight from Veronese; but the Gonzaga were particularly attached to their dogs, even celebrating their memory with epitaphs and tombstones, and the little white dog was certainly a real portrait and doubtless Eleonora's special pet. Rubens's *Adoration* evidently contained at least one other "favourite dog" of the family. It has been suggested (Schizzerotto, 1979, pp. 85 f.) that a larger dog was with the boys opposite, also in the foreground, between Francesco IV and Vincenzo II; but the available space hardly allows for this arrangement, which in any case would make for a rather obvious correspondence that is unlikely to have appealed to Rubens. Most probably the other dog or dogs appeared at the extreme left, at the feet of the halberdier (Cat. 230). Any animal included on the "male" side of the picture must have been of suitable size and character, and a hunting dog would be appropriate, even if the documentary evidence for the "greyhound" recorded by Baschet (1867, p. 308) cannot now be traced.

E.McG.

PROVENANCE: Church of Santissima Trinità, Mantua until July 1801; Commissaire des guerres Etienne-Marie Siauve, presumably sold (by September 1801) as a fragment; bought from *un francese* (?Siauve) by

231

Count C. Bevilacqua Lazise, Verona (1784-1856) (recorded in 1833); Dr. C. Bernasconi, Verona (Cat. 1851, n. 117); Bequeathed (1865) to Pinacoteca Comunale, Museo Civico, Verona (Cat. 1912, no. 133); 1 June 1936 passed to Palazzo Ducale in an exchange of pictures.
BIBLIOGRAPHY: Huemer, 1966; Norris, 1975, pp. 77f.; Huemer, 1977[1], pp. 26-28 and 1977[2], esp. p. 128; Mantua, *Rubens*, 1977, esp. p. 46; Schizzerotto, 1979, esp. pp. 83-87, 114 f.

232

Ferdinando I Gonzaga, Prince of Mantua (*c.* 1601)
Rubens (1577-1640)
Drawing, Black chalk with touches of red and white chalk on paper; 22.6 x 16.2 cm
Inscribed (by Tessin): *Ferdinando Gonzaga Cardinale di Mantova or Duca, fatto in presenza sua da P.P. Rubens. Ce portrait a eté donné à M. Crozat par M. le Comte de Cailus.*
Nationalmuseum, Stockholm (Inv. no. 1917/1863)

This is a preparatory study for the head of Ferdinando Gonzaga, one of the children shown in the *Adoration of the Trinity*. The identification of the figure given on the drawing has sometimes been questioned, as has that of Francesco on a corresponding sheet (Cat. 233). But both must be correct. Count Tessin, who inscribed the two drawings after he bought them in 1741, would hardly have used Italian or added the phrase "made in his presence by P.P. Rubens" had he been expressing a personal opinion. His inscriptions indeed must have been copied from originals dating from the reign of Ferdinando himself (1613-26), as is indicated by the words "at present Duke" on this sheet and by the fact that on the other Francesco (d. 1612) is spoken of in the past tense (Norris, 1975, pp. 73 f; Müller Hofstede, 1977, pp. 320 f).
In style these drawings clearly belong to Rubens's earliest period in Mantua, rather than to 1604, when the artist began painting the S. Trinità pictures. Besides, Tessin's identifications can hardly be reconciled with a date much later then 1601, when Ferdinando was fourteen and Francesco fifteen. In the past the considerable divergence in date between the drawings and the final *Adoration of the Trinity* seemed to present an uncomfortable, indeed impossible problem. Those scholars who wished to keep the drawings around 1601 felt obliged to deny any connection with the *Adoration*; others, convinced they were preparatory studies, pushed them forward to 1604, but then had to conclude they showed younger members of the family, namely Vincenzo (b. 1594) and the illegitimate Silvio (b. 1592). The recent discovery of the fragment of the *Adoration* which corresponds to the drawing of Ferdinando (Cat. 229) happily resolves the issue. In this Ferdinando is clearly identified by the Maltese cross on his costume, thus confirming the accuracy of Tessin's inscription. In the drawing he appears in exactly the same pose, but looks significantly younger. It is therefore evident that Rubens was planning the S. Trinità pictures long before he submitted the final *modelli*, probably in the summer of 1604 (see above, p. 215). They were presumably the "great and magnificent works" mentioned in a letter of January 1602 (Norris, 1975, p. 73); Rubens's frequent absence from Mantua, notably in 1603, must have contributed to delays in the undertaking. Ferdinando's attitude in the drawing, previously taken for one of diffidence, is now revealed as the reverent attention to his prayer book planned for the final picture. The further suggestion (Huemer, 1977[1], pp. 27 f.; 1977[2], p. 108) that Rubens represented Ferdinando and his brother Francesco (Cat. 233) with "furtive glances" to make their own covert comment on their father's pro-Spanish sympathies is wholly fanciful. Except that it incidentally glorified the Gonzaga in

220

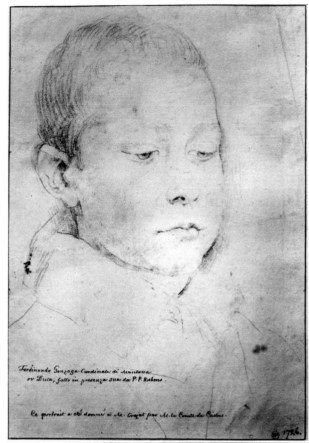

Ferdinando Gonzaga Cardinale di Mantova or Duca, fatto in presenza sua da P.P. Rubens.
Ce portrait a eté donné a M. Crozat par M. le Comte de Cailus.

232

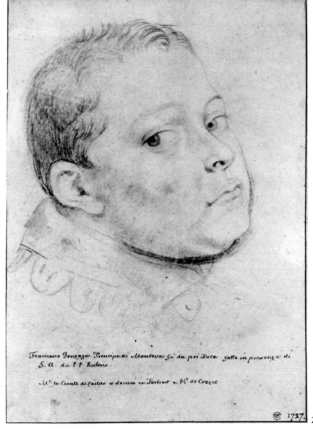

Francesco Gonzaga Principe di Mantova fu da poi Duca, fatto in presenza di S. A. da P.P. Rubens.
M. le Comte de Cailus a donné ce Portrait a M. de Crozat.

233

an obvious way, the *Adoration of the Trinity* was not intended by the artist as a "political document" (cf. Cat. 230). The poses of the figures in it are sufficiently explained by the requirements of religious decorum and pictorial variety.

E.McG

PROVENANCE: Count A.C.P. de Caylus (Paris, 1692-1765); P. Crozat (Paris, 1665-1740), sale, Paris, 10 April-13 May 1741, *Catalogue* (P.J. Mariette), no 841 or 842; Count C.G. Tessin (Stockholm 1695-1770). Bought by King Gustav III and presented to the Print Room of the Royal Museum; since 1886 part of the Nationalmuseum, Stockholm.
BIBLIOGRAPHY: Held, 1959, I , pp. 125 f, no 69 (with earlier Literature); Jaffé, 1961; Buchard - d'Hulst, 1963, I pp. 49 f (no. 27); Exh. Paris - Brussels - Amsterdam 1970-71, Bjurström pp. 45f, (no 71); Norris, 1975, pp. 73 f; Huemer, 1977[1], pp. 26-32 and 1977[2], pp. 108-11, 126-28; Exh. Vienna 1977 (Schütz), pp. 50-52 (no. 2); Mantua, *Rubens*, 1977 (Bazzotti), pp. 42-46; Müller Hofstede, 1977, pp. 318-23; Magnusson 1977, pp. 100-05, 155.

233

Francesco Gonzaga, prince and later fifth Duke of Mantua

Rubens (1577-1640)
Drawing, black chalk with touches of red and white chalk on paper; 22.5 x 16.3 cm
Inscribed (by Tessin) *Francesco Gonzaga, Prencipe di Mantova fù da poi Duca, fatto in presenza di S.A. da P.P. Rubens. Mr. le Comte de Cailus a donné ce Portrait a Mr. de Crozat.*
Nationalmuseum, Stockholm (Inv. no. 1918/1863)

As the inscription informs us, this drawing shows Francesco Gonzaga (1586-1612), the eldest son of Vincenzo I. The identification, like that on the companion study of Ferdinand (Cat. 232) is certainly correct, and both sheets can be associated with the earliest stages of Rubens's work on the *Adoration of the Trinity*, around 1601. But whereas in the finished picture of 1605 the artist represented Ferdinando as and where he had originally planned, altering the boy's stance and appearance only to take account of how he had matured in four years interval between preparatory drawing and painting, Rubens changed his mind about the placing of Francesco (see Recon-

structions I and II). Initially he had intended to put Francesco in front, at the extreme left of the family group, as is indicated by X-ray photographs of a fragment of this section of the picture now in Vienna; these show a head identical to that in the drawing here. The first figure, however, Rubens subsequently replaced with that of a younger Gonzaga child, Vincenzo. In the final scheme Francesco was moved to a more important situation, immediately behind his father. This arrangement is confirmed in the descriptions of the *Adoration*, which list the members of the family in turn from the centre outwards. Francesco's earlier pose, calculated for a low foreground position, could hardly have been adapted by the artist to the new location; as heir to the title, he must have been highest of the kneeling children, and he is unlikely to have imitated Vincenzo, by looking out of the picture, or Ferdinando, by concentrating on his prayer-book. Perhaps Francesco alone joined his parents in directing his attention to the image of the Trinity above. There remains the question of where the youngest boy, Vincenzo, appeared in Rubens's initial design. Presumably the place later accorded Francesco, next to his father, was originally Vincenzo's; his attitude, I have suggested, is reflected in the Saltram portrait (Cat. 257). Standing upright, but appropriately lower than Ferdinando, and turning to look outwards over his right shoulder, Vincenzo would have made an ideal counterpart to his sister, Margherita, on the opposite side (Reconstruction I).

E.McG.

PROVENANCE: as for Cat. 232 (Ferdinando).
BIBLIOGRAPHY: as for Cat. 232 (Ferdinando).

234

Triptych: the Virgin and Child enthroned with Saints and Donors (*c.* 1520)

Attributed to Jan Provost (*c.* 1465-1529)
Centre panel: The Virgin and Child with Saint Bernard and Benedict, 78.1 x 59.4 cm; Left wing: St. John the Baptist with an unidentified Donor 76.2 x 24.1 cm; Right wing: St Martha with an unidentified Donatrix, 76.2 x 23.3 cm. On the rever-

234

se of the wings (now detached): a Miser (?) holding a skull.
Her Majesty the Queen, (Inv. 1419)

The Gonzaga owned a large number of early Netherlandish pictures, about which unfortunately little is known. Isabella d'Este acquired two Van Eycks from a Venetian collection in 1506 (Luzio, 1913, p. 105-06), and in 1531 Federico Gonzaga had recently bought a Flemish *St Jerome* – possibly by Quentin Metsys (Luzio, 1913, p. 29; cf. pp. 117, 342, 140 etc.). In 1535 Federico purchased one hundred and twenty Flemish paintings, mostly landscapes, from a collection of three hundred offered by Matteo del Nassaro, an artist from Verona who worked at the French court and who occasionally acted as a dealer (Luzio, 1913, p. 30; Sulzberger, 1960, pp. 147-50). Vincenzo I, noted for his interest in Flemish art, acquired considerable numbers of Flemish pictures, from Italian sources (Luzio, 1913, pp. 98, n. 1, 114) and during his travels abroad, for example in Brussels and Antwerp in 1608 (Mattioli, 1976, pp. 32-43). By 1627, the Mantuan collection included seventeen paintings attributed to Bruegel, several attributed to Quentin Metsys and a version of Lucas van Leyden's *Chess Players*. Though these were highly valued, some of the "Bruegels" subsequently acquired by Charles I were considered by Van der Doort to be only "mean copies". The masterpiece among the Gonzagas' Netherlandish pictures was the small triptych by Jan van Eyck now at Dresden, which had been acquired by Vincenzo I in 1597 (Luzio, 1913, p. 176, n. 1: Mayer-Meintschel, 1966, p. 29). The Provost triptych is also of high quality. Though it is not known how it arrived in Mantua, this was perhaps another of Vincenzo's purchases. The centre panel shows the miracle of the *Lactatio Bernardi* (Réau, 1958, III, (I), pp. 213-15), but the milk from the Virgin's breast is no longer very visible. St Martha's emblem is a perforated skimmer or slice. The significance of the scene on the reverses of the wings is obscure, and none of the inscriptions there can be read, but a similar *Death and the Miser*, also attributed to Provost from a larger triptych, is in the Bruges Museum (218). The Hampton Court triptych is now always ascribed to Provost, and the style is close to that of this documented *Last Judgement* of 1525 in the Bruges Museum (117). Provost came from Mons, but from 1494 until his death he worked in Bruges.

L.C.

PROVENANCE: Listed in the Mantuan inventory of 1627, (Luzio, 1913, p. 115 (312)); acquired by Charles I (the CR brand is on the reverse of the centre panel) and probably placed at Hampton Court; apparently sold there on 17 May 1650; recovered at the Restoration (Charles II inventory, Hampton Court (198); thereafter by succession.

BIBLIOGRAPHY: Luzio, 1913, pp. 29, 98, 105, 114, 117, 140, 176; Collins Baker, 1937, pp. 259-60; London , Royal Academy, *Flemish Art*, 1953-54, no. 63.
ADDITIONAL BIBLIOGRAPHY: Bruges, *L'art flamand dans les collections britanniques*, 1956, no. 29; L. Réau, *Iconographie de l'art chrétien*, III, (I), Paris, 1958, pp. 213-15; S. Sulzberger, "Matteo del Nassaro et la transmission des oeuvres flamandes en France et en Italie", *Gazette des beaux-arts*, 6ᵉ pér. LV, 1960, pp. 147-50; A. Meyer-Meintschel, *Gemäldegalerie Alte Meister, Katalog I, Niederländische Malerei, 15. und 16 Jahrhundert*, Dresden, 1966, p. 29; M.J. Friedlander, *Early Netherlandish Painting*, IX, b, Leyden and Brussels, 1973, p. 111, no. 111 (with bibliography); D. Mattioli, «Nuove ipotesi sui quadri di 'Bruol Vecchio' appartenuti ai Gonzaga» *Civiltà mantovana*, X, 1976, pp. 32-43.

235

St Luigi Gonzaga (1568-91)
Anonymous pencil drawing (probably eighteenth century); 21.5 x 27 cm
Victoria & Albert Museum, Department of Prints and Drawings (9559.7)

2

Among the Gonzaga family's highest distinctions was to have produced a saint in Luigi, son of Prince Ferrante Gonzaga, a professional military commander of the line of Castiglione delle Stiviere. In 1577, as a page at the Medici court in Florence, Luigi took a vow of perpetual chastity at the church of the Annunziata; a severe illness strengthened his religious vocation as did the experience of receiving his first communion in 1580 from the hands of St Carlo Borromeo, who visited Castiglione delle Stiviere (about twenty miles north west of Mantua). His spiritual training continued in Spain and Milan and in 1585 he at last overcame his father's strenuous opposition and entered the Jesuit Order. For his example of a life of mortification, prayer and services to the poor and sick (he died of plague in Rome) and for alleged miracles he was beatified in 1605. Duke Vincenzo I used all the influence he could muster to obtain Luigi's canonization; many Cardinals wrote to him in January 1608 to assure him of their support (ASMAG b. 987); his son Cardinal Ferdinando, who was present in Rome for much of the period 1610-12 when the case was pending before the Congregation of Rites (of which he became a member in 1612), was an additional advocate. What happened is not clear, though in May 1612 Antonio Possevino warned Ferdinando (by then Duke) that the Jesuits were going about it the wrong way (ASMAG b. 1000); in fact Luigi was not canonized until 1726. His fame and sanctity were already assured, however, largely thanks to the Life by V. Cepari first printed in Rome (1606) and Milan (1607). Buried in the Jesuit church of Sant'Ignazio, Rome, where an altar was dedicated to him, this anonymous drawing is of his image there.

D.S.C.

BIBLIOGRAPHY: Donesmondi, II, 1616, pp. 287-89, 401-02; *Enciclopedia Cattolica*, with extensive bibliography.

236

Gonzaga banner, early seventeenth century
Two red damask panels, each *c.* 56 wide x 50 cm; with brocade, satin and embroidered silk mounted on a foreshortened stave with iron spearhead 55 cm long; two cords in gold and silver thead with tassels, 140 cm long
Dr. Giampaolo Negri, Mantua

One panel of the banner shows St George or horseback (a type used by Duke Vincenzo I on coins) slaying the dragon, with a bearded monk instead of a princess as the rescued victim; the other panel shows the Gonzaga arms surmounted by a ducal crown with below the collar of the Order of the Redeemer (see Cat. 258) which displays the device of the crucible (*crogiuolo*), the motto *Domine probasti me* and the reliquary containing the Precious Blood. Since Duke Vincenzo's chivalric Order was founded only in 1608, this excludes the possiblity that the banner could have been taken on his expeditions against the Turks (1595, 1597, 1601) as has been suggested; maybe it was not intended to have a military purpose, but was a honorific banner made for him or one of his successors as knights of the Order.

D.S.C.

BIBLIOGRAPHY: Pelati,1973, pp. 316-17, 321-22; Mantua, *Tesori*, 1974 p. 69.

237

Photograph: **The Triumphal Entry of King Henry III of France into Mantua** (1574)
Engraving from Blaise de Vigenère, *La somptueuse et magnifique entrée du treschrestien Roy Henry III de ce nom, Roy de France et de Pologne, grand Duc de Lithuanie etc. en la cite de Mantoue, avec les portraicts des choses les plus exquises, À Paris chez Nicholas Chesneau,* 1576
Bibliothèque Nationale, Paris (Bn. 4⁰. Lb³⁴.68)

The pageantry in Mantua offered in welcome to the King of France apparently began at Palazzo Te as had become customary with distinguished visitors since the Emperor Charles V; the first temporary arch through which he was to pass from there into the city bore scenes showing France holding his crown and the Gonzaga device of Mount Olympus surmounted by Faith, with the additional legend *Hic semper tuta* (Always secure here). Below were Pax and Ceres (Peace and Abundance) and on either side the figures of Mars presenting his sword and Manto (the legendary foundress of Mantua, daughter of the Theban soothsayer Tiresias) making a gesture of welcome. Blaise de Vigenère, who was to be distinguished as the first translator into French of Tasso's *Gerusalemme Liberata*, may have been sent drawings of the various arches and other temporary effects (his text includes eight engravings of them with an explanatory key) and his description of the occasion, a high point in the international prestige of Duke Guglielmo Gonzaga, corresponds closely to a manuscript account in the Gonzaga archives.

D.S.C.

ADDITIONAL BIBLIOGRAPHY: P. de Nolhac and A. Solerti, *Il viaggio in Italia di Enrico III re di Francia e le feste a Venezia, Ferrara, Mantova e Torino,* Rome etc. 1890, pp. 7, 11, 14-15, 260-62, 333-37.

238

Photographs: **Jewel inventory of Vincenzo Gonzaga** (1577)
Manuscript on paper with pen drawings
Archivio di Stato, Mantua (AG 400 *c.* 1r-1v)

These pages from an inventory of Prince Vincenzo's jewels dated 16 December 1577 (the future Duke was then only fifteen) include drawings and descriptions by the Mantuan goldsmith Giorgio Ghisi; he notes in some cases from whom the objects were acquired or to whom they were subsequently given. The greater number are gold buttons, the first page alone lists 160 (four dozen bearing rubies or diamonds), but also noted and illustrated are a gold brooch set with diamonds and rubies with a design of Solomon administering justice (Vincenzo's mother Duchess Eleonora of Austria gave this to him), a pendant in the form of a rose with six diamonds and

twelve rubies on a necklace of twelve diamond and ruby rosettes (a present from Duke Guglielmo), also a diamond brooch in the form of a cross with four rubies and two large pearls: this might well be German from the style of the settings, and is considerably later than the inventory. The same manuscript contains another inventory of the prince's jewels at Marmirolo dated 29 July 1581 (also an inventory of his clothes). Some impression can be gained of the quantity and costliness of the (totally lost) Gonzaga jewel collections. Vincenzo as Duke continued to amass jewellery, and even if many objects were given away as prestigious presents, or sold, or pawned to raise money, jewels said to be worth 1,200,000 *scudi* were found a few days after his death (letter of 24 February 1612 in ASMAG b. 2725 c. 48v, mentioned by Luzio, 1913, p. 17).

D.S.C.; A.S.C.

238

Plate with the arms of Gonzaga impaling Medici
Montelupo (?)
Sunken centre, the well forming an angle with the border.
Painted in blue, green, yellow, yellow-ochre and black.
Diam. 35.30 cm
Museo del Palazzo Ducale, Mantua (Inv. stet. no. 324)

In the centre is a cartouche with the arms of Gonzaga impaling Medici surmounted by a coronet. The remainder of the plate white.
The arms may be those of Duke Vincenzo I Gonzaga (1562-1612) and of his wife, Eleonora de' Medici, whom he married in 1584 and who died in 1611, or they may be those of Duke Ferdinando (1587-1626) and of his wife Caterina de'Medici whom he married in 1617. Another plate from this service, in a private collection at Suzzara, is illustrated "as Faenza?, end of the XVI century" in the exhibition catalogue, Mantua *Tesori*, 1974. The use of a thick, pure white ground was pioneered, if we are to believe the nearly contemporary evidence of Picolpasso, by Isabella d'Este's brother, Duke Alfonso I of Ferrara (1476-1534), though this ground-colour became known almost at once as *bianco di Faenza* and was so famous a product of the Faventine kilns that the generic term, "faience" derives from the fact. By the late 16th century, however, many other centres had imitated this Faenza fashion. Judging from photographs, it would seem that the coat of arms and cartouche are not painted with the sketchy freedom of touch habitual to Faenza practitioners of the *compendiario* style.
Hence it is here suggested that pieces from this set were perhaps made in Medici domains, and most likely at Montelupo.

J.V.G.M.

BIBLIOGRAPHY: Mantua, *Tesori*, 1974, no. 35.

239

240

Vincenzo I Gonzaga, fourth Duke of Mantua (1562-1612)
Frans Pourbus the Younger (1569-1622)
Oil on Canvas, 202 x 112 cm
National Trust, Tatton Park, Cheshire

Vincenzo, duke from 1587 to 1612, was the most exotic and vainglorious among Gonzaga rulers. Notoriously dissipated in his youth, one of the darkest clouds over his head was his confessed murder in the street in 1582 of James Crichton, an intellectual prodigy from Scotland. His first marriage to Margherita Farnese was annulled after a test of sexuality in which

she failed and he succeeded, and he again triumphed in a public test of virility with his second wife Eleonora de' Medici. As a ruler he aimed to personify majesty and magnificence regardless of cost. His coronation was spectacular and after his death he wished to be publicly displayed and then buried upon a throne (see essay by Signorini). As befitted the grandson, nephew and cousin of Habsburg emperors, he envisaged for the Gonzaga dynasty a grandiose place on the world stage, and had designs upon the thrones of Poland and Albania (Luzio, 1922, pp. 111-12, 160) as well as hopes of his son Ferdinando becoming pope, and his other son and daughter married to crowned heads. Some of his more bizarre characteristics he shared with his contemporary the Emperor Rudolph II, whose call he answered for aid against the Turks in Hungary, and whose obsessive interest he shared in natural science and magic, including alchemy. At the time of his third expedition against the Turks, he instigated experiments in chemical weapons, including two sorts of poison gas, supposed either to induce sleep or to kill the enemy (neither variety worked) (Errante, 1915, pp.60-67). But Vincenzo was also an enthusiastic patron of music and painting, his outlay of money on works of art was prodigious; as well as employing contemporary painters, both northern and Italian, he collected old masters on a vast and undiscriminating scale; through Eleonora de' Medici his agents negociated many purchases from collections in Florence as well as in Rome, Naples and elsewhere. No restraint was used in pursuit of his desires; to obtain Raphael's *Madonna della Perla* from Count Galeazzo Canossa in 1604, he bestowed on its owner a fief and a Marquisate in Monferrato (Luzio, 1913, pp. 90-91).
On a visit to Brussels in September 1599, Vincenzo encountered Pourbus who was employed by the court there, and persuaded him to come to Mantua as court painter where he remained from 1600-09 (his compatriot, Rubens was recruited in Venice also in 1600, but on a less official basis). Pourbus, the third in a dynasty of painters, had already felt the influence of the Spanish court style while in Brussels, and his large scale portraits which bestow a glacial formality on the sitters and draw attention to their status and dress more than their physical appearance, perhaps not suprisingly found favour with the Gonzaga and their relations. He painted all the ducal family, and his studio produced competent replicas which were despatched around the European courts. A fellow artist, Federico Zuccaro, described Pourbus as the *pittore e cameriere della chiave d'oro del Duca di Mantova* (d'Arco, I, p. 82), and for the Duke he travelled to Naples (where he advised him to buy two Caravaggios) and Innsbruck. In 1609 he moved to France where he became court painter to Eleonora de' Medici's sister Maria, Queen Regent of France.
Vincenzo wears an elaborate suit of half-armour decorated with the crescent moon device enclosing the monogram SIC (*sic illustrior crescam*) which he adopted in 1595 at the time of his first expedition against the Turks; his breeches appear to have been designed to match his armour. He wears the Order of the Golden Fleece around his neck (awarded to him by Philip II in 1588); at his side is an elaborately plumed helmet. Neither this nor his armour would seem to correspond either to the surviving helmet of Vincenzo's (Cat. 242), nor to any of the suits of armour in which Pourbus portrayed him e.g. the full length portrait in the Fondazione d'Arco, Mantua, which is also ornamented with the crescent moon device, as is his armour in the half-length portrait exhibited at the Royal Academy in 1953, then in the collection of Martin Asscher (*Flemish Art*, Cat. no. 261). A drawing (Nat. Gall., Edinburgh) would seem to be a study for this portrait rather than for the more mechanical portrait in Dresden. Vincenzo appears rather older here than in the painting exhibited in 1953

240

(above), his bald patch more difficult to disguise even for such a consummate flatterer as Pourbus, but it presumably dates from before 1608, the year in which Vincenzo founded his Order of the Redeemer (Cat. 258) the insignia of which he is not wearing. Behind him is a view of the lake and Mantua in the distance; the bridge appears from its structure to be the Ponte di San Giorgio much as it is represented in contemporary views. A similar view is included in the portrait of Vincenzo from the collection of Marchese Cavriani (Mantua, *Mostra Iconog.*, 1937, no. 161) and in other contemporary paintings (Cat. 281).

D.S.C., J.T.M.

PROVENANCE: Probably acquired either by Wilbraham Egerton (1781-1856) or his grandson and namesake (1832-1900); information from F. St John Gore.
BIBLIOGRAPHY: d'Arco, 1857, I, p. 82; Luzio, 1913, pp. 90-91; 1922, pp. 111-12, 160; Thieme-Becker (Burchard); Mazzoldi, III, 1965, pp. 37-82; Mantua, *Rubens*, 1977, pp. 74-75.

241

Commander's baton, probably of Duke Vincenzo I

Maker unknown; probably Spanish, late 16th century
Iron; length 81 cm
The Armouries, HM Tower of London (VIII. 75)

In the form of a hollow iron tube each end of which is closed by a plain iron cap. The surface is russetted and is covered in gold counterfeit-damascening with seven transverse panels of decoration, and two vertical tables of figures, each consisting of ten columns. The panels of decoration consist, alternately from top to bottom, of classical trophies of arms and classical battle scenes, each panel bordered by a frieze of running scroll-work. The tables are bordered by lines counterfeit-damascened in silver, and some of the decorative panels bear silver highlights. Both caps are similarly decorated with gold counterfeit-damascening – the upper with the Gonzaga eagle, the lower with the Gonzaga arms. Running round the top of the baton in capital letters are the words TAVOLE. PER. FAR. BATTAGLIE. Beneath this, written in script, and repeated on each side of the baton, are ten headings, one for each column of figures:
NVMERO DE GENTE (Number of Troops)
TANTAS POR HILERA (Number in each rank)
TANTAS HILERAS (Number of columns)
SOBRAS (Number of troops over)
FRENTE DE ESQUADRON QUADRADO DE SITIO (Number of troops forming the front of the column)
COSTADO DE ESQUADRO DE SITIO (Number of troops forming the flank of the column)
SOBRAS (Number of troops over)
FRENTE DE ESQUADRON QUADRADO DE GENTE (Number of troops forming the front of the square)
COSTADO DE ESQUADRON QUADRADO DE GENTE (Number of troops forming the flank of the square)
SOBRAS (Number of troops over)
The table given below these headings form a ready-reckoner enabling a commander to work out quickly how to marshal formations of between 12,100 and 20,000 men. The fact that the headings to these columns are written in Spanish strongly suggests that this baton was made in Spain, and this is confirmed by other known examples. In the Wallace Collection, London (A 989) is a similar baton which has been dated to about 1590, and which bears the arms of Don Rodrigo, Ponce de Léon (1545-1630) who became Duke of Arcos in 1573. In his catalogue of this Wallace baton, Mann (1962) noted that another similar baton, made for the Conde de

Lemos (presumably Pedro-Fernandez c. 1576-1622) was in the possession of the Duchess of Alba. Yet another similar baton is illustrated in a portrait of an unknown commander, attributed to Pantoja de la Cruz, in the National Museum, Poznan, Poland (1967 Cat. no. 27). The arms on the baton in this exhibition appear to be those of Duke Vincenzo I (Luzio, II, 1922, pp. 58-60) and its probable date (late 16th century) suggests that it must have been made for either Vincenzo I or his predecessor Guglielmo. Mann (1962) was in error when he ascribed this baton to Vespasiano Gonzaga Duke of Mantua. He was presumably referring to Vespasiano Duke of Sabbioneta but the arms on this baton preclude its having been made for this member of the Gonzaga family. The tables on the baton are presumably based on those which appeared in many of the military tracts that were published in the second half of the 16th century. The baton cannot be traced in the 1604 inventory of the Gonzaga armoury and its history is unknown.

G.W.

PROVENANCE: Acquired by the Armouries, HM Tower of London in 1950 from a private collection.
BIBLIOGRAPHY: Luzio, 1922, pp. 58-60.
ADDITIONAL BIBLIOGRAPHY: Sir J. Mann, *Wallace Collection Catalogues: European Arms and Armour*, II, London, 1962, p. 463.

242

Helmet of Duke Vincenzo I

Pompeo della Cesa
Burnished with engraving in gilt of leaves, flowers, stars, crowns etc.; 5275 g
Museo Poldi-Pezzoli, Milan (Inv. 2591; cat. no. 37)

Duke Vincenzo paid the Milanese armourer Pompeo della Cesa for a suit of armour on 28 July 1592, of which this helmet may be the only remaining part. It is a close helmet for foot combat at the barriers, though the decoration includes a half moon and the device "SIC" which was used upon the equipment of his troops for his first expedition against the Turks in 1595 (Errante, 1915, p. 29). The armour has been said to correspond to that illustrated in the portrait of Vincenzo in Vienna, though the helmet does not appear in that paint-

ing; none of the helmets which appear in other known portraits of him seem to correspond exactly with this helmet (Cat. 240).

D.S.C.

BIBLIOGRAPHY: Bertolotti, 1885, p. 108; Errante, 1915, p. 29; Mann, 1938, pp. 261-62; B. Thomas and O. Gamber, in Milan, *Storia*, XI, 1958, pp. 797, 803.
ADDITIONAL BIBLIOGRAPHY: ed. D. Collura, *Cataloghi del Museo Poldi Pezzoli*, 2, *Armi e armature*, Milan, 1980, no. 37, p. 31.

243

Portrait of Annibale Chieppio (*c.* 1560-1623), **secretary to Vincenzo I**
Unknown Painter (attributed to Rubens)
Oil on canvas; 66 x 53 cm
Fondazione d'Arco, Mantua,(Inv. 1103)

Conte Annibale Chieppio, whose family came from Milan, was a functionary of great influence in the court of Duke Vincenzo I and until his sudden fall from favour in 1617 (Luzio, 1922, p. 67 no. 3). Hundreds of letters drafted by him and addressed to him survive, concerning both foreign and domestic business. He certainly had a part in the supervision of Rubens's services to Vincenzo (e.g. Luzio, 1913, p. 41) but the attribution to Rubens of this presumed portrait of Chieppio is purely conjectural. Two portraits of him are listed in the inventory of his belongings dated 29 April 1623, drawn up after his death; one of him in his youth (*del signor conte Annibal d'età giovenile*) and the other, more probably the present portrait, described as only the face, on canvas (*l'effiggie del signor conte Annibale su tela solamente*): ASM, Archivio No-

tarile, Registri pergamenacei, a. 1623 (cc. 889r-912r) cc 890r, 890v. The Chieppio family inheritance passed in 1740 to the son of Francesco-Alberto d'Arco and Teresa Chieppio and so to the d'Arco family whose property, including the Palace in Mantua on the site where Annibale Chieppio lived, is now administered as a museum by the Fondazione d'Arco.

R.S., D.S.C.

BIBLIOGRAPHY: D. Mattioli in Mantua, *Rubens* 1977, p. 85, F. 19; M.G.Grassi in Amadei and others, 1980, p. 154.

244

Aeneas prepares to lead the Trojans into Exile (1602)
Rubens (1577-1640)
Oil on canvas; 146 x 227 cm
Musée National du Château, Fontainebleau (dépôt du Musée du Louvre), Inv. no. 2007.

This picture, which shows Aeneas joining the survivors of the sack of Troy to set sail for a new country, must have been part of a decorative series Rubens designed in 1602 in Mantua, presumably for Duke Vincenzo Gonzaga. It was probably the first of four extensive poetic landscapes filled with narrative incident, displayed beneath the larger ceiling painting which artfully sums up the role of the gods in the *Aeneid*. Of the other episodes only meagre traces survive, but it is clear that Rubens's version of Virgil's story emphasised the Trojans' settlement in Italy; the picture devoted to Dido, whose love would have detained Aeneas for ever in Carthage, represented her desertion and tragic end and must have set this against a background of departing Trojan ships. Indeed, the *Battle with Turnus*, the conclusion of the poem that

brought security to the immigrants, evidently included specific Mantuan allusions (See also introductory passage preceding Cat. 228).

For his opening scene Rubens chose not the familiar Flight
from Troy, with Aeneas rescuing his father and son amid a
night of confusion and flames, but its aftermath, a morning of
new hope for the refugees, their blazing city in the far distance. The artist's inspiration was the close of the second book
of the *Aeneid*; day breaks over the peak of Mount Ida as
Aeneas finds the pathetic gathering of mothers and children,
older men and youths "all packed up and resolved to be taken
across the seas to any land (he) may chose for them" (II,
796-802). Rubens has given vivid expression to their intention by depicting the Trojans on the shore and already load-
ing up, in anticipation of the event which Virgil puts off
until such time as they have actually built themselves ships
(III, 1-12). On the morning after the sack Virgil's Trojans
simply made for the mountains (II, 802-4) after meeting outside the town at a deserted shrine of Ceres, near an ancient
cypress tree; this, the spot designated earlier by Aeneas (713-
15; 742), Rubens reconstructed in the background with imaginative exactitude. His attention to the effective visual translation of the poem led the artist to combine elements from
two separate encounters at the ruined temple. For Aeneas is

depositing his father and son, as he did when he first arrived
and left them with his friends and servants (741-48). The hero
is seen wearing the lion skin that Virgil had him put on to
protect his shoulders before he took up the old man to carry
him from Troy, and Anchises himself is still clutching the
images of the Penates, those ancestral guardian deities that
were to be transported to Italy (717-24). Since there is no
account of their appearance in the *Aeneid* Rubens represented
these as Mars and Venus, appropriately combining the mother of Aeneas and protector of his descendants with the god
who later fathered Romulus and became the patron of martial
Rome. The boy Ascanius leans close to Aeneas's side, ex-
hausted after the effort he has made to keep up with his father
(cf. 723f.).

But Rubens shows Aeneas bringing Anchises and Ascanius at
daybreak, and to that company, now much swelled in number, to which Virgil says the hero returned alone, having
spent the night vainly searching for his lost wife. The poet's
vague but suggestive characterisation of this larger group, the
miserabile vulgus "all gathered for exile", left the artist free to
invent the touching details – wounded soldiers, weary infants
and suppliant mothers – drawing generously, as Foucart has
noted, on a variety of artistic models, especially on Giulio
Romano and the Venetians. The picture is, however, a testi-

mony to Rubens's scholarly sensitivity as well as to his response to Italy — its landscape in particular: a brilliant fusion of his native Flemish tradition with the art of Titian and an evocative expression of the verses of the ancient Mantuan poet.

E.McG.

PROVENANCE: see bibliography.
BIBLIOGRAPHY: Foucart in Exh. Paris, *Rubens*, 1977, pp. 151-53, no. 110.

245

Photograph: **The Galleria della Mostra in the Palazzo Ducale, Mantua** (*c*. 1592-1608)

A gallery for the display in particular of the vast Gonzaga collections of antique sculpture was desired by Duke Guglielmo, but it was not until the reign of his son Vincenzo that work began on the great *Galleria della Mostra* (65 m long), overlooking the *Cortile della Cavallerizza* already built by Giovanni Battista Bertani. First directed by Giuseppe Dàttari (work on the ceiling was in progress in 1592) its completion was supervised by Giovan Battista Viani. It is not known what sculptures were originally displayed in it, though over a hundred paintings, including Cat. 267 and *The Triumphs* of Mantegna, were listed there in 1627 (Luzio, 1913, pp. 103-9). Its appearance today is largely the result of a long programme of restoration in 1931-33. After years of neglect in 1876 the ceiling had collapsed, but a section with the original designs of Gonzaga devices and mottoes was preserved and copied.

D.S.C.

BIBLIOGRAPHY: Luzio, 1913, pp. 35-43. 103-09; Marani and Perina, 1965, pp. 117, 165, 186, 428; Paccagnini, 1969, pp. 160, 176.
ADDITIONAL BIBLIOGRAPHY: C. Cottafavi and N. Giannantoni, *Galleria della Mostra nel Palazzo Ducale di Mantova*, Mantua, 1934.

245

246

Busts and statues in Whitehall Gardens
Bound volume of 67 sheets of drawings, pencil and bistre wash, and red chalk and pale brown wash; 24 x 18 cm, and 33 x 21 cm
Her Majesty the Queen, Royal Library, Windsor Castle (Inv. A 49)

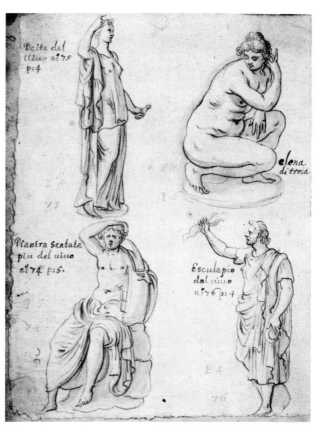

246

The volume is inscribed on the fly-leaf "M. Delany given me by Sir John Stanley", and on the following page "Drawings of Statues & Busts that were in the Palace at Whitehall before it was burnt. Preserved by Sr. John Stanley Bart. who belonged to the Lord Chamberlaynes office at the time the Palace was burnt down". Sir John Stanley (d. 1744) was Secretary in the Lord Chamberlain's office from 1689. Mrs Mary Delany (1700-1788) was his wife's niece.
The drawings fall into three distinct groups. The first group, mostly in pencil and bistre wash, comprises forty sheets carrying 157 drawings of busts. The second group, apparently by the same hand, but in red chalk and pale brown wash, consists of sixteen sheets with 64 drawings of statues or groups. The third group consists of eleven sheets with 38 drawings of busts. This group, in pencil and bistre wash, is on thicker paper of larger format, and is clearly by a different hand. The drawings in the first two groups have all been cut at one side or the other, and are clearly only half sheets, some of which can be matched together. It appears that the drawings were originally done on sheets some 26 cm in width, which were cut in half for convenience in binding.
In the first two groups of sheets each drawing is accompanied by a name or description in Italian and a number, written in brown ink.
The title on the spine and the inscription inside the front of the volume are in fact largely misleading. Although early writers like Michaelis took them at their face value, it was first conjectured by Lange, and more recently in very positive terms by Norton, that the drawings in fact represented sculptures in the Ducal collections at Mantua before their purchase by King Charles I. This point was conclusively proved in 1959 in a very thorough study by Scott-Elliot, who showed that the first two groups of drawings could be related very

precisely to items in the inventory compiled in Mantua in 1627 after the death of Duke Ferdinando Gonzaga, to a list of sculptures in the Palazzo Ducale, Mantua compiled for King Charles I later in the same year by the merchant Daniel Nys, and to items in the inventory compiled under the Commonwealth for the sale of the King's goods in 1649-51.

In a letter written from Italy in early 1629 to Lord Dorchester Daniel Nys states that he will send by the next courier drawings of the Mantuan statues, and in letter written one week later he states that he has actually sent the drawings rolled up inside prints of the Mantegna *Triumphs*, the originals of which he also of course sold to the King eventually. As Scott-Elliot has demonstrated, there can be no doubt that the drawings of the first two groups in the volume are the drawings referred to in Nys' letters.

The drawings of the third group would actually appear to show busts in the Royal collection after the Reformation.

The drawings in the first two groups, therefore, provide a visual record of the greater part of the great collections of antique sculpture in the Palazzo Ducale at Mantua as they were immediately before the sale and the sack. In some cases they provide a valuable record of important sculptures which are now lost without trace: sheet no. 8914, for instance, contains the only surviving representation of Michelangelo's famous *Sleeping Cupid*, acquired for Mantua by Isabella d'Este in 1502, which probably perished in the Whitehall fire of 1698.

Others of the statues which appear in the drawings still survive. The sheet shown here (no. 8911) shows, described as *Elena di Troia* the marble of a crouching Venus, known as "Lely's Venus" (Cat. 249 in the present exhibition), which was bought by Sir Peter Lely at the Commonwealth sales and later returned to the Royal collections.

A.F.R.

BIBLIOGRAPHY: Noel Sainsbury, 1859, pp. 329-30; Lange, 1898; Norton, 1957, pp. 251-57; Scott-Elliot, 1959.
ADDITIONAL BIBLIOGRAPHY: A. Michaelis, "Die Privatsammlung Antiker Bildwerke in England", *Archäologische Zeitung*, LXX, 1873, pp. 1-70; A. Michaelis, *Ancient marbles in Great Britain*, 1882, pp. 28, 30-31.

247

Bust of Marcus Aurelius as a Young Man

Marble; h overall 65 cm; the nose is restored, the bust has been broken and repaired
Her Majesty the Queen

Marcus Aurelius was born in 121 AD; he was the son of Annius Verus of Spanish origin, who was the brother of Faustina the Elder (see Cat. 248). In 138 he was adopted by the Emperor Antoninus Pius, and betrothed to Antoninus's daughter, Faustina the Younger, his cousin, whom he married in 145. He became Emperor in 161.

Formerly in the Gonzaga collections in Mantua, this bust was among the works of art sold to Charles I in 1627-28. This is known from the fact that this bust, labelled *Marco Aurelio giovine*, is represented in a volume of drawings from the Royal Library, Windsor Castle, which illustrates the antique sculpture at Mantua (Cat. 246).

In this portrait bust Marcus Aurelius is represented with his head turned slightly to the right. He is shown with a beard, a fashion which was revived by the Emperor Hadrian, and wears a military cuirass. Although a considerable number of portrait busts of Marcus Aurelius as Emperor are known, there are relatively few examples of him when younger. There is, however, a portrait of him as young man, which is

247   248

similar to this example, in Rome in the Museo del Foro Romano.

M.L.

BIBLIOGRAPHY: Scott-Elliot, 1959, p. 218ff. ill. 14.
ADDITIONAL BIBLIOGRAPHY: M. Wegner, *Die Herrscherbildnisse in antoninischer Zeit*, Berlin, 1939, p. 193, pl. 18.

248

Bust of Faustina the Younger

Marble; h overall 79 cm, h of bust 60.5 cm
Her Majesty the Queen

Faustina the Younger was born *c*. 125-30 AD, the daughter of the Emperor Antoninus Pius and of Faustina the Elder (see Cat. 122, 123). In 145 she married her cousin Marcus Aurelius who became Emperor in 161 (see cat. 247). She accompanied her husband on his northern campaigns, and on his expedition to the east in 175, where she died.

It is possible to identify this bust as part of the collections of the Duke of Mantua which were sold to King Charles I as it is illustrated in a volume of drawings from the Royal Library at Windsor Castle which were made to show the antique sculpture in Mantua involved in the sale (see Cat. 246).

In this bust a young woman is portrayed, the head being turned slightly to the left. Her hair is parted in the centre, and brought down in waves on each side of the face. She is wearing a tunic and cloak. The bust most probably represents Faustina the Younger, as a number of other similar portraits are usually taken to represent her. However some scholars have identified them with her daughter Lucilla, who is portrayed on coins with similar features and hairstyle.

M.L.

BIBLIOGRAPHY: Scott-Elliot, 1959, p. 218ff.
ADDITIONAL BIBLIOGRAPHY: For other examples of portraits of Faustina the Younger, and for portraits of Lucilla see J. J. Bernouilli, *Römische Ikonographie*, II, 2 Stuttgart, 1891, 189ff, 221ff, pls. 53, 54, 59; *British Museum, Catalogue of Sculpture in the Department of Greek and Roman Anti-*

quities, vol. 3, 1904, no. 1905, p. 161; H. Stuart Jones, *Sculpture of the Museo Capitolino*, vol. I, Oxford, 1912, text p. 126 no. 53, pl. 32, & p. 198 no. 39, pl. 52; M. Wegner, *Die Herrscherbildnisse in antoninischer Zeit*, Berlin, 1939, p. 212, pl. 36; p. 220 pl. 34; p. 222, pl. 35.

249

Crouching Venus known as the Lely Venus

Italian marble; over life size. The fingers of the right hand, and the left arm below the elbow have been restored.
On loan from Her Majesty The Queen to the British Museum.

This statue representing the goddess Venus crouching to wash herself is an antique Roman copy of a Greek original of the third century BC. This statue was formerly in the collections of the Dukes of Mantua; it was among the large number of works of art sold to King Charles I from the Gonzaga collections in 1627-28. The figure is shown labelled *Elena di Troia* in a volume of drawings now in the Royal Library at Windsor Castle made to illustrate the antique sculpture in Mantua when negotiations of its sale to Charles I were in progress (Cat. 246). The statue is also mentioned in correspondence about the sale of antiquities from Mantua; the agent Daniel Nys writing to Lord Dorchester, Charles's Secretary, referred to *une figure de femme accroupie de marbre, aucuns disent*

249

Venus delli Ely, autres Hélène de Troye, c'est la plus belle statue de tous estimée à 6 mille escus. A later annotation beside the drawing in the volume from Windsor records that the statue was bought by Lely the painter from the collection of Charles I. It was reacquired for the royal collections by Charles II in 1682. This statue which is one of several surviving antique versions of the Greek original, shows the goddess half-kneeling on the right knee, sitting on the heel and bending forward; the left arm is brought across close to the body to touch the right thigh, while the right arm is brought up to near the left shoulder. The head is turned to the right. The belief that this composition was created by a Bithynian sculptor of the third century BC, called Doidalses, has been discredited, as it has been shown that such an interpretation could not be extracted from a corrupt passage of the text of Pliny the Elder (*Historia Naturalis*, XXXVI, 35) on the history of art. However, it is still generally agreed among historians of ancient art that the original Greek statue, from which this statue is derived, was the creation of a sculptor of the third century BC, as many trivial actions and everyday activities were first represented in sculpture at this time.

M.L.

BIBLIOGRAPHY: Scott-Elliot, 1959, pp. 218-27, esp. pp. 218-20, fig. 13.
ADDITIONAL BIBLIOGRAPHY: F. Haskell & N. Penny, *Taste and the Antique*, London, 1981, p. 321. C.M. Robertson, *History of Greek Art*, Cambridge, 1976, pp. 556-57 for the type; C. Vermeule, *AJA*, 59, 1955, p. 149-50; C. Vermeule, *AJA*, 60, 1956, p. 461; P.P. Bober & R.O. Rubinstein, *Antique Sculpture and Renaissance Artists*, forthcoming, Cat. no. 18.

250

A Poet
Domenico Fetti (*c.* 1589-1623)
Oil on canvas, 140 x 110 cm
Artemis Group, London

This is one of a pair of over life-size paintings of poets (its companion is in the National Museum, Stockholm). That the subjects are poets is suggested by the attributes of laurel wreaths and books, and their dependence on Titian's series of eleven emperors (Cat. 168-178) makes it likely that they date from Fetti's Mantuan sojourn. He may have also copied Titian's emperors (Artemis Catalogue, 1977, no. 1). It has been suggested that the Stockholm painting of an elderly, cadaverous man, also dressed in a robe fastened by a cameo and holding a pen and book, represents Virgil, but this present painting bears a close resemblance to the terracotta bust (Cat. 99) then believed to be a likeness of Virgil. Fetti worked as Duke Ferdinando's court artist from 1613-23; he was sent to Venice to buy paintings for the Villa Favorita in 1621, but he himself is not recorded as having contributed anything to its decoration. The Favorita (Cat. 271) was Ferdinando's chief undertaking as a patron of the arts; it also was a great drain on his financial resources. Among many other works, the Duke commissioned a series of paintings of Apollo and the Nine Muses from Baglione (Askew, 1978, pp. 274-95); a series of Mantuan poets could also have appealed to him. The scale of the poets is in keeping with the paintings ordered for the Favorita; for the old Ducal Palace Fetti painted many of his small scale parables (Askew, 1961, pp. 21-45). The 1627 inventory lists twenty-three portraits by Fetti in the *Galleria della Mostra* (Luzio, 1913, p. 108, no. 266).

J.T.M.

PROVENANCE: Dr and Mrs Oscar K. Cosla, given by them to Baldwin-

Wallace College, Berea, Ohio; on loan to the Museum of Fine Arts, Maryhill 1949-65; Artemis Group, 1977.

BIBLIOGRAPHY: Luzio, 1913; Askew, 1978, pp. 274-95.

ADDITIONAL BIBLIOGRAPHY: P. Askew, "The Parable Paintings of Domenico Fetti", *Art Bulletin*, XLII, 1961, pp. 21-45; *An Exhibition of Paintings by Fetti and Magnasco* (Exhibition Catalogue), Artemis Group, London, 1977, nos. 1 and 2.

251

Il Ballarino (Venice, 1581)
F. Caroso
Private Collection

Caroso, a dancing master, wrote two large manuals of crucial significance for their precise descriptions of sixteenth-century dance steps, the *Nobilità di dame* (Venice 1600) and *Il ballarino* (Venice 1581). Taken together they present a valuable panorama of the basic rules for dancing as well as a considerable repertory of over 100 dances, for the most part *balletti*, direct descendents of fifteenth-century *balli*. Caroso's patrons were the Caetani, the ruling family of Sermoneta where he was probably born about 1530, and many of his dances are dedicated to other Roman ladies. *Il ballarino* itself is dedicated to Bianca Cappello, Grand Duchess of Tuscany, and includes pieces inscribed to members of the Este, Sforza, and other north Italian noble families. A prominent position is allocated to the dance Este-Gonzaga, dedicated to Margherita Gonzaga, wife of Duke Alfonso II d'Este of Ferrara, and the founder of the so-called *Balletto della duchessa* about this time. This ensemble of dancers were carefully rehearsed by Margherita to perform specially-choreographed dances of considerable elaboration during the 1580's. Other pieces are addressed to Eleonora Gonzaga of Austria, Duchess of Mantua (fol. 9ᵛ), and Margherita Farnese Gonzaga, Princess of Mantua (fol. 30ᵛ).

I.F.

BIBLIOGRAPHY: DBI.

252

Portrait of a young musician, possibly Monteverdi
(1567-1643)
Unknown (? Cremonese) painter
Oil on Canvas; 75 x 56 cm
Ashmolean Museum, Oxford (Inv. A 863 a)

Monteverdi came from Cremona to Mantua *c.* 1590 and was by 1592 employed as a viol player by Duke Vincenzo I, to whom he dedicated his third book of madrigals. He accompanied Vincenzo to Hungary in 1595 and to Flanders in 1599, the same year that he married a Mantuan court singer, Claudia Cattaneo; in 1602 he was appointed *maestro di cappella*. It was first suggested by M.L. Huggins that this painting might be of the young Monteverdi, since its earliest known provenance is his home town of Cremona (Stradivari Collection); the clothes are of the late sixteenth century and a bass viol is in his hand while a violin with a bow is on the wall behind. A sheet of music (unidentified) with some words for vocal accompaniment is visible, while an ink bottle with a quill and case for music in the foreground might be intended to emphasize that the player was also a composer. Other names have been put forward, however, including that of the violin maker Gaspare da Salò (Geiser, 1974). There is no known early portrait with which to compare it; the portrait at Castle Howard of a *Musician* thought to be Monteverdi would be from his Venetian period, many years later, and the print of 1644 is posthumous.

D.S.C.

PROVENANCE: Giacomo Stradivari; J.B. Vuillaume (before 1882); W.H. Hill (after 1891); Ashmolean Museum (1952).
BIBLIOGRAPHY: Grove, 1980.
ADDITIONAL BIBLIOGRAPHY: M.L. Huggins, "A supposed portrait of Stradivari", in W.H., A.F. and A.E. Hill, *Antonio Stradivari, His Life and Work*, London 1902, pp. 279-85.

251

252

253

L'Orfeo, Favola in Musica (2nd edition; Venice, 1615)
C. Monteverdi (1567-1643)
Bodleian Library, Oxford (MS.20 Art)

L'Orfeo is Monteverdi's first extended work for the stage, and
the sixth *dramma per musica* to be written. Although officially
sponsored by the Accademia degli Invaghiti, a group of high-
ranking courtiers and local nobility who assembled for the
purposes of oration and versification on what they believed to
be classical models, the real instigator of the work seems to
have been Prince Francesco Gonzaga. A series of letters between him and his brother Ferdinando, who also possessed
strong artistic interests, oulines the gestation and preparation
of the work from early in 1607. From these letters, and from
other evidence, it would seem that the opera was produced on
a modest scale with doubling of parts, minimal stage appara-
tus, and small instrumental forces. The principal parts were
taken by the Florentine castrato Giovanni Gualberto, and the
distinguished tenor Francesco Rasi who was then in Gonzaga
service but who had been employed earlier by the Medici.
L'Orfeo was given for the first time on 23 February as part of
Carnival, and was repeated on 1 May; a projected third performance in honour of the visit of the Duke of Savoy never
took place. The first edition of the score appeared in Venice in
1609, and discrepancies between it and the published libretto
produced for the first performance suggest that in some respects it may not represent Monteverdi's original conception
as given in 1607.

I.F.

BIBLIOGRAPHY: Davari, 1884; Vogel, 1887, Schrade, 1964, Grove, 1980,
12, pp. 514-34.

234

254

Gonzaga wedding festivities (May 1608)
F. Follino, *Compendio delle sontuose feste per le reali nozze del
Serenissimo Principe d. Francesco Gonzaga con la Serenissima in-
fante Margherita di Savoia*, Mantua, 1608
Private Collection, London

Prolonged celebrations followed the marriage of Prince Francesco Gonzaga to Margherita of Savoy, which was expected
to ensure a long and secure succession. Federico Follino (dates
unknown, d. *c.* 1620) according to his dedication compiled
this account for the benefit of Margherita Gonzaga Duchess
of Lorraine, who had not been able to come. The festivities,
coinciding with the institution of the Order of the Redeemer
which Follino also describes (pp. 20-77) included the first
performances of Monteverdi's opera *Arianna* and his *Balletto
delle Ingrate* and Follino gives a version of Rinuccini's libretto
in each case (pp. 29-65, 124-34), the production of Guarini's
Idropica is also described at length (pp. 73-99). Other entertainments for Duke Vincenzo's many guests included tourna-
ments and wild boar hunts, but the most spectacular event of
all (which had to be postponed several times because of high
wind) was the mock naval battle with firework displays on
the Lake. This was devised by Gabriele Bertazzolo whose
separate description and two engravings of the event were
also incorporated in Follino's book (pp. 67-72). Thousands of
coloured paper lanterns illuminated the Ducal Palace, Castel-

253

lo S. Giorgio and an artificial castle on an island in the Lake which was supposedly held by Turks against an attacking Christian fleet; the latter won its victory in spite of a Turkish armada coming to the relief of the castle. Bertazzolo, it has been suggested, originally devised all this to celebrate Duke Vincenzo's return from his last campaign against the Turks (1601) but because the campaign had been such a fiasco the spectacle had been cancelled (Errante, 1915, p. 79).

D.S.C.

BIBLIOGRAPHY: Errante, 1915, D.B.I.

255

Mascherata dell'Ingrate (Mantua, per gli heredi di Francesco Osanna, stampator Ducale, 1608)
C. Monteverdi (1567–1643)
Private Collection

Monteverdi contributed a number of items to the celebrations marking the marriage of Francesco Gonzaga to Margherita of Savoy in 1608, including the opera *L'Arianna*, the music for the prologue to *L'Idropica*, and the full-length ballet *Il ballo dell'ingrate*. Although the libretto for the *ballo* appeared in 1608, the score itself was not published until thirty years later, and comparisons between the two reveal considerable discrepancies, presumably a reflection of changed artistic fashions. Further details of the original performance are supplied by Follino's *Compendio* (Cat. 254). The scene is set in Hades, and opens with a dialogue in which Cupid and Venus intervene with Pluto to permit the *ingrate* to ascend to earth.
This granted the *ingrate* emerge and dances ensue. Following

a moralistic *arioso* from Pluto, interspersed with a recurring instrumental passage, the *ingrate* return to Hades. As they do so, one of them sings a final lament. The parallels between the *ballo* and Acts III and IV of *L'Orfeo*, composed for the Carnival of 1607 (Cat. 253), are striking. Although little is known about the Mantuan productions of either, it seems likely that whereas *L'Orfeo* was planned on a modest scale, the *ballo* was intended for elaborate presentation in the manner of the Florentine *intermedi*.

I.F.

BIBLIOGRAPHY: As for Cat. 253.

255

MASCHERATA
DELL'INGRATE.
BALLO DEL SERENISS. SIG. DVCA,
DANZATO PER LE NOZZE DE' SERENISSIMI
PRINCIPE DI MANTOVA,
ET INFANTA DI SAVOIA.

In Mantova, per gli Heredi di Francesco Ofanna Stampator
Ducale. 1608. Con licenza de' Superiori.

Il Lamento d'Arianna (Venice, 1623)
C. Monteverdi (1567-1643)
Private Collection

Monteverdi seems to have begun work on his opera *L'Arianna* (Ariadne) in the last months of 1607. It was originally hoped to produce it during Carnival of the following year, but in the event Marco da Gagliano's *La Dafne* was substituted. The work was finally given in May 1608 as part of the Mantuan festivities celebrating the marriage of the heir-apparent, Francesco Gonzaga, to Margherita of Savoy. Final preparations for the performance were complicated by the death from smallpox of the young singer Caterina Martinelli who was to have taken the title-role. Eventually the part was played by Virginia Andreini, a member of a visiting company of players, the Comici Fedeli. Several versions of Arianna's lament, "Lasciatemi morire", are known, the only music from the opera to survive. Andreini's performance of this song was apparently enthusiastically received, and it was evidently the only excerpt from the work to find its way into print. Disguised as a five-voice madrigal, the piece apears in Monteverdi's *Il sesto libro de madrigali a cinque voci* (Venice, 1614), the first of his madrigalian publications to appear after the first production, and was subsequently printed in the monodic version shown here (pp. 38-39).

I.F.

BIBLIOGRAPHY: As for Cat. 253; also Ademollo, 1888; Reiner, 1974.

256

257

Vincenzo, Gonzaga, (formerly believed to be Francesco), later Duke Vincenzo II of Mantua
Rubens (1577-1640)
Oil on canvas (on board); 67.3 x 57.2 cm; (1602-3)
National Trust, Saltram House, Plympton.

This portrait has been convincingly identified with a half-length figure in armour "done... by... Rubens when he was in Italie" which was in the collection of Charles I in 1639 (Jaffé, 1961). The inventory of this date which records the picture calls the sitter "the deceased young Duke of Mantuas brother". The description is, however, misleading; for it seems that it must refer either to Francesco or to Ferdinando Gonzaga, the elder brothers and predecessors of Vincenzo II (b. 1594; Duke, 1626-27). Rubens's picture in fact shows

257

Vincenzo himself. Stylistic considerations indicate that the picture was painted between 1602 and 1603. Obviously therefore the sitter cannot be Ferdinando, as his different appearance just before and after this date is documented in Rubens's *Adoration of the Trinity* and in his preparatory drawing (Cat. 229, 232). Nor can it be concluded that the Saltram picture represents Francesco, as is usually assumed. For it is Francesco who appears in Rubens's other surviving portrait drawing for the *Adoration* (Cat. 233), and this study, made around 1601 certainly does not show the boy in the Saltram portrait; we would then have to believe that in the course of a year or so Francesco had not just radically altered but been amazingly rejuvenated. On the other hand, as has often been noted, the child in the Saltram picture in fact bears a striking resemblance to a different member of the Gonzaga family who was included in Rubens's *Adoration*, namely the boy in the Vienna fragment. This fragment certainly does not show Francesco (b. 1586) as is sometimes maintained, but rather Vincenzo, aged ten in 1605 (cf. Cat. 232). The present portrait clearly depicts the same Vincenzo, appropriately younger by about two years, and not yet so plump.
It has been observed (Müller Hofstede, 1977, p. 302) that this independent portrait by Rubens of a member of the ducal family is unusual. The official Gonzaga portraitist was Pourbus; it was his image of Vincenzo I that Rubens took to Spain in 1603 even if the Duke of Lerma then wanted the artist to produce another one of his own from memory (Rooses-Ruelens, 1887, p. 171). It is tempting to suppose that the Saltram *Vincenzo II* might have had just such an origin. Jaffé has pointed to the lack of assurance in the treatment of the body, notably in the projecting arm, and the summary hand-

ling of some details of costume. This, as well as the stark background, suggests that the figure was not studied from life. The same is not true for the much more impressively painted collar and head. The implication is that Rubens produced this portrait, perhaps rather hastily, from an existing study of Vincenzo's head alone. A drawing of this kind must have been made along with those of Ferdinando and Francesco (Cat. 232, 233) in connection with the *Adoration of the Trinity*. It therefore seems more than likely that the Saltram portrait, which shows Vincenzo at about the age of eight, was elaborated from a preparatory study for the S. Trinità picture done perhaps a year before. Rubens's original plan for the *Adoration* apparently had Vincenzo standing immediately behind his father, not kneeling and leaning forward in the foreground as he finally appeared (Reconstructions I and II; Cat. 229); the pose of the head in the present portrait fits well enough his position in this first arrangement.

E.McG.

PROVENANCE: Charles I (bought before 1625 probably in Spain in 1623); sold to Mr. Bass, 19.12.1651; Saltram House (first recorded 1819).
BIBLIOGRAPHY: Jaffé, 1961; Huemer, 1977[2], II, pp. 127f, no. 15, (with earlier bibliography); Exh. Antwerp, 1977, p. 49, no. 13; Müller Hofstede, 1977, p. 302, no. 81.

258

Vincenzo II Gonzaga (1594-1627), last Duke of the original line, as a Knight of the Order of the Redeemer (*c.* 1621) [Pl. 97]
Attributed to Justus Sustermans (1597-1681)
Oil on canvas; 196 x 109 cm
Museo del Palazzo Ducale, Mantua (Inv. 197)

Vincenzo, youngest of the three sons of Duke Vincenzo I, disgraced the family when after he became a Cardinal (1615) it emerged that he had already married a widow much older than himself, Isabella Gonzaga da Novellara; Pope Paul V refused to annul the marriage and he had to renounce the cardinalate. In so far as his character and career have been studied at all, he has been portrayed as one of the most decadent, puerile and sickly of the Gonzaga lineage (Luzio, 1913, pp. 54-62) interested above all in dwarves and parrots. During his short reign as Duke (29 October 1626-26 December 1627) it was he who first authorized the sale of works of art to Charles I (see essay by Howarth and Cat. 274-276). If indeed painted by Sustermans, the portrait was presumably done when the artist visited Mantua in *c.* 1621 to paint Vincenzo's sister Eleonora (see Cat. no. 273), during the reign of Duke Ferdinando Gonzaga. Vincenzo is shown wearing the robes and collar with a pendant of the Order of the Redeemer, founded by his father in 1608 and to which he had been admitted in April 1609 (Cottafavi, 1935, p. 251, and see Cat. 236, 240). Presided over by the reigning Duke, the membership limited to twenty, its declared purpose was to defend the Catholic faith and honour the Blood of Christ; the church of Sant'Andrea, where the famous relic was preserved, therefore became the chapel of the Order and its choir was intended to contain the arms of each knight. The collar, decorated with the ancient Gonzaga device of the crucible (see above Cat. 62 and essay by Praz) was intended to remind the wearer of a comparison between fine gold tried by fire and his obligation to prove himself by works of virtue to God and the world; the motto *Domine probasti* was also used with the crucible on the crimson mantle fringed with gold (part of one mantle of the Order survives as a chasuble in the sacristy of the church

of Santo Stefano, Verona). The pendant to the collar bears the image of the reliquary urn containing the Precious Blood at Sant'Andrea.

D.S.C.

BIBLIOGRAPHY: Mantua, *Mostra Iconog.*, 1937, p. 45, no. 204; Ozzòla, 1949, p. 3, n. 14; Cottafavi, 1935; Pelati, 1973, p. 315.

259

259

Quarter Ducat of Duke Vincenzo I (1596)
Gold coin; diam 16 mm, weight 0.87 g
British Museum, Department of Coins and Medals (1910, 10, Spink, 6, 19)

Under Duke Vincenzo gold coins smaller than the ducat were minted; this *quarto di zecchino* has the reliquary of the Precious Blood and Imperial eagle on the obverse, and an hourglass with a compass and the device "NEC CITRA NEC ULTRA" on the reverse above the date. An even rarer gold *quartino* has Virgil's head on the obverse and the device "SIC" with the half moon on the reverse.

D.S.C.

BIBLIOGRAPHY: CNI, IV, p. 318, 21; Magnaguti, II, 1915, pp. 33-34.

260

Francesco Gonzaga, fourth Duke of Mantua and fifth Duke of Monferrato (1586-1612)
Guillaume Dupré (c. 1576-1643)
Medal (uniface); bronze; diam. 165 mm
British Museum, Department of Coins and Medals (Inv. M. 2149)

Dupré, a leading medallist at the French Court in the early

260

261

seventeenth century, came to Italy in 1612; through Queen Marie de' Medici, sister of the Duchess Eleonora Gonzaga, the links with Mantua at that period were strong and Cardinal Ferdinando Gonzaga had spent the winter of 1611-12 at Paris. Dupré's portrait of the twenty-six year old Duke in the year of his accession (February) and death from small pox (December) shows him obese looking, heavy-jowelled and prematurely old.

D.S.C.

BIBLIOGRAPHY: Jones, 1979, p. 75.

261

Ducatone of Cardinal Duke Ferdinando (1613)
Silver coin; diam 43 mm; weight 31.46 g
British Museum (SSB 101-60)

The coins of Duke Ferdinando (still a Cardinal until 1615) were unequalled in number and fine quality by those of any contemporary ruler in Italy, even the Pope (Magnaguti, II, p. 52) and included an enormous twelve ducat gold coin. This double *scudo* or *ducatone* bears on the obverse a portrait of the Cardinal wearing a biretta and the collar of the Order of the Redeemer over his mozzetta.

D.S.C.

BIBLIOGRAPHY: CNI, IV, p. 339, 10 var.; Magnaguti, II, 1915, pp. 52-53.

262

Ducatone of Cardinal Ferdinando (1613)
Silver coin; diam 44 mm; weight 31.41 g
British Museum (1851-3-8-4; Milan Tray, 1)

As Cat. no. 261 but showing the reverse with Ferdinando's favourite device of the sun with the motto "NON MUTUATA LUCE" ("not with borrowed light" i.e. the House of Gonzaga shines on its own).

263

263

Tallero of Cardinal Duke Ferdinando (1613)
Silver coin; diam 42 mm; weight 26.4 g
British Museum (1919-2-14-54)

The coins of Cardinal Duke Ferdinando displayed a variety of religious imagery. The *tallero*, an equivalent of the German *thaler*, which has on its obverse the Gonzaga arms with the Cardinal's hat and a crown labelled "FIDES", provides on its reverse a variation on the image of the Precious Blood; here the relic is presented by its finder St Longinus to St Andrew, its custodian in Mantua. This type had already appeared in 1612, however, on the silver *scudo* and pretentious twelve

ducats (*zecchini*) gold coin of the short-lived Duke Francesco IV.

D.S.C.

BIBLIOGRAPHY: CNI, IV, p. 339, 13; Magnaguti, II, 1915, pp. 46-47, 54.

264

Presentation coin of Duke Vincenzo II (1627)
Gold strike of *ducatone*; diam 43 mm, weight 39.17 g
British Museum (1864-3-1-8; Milan Tray, 1)

The *ducatone* was normally minted in silver so this example in gold must have been exceptional; moreover, it was struck at the time when Gonzaga financial difficulties had reached their peak. Vincenzo's head appears on the obverse, and on the reverse is a device of a dog with the motto "FERIS TANTVM INFENSVS" (enraged only by wild animals) which one might take as an appropriate enough motto for an ineffectual ruler.

D.S.C.

BIBLIOGRAPHY: CNI, IV, p. 357, as 8/7; Magnaguti, II, 1915, pp. 64-65.

264

265

Tasso's epic poem published in Mantua (With revisions by Scipione Gonzaga) (1584)
Torquato Tasso, *Gerusalemme Liberata. Poema Heroico...*, In Mantova/per Francesco Osanna MDLXXXIIII
British Library (G 11109 [1])

The capture of Jerusalem in the first Crusade (1099) led by Godfrey of Bouillon was already the theme for a poem Tasso began in 1559, at a time when fears of the Turkish danger were acute in Italy, but he put it aside for years; in 1575, when he went to stay with Scipione Gonzaga in Rome (Cat. 266) his poem was finished though not to his satisfaction. Scipione wrote a copy in his own hand (the manuscript reappeared in public only in 1968), but this cannot be identified with Scipione's rapid transcription referred to by Tasso in letters, and corresponds more to the version printed in Venice under the title *Goffredo* in 1582 and 1584 than to the edition bearing the title *Gerusalemme Liberata* (Parma and Ferrara, 1581) which was supervised by the poet's friend Febo Bonnà. The Mantuan edition shown here, incorporating the revisions suggested by Scipione and others, was to be accepted as the most authentic text for the next three centuries. Francesco Osanna, the Ducal printer, may have met Tasso in 1578, and he published a selection of the *Rime* in 1581; later they became close

265

friends and Tasso declared he had never felt greater affection for anyone else. During his long confinement for supposed madness, Tasso began to react against his own work and plan a revision, more orthodox in its religious allusions, which was to appear as the *Gerusalemme Conquistata* (first printed in 1593); but in spite of the controversy the *Liberata* aroused (some critics denounced it as immoral and obscure) it had an immense success, not least in England where it influenced the poetry of Spenser, and in the Gonzaga court it contributed to the romantic crusading militancy, credulity and chivalric fantasy of Duke Vincenzo. As well as numerous Italian printings, translations soon appeared; an incomplete version in English by Richard Carew, *Godfrey of Bulloigne* (1594) was followed by the much superior version of Edward Fairfax, *Godfrey of Bulloigne, the Recoverie of Jerusalem, done into English heroicall verse* (1600).

D.S.C.

BIBLIOGRAPHY: Brand, 1965; Tasso ed. Caretti, 1979.
ADDITIONAL BIBLIOGRAPHY: A. Magnaguti, "Il tipografo di Tasso: messer Francesco Osanna", *Atti Acc. Virgiliana*, XXV, 1939, pp. 157-68; D. Rhodes, "Some notes on Francesco Osanna of Mantua, Torquato Tasso and others", *British Museum Quarterly*, XXXI, 1966, pp. 1-2; L. Caretti, "Il Codice Gonzaga della Liberata", in G. Pozzi et al. *Tra Latino e volgare per Carlo Dionisotti*, vol. 1, Padua, 1974, pp. 318-30.

266

Photograph: **Letter of the poet Torquato Tasso (1544-95) with two sonnets addressed to Duke Vincenzo I;** Rome, 10 November 1590
Archivio di Stato, Mantua (Autografi, b. 9 cc. 106-07)

Torquato Tasso, one of the greatest Italian poets and a self-tormented victim of persecution mania, was associated from 1565 with the d'Este of Ferrara, but he had longer and happier links with the Gonzaga. His father Bernardo Tasso ended his career in Duke Guglielmo's service (he died as governor of Ostiglia in 1569); Torquato visited him at Mantua in 1563 and in 1564-65 addressed love sonnets to the daughter of a Man-

tuan merchant. When studying at Padua he became a close friend of Scipione Gonzaga (who was to become a Cardinal in 1587); Scipione invited him to Rome in 1575 and acted as one of his principal editorial revisers and advisers (Cat. 265). After Tasso's return to Ferrara (1579), at the time Duke Alfonso II d'Este married Margherita Gonzaga, Alfonso became convinced that Tasso was mad and had him confined to the hospital of Sant'Anna in Ferrara until, thanks to the future Duke Vincenzo Gonzaga, he was released in 1586 and went to Mantua. From 1587 to 1590 on his wanderings he went back to Scipione Gonzaga's house in Rome. Tasso in the letter shown here, as well as asking Duke Vincenzo for a printing concession, congratulates him upon a discovery of gold bars (a reference presumably to a rumour about Vincenzo's experiments in alchemy) and both sonnets celebrate this. In the first, Tasso reflects that Vincenzo prefers the splendours of the earth (gold and diamonds) to its sons, men who make wars, and this is a token of his power; in the other, that splendour is assured to Vincenzo by the favour of the moon's rays and the world is preparing as many sceptres for his hand as there are stars. Tasso accepted Vincenzo's invitation and early in 1591 returned to Mantua, writing there in gratitude his *Genealogia della Casa Gonzaga*; later in the same year, when Vincenzo set off for a visit to Rome, the poet accompanied him.

D.S.C.

BIBLIOGRAPHY: Brand, 1965; Tasso ed. Caretti, 1979.
ADDITIONAL BIBLIOGRAPHY: Letter published in C. Guasti, *Le lettere di T. Tasso*, vol. V, Florence, 1855, p. 12; the sonnet "Quella, che trasse..." was published in Tasso's lifetime: *Delle rime del Sig. Torquato Tasso*, 1, Brescia, 1592, fol. 3v; both sonnets in *Dodici lettere e Due sonetti di T.T.*, Casalmaggiore, 1850, pp. 12-13 and now in T. Tasso, *Opere*, ed. B. Maier, II, Milan, 1964, pp. 230-32.

267

Erminia and the Shepherd (1620)
Guercino (Giovanni Francesco Barbieri) (1591-1666)
Canvas 149 x 178 cm. Traces of an inscription and a date (162-) on the knife blade
City Art Gallery, Birmingham

Guercino's first contact with Mantua came when a collection of his anatomical drawings for the instruction of artists was engraved in Venice and dedicated to Duke Ferdinando in 1619. The frontispiece shows a woman, the personification of art, painting the ducal arms on a canvas. This act of ingratiation was effective, for Guercino's pupil Gennari, who delivered the book to Mantua, returned to his master with a request from the Duke that he make a painting "to his own whim" (*à suo capriccio*). In September 1619 Guercino wrote to Ferdinando asking for the subject and measurements required. The following year Guercino delivered this painting to Mantua where he stayed for fifteen days and was made a knight. Although it has been suggested that on account of its scale it was destined for the Villa Favorita (Askew, 1978, p. 286), in the 1627 inventory made after Ferdinando's death "A painting by Guercino of Cento depicting a subject of Tasso's" was in the *Galaria della Mostra* in the Palazzo Ducale (Luzio, 1913, p. 106; cf. Cat. 245).
The subject is taken from the epic poem *Gerusalemme Liberata* by Torquato Tasso (1544-95) (Cat. 265, 266). The somewhat turgid descriptions of battle between crusaders and saracens are interspersed with pastoral interludes which provided the subject-matter for numerous seventeenth century painters. Guercino illustrated a passage at the beginning of Canto VII when Erminia, a pagan princess in love with the crusader

239

Tancred, dressed in the armour of the virago Clorinda, is chased away from the Christian camp and carried by horse into Arcadia. Here she comes across an old shepherd weaving baskets (*E Vede un uom canuto a l'ombre amene / Tesser fiscelle a la sua gregge acanto*, Canto VII, stanza VI). He is frightened by her warrior's dress, but this she removes and they enter into a discussion of the merits of pastoral life, the debate which is shown in this painting. In this early work of Guercino's, Erminia is depicted as a healthy peasant girl: his later paintings of the subject show her more idealized in appearance. Evidently both the subject and the artist appealed to the Gonzaga, for in 1651 Duke Carlo II acquired Guercino's painting of another episode from the same poem (*Erminia discovers the wounded Tancred*, Castle Howard).

J.T.M.

PROVENANCE: Mantua, Palazzo Ducale, 1627 inventory; 18th and 19th centuries in private collections in Paris; 1961 bought by Colnaghi (Colnaghi Exhibition, 1962, no. 8); 1962 bought by City Art Gallery, Birmingham.
BIBLIOGRAPHY: Luzio, 1913, p. 106; Askew, 1978, p. 286.
ADDITIONAL BIBLIOGRAPHY: R. Lee, "Erminia in Minneapolis" in *Studies in Criticism and Aesthetics: Essays in honor of Samuel Holt Monk*, Minneapolis, 1967, pp. 36-57; Bologna, *Il Guercino: i dipinti*,ed. D. Mahon, 1968, pp. 85-86, no. 37; Bologna, *Il Guercino: i disegni* ed. D. Mahon, 1968, p. 60.

268

Gonzaga Historiography
Antonio Possevino, *Gonzaga* (Mantua, 1628)
British Library (803.1.2)

Possevino, nephew and namesake of a famous Jesuit missionary who went to Russia, was a physician, savant and wit much favoured by the Cardinal Duke Ferdinando Gonzaga, whose brother Francesco had first commissioned him to write in Latin a History of the dynasty. Possevino's unpublished letters record progress on the work; on 4 September 1614 he had only reached Guido Gonzaga, 2nd Capitano of Mantua but on 10 January 1615 he reported to Ferdinando that in the course of ten months labour, having read many historical works and an enormous load of original documents, he had written about a thousand pages which would come to about 400 pages set in a decent type (ASMAG, b. 1006, b. 1010). Clearly he found the labour wearisome; he hardly attempted to go beyond received wisdom, and devoted too much space to early history and legend. Only in Book III did Possevino reach the expulsion of the Bonacolsi and in Book VII he at last arrives in the sixteenth century. Book VIII, lasting from the visit to Mantua of Henri III in 1574 to the death of Duke Francesco in 1612, completes the work. Although he apparently had access to the Ducal archives, Possevino was ridiculed for falsification and inaccuracy (Luzio, 1922, pp.

16-17). Nevertheless it was a monumental publication and Domenico Fetti was commissioned to engrave for it copies of portraits of the entire line of Gonzaga rulers; Possevino was worried that these would not be ready, according to a letter of 12 December 1616 (Luzio, 1913, p. 286) but the 1617 edition includes the portraits as well as genealogical tables. That it had a success is indicated by the publication of another edition in 1628; this did not include the portraits, although (curiously) they happen to be bound into the present copy, which contains also the title-page of 1617, designed by the architect Nicolò Sebregondi.

D.S.C.

BIBLIOGRAPHY: Faccioli, 1962, pp. 473-74.

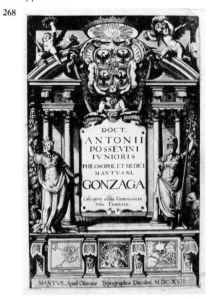

268

269

Photograph: **The Palazzo Nuovo, Maderno: a Gonzaga villa on Lake Garda**
Pencil drawing on paper, 1641
Archivio di Stato, Mantua (Archivio Gonzaga b. 3168, filza 1587-1699)

In addition to all the Gonzaga residences on Mantuan territory, Duke Vincenzo I had a summer palace built at Maderno, near Salò on the western shore of Lake Garda. From 1602-06 he was acquiring property there and the project was to include the so-called Palazzo Vecchio on three floors, the Palazzo Nuovo on five floors and the Casino or pavilion on the hill among lemon groves. The architect was Antonio Maria Viani who may already have been drawing up plans in 1603 (Luzio, 1913, p. 73, n. 3) but the main building campaign was in 1606-08; already in October 1606 it was reported that 25.000 *scudi* had been spent. After a period of disuse the site was surveyed in 1641 by Nicolò Sebregondi, who had been Duke Ferdinando's architect for his villa palace of La Favorita outside Mantua.

D.S.C.

BIBLIOGRAPHY: Fossati, 1969, pp. 30-47; Ferrari, 1970, pp. 276-77.

270

Photograph: **Bosco della Fontana, Marmirolo** (1592-95)

The palatial hunting lodge of Bosco della Fontana stands in a wooded park about three miles north west from Mantua. This setting is all that remains of the forest and game reserve of Marmirolo, one of the earliest and largest estates in Gonzaga possession which formerly included the castles and successive villas of Goito and Marmirolo, with Renaissance buildings and works of art of which no traces remain. Bosco della Fontana was designed for Duke Vincenzo I by Giuseppe Dàttari of Cremona (completed by Antonio Maria Viani) and suggests some lingering influence of Giulio Romano.

D.S.C.

BIBLIOGRAPHY: Marani and Perina, 1965, pp. 171-72, 194.
ADDITIONAL BIBLIOGRAPHY: G. Amadei and E. Marani, *Il Bosco della Fontana presso Mantova*, Mantua, 1975.

271

Photograph: **Villa La Favorita, built for Duke Ferdinando Gonzaga** (*c*. 1613-24) [Pl. 41]

Duke Ferdinando's grandiose palace near the earlier villa of Porto, facing south towards Mantua over the lake, was the final expression of Gonzaga magnificence in a major building project. Designed by Nicolò Sebregondi, who had worked for him in Rome, it was already roofed and habitable by 1616, though the building and furnishing and layout of the pleasure gardens continued for the next eight years. An elaborate double curving stairway led down from the piano nobile of the central section of the palace, and the scale of the state rooms can be imagined from the size of some of the paintings for them which survive (e.g. the four Hercules paintings by Guido Reni now in the Louvre). Ferdinando employed a team of painters imported from Rome, Bologna and elsewhere for the decorations, and purchased in bulk separate paintings and other works of art. Fountains, fishponds, specially designed gardens, woods and artifical mounds adorned the grounds. Vandalized, turned into a hospital in the late eighteenth century, abandoned then largely destroyed by fire during the First World War, only a shell of one wing of the Villa Favorita now survives.

D.S.C.

BIBLIOGRAPHY: Luzio, 1913, pp. 47-48, 292-99; Marani and Perina, 1965, pp. 175-76, 420-21, 472-74; Askew, 1978.

272

Photograph: **Fireworks to celebrate the marriage of Eleonora Gonzaga to Emperor Ferdinand II** (1622) [Pl. 1]
Anonymous
Engraving; original 26.6 x 38.4 cm
British Museum, Department of Prints and Drawings (F/H 1622; 1870-10-8/2972)

This was one of the last occasions of costly public rejoicing in Mantua before the disasters of 1627-30. Before Eleonora (see Cat. no. 273) left for the marriage ceremony in Innsbruck, there were several weeks of festivity in Mantua, culminating in the firework display on 19 January 1622. Already a theatrical centrepiece had been set up in the Piazza San Pietro (now Piazza Sordello) representing the device of Mount Olympus surmounted by the altar of Faith. The "mountain" displayed real trees and contained four grottoes and was surrounded by a balustrade decorated with flowers. Bertazzolo, the designer, described the night scene, watched by Eleonora seated beneath a *baldacchino*. There were two thousand soldiers on parade, and the vast crowd included many from far afield who wanted to see an Italian Empress. Over four thousand coloured lanterns decorated the towers, crenellations and chimneys of the surrounding buildings, in addition to the lights upon the "mountain" and its surrounding balustrade. From it emerged a figure in white representing Faith followed by others personifying virtues; the display then began and amid the rockets, revolving wheels, squibs, fire and smoke puffs; the supreme spectacle was when the feathers of the great imperial eagle over the altar came alight and flames emerged from its mouth while a triple wheel revolved and exploded, scattering a dense shower of gold sparks: for more than fifteen minutes the piazza seemed as light as at midday. The spectacle ended with a great salvo of artillery.

D.S.C.

BIBLIOGRAPHY: Bertazzolo, 1622, pp. 6-30.

273

Eleonora Gonzaga (1598-1655), bride of Emperor Ferdinando II, 1622

Lucrina Fetti (known 1614-29), after Justus Sustermans (1597-1681)
Oil on canvas; 193 x 118 cm
Museo del Palazzo Ducale, Mantua (Inv. 6832)

The marriage early in 1622 of Eleonora, youngest daughter of Duke Vincenzo I, to the Emperor Ferdinand II, raised the Gonzaga dynasty to its highest level of secular dignity; in addition to the celebrations (see Cat. no. 272) it cost her brother Duke Ferdinando a dowry of 150,000 *scudi* (Luzio, 1913, p. 7) though in return she received from her husband a diamond wedding ring worth 15.000 *scudi* and three diamond necklaces or chains, to one of which, worth over 40.000 *scudi*, was attached a pendant imperial eagle in gold with the Emperor's portrait on its breast (Bertazzolo, 1622, p. 7). Since her mother's death in 1611 Eleonora had lived at the conventual establishment of Sant'Orsola (see Cat. 227) supervised by her aunt Margherita Gonzaga (d. 1619) where Lucrina, sister of the painter Domenico Fetti, was resident as a nun (renamed Giustina).

This portrait is signed on the back "Suor Lucrina Fetti romana in S. Orsola, Mantova, ha fatto, 1622" but it is a close copy of a portrait in Vienna by Justus Sustermans (Porträtgalerie, 1976, no. 241 inv. no. 7146). According to Filippo Baldinucci (1625-96) Sustermans had been allowed to leave the Medici court at Florence sometime after 1620, in order to paint Eleonora's portrait at Mantua. In both versions of the portrait Eleonora is wearing a ceremonial chain of state and a dress of white Italian brocade with gold thread and Venetian lace – perhaps her wedding dress – and on the left side of her waist hangs a pendant with the imperial monogram, not the pendant mentioned above. The main differences are that Sustermans placed in Eleonora's left hand a handkerchief and her right hand is stroking a small dog on the table, whereas Lucrina moved Eleonora's right hand over her body, so that she is holding the pendant by its chain, while a crown and a letter addressed *Alla Sacra Maesta dell'imperatrice Gonzaga. Mantova* lie on the table as though to emphasize her exalted rank.

Eleonora was much painted; a child portrait of her, sometimes attributed to Rubens, survives at Vienna (Porträtgalerie, no. 240 inv. no. 3339) and was also copied by Pourbus (Palazzo Pitti, Florence). Other portraits of her attributed to Sustermans also survive; one at Vienna (Heinz, 1963, p. 145; Porträtgalerie no. 242 Inv. no. 1734) shows her in a dark dress,

this time wearing the diamond wedding ring and with the lapdog at her feet; Sustermans is reported by Baldinucci to have followed her to Vienna in 1623-24. She has, however, been wrongly identified as the subject of another state portrait attributed to Lucrina Fetti and formerly at Sant'Orsola (Palazzo Ducale Mantua, inv. no. 6326; Ozzòla no. 18) This is of an Empress, crowned and holding orb and sceptre, who has also been wrongly indentified as the later Eleonora Gonzaga, sister of Duke Carlo II, who in 1651 married Emperor Ferdinando III (Askew, 1976). In fact this is the copy of a portrait painted in 1613 by Jeremias Günther (Heinz, 1963, p. 195 Inv. no. 3092) of the Empress Anna, daughter of Anna Caterina Gonzaga and Archduke Ferdinando of Austria; she was wife of the Emperor Matthias II (d. 1618) and a cousin of our Empress Eleonora. The confusion probably arose through an engraving by W. Kilian of Frankfurt based on the portrait of Empress Anna but labelled Eleonora (Heinz, 1963, pp. 131, 193).

D.S.C., A.S.C.

BIBLIOGRAPHY: Bertazzolo, 1622; Intra, 1895; Mantua, *Mostra Iconog.* cat., 1937, p. 47, no. 214; Ozzòla, 1949, p. 4 no. 19.

ADDITIONAL BIBLIOGRAPHY: ed. F. Ranalli, F. Baldinucci, *Notizie dei professori del disegno*, IV, Florence, 1846, pp. 479f.; G. Heinz, "Studien zur Porträtmalerei an den Höfen der Österreichischen Erblande", *Jahrbuch der Kunsthistorischen Sammlungen in Wien*, 59, 1963, pp. 99-224; G. Heinz, K. Schütz and others, *Porträtgalerie zür Geschichte Österreichs von 1400 bis 1800*, Vienna, 1976; P. Askew, in A. Sutherland-Harris and L. Nochlin, *Women Artists*, Chicago, 1976, pp. 124-27.

VII   Disintegration

Self Portrait (*c.* 1640) [Pl. 96]
Nicholas Lanier (1588-1666)
Oil on canvas, 66 x 58.4 cm. Inscribed "made and / paynted by Nich: Lanier", and the music for a three voice canon with the words "Thus. thus. at last wee must reducéd / be to naked boanes and dust".
Oxford University Faculty of Music.

Lanier, composer, lutenist, and amateur painter, came from a family of musicians working in the royal household from the time of Elizabeth I. In 1617 he composed the music for Ben Jonson's masque *Lovers made Men*, in which he also sang and for which he painted the scenery. He was appointed Master of Music to Prince Charles in 1618, and effectively became Master of the King's Music in 1625 and later Keeper of the King's Miniatures. During the royal ocupation of Oxford (1642-44) Lanier seems to have been made a Doctor of Music, and this self portrait was probably presented to the Music Faculty then. During the time of the Commonwealth he travelled in the Low Countries, but was reinstated as Master of the King's Music in 1660.

His career as collector and conoisseur began in June 1625 when he was sent by Charles I to Italy "to provide for him some choice Pictures", as Lord Conway writes to the ambassador in Venice, adding "It will be one speciall parte of y^r and his care not to make knowne the cause of his cominge, because that would much enhance the prices" (Noel Sainsbury, 1859, pp. 321-2). This subterfuge was maintained by the King's agent in Venice, Daniel Nys, a man of uncertain nationality, who was already negotiating to buy the Mantuan collection. In August 1625 Nys wrote a letter of introduction for Lanier to Striggi, the Mantuan Chancellor, saying that the musician was travelling to Mantua on the pretext of going to Rome for the *Anno Santo*, but in fact to inspect the collection, (Luzio, 1913, p. 137). After a sojourn in Genoa, where he may have been painted by Van Dyck (Kunsthistorisches Museum, Vienna), he reached Rome by December, where he sought an export licence for many paintings including a portrait of himself. In the summer of 1626 Lanier was in London, presumably reporting to the King on the Mantuan collection, but returned to Venice in September 1627. Duke Ferdinando had died the previous November, and Nys and Lanier moved in to bargain hard for the Mantuan collection, particularly the "marbles", some of which Lanier was buying for the Duke of Buckingham. By this time the Mantuan officials were growing mistrustful of the two agents, believing them to be double-crossing the English King himself. Lanier had further dealings in Genoa with Orazio Gentileschi's sons; he was said to have been the lover of their sister, Artimisia.
From January to April 1628 Lanier supervised the packing of Mantuan paintings and sculpture on the London boat the *Margaret* which sailed from Venice. He himself left in May, travelling via Switzerland and Brussels with two paintings by

Correggio (the Louvre *Allegories*) and one by Raphael.
Lanier was one of the first to recognise the importance of drawings: "He used to contract for a piece, and at the same time agree to have a good parcel of waste paper drawings... for himself" (North, ed. 1890, p. 202). These drawings he marked with a star (e.g. above Cat. 166). He also has a more dubious innovation to his credit, that of blackening and rolling copies of paintings to make them appear old.
This self portrait, the only painting of his to survive, shows his in the dual rôle of composer and painter. Although the three voice canon is not recorded amongst his works, Iain Fenlon sees no reason to doubt his authorship. Despite the melancholy tone of the words, Lanier appears to have had a great capacity to survive the vicissitudes of seventeenth century court life.

J.T.M.

PROVENANCE: Presented by the artist to the Music Faculty, Oxford University.
BIBLIOGRAPHY: Noel Sainsbury, 1859, pp. 311-13, 315, 320ff; Luzio, 1913, pp. 69, 137 ff; Millar, 1972, p. 95 No. 1; Groves, 1980, 10, pp. 454-55.
ADDITIONAL BIBLIOGRAPHY: R. Poole, "The Oxford Music School and the Collection of Portraits formerly Preserved there", *The Musical Antiquary* iv. 1913, p. 142; I. Spink, "Lanier in Italy", *Music and Letters*, 40, July 1959, pp. 242-52.

Daniel Nys' Bargaining for Gonzaga pictures
a) Photograph: Letter of Daniel Nys to Alessandro Striggi, Venice, 24 April 1627
Manuscript in Italian on paper, autograph
Archivio di Stato, Mantua (Archivio Gonzaga, b. 1558)

Daniel Nys, agent for Charles I, itemizes in this letter the four successive lists of paintings which Duke Vincenzo II had already offered to sell; on the second list, for instance, appear Titian's twelve (in fact eleven) *Roman Emperors* (Cat. 168-78) and on the third are included Correggio's *Allegories* of *Vice* and *Virtue* painted for Isabella d'Este (Pl. 52, 53) *duo quadri Coregio della Grota* – the total asking price being 62.423 *ducatoni* or 42.998 *scudi* of Mantua. Nys however made a bid also to include Mantegna's *Parnassus* and Costa's *Allegory* (Pl. 89, Cat. 114) – *il ballo del Mantegna et quadro del Costa Vecchio della grota* – offering a round figure of 50.000 Mantuan *scudi*.

D.S.C.

BIBLIOGRAPHY: Luzio, 1913, pp. 71-74, text pp. 140-41; essay by Howarth above.

b) Photograph: Letter of Daniel Nys to the same, Venice, 1 May 1627
Manuscript in Italian on paper; autograph
Archivio di Stato, Mantua (Archivio Gonzaga, b. 1558)

A reply to the above had made clear to Nys that there was no hope of having either the *Parnassus* or the *Costa*; accepting this disappointment, he asked for confirmation that he could get the two pictures by Correggio. A letter of 14 May shows that he had this assurance, but he found the bargain was getting a little harder, since the asking price without the extra items had risen to 50.000 *scudi*. By July a first instalment of the sale had been agreed.

D.S.C.

BIBLIOGRAPHY: As for Cat. 275a.

276

Charles I (1628) [Pl. 101]
Gerrit van Honthorst (1599-1656)
Oil on canvas 76.2 x 63.8 cm
National Portrait Gallery, London (no. 4444)

Honthorst, a Dutch Catholic painter who had worked in Rome from 1610-20 where he was influenced by Caravaggio, came to England, probably in April 1628, and stayed until 8 December of the same year, when he was handsomely rewarded by Charles I for his services. Sir Baltazar Gerbier, in a letter to the Duke of Buckingham's secretary says "I trust you will not forget to bring Mr Honthorst: for the Duke (of Buckingham) intends to employ him as well as His Majesty who will give him cause not to complain of crossing the sea" (5 April 1628) (Judson, 1959, p. 11). Joachim van Sandrart, Honthorst's assistant who accompanied him to England, implies that the chief undertaking was the large allegory of *Apollo and Diana* painted for the Banqueting Hall, Whitehall (now at Hampton Court), in which the King and Queen are represented as Apollo and Diana respectively, and the Duke of Buckingham appears in the rôle of Mercury. However Honthorst painted court portraits as well, including the large group of the *Duke of Buckingham and his Family* (Royal Collection) which hung in the King's bedroom at Whitehall. It has been suggested by Sir Oliver Millar that this portrait of Charles I may be a preliminary study for the head of Apollo in the Hampton Court painting, but the very intimacy and informality of the pose, almost certainly taken from life, might suggest that it was made for a member of the royal household (his favourite, Buckingham, was assassinated in June 1628). He is shown reading a letter or document, and wearing the blue sash of the Order of the Garter. It was in these years that his agent, Daniel Nys, was continuing negotiations to buy the Mantuan collection of paintings, while at home the King was attempting to force Parliament to vote him the most unpopular levy of Tonnage and Poundage.

J.T.M

PROVENANCE: Henry Farrer Esq. Sold at Christies 15 June 1866, lot 122. Subsequent history unknown; Paris art market in the early 1950's, M. Ulysse Moussali. Bought by the National Portrait Gallery in 1965.
BIBLIOGRAPHY: Millar, 1972, no. 78
ADDITIONAL BIBLIOGRAPHY: O. Millar, "Charles I, Honthorst, and Van Dyck", *Burlington Magazine*, XCVI, 1954, p. 36; J.R. Judson: *Gerrit van Honthorst, a Discussion of his position in Dutch Art*, 1959; *The Orange and the Rose*, Victoria & Albert Museum, 1964-5, no, 26, *France Ecosse*, Archives Nationales, Paris, 1965, no. 375; National Portrait Gallery Annual Report 1965-66, pp. 26-27.

277

Abraham van der Doort's catalogue of Charles I's collection
Bodleian Library, Oxford (Ms Ashmole 1514)

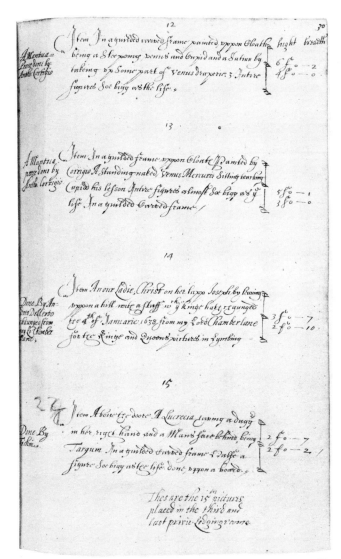

277

Abraham van der Doort (c. 1575-1640), a Dutch craftsman particularly skilled in coin design, had been connected with the court of Emperor Rudolph II and later with the Princes of Wales Henry (d. 1612) and Charles. His appointment as Keeper of the Cabinet Room, which carried special responsibility for the royal collection of coins and medals, was confirmed by Charles I in 1625. During the 1630's he undertook to compile a comprehensive list of the King's collection of works of art, including the many recent acquisitions from Mantua. The inventory survives in a number of versions (a fair copy for the King himself is at Windsor). The manuscript shown here was evidently van der Doort's working copy, and the scribe's neatly written entries are much annotated and corrected in a Dutch hand; the text is open at fol. 30r which itemizes one of Correggio's paintings originally commissioned by Duke Federico "a standing naked Venus Mercuris sitting teaching Cupid his lesson" (now in the National Gallery, London; Pl. 98).

Van der Doort was evidently under great strain, surrounded by jealous courtiers, and committed suicide.

D.S.C.

BIBLIOGRAPHY: Millar, 1960.

Addendum to van der Doort's catalogue of Charles I's collection
Victoria & Albert Museum, Library (MS A.A. 17)

Someone with access to van der Doort's inventory (but who cannot be identified with any of the scribes who compiled the surviving manuscripts) wrote this abbreviated and in parts variant version of it in *c.* 1640; Sir James Palmer (1584-1658), a member of the King's circle, has been suggested as the possible author. It includes some additional items and altered attributions. The long list of contents "In his Ma(jest)ties Closet by the Privy Gallerie in Whitehall" describes here Mantegna's *Death of the Virgin* (Pl. 22; Prado, Madrid): "A peace of Eleaven figures being the Death of our Ladie some Apostles standing by her with Tapers in their handes by Andrea Montania". This omits the wholly misleading description, in the van der Doort original, of the view through the window behind these figures as a view of the town of Mantua, rather than a view in the other direction of the bridge and fortified suburb of S. Giorgio.

D.S.C.

BIBLIOGRAPHY: Millar, 1960.

279

Sleeping Cupid, (*c.* 1635-40)
Francesco Fanelli (active 1609; d. *c.* 1665)
Bronze statuette; h. 11.1 cm, length 24.8 cm
Victoria & Albert Museum (A. 2-1981).

The statuette is signed underneath with a large raised capital F, applied in the wax. Another version of about half the size (length 10.7 cm; private collection, Suffolk) has the signature "F.F.F." (Franciscus Fanellius Florentinus) incised underneath in the wax. The bronze is generally consistent in facture with statuettes and reliefs by Fanelli, but is more highly worked than the great majority of Fanelli's bronzes.
Fanelli came to England in about 1631 after working for a period in Genoa. By 1635 he was in the employ of King Charles I, and in 1640 described himself as "sculptor to the King of Great Britain". By 1640 bronzes by him were recorded by Van der Doort in his inventory of the King's collection at Whitehall, and two of these are still in the Royal collection at Windsor Castle. Fanelli appears to have left England at about the time of the outbreak of the Civil War, and is last recorded in France in the early 1660's.
The figure is based on one of the three marble *Sleeping Cupids* which Charles I acquired from the Ducal collections in Mantua, all of which are now lost. One of these was antique, supposed to be by Praxiteles, one was supposedly by Jacopo Sansovino, and the third was by Michelangelo. All three are shown on a sheet (no. 4914) in the volume of drawings preserved at Windsor of marbles which the King acquired from Mantua (see Cat. 246), although the respective authorship of the three marbles is not indicated on the sheet. Fanelli's bronze is based on the marble numbered 29 on the sheet, which Lange attempted to prove was the *Cupid* by Michelangelo, but which in fact is likely to be the antique ascribed to Praxiteles (as argued by Norton, the *Cupid* at the upper right of the sheet numbered 28, is likely to be Michelangelo's).
Fanelli's bronze follows the basic pose of the marble fairly closely, but omits the club which the marble *Cupid* holds in his right hand, and re-arranges the hands in a more natural-

279

istic way with the right hand placed under the head. The left hand, instead of being turned back under the head as in marble, is now turned outwards, following the *Cupid* numbered 28 on the sheet of drawings, which is probably Michelangelo's *Cupid*. The smaller version of the bronze follows the marble more closely, and is probably an earlier version.
The antique *Cupid* ascribed to Praxiteles and the *Cupid* by Michelangelo both belonged to Isabella d'Este, and were two of the most important features in her *Grotta* in her rooms in the *Corte Vecchia* of the Palazzo Ducale at Mantua.

A.F.R.

PROVENANCE: Bought at Christie's, London, 9th December, 1980, lot 200.
BIBLIOGRAPHY: Lange, 1898; Norton, 1957; Scott-Elliot, 1959.
ADDITIONAL BIBLIOGRAPHY: J. Pope-Hennessy, "Some bronze statuettes by Francesco Fanelli", *Burlington Magazine*, XCV, 1953, pp. 157-62; A. Radcliffe and P. Thornton, "John Evelyn's cabinet", *Connoisseur*, CXCVII, 1978, pp. 254-62.

280

Plague in Mantua
Giovanni Battista Susio, *Libro del conoscere la pestilenza...*
Mantua, Giacomo Rufinello, 1576
British Library (543 d. 35 (2))

The catastrophic plague of 1630 during the siege of Mantua was the first major outbreak since that of 1575-77. Susio (1520-83) who had graduated in arts and medicine at Bologna in 1542 and wrote various works on venesection (bloodletting) dedicated this pioneer treatise (dated 1 January 1576) to Duke Guglielmo Gonzaga; although his main argument was to confute astrological prediction of the plague's coming and to demonstrate that the epidemic disease already causing many deaths the previous year was not plague at all, he made a serious contribution in his discussion of the problem of contagion and practical measures which should be taken by health authorities. The book contains also an address from the printer to the reader apologizing for typographical errors or other shortcomings owing to the haste with which it had been produced to satisfy demand. A sequel, still insisting that the plague in 1576 was not true plague, was published in Brescia in 1579. Susio died at Mantua.

D.S.C.

BIBLIOGRAPHY: Rhodes, 1957, p. 29; Lodigiani and Zanca-Galassi in Mantua, *Convegno*, 1978, pp. 363-73, 404-05.
ADDITIONAL BIBLIOGRAPHY: R.J. Palmer, *The control of plague in Venice and Northern Italy 1348-1600*, unpub. Ph. D., University of Kent, 1978.

St Francis intercedes for the relief of Mantua from plague, c. 1620
Francesco Borgani (c. 1557–1624);
Oil on canvas; 320 × 197 cm
Museo del Palazzo Ducale, Mantua (Inv. 4189)

Borgani is one of the few native painters of Mantua who gained some modest distinction (another was Ippolito Andreasi, many of whose large altarpieces survive and with whom Borgani collaborated in decorating the castle of Goito c. 1584–87). As a painter around the court of Vincenzo I he was copying paintings by Titian for Rubens to take with him to Spain in 1603 and he was involved in setting up the *Galleria della Mostra* (Cat. 245); in a letter of 8 September 1612 he mentioned his continual work there and his refurbishing of many Titians to hang in the gallery (*ho accomodato molti quadri di Titiano*). Borgani's principal works, like Andreasi's, were paintings of religious subjects, and include *The Finding of the Precious Blood* in Sant'Andrea and various altarpieces at Viadana. The present work was executed for the church of Sant' Agnese, Mantua, where it remained until 1876. Exactly when it was painted, or to which outbreak of plague it refers, is uncertain; the 1576–77 plague is too early and the 1630 plague too late, but it might have been intended as a reminder of the former and a general invocation against the possibility of recurrence. In fact the great plague of 1630, following on top of the succession crisis and siege, was to add yet another catastrophe to Gonzaga Mantua.

The view of the city beyond a gruesome foreground littered with human skulls and bones shows the Ponte San Giorgio leading to the Castello, with the tower of Santa Barbara clearly visible and also the *loggia* of Eleonora de' Medici which confirms that the painting cannot be very early. So similar is this view to the one in a painting by Domenico Fetti of *The Madonna and young Christ, Sant'Anselmo and St Carlo Borromeo* (Istituti Gonzaga e Opere Pii Annessi, Mantua) that it may be Borgani copied it, or vice-versa.

D.S.C.

BIBLIOGRAPHY: Ozzòla, 1949, no. 248. Marani and Perini, 1965, p. 469; D.B.I.
ADDITIONAL BIBLIOGRAPHY: I. Sarzi-Bona, *Francesco Borgani* (unpublished thesis, Univ. of Bologna, 1974–75)

282

Photograph: The siege and Capture of Mantua, 1629–30
Print, original 38.5 × 48.3 cm; unsigned
Biblioteca Comunale, Mantua (Album B4)

The succession of Carlo Gonzaga of the Nevers line after the death of Vincenzo II (December 1627) brought about a European war and sealed the fate of Mantua. Carlo was supported by France, and his son was hastily married to Maria, surviving daughter of Duke Francesco (d. 1612), but the Emperor Ferdinand II refused to recognize Carlo's claim to be heir by descent. To be vassals of the Empire had always been a source of Gonzaga pride; now the price had to be paid. The Emperor demanded the resumption to himself of Mantua as an Imperial fief, and the Guastalla line of the Gonzaga, hoping to be invested with the Dukedom, supported this. In March 1629 a French army, in defence of Carlo's claim also to be Duke of Monferrato, began hostilities against Savoy and Spain; Imperial troops led by the generals Collalto and Aldrighen were sent to Mantuan territory, which suffered devastation, and

the long siege of the city began in September. The unusual site and long impregnability of Mantua and the horror of the outcome clearly made the Siege a popular subject for souvenir prints, many versions of which survive. Plague in the besieged city slaughtered thousands and the diseased corpses could not be buried properly; on 18 July (allegedly after betrayal by a Swiss guard of the Castello di San Giorgio) the defences were broken and the city fell. The sacking lasted for three days, during which all manner of atrocities were allowed. Carlo's submission apart from other material losses involved the surrender of much of the Gonzaga dominion, though he was confirmed and invested as Duke; the Imperial troops were withdrawn in September. Thus ended three centuries of Gonzaga ascendancy at Mantua, in mass mortality, shame and ruin.

D.S.C.

BIBLIOGRAPHY: Mazzoldi, III, 1963, pp. 95–116.
ADDITIONAL BIBLIOGRAPHY: R. Quazza, *La guerra per la successione di Mantova e Monferrato* (1628-1631) Mantua, 1926; G. Schizzerotto et al., *Mantova 1630 fra guerra e Peste*, Mantua, 1973.

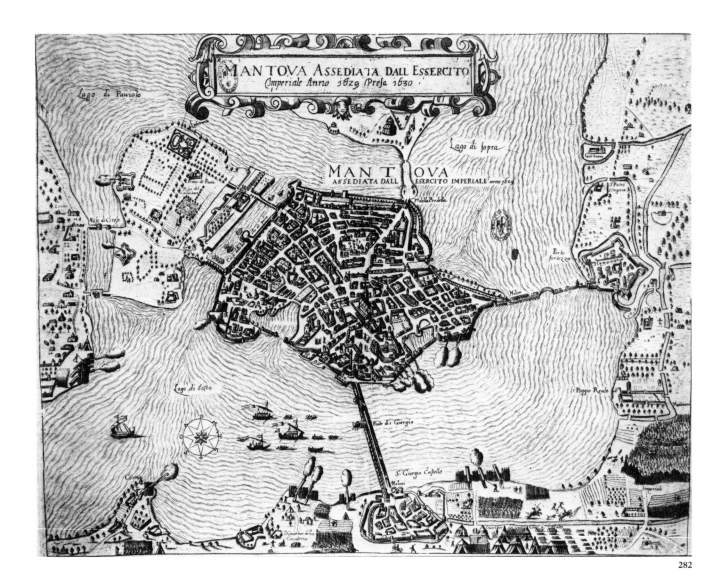

282

248